CU00657905

The Fourth Wave

Violence, Gender, Culture & HIV in the 21st Century

The Fourth Wave

Violence, Gender, Culture & HIV in the 21st Century

EDITORS

Jennifer F. Klot and Vinh-Kim Nguyen

A publication developed in the context of a project led by the
UNESCO Division for Gender Equality in the Office of the Director-General
in collaboration with the Division for Cultural Policies and
Intercultural Dialogue of the Culture Sector.

The designations employed and the presentation of material throughout this publication do not imply the expression of any opinion whatsoever on the part of UNESCO concerning the legal status of any country, territory or area or of its authorities, or concerning the delimitation of its frontiers or boundaries.

The ideas and opinions expressed in this publication are those of the authors and do not necessarily reflect the views of UNESCO and its Member States.

ISBN 9-789231-041587

© 2011 UNESCO
All rights reserved.
No part of this book may be reproduced in any form
without written permission from the publisher.

Published by UNESCO
7, place de Fontenoy
75352 Paris 07 SP
France

Contents

Foreword

Lydia Ruprecht

In this third decade of the AIDS pandemic, and despite strengthened political and financial commitments to women's empowerment and gender-responsive programming, women – and particularly young women and girls – constitute a growing proportion of those affected and infected (see UNAIDS, 2008; and UNAIDS/WHO, 2006).

This trend can be attributed in part to inadequate or inappropriate implementation of policy commitments to gender equality (see Forss and Kruse, 2004; UNAIDS, 2007; and UNIFEM, 2008). However, this is only half the story. In different settings and epidemics, mainstream approaches ignore the most basic driver of the pandemic: the unequal power relations between women and men, girls and boys. The power structures that determine women's and men's different abilities to protect themselves from infection; to access quality prevention, treatment and care; and to cope with the consequences of the pandemic are poorly understood. These structures have also received scant policy attention, making it difficult for practitioners and policy-makers to understand the specificities of each epidemic and to identify what should be done differently to address them.

We must develop more sophisticated analyses of how gender dynamics operate in a given cultural context so that we can formulate appropriate policy responses. Only on this basis can we design programmes that challenge disempowering and harmful gender norms that perpetuate women's vulnerability (UNAIDS, 2009). If we do not do this, the effectiveness of intervention strategies and prevention policies will continue to be limited.

The designations employed and the presentation of material throughout this publication do not imply the expression of any opinion whatsoever on the part of UNESCO concerning the legal status of any country, territory or area or of its authorities, or concerning the delimitation of its frontiers or boundaries.
The ideas and opinions expressed in this publication are those of the authors and do not necessarily reflect the views of UNESCO and its Member States.

In order to respond to gaps in awareness and understanding, the UNESCO Division for Gender Equality, in collaboration with the Division for Cultural Policies and Intercultural Dialogue, commissioned the Social Science Research Council (SSRC) to co-publish this volume that seeks to explore the sociocultural and gendered drivers of vulnerability and disempowerment.

This work has been undertaken in the context of UNESCO's firm commitment to gender equality as one of its two global priorities, alongside a focus on Africa. It also reflects the organization's ongoing efforts to promote its conviction that quality HIV and AIDS programmes must be based on holistic, rights-based and culturally appropriate approaches that seek to involve people living with HIV in a meaningful way and to promote and foster gender equality (UNESCO, 2007).

We recognize the difficulty of operationalizing these policy commitments and hope that this publication will support decision-makers and practitioners working at both international and national levels by providing gendered analyses of epidemics and responses to them and by shedding new light on well-known challenges. By placing gender and culture at the centre of the discussion, this volume aims to help our readers articulate new entry points for effective gender-responsive and – hopefully – gender-transformative interventions that support tailored strategies.

We thank all the contributors who have made this intellectual exploration possible. UNESCO is pleased to have collaborated with the SSRC, Jennifer Klot and Vinh-Kim Nguyen to make this important contribution to the growing body of knowledge on gender, culture and HIV.

References

Forss, K. and Kruse, S. E. 2004. *An Evaluation of UNESCO's Response to HIV/AIDS.* Oslo, Centre for Health and Social Development.

UNAIDS (Joint United Nations Programme on HIV/AIDS). 2007. Programme Coordinating Board (PCB) Archive, 20th PCB meeting, June. http://www.unaids. org/en/AboutUNAIDS/Governance/PCBArchive/20070625-pcb20.asp (Accessed 13 June 2009.)

——. 2008. *2008 Report on the Global AIDS Epidemic.* Geneva, UNAIDS.

——. 2009. *UNAIDS Action Framework: Addressing Women, Girls, Gender Equality and HIV.* Geneva, UNAIDS.

UNAIDS/WHO (Joint United Nations Programme on HIV/AIDS/World Health Organization). 2006. *AIDS Epidemic Update.* Geneva, UNAIDS/WHO.

UNESCO (United Nations Educational, Scientific and Cultural Organization). 2007. *UNESCO's Strategy for Responding to HIV and AIDS.* Paris, UNESCO.

UNIFEM (United Nations Development Fund for Women). 2008. *Transforming the National AIDS Response – Mainstreaming Gender Equality and Women's Human Rights into the 'Three Ones'.* New York, UNIFEM.

Introduction

Jennifer F. Klot and Vinh-Kim Nguyen

The HIV and AIDS pandemic both fuels and is fuelled by inequalities across gender, race, ethnicity and class. Its effects vary across different settings and regions of the world and are also shaped by armed conflicts, natural disasters, environmental degradation, state incapacities, famine and poverty. Its refractory impacts on women and girls – and humanity writ large – are nothing short of catastrophic.

The third decade of the pandemic is characterized by subepidemics that are now coursing through many parts of the globe and among groups previously considered to be unaffected. Growing and disproportionate impacts are now being seen among young women and girls, particularly in sub-Saharan Africa, where young women between 15 and 24 years old are at least three times more likely to be HIV-positive than young men. Nearly half the 30.8 million people living with HIV worldwide are women between the ages of 15 and 49. Between the ages of 15 and 24, gender disparities are even more extreme, with women 1.5 times more likely to be living with HIV than young men (UNAIDS, 2008).

This volume, commissioned by UNESCO, attempts to answer crucial and defining questions about why and how responses to the HIV pandemic are failing women. We began our search for answers in 2005 by reviewing thousands of citations across social science, public health and policy literatures (Nguyen et al., 2006).[1] Although we found a heartening increase in research on the sociocultural dimensions of the pandemic, we were alarmed by the absence of gender analysis and the dearth of critical, feminist and comparative approaches.

The designations employed and the presentation of material throughout this publication do not imply the expression of any opinion whatsoever on the part of UNESCO concerning the legal status of any country, territory or area or of its authorities, or concerning the delimitation of its frontiers or boundaries.
The ideas and opinions expressed in this publication are those of the authors and do not necessarily reflect the views of UNESCO and its Member States.

The vast majority of the literature addressing the intersections between gender, culture and HIV tends to focus on specific groups of women or specific practices rather than on how gender organizes relational interactions within families, communities and institutions in everyday life.[2] Risks relating to HIV continue to be assessed mainly in terms of 'vulnerable groups' and 'high-risk behaviours' rather than in relation to the socio-structural and environmental factors that shape individual behaviour and place particular groups at disproportionate risk. While a confluence of factors – from poverty and conflict to age and family status – are broadly recognized as significant in determining risk behaviours, HIV and AIDS policies and programmes have yet to distinguish adequately among and adapt specifically to varied circumstances or key populations.

We conceived of this project to deepen analysis about the feminization of the epidemic and the emergence of gender as a powerful force driving HIV transmission. We wanted to provide more than a simple account of the biological and social differences between men and women by exploring the mutually reinforcing ways that sociocultural, political and economic factors interact and influence physiological susceptibility to HIV. Further, we wanted to understand how these dynamics are linked to broader geopolitical forces, how they play out in everyday life and, most important, why they place some people at risk while shielding others.

With UNESCO's support, we brought together thirty-four accomplished authors, including senior policy-makers, practitioners and young scholars, to offer original insights and empirical analyses of the biosocial factors that are shaping the gendered course of the pandemic and responses to it. Their chapters in this volume chart the changing sociocultural and geographical distribution of HIV, including emerging epidemics in India and China, less-developed or under-recognized epidemics in areas like the southern Caucasus, and advanced pandemics, such as in sub-Saharan Africa. These changes in distribution reflect broader historical shifts as well as contemporary geopolitical dynamics fuelling wars and economic turmoil, which, in turn, drive migration patterns and create new economic vulnerabilities and social constructions of masculinity and femininity.

The chapters in this collection expose the inadequacy of current frameworks and tools for understanding and measuring the pandemic and its social and relational impacts. Taken together, they represent what we are calling the 'Fourth Wave': an analysis of HIV risk and response that examines the cultures of violence and deprivation that can shape relationships and determine how individuals negotiate and express their various sexual, familial, professional, political and economic identities and roles. This volume shows how early models of successful HIV prevention and response in the United States and Europe – rooted in human rights approaches, identity politics and gay activism – are far less applicable in settings where sexual identity is less a factor of HIV risk than are age, class and geography.

The new contours of the pandemic in sub-Saharan Africa, India, the Russian Federation and China require new modes of analysis. These epidemics are taking place in settings where there are varying degrees of political will to respond, under-resourced health care systems, limited access to treatment and care, and judicial systems that may not be willing or able to protect individual rights to health care or against stigma and discrimination. Whether it is widow inheritance in Uganda, access to treatment in South Africa, male migration in the southern Caucasus or forced displacement in Burundi, this collection of studies exposes the stark limitations of the dominant discourse in capturing and addressing the gender dimensions of HIV and AIDS and its differential impacts on women and girls as compared to men and boys.

The fourth wave: Unpacking the 'feminization' of HIV

In the third decade of the pandemic, women – and particularly young women and girls – constitute a growing proportion of those infected and affected across very different epidemiological situations. Despite a growing awareness of these trends and the emergence of advocacy campaigns focusing on women, the 'feminization' of the pandemic has yet to be adequately explained. Thus far, efforts to respond to women's physiological and social vulnerabilities have focused mainly on decreasing their risk of exposure through behaviour change and reducing social vulnerability through measures designed to improve their socio-economic and legal statuses. The failure of these interventions – and especially of those seeking to change male risk behaviour by 'empowering' women with AIDS information and education – shows that the links between information, knowledge and behaviour change are neither simple nor direct. To the contrary, it suggests the need for focus on the broader circumstances that structure gender relations and layer economic and social difference onto biological difference.

By introducing the notion of a fourth wave, we offer a new paradigm for understanding the risks, causes and consequences of the pandemic. We use the metaphor of the wave to convey fluidity, movement, overlap and undertow:

to highlight factors that are not visible at the surface but that crucially shape direction, force and velocity and that take into account previously unsuspected elements even as new waves break through the old. In the early stages of the pandemic, the first wave of analysis was largely behavioural and drew attention to groups considered to be at high risk of HIV, such as injecting drug users, gay men and sex workers. The second wave emphasized biomedical approaches, prevention technologies and a push to develop microbicides, antiretroviral therapies and a vaccine. During this wave, activist social movements made claims on the public and private sectors to protect individual human rights to health care, to provide access to treatment and to prevent stigma and discrimination. The subsequent third wave theories of HIV-transmission risk incorporated a range of social and structural factors, such as poverty, migration and conflict, into analyses of HIV-transmission risk within and across key populations and among the HIV negative population.

The fourth wave described in this volume expatiates on two mutually reinforcing factors of HIV risk: gender and violence. Each of the chapters in this collection illustrates how different sociocultural constructions of masculinity and femininity embed sexual interactions within a broader framework of meaning and across a continuum of violence, force, coercion, desire and choice. They show how the risk of HIV infection is less a factor of sexual identity and more about how power is exercised differently by men and women and boys and girls across different settings: in prisons, refugee camps and openly gay communities or within abusive and violent families and other cross-generational and interpersonal relationships. From this perspective, the sexual transmission of HIV – between men and women as well as between men who have sex with men and with women – becomes a small part of a much larger picture that is constantly shifting as globalization, the media and a veritable industry of HIV and AIDS constituencies continually reset the political, economic, social and cultural frames within which gender is expressed.

This fourth wave discussion brings into focus the onerous question at the heart of this volume: why have we so spectacularly failed to protect young women and girls from HIV, despite best intentions? It asks if this failure might also explain how newer subepidemics have expanded the demographic geography of risk. Veena Das, Didier Fassin, Mary Crewe and Philip Setel introduce, respectively, each section of this volume and tie together a selection of essays that address four central themes: (1) the intersections between global and local forces in shaping vulnerability to HIV; (2) the mixed success of international interventions to protect women; (3) the gendered nature of local responses to

HIV interventions, focusing specifically on unintended and unexpected outcomes; and (4) the challenges of measurement, data collection and analysis of the pandemic and its causes and consequences.

Gender, culture and HIV

The chapters in Section I suggest that gender has been underutilized as an analytical tool. Focusing on the new geography of HIV, they show how globalization shapes vulnerability to HIV along strongly gendered lines. As Colleen O'Manique points out, some of the global economic and social forces that determine HIV risk disproportionately affect Africa, suggesting that the feminization of the pandemic in sub-Saharan Africa is not so much a product of local biological or social factors as of the ways in which global forces have exacerbated vulnerabilities. Chapters also show how focused analyses of women's vulnerability may also detract attention from the more insidious and pervasive role of gender. This is clearly visible in the way that social capital works more for South African boys than girls in providing protection from sexually transmitted HIV infection (Kelly Hallman) and in the ways that gender is at stake even in non-sexual forms of HIV transmission, such as through drug use or the illicit markets for blood products (Shao Jing).

The language of vulnerability and disempowerment, whether deliberately or not, offers up a convenient representation of women as victims. This glosses over the ways in which socio-economic conditions may lead men and women into situations where they are vulnerable (Cynthia Buckley). It leaves unaddressed the possibility that behind the metaphor lie very real forms of sexual violence that may be far more widespread and systematic than has been acknowledged (Johannes John-Langba). Moreover, the metaphor of woman as victim elides the subtle ways in which male social vulnerability is produced through prevailing masculinities that discourage educational achievement and sanction self-destructive behaviour (David Plummer). It is a metaphor that shuts down thinking and obfuscates difficult but necessary questions about individual agency.

The chapters in Section II show how the absence of gender analysis may undermine – and in some cases inadvertently exacerbate – efforts to address gender inequalities that shape exposure and vulnerability to HIV infection. Anthropologists Paul Farmer and Didier Fassin have strongly asserted that culture has often been used to 'blame the victims', falsely attributing the spread of HIV to 'cultural practices' – and reproducing crude stereotypes of 'victims' while leaving unexamined social and economic fault lines that fuel HIV's spread (Farmer, 2004). Similarly, the chapters in this section show the importance of culture as an analytical tool, not for categorizing the 'victims', but for bringing critical scrutiny to various 'cultures of intervention and response' within international organizations, the AIDS industry, governments, faith-based organizations and non-governmental and community groups.

The metaphor of women as victims sustains the 'logic of rescue' that permeates the marketing of efforts to combat HIV by corporate philanthropy (Lisa Ann Richey). The perceived need to rescue victims and save lives creates a global state of emergency, with a system of triage that is visible in the kinds of interventions that are developed and the particular groups given priority for rescue (Judy El-Bushra, Alton Phillips). Even Brazil's policy, which is held up as a model of state-supported social protection, has been unable to fully address the gendered aspects of the country's epidemic as it 'feminizes, heterosexualizes and interiorizes' (Inês Dourado, Vera Paiva and Francisco Inácio Bastos). Chapters in Section III examine local cultures of response to global HIV interventions. In these cases, the metaphor of women as victims rationalizes avoidance of uncomfortable issues of sexuality, desire and pleasure (Hakan Seckinelgin), whereas the rescue paradigm of response may inadvertently increase gender vulnerabilities as it singles out women – or men – for protection or creates new forms of gender relations. Treatment programmes may unexpectedly spur patients to have children and establish new families (Joséphine Aho and Vinh-Kim Nguyen), or men may become 'victims' as gendered norms endorse the rape, beating or murder of men who have sex with men (Robert Lorway). Chapters demonstrate how international responses are embedded with unexamined assumptions about gender that do not reflect local values and may even undermine pre-existing systems that actively work to protect women (Stella Nyanzi, Margaret Emodu-Walakira and Wilberforce Serwaniko). Gender is, in effect, 'lost in translation' (Orkideh Behrouzan), a phenomenon that is also visible in some treatment programmes where the fact that women outnumber men is strongly attributable to gender norms (Nicoli Nattrass).

The fourth and final section of the volume provides a critique of the mechanisms by which the measurement and construction of 'objective' epidemiological data may actually obscure the identification of evidence that may be most significant for understanding how gender, violence and HIV interact and are mutually reinforcing. Chapters expose the limitations associated with dominant methods of knowledge production that privilege biological factors over social and cultural drivers (Catherine Pirkle). They call for the overhaul of frameworks and categories of measurement to better account for and respond to the economic and social causes and consequences of the pandemic for women. Patrick Heuveline and Jeremy Seekings interrogate standard units of analysis, such as 'orphans' and 'households', raising troubling questions about how these category assumptions may unwittingly obfuscate understanding about the factors most significant for improving HIV prevention and response. Charlotte Watts shows how current indicators and methods for quantifying HIV risk obscure the underlying drivers and contextual factors that contribute to coerced and unsafe sex. And, at the macroeconomic level, Rania Antonopoulos and Taun Toay call for an accounting of the yet unmeasured costs to women and young girls of providing unpaid care for those infected and affected by HIV.

Implications for policy

Together, the chapters in this volume demonstrate the critical importance of gender analysis for effective HIV prevention and responses to the pandemic and point to seven important policy implications.

First is the urgent need for new paradigms, tools and approaches for defining and measuring HIV risks and impacts. This implies both a scientific and an epistemic challenge of moving beyond prevailing biomedical, epidemiological frameworks that focus on individual behaviour and fail to specify structural risk factors across different geographic and cultural settings. Population-level data of HIV incidence and prevalence reveal little about who is most at risk and why. Accurate measures are almost impossible to obtain in situations affected by conflict and natural disasters, whereas standard measurement tools reveal little about the actual determinants of risk, consequences or opportunities for response. Renewed focus must be given to understanding and measuring the dynamics shaping sexual interactions, family relationships and social functioning.

Second is the need to rethink the hidden assumptions and values that are embedded in HIV interventions. Too often, Western concepts of sexuality, the family unit and gender roles and identities are assumed to be universally understood and accepted across cultures. When used as a basis for allocating HIV resources, these assumptions may unintentionally increase HIV-related risks by excluding categories of vulnerable people (married women, perpetrators of sexual violence, indigenous populations) or by stigmatizing groups of people regardless of HIV status (widows, orphans, the military).

The third policy implication calls for urgent recognition of violence, and especially sexual violence, as a physiological and social factor of HIV risk. Although sexual violence – particularly in conflict situations – has long been associated with increased vulnerability to HIV infection, it has yet to be identified as a specific factor in epidemiological models of risk transmission or even as an entry point for HIV prevention and response. The dissonance between widely accepted 'grey' literature documenting these links and the biomedical and epidemiological 'science' of HIV measurement is fuelling a growing debate in the humanitarian, security and public health arenas. Chapters in this volume associate degrees of power and choice with levels of HIV risk in relationships and families and across a continuum of violence ranging from survival and transactional sex and forced and early marriage to intimate-partner violence between men who have sex with men and forced sex between widows and leverites.

Fourth is the yet unmeasured costs and consequences of HIV and AIDS–related care for family care arrangements. As family and community networks are being pushed beyond their capacities, the notion of 'resilience' is fast becoming a euphemism for the absence of state-supported care and treatment. Women and girls are the principal providers of unremunerated physical and psychosocial care. Chapters in this volume speak to the longer-term impacts of increased care burdens on lost educational opportunities and the economic, political and social status of women. They explore how state provision of care and treatment may shift the costs of care among the public, private and family sectors. And they call for the cost and value of caregiving to be considered within macroeconomic and sector-specific employment planning, workplace and social protection policies, and health system reforms and expenditures.

Fifth is the growing realization that the most effective way to reduce vulnerability to HIV among women may be to increase HIV prevention efforts for men. Despite the near-universal fact that women and girls have less power than men to control the terms of sexual interactions and the circumstances under which forced, coerced or consensual sex takes place, they continue to be the principal recipients of HIV information and education campaigns. Chapters in this volume suggest that HIV prevention directed at men may increase their health-seeking behaviours, reduce violence and stigma related to status disclosure and, given the increased biological risk associated with male-to-female and male-to-male transmission, even reduce overall prevalence.

The sixth implication for policy is the need to situate HIV risk analysis within a larger geopolitical context. Chapters in this volume show that HIV interventions for women and girls may be more dramatically shaped by health sector reforms and transportation, education and macroeconomic policies than by any single HIV intervention. Without public policies and support for women's property rights, education, livelihoods and access to health care, unsafe transactional sex can become one of the only alternatives for survival. It is only by connecting 'bottom-up' and 'top-down' analyses of HIV drivers and impacts that interventions can most effectively reach those who are at greatest risk.

Seventh is the need to assess the beneficence of the new financial instruments that have been created to mobilize and disburse resources to combat the pandemic. Mechanisms such as the Global Fund, PEPFAR and (PRODUCT) RED have generated unlikely collaborations between pharmaceutical companies, defence contractors, faith-based organizations and the fashion industry. Chapters in this volume expose how the political, ideological and development agendas of the governments, corporations and individual philanthropists engaged in these collaborations may also unduly influence the ways in which resources are mobilized and allocated. This can be seen in how the language of victim and rescue has been used to generate political traction, particularly for the publics in wealthy nations and in the countries identified as major recipients of bilateral funding for HIV. New forms of accountability are needed to ensure that resources are allocated according to need, that criteria are transparent and that impacts – both intended and unintended – are taken into account.

Conclusion

Although the epidemiology of the HIV and AIDS pandemic continues to be explained largely in biomedical and behavioural terms, more attention is now being paid to the social, political and economic factors that shape individual behaviour and the effectiveness of responses. But even this growing attention is not nearly enough. For young women, mutually reinforcing biological and social vulnerabilities form a particularly toxic combination that is driving a feminization of the pandemic in some of the hardest-hit countries in the world. We continue to be concerned that the focus of HIV interventions – on children in isolation from their social and family context, on prevention technologies and on celebrity aid – may be deflecting attention from broader forms of social and gendered violence that shape HIV risk for both women and men.

If the deeply rooted social and cultural norms that increase risks for girls, young women and other at-risk populations are not understood and taken into account, HIV prevention strategies will continue to be ineffectual as the pandemic unfolds over generations. Addressing the gender dimensions of the pandemic will require a far deeper understanding about how to support families and communities as they negotiate the pandemic's repercussions for household restructuring, gender and intergenerational relations, reproductive decision-making, livelihood choices, education planning and civic participation. Equally urgent is the need to develop the knowledge necessary for strengthening national response capacities so that those most affected by HIV and AIDS do not also have to shoulder their associated burdens alone.

The prevailing institutional logic of international response must be adapted to realities on the ground as experienced by those most affected by HIV and AIDS. And this will require that careful attention also be paid to local voices and regional differences. In addition, we need to study how international interventions are themselves shaping the course of the pandemic and how they interact locally to structure biosocial vulnerability in gendered terms.

Acknowledgements

We are grateful for having had the rare opportunity to bring together, in one volume, such a compelling and diverse community of practice, representing multiple disciplines and regions of the world. We hope the depth and range of analyses offered will contribute to new ways of thinking about the AIDS pandemic and its gender and socio-cultural dimensions. We gratefully acknowledge UNESCO's partnership in this vision and, particularly, Lydia Ruprecht's leadership and the contributions made by Katérina Stenou, Susanne Schnuttgen, Jeanne Lawler, Ariana Stahmer, Manilee Bagheritari, Dominique LaRochelle and Aylin Taftali.

The realization of this vision would not have been possible without the SSRC's talented and dynamic team, their initiative, commitment, enthusiasm and many hours. We thank Dinasas (Dinu) Abdella for her exceptional support in managing the project and organizing the first meeting of authors that took place in Paris, in 2007. Alton Philips provided foundational research assistance during the project's development. Tanja Mrdja managed an extensive editorial review process and Dana Huber provided exacting editorial support during the final stages of production. The SSRC's agile, creative and meticulous production team was led by Editorial Director Paul Price and Production Manager Debra Yoo. Editorial Advisor Manjari Mahajan's contributions were, in a word, indispensable. We are thankfully beholden to her. Additionally, we want to thank Mark Bloch and Nina Allen for their careful editing of early versions of the manuscript.

We also extend deep appreciation to our Canadian collaborators Pr Maria Victoria Zunzunegui, Catherine Pirkle, colleagues at the Global Health Group at the Centre de Recherches du Centre Hospitalier de l'Université de Montréal (CRCHUM), colleagues at the Clinique Médicale l'Actuel, and the Département de Médecine Sociale et Préventive at the Université de Montréal.

Notes

1. For information on UNESCO's Culture, HIV and AIDS program, see http://www. unesco.org/culture/aids.
2. Notable exceptions include *AIDS, Sexuality and Gender in Africa: The Struggle Continues* (Baylies, 2000); *Women and HIV/AIDS: An International Resource Book* (Berer and Ray, 1993); and *The Relationship Between Gender Roles and HIV Infection in Namibia* (Lipinge et al., 2004).

References

Baylies, C. 2000. *AIDS, Sexuality and Gender in Africa: The Struggle Continues*. London, Routledge.

Berer, M. and Ray, S. 1993. *Women and HIV/AIDS: An International Resource Book*. London, Pandora Press.

DeBruyn, M. 1992. Women and AIDS in developing countries: The XIIth international conference on the social sciences and medicine. *Science and Medicine*, Vol. 34, No. 3, pp. 249–62.

Farmer, P. 2004. An anthropology of structural violence. *Current Anthropology*, Vol. 45, No. 3, pp. 305–25.

Goldstein, N. and Manlowe, J. (eds). 1997. *The Gender Politics of HIV/AIDS in Women: Perspectives on the Pandemic in the United States*. New York, NYU Press.

Kalipeni, E., Flynn, K. and Pope, C. 2009. *Strong Women, Dangerous Times: Gender and HIV/AIDS in Africa*. Hauppauge, NY, Nova Science Publishers.

Lipinge, S., Hofne, K. and Friedman, S. 2004. *The Relationship Between Gender Roles and HIV Infection in Namibia*. Windhoek, University of Namibia Press.

Nguyen, V., Klot, J., Phillips, A. and Pirkle, C. 2006. *Culture, HIV and AIDS: An Annotated Bibliography*. Paris/New York, UNESCO/SSRC. http://unesdoc.unesco.org/images/0014/001472/147244M.pdf or http://www.ssrc.org/publications/view/6A6F9BF1-4059-DE11-BD80-001CC477EC70/

Patton, C. 1994. *Last Served? Gendering the HIV Pandemic*. London, Taylor and Francis.

Quinn, T. C. and Overbaugh, J. 2005. HIV/AIDS in women: An expanding epidemic. *Science*, Vol. 308, No. 5728, pp. 1582–583.

UNAIDS (Joint United Nations Programme on HIV/AIDS). 2008. *2008 Report on the Global AIDS Epidemic*. Geneva, UNAIDS. http://www.unaids.org/en/KnowledgeCentre/HIVData/GlobalReport/2008/2008_Global_report.asp (Accessed 1 June 2009.)

Section I: The New Geography of HIV

Introductory Essay

Veena Das

The threat of the HIV and AIDS epidemic in both public literature and policy documents is habitually presented with the aid of statistics that highlight the very large numbers of people living with HIV and AIDS around the world. Yet, when viewed as a biosocially produced disease, as experienced by subjects (either patients or caregivers), HIV and AIDS is not a single disease but a cluster of conditions. With the availability of antiretroviral (ARV) therapies and in contexts where health delivery systems function well and patients have the material and social resources to access the right combination of drugs, HIV and AIDS may be defined as similar to other chronic diseases. Conversely, in countries (or among different populations within the same country) where overall health care systems are fragile and where social ties have become corroded by long-term chronic violence or grinding poverty, HIV and AIDs might be seen as one of the several fateful conditions that lead to dissolution of social ties, unbearable care burdens and early death, even when antiretroviral drug therapy is available through national or global programmes of intervention.

The chapters in this section concentrate on the social configuration of the disease and its implications for African countries that have experienced civil wars and apartheid and for post-liberalization communist countries in which new kinds of economic and social stressors have made certain populations much more vulnerable to HIV. A theme that unites all the chapters in this section is the move away from public health or epidemiological perspectives that privilege the individual as both the bearer of risk and the locus of action.

The designations employed and the presentation of material throughout this publication do not imply the expression of any opinion whatsoever on the part of UNESCO concerning the legal status of any country, territory or area or of its authorities, or concerning the delimitation of its frontiers or boundaries.
The ideas and opinions expressed in this publication are those of the authors and do not necessarily reflect the views of UNESCO and its Member States.

Instead of asking how individual behaviour might be targeted for intervention to reduce the risk of harmful sexual practices, these chapters ask how structural features at the macro level – such as structural adjustment programmes and related market-oriented reforms or widespread sexual and reproductive violence in chronic warfare – affect not only the incidence and prevalence of HIV and AIDS but also the different ways in which it affects men and women.

One of the features of HIV and AIDS as it has been reconfigured in the context of Africa is what many scholars are describing as the 'feminization' of the epidemic. This not only means that the proportion of young women aged between 16 and 30 living with HIV and AIDS has been steadily rising but also that the responsibility of caring for patients and families is now being shouldered disproportionately by women. The chapters in this section call for a radical rethinking of how we perceive these issues, from individual-level analyses to HIV and AIDS in the context of social networks of relations. Thus, Colleen O'Manique's chapter draws specific attention to the ways in which economic developments at the macro level can affect livelihood opportunities for women and force them into survival strategies involving high-risk transactional or commercial sex. O'Manique argues that the role of women as caregivers has been seriously neglected in economic analysis, which, in turn, impacts our understanding of the HIV and AIDS epidemic as it affects the lives of women.

When we begin to think of HIV and AIDS as a cluster of conditions, it also becomes evident that vulnerable populations might be seen as an extension of other vulnerable groups affected by civil wars, apartheid or economic catastrophes that were exacerbated by particular alignments with larger global processes. Thus, the South African apartheid regime and its systematic policies of racial discrimination had deleterious effects on families and on relations between generations and the sexes. How did the systematic eroding of familial ties during the apartheid era create or exacerbate the vulnerability of young women to HIV and AIDS, and why has gender been neglected in efforts to map the contours of the epidemic? Kelly Hallman's chapter puts the conceptual issue as follows: '"Gendered" here does not simply refer to differences between women and men but rather to the complexities of power relationships that have evolved between them within a context that has been deeply altered by state-mandated distortions of structures of production, physical mobility, family arrangements and social relations.' This attention to social relations, not as organic to society, but as a phenomenon that has been deeply distorted by state-mandated policies, is crucial in gaining an understanding of why general theories pertaining to, say, the impact of social capital on health that might work in stable but otherwise resource-constrained neighbourhoods are unlikely to work in post-conflict societies.

To recapitulate briefly: Theories of social capital that postulated that membership in voluntary organizations could be treated as a good index of the robustness of civil society were first formulated by political theorists and then used in the health sciences to argue that social networks can bolster health-enhancing behaviours and serve as a buffer to the health-damaging stressors frequently encountered in low-resource environments. But low-resource environments are not the same everywhere. One has to ask if the concept of social capital is robust enough to take into account the kinds of environments in which social relations bear the mark of ongoing chronic violence, as was the case of the apartheid regime, which depended on a deliberate destruction of the social ties of black communities.

A good example of this is provided in Hallman's chapter, which looks at the prevalence of HIV and AIDS in the South African province of KwaZulu-Natal – a region that experienced some of the worst violence during the struggle to end apartheid. KwaZulu-Natal also has the highest levels of HIV prevalence in South Africa, especially among young people, and in particular among young women. Analyzing the results of national surveys that seek to measure the impact of social capital (as indexed by community trust, reciprocity and individual membership in communities or groups) on adolescent sexual risk, Hallman finds that results are ambiguous at best. For example, it is not group membership per se that determines whether such membership would be protective or foster dangerous sexual practices but membership in *which kind of groups* that is crucial. Obviously, belonging to a street gang might promote cohesion among young men, but it has different implications for health behaviour than the fact of belonging to an economic self-help group.

One of Hallman's conclusions is that:

> Girls in more cohesive communities appear able to practise safer behaviours relative to girls who reside in less cohesive communities. Most of the differences, however, *are not statistically significant,* with the exception of the outcome 'ever experienced non-consensual sex', which is significant at the $p \leq .05$ level. Among males, differences by degree of community cohesiveness are also in the hypothesized direction, *but none are statistically significant.*

I note that the differences for both girls and boys in relation to group membership are not statistically significant and one implication is that theories of social capital work when they do and don't when they don't. This conclusion might be disconcerting if we are looking for 'magic bullet' solutions in policy interventions to contain the epidemic. However, this research is significant for arguing that we cannot dissociate larger questions of democratic reform, social justice and attention to provisioning in general from policies and programmes to contain or prevent HIV/AIDS.

One of the most neglected aspects of research and policy interventions on HIV and AIDS is to show how sexual and reproductive violence is folded into the experience of the disease. The typical picture of adolescent sexuality in the public health literature in North America is that of an experimenting subject whose one-night stands or frequent changes of partners are seen as constituting dangerous practices. Even in the United States, for instance, the exposure of young girls (and boys) to HIV and AIDS due to sexual violence within their families and communities has received little attention. In the case of countries in which long-term civil war was coterminous with sexual slavery, widespread rape and reproductive violence, HIV risks from violence have been similarly under-explored. It is not surprising that Johannes John-Langba's chapter on post-conflict transition in Sierra Leone finds low levels of knowledge about HIV and AIDS in conflict-affected communities, as well as skepticism regarding the motives of NGOs and HIV and AIDS workers, who are seen to be exploiting the epidemic as a means of extracting money from international donors. These perceptions are best understood in the context of the war in Sierra Leone, in which systematic violence was perpetrated against women and girls, including sexual slavery, forced pregnancy, abduction, enslavement and torture. Many women, together with their families and community members, lost their lives or their limbs or were forced to witness or engage in horrendous acts, including killing their own family members. The overall number of girls and women affected by this violence is estimated to be in the range of 250,000, or 33 per cent of the total female population. The reproductive health problems that women in Sierra Leone continue to face, coupled with the poor medical environment in which treatment is not easy to access, compels us to understand what reported attitudes towards HIV and AIDS truly mean. Thus, for example John-Langba reports that, in a focus group discussion, a number of girls said that 'they do not believe AIDS existed' as they had never seen any sufferer. John-Langba interprets this as an indication of denial about the existence of HIV and AIDS. It is equally possible to read this as a critique of global practices and programmes that target the conditions affecting the security of the international order or the delivery of global public goods rather than the local conditions that people can see as constituting the suffering they are experiencing here and now. This is not to argue that the threat of HIV and AIDS is overstated, but that for the young women suffering from adverse reproductive health conditions as a consequence of brutal violence, it is the absence of attention to the here and now that stands in need of explanation and not their lack of knowledge of HIV and AIDS.

A major contribution of the chapters in this section is that they shift the focus from individual behaviour to the social context within which individuals are embedded. The authors are careful to avoid a binary distinction between, say, individual and community or individual and society. Instead, they speak of gendered norms, of social networks, of neighbourhoods or of families. It is important to realize that there are different social thresholds and associated implications – be they at the level of neighbourhood or the family. David Plummer, for instance, in his chapter on what can be termed a crisis of masculinity, points to the growing imbalance in the educational achievements of boys and girls in the Caribbean – with boys increasingly excluding themselves from the sphere of education. Plummer interprets this as evidence of the changing norms of masculinity in the Caribbean, where boys are increasingly asserting their masculinity and seeking to enhance their prestige within peer groups by joining gangs, engaging in crime and having multiple sexual partners. From a health intervention perspective, such macho behaviour exposes boys to the risk of dangerous sexual behaviour. From a social science perspective, the complexities of the problem also point to significant differences in the ways in which youth culture in different Caribbean countries is aligned with the macho urban culture of African-American youth in urban North America. Social science analysis would also include an assessment of a long history of the paradigm of the masculinity crisis, with reference to the African-American or Caribbean family, which subverted the role that racism or the racial practices of the colonial powers played in contributing to and defining this 'crisis of black masculinity'. On a cautionary note then, I am wary of isolating the practices of masculinity as the 'risk factors' without first embedding them in the structural features to which others in this section have drawn attention.

While a history of violent conflicts, as in South Africa, Sierra Leone or Liberia, is extremely important in understanding the relation between sexual violence and vulnerability to HIV and AIDS, the chapters on the southern Caucasus region in the former Soviet Union (Cynthia Buckley) and on China (Shao Jing) draw attention to the importance of everyday economic strategies used by families and the implications of these strategies for understanding vulnerability to HIV and AIDS. Cynthia Buckley's chapter argues that it is important to expand our understanding of the ways in which male out-migration, directly and indirectly, alters the risks faced by migrant families generally and the wives of male migrants specifically. Although the rates of HIV infection are relatively low in the region, its geographical location close to regions of high HIV prevalence makes it likely that the economic strategies followed by households, such as seasonal migration of male heads of households to these regions, would expose them to HIV and AIDS, placing wives at increased risk of infection and creating new economic burdens on the family. Treating the household as the unit of analysis captures the impact of HIV and AIDS better than concentrating on individual subjects.

Finally, the chapter by Shao Jing is a masterly demonstration of how changing economic policies, technologies of governance and gendered norms together constitute the conditions of possibility for the different trajectories of HIV and AIDS epidemics in post-liberalization China. I use the term epidemic in the plural because one could read Shao Jing as saying that under the agreed meta-narrative of the nature of the HIV and AIDS epidemic in China, there are other more local epidemics that are eclipsed. The story of these local epidemics can shed light on what Jing calls the 'poverty of epidemiology' and, by implication, of the narrowly focused public health understandings of what constitute effective interventions.

Jing shows that whereas there is an official acknowledgement in China of the fact that HIV and AIDS is now not only a disease of key populations, such as female sex workers, but also of the HIV negative population through the risk of sexual transmission, the connection between these two sites is not well understood. Thus, the very same gendered norms that make female sex workers consider condom use an obstacle to genuine sexual enjoyment and privilege the sexual pleasure of their male clients over their own safety also make married women regard the use of condoms as getting in the way of trusting relations between spouses. It is the generality of gendered norms that make women see issues of intimacy through the eyes of their male partners rather than through concerns for their own health.

Further, looking at other roots of transmission, such as the sale of blood products, we see how gender operates in everyday relations. Jing shows how economic liberalization led to the simultaneous emergence of diverse markets that included markets for cheap migrant labour from rural areas and markets for cash crops and blood products. Market fluctuations in the demand for agricultural products led impoverished rural women in Henan Province in central

China to become plasma sellers. Yet, the safety of plasma donors seems not to have been of any concern for the state or for the buyers of blood products in the medical market. Simple technical failures, such as the use of unsterile instruments and the breaking of plastic blood bags, resulted in close to 45 per cent of women in some villages of the province becoming infected with HIV. Similar distortions in the health delivery system meant that even when antiretroviral therapies were made available to those infected, there were no systematic provisions for clinical testing, monitoring side effects and ensuring adherence. It is thus not a framework of causes and effects but of an assemblage in which several conditions combined to give a particular shape to the epidemic in post-liberalizing China.

The chapters in this section raise a new set of questions, and even when they use traditional datasets, the results are interpreted in novel ways. The most important conclusion for both researchers and policy-makers in the analyses offered here is that the HIV and AIDS epidemic is a cluster of conditions through which vulnerability is constituted, requiring a much better understanding of how sexual violence, economic destitution and gendered norms shape particular impacts. For HIV interventions to have long-term impact, there must be new approaches to drug policies, markets for blood products, and sexual services. In addition, health care systems need to ensure access to ARVs as well as other services that can help ensure greater compliance to existing therapeutic regimes without jeopardizing the social and economic survival of those living with HIV. Just as the epidemic shows spatial variation, so it will change with time; without addressing the kind of structural conditions that have been brought to light in these chapters, there are no effective ways in which prevention and treatment can keep abreast of changing HIV epidemics and their interaction with other grievous conditions that threaten health and well-being and the stability of the international order.

CHAPTER 1

Globalization and gendered vulnerabilities to HIV and AIDS in sub-Saharan Africa

Colleen O'Manique

The connections between global structural economic arrangements and vulnerabilities to HIV and AIDS at the local level are non-linear and complex. However, there is little doubt that these global structural transformations have played an important role in shaping the HIV and AIDS pandemic in sub-Saharan Africa, as well as the policy responses that have been formulated to combat the pandemic. Macro-structural arrangements determine who receives treatment once infected as well as who shoulders the burden of care of people living with HIV and AIDS, children orphaned by AIDS, and much else. Yet, despite the profound impact of global economic structures on local communities, the policy implications of these macro-structural arrangements remain under-explored.

This chapter highlights some of the ways in which the governance of the global political economy contributes to vulnerability to HIV and AIDS in sub-Saharan Africa, particularly among women and girls. By vulnerability, I mean the ways in which women or men are at risk of being exposed to HIV and of being stigmatized and marginalized in terms of care and support once infected. Vulnerability also refers to the many ways in which the livelihoods of women and men are undermined and their resilience weakened in HIV-affected households and communities.

The rules of global governance are a form of structural power that imposes constraints on political and economic interactions, from within local communities and at the global level. Though seemingly remote from local

The designations employed and the presentation of material throughout this publication do not imply the expression of any opinion whatsoever on the part of UNESCO concerning the legal status of any country, territory or area or of its authorities, or concerning the delimitation of its frontiers or boundaries.
The ideas and opinions expressed in this publication are those of the authors and do not necessarily reflect the views of UNESCO and its Member States.

communities, structural power plays a role in shaping risk environments and circumscribing the range of possibilities in national and local responses, including the responses of an increasingly diverse group of civil society and private actors. This chapter will especially focus on international laws governing intellectual property; trade, investment and subsidy regimes; and the conditions attached to national debt and development assistance, all of which contribute to the contexts within which the pandemic unfolds and to local capacities to respond to HIV and AIDS.

One clear lesson of the pandemic is that those most socially, politically and economically marginalized are often the most vulnerable to HIV infection. In the areas hardest hit by HIV and AIDS, these people are increasingly women. The UNAIDS annual report on the epidemic for 2007 (UNAIDS, 2008) points to the continuing and hugely disproportionate impact of HIV and AIDS on sub-Saharan Africa. The statistics are alarming: 68 per cent of adults and 90 per cent of children infected with HIV live in this region; 76 per cent of all AIDS deaths have occurred here; infection rates in the 15–49 age group exceed 15 per cent in most southern African countries; and in 2007, almost 61 per cent of adults living with HIV in sub-Saharan Africa were women.

Our knowledge of the HIV and AIDS pandemic has been limited by ways of seeing and knowing that leave out important pieces of the puzzle. A key piece that is often left out is how structural power, in its present configuration, has contributed to the growing feminization of the pandemic. Feminist political economists have recognized that the rules governing the global political economy are inscribed with gendered meanings (Marchand and Sisson Runyan, 2000). Gender here refers to the varied and shifting understandings of what it means to be a man or a woman in specific historical and social contexts. Gender relations are constantly negotiated in relation to other relational divides, such as class, race, ethnicity and sexuality. Gender relations, thus, not only shape relationships between individuals but also cultural and institutional practices from the very local to the global level.

One of the reasons why the links between the global political economy and the feminization of the HIV and AIDS epidemic are seldom made has to do with existing dominant frameworks for understanding the epidemic. The main frameworks for conceptualizing the pandemic are still predominantly biomedical and epidemiological. For instance, within mainstream accounts of risk and vulnerability, gender relations have been largely understood through a focus on individual sexual behaviour, which is perceived to be amenable to change through education and empowerment campaigns. The central role of women in formal, informal and caring economies has been neglected, as have the implications of gender relations in the links between poverty and HIV and AIDS. Many similar examples illustrate how biomedical frameworks can mask the impacts of the past thirty years of neoliberal economic restructuring on the feminization of the pandemic.

The term 'neoliberalism' here is understood as the political and economic doctrine that proposes that collective human interest is best advanced by unleashing entrepreneurial freedom within a governing framework characterized by strong individual property rights, free markets and free trade. The application of this doctrine has resulted in deregulated global financial markets, weakened institutions for social and labour protection, and diminished government services. It has cut top tax rates and liberalized capital markets and the trade of international goods and services. The necessities of life – water, health care, education – have become increasingly privatized and commodified (Harvey, 2005). The gender dimensions of neoliberal ideology are reflected in the devaluation of subsistence, informal and unpaid household labour – labour that is critical to human survival and that is largely shouldered by women (Bakker and Gill, 2003; Mohanty, 2004).

This chapter will argue that the neoliberal rules governing the global political economy are not simply a backdrop but a key contributor to the pandemic and its increasing feminization. It will examine the connections between globalization and the feminization of HIV and AIDS by focusing on the impacts of structural adjustment programmes, international intellectual property laws and agricultural trade policies. All of the above are seemingly removed from the day-to-day hardships faced by people who have been affected by the AIDS epidemic, but I will try to show that these macro-level policies have a gender-specific impact on the AIDS epidemic.

Understanding the vulnerability of women to HIV and AIDS: Some common approaches

The pandemic in sub-Saharan Africa, including its gender dimensions, has been understood primarily through narrow cultural and biomedical perspectives. In the late 1980s, the first accounts of women's particular vulnerability to HIV focused on their unique biological risk factors, as well as on the 'high-risk' sexual behaviours of both men and women that placed women at greater risk. The focus was on the 'promiscuity' of 'high-risk groups', such as sex workers, migrating men and long-distance lorry drivers, and the factors contributing to high-risk sexual behaviour, such as the breakdown of traditional cultural codes governing sexuality, increased rural-to-urban migration, alcohol consumption and deeply entrenched patriarchal cultures that placed men in control of women's sexuality and labour (see, for example, Killewo et al., 1989; Piot et al., 1987; Serwadda, 1985).

However, by the early 1990s, this individual behaviour paradigm was challenged. Critics pointed to the sometimes stigmatizing, racist and ahistorical biases in biological and cultural explanations. Instead of offering cultural or biological explanations for individual behaviour, they drew attention to the influence of broader sociocultural, political, legal and economic conditions that increased the risk and vulnerability of women (Barnett and Whiteside, 2002; Schoepf, 1991a and 1991b). These factors included the limited income-earning options of impoverished women in both formal and informal economies, which, coupled with their central roles in domestic labour, forced them to resort to 'survival' sex to provide for their families. They also referred to women's disadvantaged sociocultural and legal position with respect to property, land ownership and inheritance (Izumi, 2006) and to the impact of the increasing informalization of economies and related migration and household mobility (Hunter, 2007; O'Manique, 2004).

The critique of the individual biomedical approach additionally pointed out that women could not be 'empowered' to have safer sex without also taking into consideration the behaviour of men. What was relevant was the local context shaping gendered power relations, such as the asymmetrical economic and legal standing of men and women within the household.

In line with these critiques, an important 2001 World Bank Policy Research Report, *Engendering Development Through Gender Equality in Rights, Resources and Voice* (2001), advocated programmes to strengthen the empowerment of women by focusing on their centrality to family survival, economic growth, poverty reduction and household well-being, particularly in contexts where public health care systems and social safety nets were weak or non-existent. This analysis pointed to the need for the economic empowerment of women and refocused attention on microcredit and microenterprise development for women in HIV-affected communities; this development approach rapidly became ubiquitous as an empowerment strategy for women. However, this approach sometimes masked the fact that a lack of credit was not the main cause of poverty, nor could credit stand in for decent health and social policies or access to secure employment (Bond, 2007; Rankin, 2001).

At the same time that microcredit and microenterprise programmes for women were becoming popular, campaigns by civil society and women's organizations were directed at changing discriminatory laws and practices that denied women access to income and property, thereby exposing the injustices faced not only by women but also by the majority of the poor in various local settings (Izumi, 2006). However, these kinds of interventions had a limited impact because resources for collective action were often unavailable (Baylies and Burja, 2000).

The critiques of individual behavioural approaches also drew attention to structural factors that frame risk. Research has shed light on the connections between national political economies, state responses and the broader macro-structural factors that shape risk environments, such as debt, structural adjustment programmes (SAPs), intellectual property and trade law, and investment patterns (Barnett and Whiteside, 2002; Nattrass, 2003; Poku and Whiteside, 2004). Scholars have modeled the effects of HIV epidemics on governance and democracy, national security and the economy (Fourie, 2004; Ostergard, 2004, Price-Smith, 2003). However, these critiques have seldom shed light on the impact of structural power on the everyday lives and choices of women, men and children.

Structural adjustment programmes and their implications for HIV and AIDS

Recent changes in the political economy of sub-Saharan Africa are important in explaining the distribution and scale of the pandemic. The spread of HIV in the Great Lakes region of Africa, beginning in the late 1970s, roughly corresponded to the advent of neoliberal SAPs, which contributed to weakening of the capacity of states to provide adequate health services. We cannot know with certainty whether the course of the HIV pandemic would have been different had it not emerged alongside Africa's debt crisis and the introduction of SAPs, but a body of research produced in the 1980s and 1990s pointed to the role of SAPs in undermining health systems, local economies and the social determinants of health (Schoepf, 1991b; Schoepf et al., 2000). Structural adjustment policies represented a shift in control of social and economic policy away from the nation-state and towards global institutions, such as the World Bank and the International Monetary Fund. The basic prescriptions of SAPs focused on currency devaluation, the diversion of production and trade towards export markets, the trimming of state budgets and the retrenchment of public sector employees, and privatization and the establishment of user fees for public services (Gershman and Irwin, 2000; Poku, 2004).

From the start of the epidemic, National AIDS Programmes (NAPs) were implemented through weak ministries of health, which were already subject to budgetary and human resource constraints and had been further weakened by SAPs (O'Manique, 2004). Again, there are variations from one country to another, but generally speaking, the health and social systems inherited from colonial administrations were already beleaguered and primarily served the urban middle classes. Structural adjustment policies linked to debt rescheduling foreclosed the possibility of providing and extending basic health care and other social necessities (Cheru, 2002; Green, 1989). Neoliberal restructuring undermined the capacity of individual states to restrain financial markets and control the investments and activities of economic enterprises for developmental purposes. Today, political authority and the protection of citizenship rights are conceded to 'sovereign' states, but the state system is inseparable from the rules governing the global market economy (Brysk, 2002). The SAPs of the 1980s and 1990s served to entrench the notion that it is not the responsibility of states to provide services; government accountability tilted towards external financiers, with local and international non-governmental organizations and the private sector becoming subcontractors in the delivery of basic services where the state had opted out (Stewart, 1997). The World Bank and related communities of experts – dominated by economists – became central to the design of health systems and also HIV and AIDS policies (Lee and Goodman, 2002).

The erosion of public services due to the implementation of SAPs disproportionately affected women. The impacts of SAPs on women and gender relations have been extensively documented and include the intensification and lengthening of the work day in both the productive and reproductive spheres to make up for income loss; increased household expenses due to the increased commodification of necessities; decreased participation of girls in school due to user fees as well as the need for their labour in the household; the deterioration in the health status of women and girls, particularly among the poorest, who cannot afford health services; the rise in women's participation in licit and illicit informal sector activities; and increased acts of violence against women (Petchesky, 2003; Peterson, 2003). In contexts where HIV was prevalent and spreading, SAPs removed the social support structures needed by individuals caring for sick family members and paying for necessities and diverted their labour towards income-generating strategies to pay for medicines, food and funerals (Barnett and Whiteside, 2002; Baylies, 2002).

In many parts of sub-Saharan Africa, women are responsible for subsistence and smallholder food production and securing access to water and fuel, as well as household chores, such as cooking, cleaning, caring for and socializing children and the care of older people. The HIV and AIDS pandemic, with its growing numbers of sick adults and children and orphans, increased the burdens that many women had to shoulder. This increased workload sometimes obliged women to give up waged labour or, conversely, to increase their working hours to meet AIDS-related expenses. Girls are also drawn into the care or wage economies in times of economic need. Yet, the very categories that are used by most macroeconomic models exclude consideration of the unpaid labour routinely done by women. By not problematizing them nor accounting for them in economic analyses, existing gender relations that disfavour women are often further reinforced (Bakker and Gill, 2003). These silences in macroeconomics are especially problematic in the context of the AIDS pandemic, which has created disproportionately large care burdens for women in countless communities across sub-Saharan Africa.

Trade, TRIPS and AIDS: Access to treatment for HIV in the global market

SAPs have not been the only global issue that has had a gendered impact on the unfolding of the response to the pandemic. The global market is governed by a number of World Trade Organization (WTO) trade agreements. Trade-Related Aspects of Intellectual Property Rights (TRIPS), which requires WTO members to increase and enforce intellectual property rights, has been perhaps the most controversial WTO agreement in relation to the HIV and AIDS pandemic. Under TRIPS, patent-holders have exclusive rights to their inventions for a period of no less than twenty years, which has led to a monopoly on setting prices for patent-protected antiretroviral drugs. Civil society groups, including Treatment Action Campaign in South Africa, the Third World Network, and Médecins Sans Frontières, have brought the injustice of this legal framework that privileges private profit over human life to the world's attention. But the basic framework has remained unchanged since TRIPS came into effect in 1995 (Thomas, 2003) despite the Ministerial Declaration on the TRIPS Agreement and Public Health adopted at the Doha Ministerial Conference in 2001, which allowed for the granting of compulsory licenses in 'national emergencies' (Heywood, 2004).

Implications of TRIPS are especially salient since the treatment of AIDS through antiretroviral drugs has become the most popular item on the HIV agenda for international donors. Recent data from the World Health

Organization puts access to antiretroviral therapy (ART) in sub-Saharan Africa at 30 per cent, up from 21 per cent in 2006 (WHO, 2009). With the increase in the production and distribution of generic drugs, life-extending treatment has been supplied through a range of mechanisms: brokered country-specific price breaks for individual drugs or combinations, corporate donations, the United States President's Emergency Plan for AIDS Relief (PEPFAR) and the Global Fund to Fight HIV/AIDS, Tuberculosis and Malaria. 'Saving African Lives' through the provision of ART has also become a marketing strategy for a range of Western corporations through (PRODUCT) RED, which is discussed by Lisa Ann Richey elsewhere in this volume. In these marketing campaigns, shoppers in the North are told that they can keep their 'African brothers and sisters alive' with just '2 pills a day' through their purchases of specific products that channel resources to the Global Fund (http//www.joinred.com/Home.aspx). These acts of 'compassionate consumption' mask and silence the relationship between overconsumption in the North and the grim state of public health in the South (Labonte and O'Manique, 2008).

An open question is what will happen when pilot projects and existing funds, such as PEPFAR, for the scaling-up of ART come to an end. What will happen when those receiving ART require different formulations than those currently under WTO patent protection or for which price breaks have not been negotiated? After all, people living with HIV and AIDS need to be treated throughout the course of their lives and will need new formulations when they develop resistance to the current combination of drugs (MSF, 2009). The drugs that are effective today will not be tomorrow. Kenneth Shalden (2007) has argued that TRIPS has engendered changes that threaten the future supply of high-quality, generic antiretroviral drugs needed for AIDS treatment, which in turn creates a challenge for the scaling-up and the long-term maintenance of treatment regimens. According to such arguments, TRIPS has transformed market structures by dramatically reducing incentives to invest in the production of generic versions of new antiretroviral drugs that are known as 'hybrid generics' – drugs that have high production costs but low prices. Shalden hypothesized that there will be little economic incentive to produce such new drugs, regardless of existing intellectual property provisions that allow firms to do so. Similarly, there will be little incentive to grant compulsory licenses or use parallel imports in the case of a 'health emergency.' The costs of reverse-engineering, producing and marketing these new drugs are quite high, as are the transaction costs that derive from the legal environment. It is therefore 'an activity with exceptionally thin [profit] margins' (p. 571).

Efforts to scale-up treatment are also hampered by bottlenecks, such as the inadequate human and physical capacity in relevant health sectors and the absence of other conditions necessary to the health of people living with HIV and AIDS, such as access to nutritious food, primary health care and treatment for other endemic health conditions (Schoepf et al., 2000; Stillwaggon, 2006). Moreover, the focus on ART has diverted attention from some of the other factors that contribute to poor health, either alongside HIV or on their own. The social determinants of health are equally neglected. Laurie Garrett (2007) recently reported that while many HIV-positive mothers are given ART to manage their infection and prevent the transmission of the virus to their babies, some of them still cannot obtain even the most basic obstetric and gynecological care or immunization for their infants. Although women have been among the first to receive ART in certain contexts because of campaigns to prevent mother-to-child transmission and their more frequent contact with the health care system, this may change as treatment programmes move into the general population (Cohen et al., 2007, p. 383). Cohen et al. speak to the range of factors that may impede the access of women to ART unless the systemic barriers to health care are addressed, including sexual coercion and fear of retaliatory violence in the case of a positive HIV test, and unequal access to education, property and income (p. 384).

Much analysis of TRIPS and the HIV and AIDS epidemic has focused on the issue of affordability of ART. Less attention has been paid to the manner in which the current intellectual property architecture shapes drug research agendas. The only common prevention technology that exists – a full three decades into the pandemic – is condoms, which, if used consistently, eliminate the possibility of pregnancy and are often difficult for women to use without the consent of male partners. Microbicides are being developed, some of which are non-contraceptive tools, a technology that would give women the power to protect themselves from infection. But research has moved at a snail's pace and depended on a broad-based advocacy campaign and funding from donors, governments and multilateral institutions since it is 'not in the economic self-interest of pharmaceutical companies to fill this R&D gap' (Global Campaign for Microbicides, 2009). According to the Global Campaign for Microbicides, there are currently nine clinical trials being undertaken around the world, but it could be more than a decade before any microbicides are approved for use. Therapeutic or preventive vaccines and pediatric formulations of ART fall into the same category, as the main beneficiaries live in the global South, and are simply not profitable for private industry to develop. At the centre of the debate are the contradictions of a global market-based system that puts profit before the interests of people who could benefit from these drugs.

This is not to say that the scale-up of ART is not critically important, nor that vertical programmes focusing exclusively on HIV and AIDS are not needed. However, it is important to point out that these programmes are often skewed by the priorities of Western donors, who are attracted to technological 'quick fixes' with results that can be easily measured in quantifiable terms, which are easy to market to their national constituencies. Some argue that the scale-up of ART will encourage investment in the infrastructure and human resources needed to run the programmes: states and donors will dedicate resources to the health sector in order to shore up the capacity to deliver ART, with potentially positive spin-off effects for health services in general (UNAIDS, 2008, p. 154). However, it remains to be seen whether this can happen. The provision of ART is critically important. But it is not enough.

Agriculture, trade and the risk environment for HIV

Access to drugs and intellectual property laws is just one aspect of the complicated relationship between trade and HIV and AIDS. An understanding of the links between trade policies and the food security crisis in certain parts of sub-Saharan Africa and between these elements and local epidemics lies much further out on the margins of AIDS research and policy. In early 2000, Alex de Waal put forth the 'new variant famine' hypothesis. New variant famine is 'an episode of acute food insecurity fuelled by the loss of human capacity in agriculture' that has resulted from the HIV and AIDS pandemic and that, according to de Waal and Tumushabe, is 'threatening a social calamity on a scale not witnessed before in the continent' (de Waal and Tumushabe, 2003, p. 2). The hypothesis posits a new kind of acute food crisis in which there is no expectation of a return to sustainable livelihoods. In the past, households and communities were able to withstand periodic drought or a food emergency, and once the crisis was over, there was a return to a 'normal' situation. However, agrarian households that are affected by HIV and AIDS are more susceptible and less resilient to external shocks. When family members are dying or too ill to farm and bring in the harvest, acute food crises have more permanent effects. AIDS-related mortality and morbidity have the potential to permanently undermine household subsistence in many areas of high HIV prevalence.

The synergies between HIV and AIDS, household food security and the overarching macroeconomic frameworks and conditionalities that shape agricultural sector policies are poorly understood. The WTO Agreement on Agriculture poses a challenge for self-sufficiency in the South since only monetized transactions are counted as productive, whereas subsistence agriculture, indigenous labour practices, seed saving and other forms of commons management lie outside of the model (McMichael, 2004). It has been long recognized that, in most African countries, women form the backbone of subsistence food provision and that their contribution to household food security has suffered disproportionately from the drive to export products, at the expense of food production for domestic consumption. The promotion of export crops has reinforced the bias against the subsistence sector, and women farmers have been neglected in terms of access to credit and extension services, labour-saving technologies and transport facilities.

The billions of dollars in farm subsidies and price supports provided by the United States and European Union countries place African exporters at a competitive disadvantage and undermine the potential gains that might result from trade liberalization. Subsidies keep global prices artificially low, undermine rural livelihoods and food security through unfair competition in local markets and result in lost market share in export markets, particularly as African countries cannot compete with the prices of dumped or subsidized commodities (Oxfam, 2006). Donna Lee's (2007) recent analysis of domestic subsidies for cotton producers in the United States puts the cost to Central and West African cotton farmers at an estimated US$1 billion in lost export revenues. While cotton production in Africa increased by 14 per cent between 1999 and 2002, export earnings fell by 31 per cent. Single commodity producers are the hardest hit. As Lee states, 'cotton production and exports play a vital strategic role in the … continued underdevelopment of the 33 net cotton export countries' (p. 141). The impacts on farming households could not be more profound: they cannot earn enough income to send their children to school, to buy basic necessities or to feed their families. While seemingly removed from the HIV and AIDS epidemic, these issues determine sustainable livelihoods in rural agricultural households and the associated resilience and capacity of those households to deal with health emergencies.

Conclusion

The scale-up of HIV prevention strategies and antiretroviral therapy has not been matched by policies that address the structural factors that contribute to the transmission of HIV and place certain people at greater risk. Indeed, some of the current policies and institutional cultures that shape responses serve to mask the structural power that will continue to condition the political geography of the pandemic and undermine local and national responses. Despite the vast and complex web of private and public initiatives, the growing list of foundations and celebrities embracing the cause, and the exponential growth in the production of scientific knowledge about HIV and AIDS, the pandemic continues to exact a devastating toll and will likely do so for many decades to come.

What does this mean for research and policy? Our construction of the disease and the epidemic matters as it shapes how responses are conceptualized and implemented. Integrating an understanding of the gendered nature of globalization into analyses of the pandemic in sub-Saharan Africa and elsewhere will help to demystify global processes and clarify what needs to change and where pressure needs to be directed in a macro-policy framework.

The response to HIV and AIDS is not just a question of health policy. Claims that globalization has produced higher standards of living and well-being across the board (Wolf, 2004) are contradicted by realities on the ground, as reflected in the persistence of inequalities and human rights abuses that are shaping individual epidemics within the global pandemic. We therefore need analyses that relate local understandings with meso- and macro-level analyses of global political economic frameworks and HIV and AIDS responses. Collaboration and interdisciplinary research that bring together specialist knowledge of biomedicine, anthropology, public health, political economy, human rights and feminist and gender analysis will usefully inform mainstream technical approaches and draw attention to the structural violence within which HIV epidemics are embedded. A gender lens can be a galvanizing force to bring about systemic change.

References

Bakker, I. and Gill, S. 2003. Ontology, method and hypotheses. I. Bakker and S. Gill (eds), *Power, Production and Social Reproduction*. Basingstoke, United Kingdom, Palgrave MacMillan.

Barnett, T. and Whiteside, A. 2002. *AIDS in the Twenty-First Century: Disease and Globalization*. Basingstoke, United Kingdom, Palgrave MacMillan.

Baylies, C. 2002. HIV/AIDS and older women in Zambia: Concern over self, worry over daughters, towers of strength. *Third World Quarterly*, Vol. 23, No. 2, pp. 351–76.

Baylies, C. and Burja, J. 2000. The struggle continues: Some conclusions. C. Baylies and J. Burja (eds), *Aids, Sexuality and Gender in Africa*. London, Routledge.

Bond, P. 2007. Microcredit evangelism, health and social policy. *International Journal of Health Services*, Vol. 37, No. 2, pp. 229–49.

Brysk, A. 2002. Transnational threats and opportunities. A. Brysk (ed.), *Globalization and Human Rights*. Berkeley, Calif., University of California Press, pp. 1–16.

Cheru, F. 2002. Debt, adjustment and the politics of effective response to HIV/AIDS in Africa. *Third World Quarterly*, Vol. 23, No. 2, pp. 299–312.

Cohen, J., Kass, N. and Beyrer, C. 2007. *Human Rights and Public Health Ethics: Responding to the Global HIV/AIDS Pandemic*. C. Beyrer and H. F. Pizer (eds), Baltimore, MD, Johns Hopkins University Press, pp. 362–90.

de Waal, A. and Tumushabe, J. 2003. HIV/AIDS and Food Security in Africa: A Report for the UK Department for International Development. A report for DFID, draft, London.

Fourie, P. 2004. Multi stakeholders with multiple perspectives: HIV/AIDS in Africa. *Development*, Vol. 47, No. 4, pp. 54–99.

Garrett, L. 2007. The challenge of global health. *Foreign Affairs*, Vol. 86, No. 1. http://www.foreignaffairs.org/20070101faessay86103/laurie-garrett/the-challenge-of-global-health.html

Gershman, J. and Irwin, A. 2000. Getting a grip on the global economy. J. Y. Kim, J. V. Millen, A. Irwin and J. Gershman (eds), *Dying for Growth*. Monroe, Maine, Common Courage Press, pp. 11–43.

Global Campaign for Microbicides. 2009. *About Microbicides*. http:www.globalcampaign.org/about_microbicides.htm (Accessed 9 April 2009.)

Green, R. H. 1989. The broken pot: The social fabric, ecology, disaster and adjustment in Africa. Bade Onimode (ed.), *The IMF, the World Bank and African Debt: The Social and Political Impact*. London, Zed Books, pp. 31–55.

Harvey, D. 2005. *A Brief History of Neoliberalism*. Oxford, United Kingdom, Oxford University Press.

Heywood, M. 2004. Drug access, patents and global health: 'Chaffed and waxed sufficient'. N. K. Poku and A. Whiteside (eds), *Global Health and Governance: HIV/AIDS*. Basingstoke, United Kingdom, Palgrave MacMillan, pp. 27–41.

Hunter, M. 2007. The changing political economy of sex in South Africa: The significance of unemployment and inequality to the scale of the AIDS pandemic. *Social Science and Medicine*, Vol. 61, pp. 689–700.

Izumi, K. 2006. *Reclaiming Our Lives: HIV and AIDS, Women's Land and Property Rights and Livelihoods in Southern and East Africa*. Cape Town, HSRC Press.

Killewo, J., Lwihula, G., Sandström, A. and Dahlgren, L. (eds). 1989. *Behavioural and Epidemiological Aspects of AIDS Research in Tanzania*. Proceedings of a workshop held in Dar Es Salaam, Tanzania, December, 1989. SAREC Documentation report (published in 1992).

Labonte, R. and O'Manique, C. 2008. Rethinking (Product) RED. *Lancet*, Vol. 371, No. 9624, pp. 1561–563.

Lee, D. 2007. The cotton club: The Africa Group in the Doha development agenda. D. Lee and R. Wilkinson (eds), *The WTO after Hong Kong*. New York, Routledge.

Lee, K. and Goodman, H. 2002. Global policy networks: The propagation of health care financing reform since the 1980s. J. Y. Kim, J. V. Millen, K. Lee, K. Buse and S. Fustukian (eds), *Health Policy in a Globalizing World*. Cambridge, United Kingdom, Cambridge University Press.

Marchand, M. H. and Sisson Runyan, A. (eds). 2000. *Gender and Global Restructuring, Sightings, Sites and Resistances*. New York, Routledge.

McMichael, P. 2004. *Global Development and the Corporate Food Regime*. Sustaining a Future for Agriculture Conference, Geneva, 16–19 November 2004. http://www. agribusinessaccountability.org/pdfs/297_GlobalDevelopment and%20the%20 Corporate%20Food%20Regime.pdf (Accessed 16 February 2009.)

Mohanty, C. T. 2004. *Feminism Without Borders*. Durham, NC, Duke University Press.

MSF (Médicins Sans Frontières). 2009. *Special Report: HIV/AIDS Treatment in Developing Countries*. Geneva, MSF. http://www.dwb.org/publications/article. cfm?id=3742&cat=special-report&ref=footer-features

Nattrass, N. 2003. *The Moral Economy of AIDS in South Africa*. Cambridge, United Kingdom, Cambridge University Press.

O'Manique, C. 2004. *Neoliberalism and AIDS Crisis in Sub-Saharan Africa: Globalization's Pandemic*. Basingstoke, United Kingdom, Palgrave Macmillan.

Ostergard, R. 2004. Politics in the hot zone: AIDS and national security in Africa. N. K. Poku and A. Whiteside (eds), *Global Health and Governance: HIV/AIDS*. Basingstoke, United Kingdom, Palgrave MacMillan, pp. 123–42.

Oxfam. 2006. *Causing Hunger: An Overview of the Food Crisis in Africa.* (Briefing Paper #91.) http://www.cfr.org/publication/11625/oxfam.html (Accessed 26 February 2009.)

Petchesky, R. 2003. *Global Prescriptions: Gendering Health and Human Rights.* London, Zed Books.

Peterson, S. V. 2003. *A Critical Rewriting of Global Political Economy: Integrating Reproductive, Productive and Virtual Economies.* New York, Routledge.

Piot, P., Kreiss, J. K., Ndinya-Achola, J. O., Ngugi, E. N., Simonsen, J. N., Cameron, D. W., Taelman, H., Plummer, F. A. 1987. Heterosexual transmission of HIV. *AIDS,* Vol. 1, pp. 199–206.

Poku, N. K. 2004. Confronting AIDS with debt: Africa's silent crisis. N. K. Poku and A. Whiteside (eds), *Global Health and Governance: HIV/AIDS.* Basingstoke, United Kingdom, Palgrave Macmillan, pp. 33–49.

Poku, N. K. and Whiteside, A. (eds). 2004. *Global Health and Governance: HIV/AIDS.* Basingstoke, United Kingdom, Palgrave Macmillan.

Price-Smith, A. T. 2003. *The HIV/AIDS Pandemic as a Threat to Governance and National Security: The Case of South Africa.* Annual meeting of the International Studies Association, Portland, Oregon.

Product RED. http://www.joinred.com/Home.aspx (Accessed 4 March 2009.)

Pogge, T. 2005. Recognized and violated by international law: The human rights of the global poor. *Leiden Journal of International Law,* Vol. 18, pp. 717–45.

Rankin, K. 2001. Governing development: Neoliberalism, microcredit and rational economic woman. *Economy and Society,* Vol. 30, No. 1, pp. 18–37.

Schoepf, B. G. 1991*a*. Ethical, methodological, and political issues of AIDS research in Central Africa. *Social Science and Medicine,* Vol. 33, No. 7, pp. 749–63.

Schoepf, B. G. 1991*b*. Political economy, sex, and cultural logics: A view from Zaire. *African Urban Quarterly,* Vol. 6, Nos 1/2, pp. 94–106.

Schoepf, B. G., Schoepf, C. and Millen, J. V. 2000. Theoretical therapies, remote remedies: SAPs and the political ecology of poverty and health in Africa. J. Y. Kim, J. V. Millen, A. Irwin and J. Gershman (eds), *Dying for Growth: Global Inequality and the Health of the Poor.* Monroe, Maine, Common Courage Press.

Serwadda, D. 1985. Slim disease: A new disease in Uganda and its association with HTLV-III Infection. *Lancet,* Vol. 19, pp. 849–52.

Shalden, K. C. 2007. The political economy of AIDS treatment: Intellectual property and the transformation of generic supply. *International Studies Quarterly,* Vol. 51, No. 3, pp. 559–81.

Stewart, S. 1997. Happy ever after in the marketplace: Non-government organisations and uncivil society. *Review of African Political Economy,* Vol. 24, No. 71, pp. 11-34.

Stillwaggon, E. 2006. *AIDS and the Ecology of Poverty.* New York, Oxford University Press.

Thomas, C. 2003. Trade policy, the politics of access to drugs and global governance for health. Kelley Lee (ed.), *Health Impacts of Globalization: Towards Global Governance,* Basingstoke, United Kingdom, Palgrave Macmillan, pp. 177-191.

UNAIDS (Joint United Nations Program on HIV/AIDS). 2008. *UNAIDS Annual Report 2007: Knowing Your Epidemic.* New York/Geneva, UNAIDS.

WHO (World Health Organization). 2009. *Millennium Development Goal 6.* www.who. int/hiv/topics/mdg/info/en/print.html (Accessed 22 April 2009.)

Wolf, M. 2004. *Why Globalization Works.* Boston, Mass., Yale University Press.

World Bank. 2001. *Engendering Development Through Gender Equality in Rights, Resources, and Voice.* New York, World Bank/Oxford University Press.

CHAPTER 2

Social exclusion: The gendering of adolescent HIV risk in South Africa

Kelly K. Hallman

Young people coming of age in South Africa at the beginning of this new millennium face a number of challenges. Although the country has been a modernizing constitutional democracy since 1994, the legacy of the apartheid era continues to have an impact on the daily lives of most inhabitants. The country's complex historical, sociocultural and political environment – where stigma and denial hold sway – has increased socio-economic inequalities and fuelled the spread of the HIV and AIDS epidemic, deepening its impact on individuals, families and communities. Nowhere is this more pronounced than in KwaZulu-Natal, the province that experienced some of the worst violence during the struggle to end apartheid. KwaZulu-Natal has the highest levels of HIV prevalence in South Africa, especially among young people, and in particular young women. In sub-Saharan Africa, 75 per cent of 15–24-year-olds living with HIV are female (UNAIDS, 2006). A nationally representative survey in South Africa in 2005 (Shisana et al., 2005) found that HIV prevalence among 15–24-year-olds was 16.9 per cent for females and 4.4 per cent for males – a nearly four fold difference. The gendered ratio of new infections among this age group was even more extreme at eight-to-one female (incidence of 6.5 per cent versus 0.8 per cent per year). The national HIV prevalence among 15–24-year olds is 10.3 per cent; KwaZulu-Natal has by far the highest level at 16.1 per cent. Young women and young men are both increasingly exposed to competing and often contradictory influences regarding lifestyles that are healthy, appropriate and socially desirable; these influences have ranged from the norms propagated by community elders to those of sophisticated global media campaigns.

The designations employed and the presentation of material throughout this publication do not imply the expression of any opinion whatsoever on the part of UNESCO concerning the legal status of any country, territory or area or of its authorities, or concerning the delimitation of its frontiers or boundaries.
The ideas and opinions expressed in this publication are those of the authors and do not necessarily reflect the views of UNESCO and its Member States.

Although a multitude of programmes focusing on individual behaviour change exist to curb the spread of HIV – with many designs influenced by programmes in the North – the effectiveness of such approaches at quelling this increasingly gender- and age-stratified epidemic can be characterized as anaemic at best and harmful at worst. Members of HIV-affected communities have called for a shift from individual behaviourally focused interventions to those that acknowledge and address historically imbued, gendered environmental and structural risk factors faced by young women and young men of various ages, races and socio-economic groups. 'Gendered' here does not simply refer to differences between women and men but rather to the complexities of power relationships that have evolved between them within a context that has been deeply altered by state-mandated distortions of structures of production, physical mobility, family arrangements and social relations.

This chapter, which draws on a larger and ongoing study, aims to assess the impact of a selection of these structural factors on gendered HIV risks for young people. The particular focus is to investigate among adolescents in KwaZulu-Natal the influences of social capital within their communities while controlling for two other key aspects of structural risk in the South African environment: poverty status and orphanhood. A handful of studies from sub-Saharan Africa have examined the relationship between adolescent sexual experiences and voluntary group membership (Camlin and Snow, 2008; Campbell et al., 2002; Gregson et al., 2004), but none has assessed the associations with perceived levels of community reciprocity and trust. This research attempts to begin to fill this gap by examining the associations by gender between adolescent sexual risk experiences/behaviours and two dimensions of social capital, namely: community trust and reciprocity, and individual membership in community groups. Measures of community trust and reciprocity are based on questions asked of each adolescent about own-friendship networks; perceptions of community trust, cohesion and reciprocity; perceived levels of community crime and safety; and if s/he would be happier if s/he lived in a different community. Individual membership in community groups is measured by responses to questions about membership in nine types of groups.

The concept of social capital

Putnam's (1993, 1995, 2000) concept of social capital has been used to explore the link between health and community networks and trust. For Putnam, social capital refers to the cohesion within a community that results from high levels of civic engagement, in particular membership in voluntary community groups, which is in turn allegedly associated with reciprocity, trust and positive local identity. Research on this concept in relation to health asserts that social networks and support can bolster health-enhancing behaviours and thus serve as a buffer to the health-damaging stressors frequently encountered in low-resource environments (Kawachi and Kennedy, 1997; Tawil et al., 1995). The mechanisms through which this occurs are likely to be complex and are not yet well-understood. Baum (1999) emphasized that whereas greater social capital may lead to more positive health outcomes in some settings, not all forms of social capital are necessarily positive and health-enhancing, for example, membership of youths in gangs. Moreover, some tight-knit communities may be distrustful and exclusionary and therefore potentially health-damaging to individuals who are viewed as not belonging. In Namibia, Lorway (see Chapter 14) found that associating with international HIV gay groups increased social capital at some levels but also caused violence and discrimination at others. Campbell et al. (1999) further argue that social capital is a resource that is not uniform or equally available to all individuals within a community and that the impact of community norms of trust and reciprocity on health and health behaviours might vary greatly according to a person's age, gender, socio-economic status and ethnicity.

Social capital has been measured in a variety of ways and can potentially influence adolescent behaviours and outcomes in a number of ways. Membership in groups and other social networks can offer encouragement for the reinforcement and sustainability of positive (or negative) behaviours (Latkin and Knowlton, 2005). Members of social networks can act as sources of insurance and credit during times of economic hardship. This may, in turn, lessen the desire to engage in sexual relationships for economic support (Baylies, 2000; Cohen, 1998). In the event of parental morbidity, trusted friends and extended family may offer assistance with care and provide psychosocial support to an adolescent. These sources of social support may reduce the possibility of psychological distress – and the accompanying depression and negative acting-out behaviours – and of performing poorly in or dropping out of school (Hartell and Chabilall, 2005). The same may hold true after the occurrence of a major household event, such as parental death (Campbell et al., 2005). As described in other research (Lester et al., 2006; Wood et al., 2006), parental loss is highly complex and its consequences for adolescents vary according to gender, developmental stage, innate resilience, quality of available care and social support networks. In addition to individual networks and membership in voluntary community groups, perceptions of the community, trust in community institutions and neighbours, perceptions of local social cohesion and mutual respect, and perceptions of solidarity, support and reciprocity can all influence the extent to which social, health and other types of supports and services are sought and utilized by adolescents (Harpham et al., 2005). They also reflect the degree to which parents and other community members are able to jointly exert social norms and informal social control to influence the values and behaviours of children and adolescents (Browning et al., 2004).

Evidence on social capital and HIV risk

Although many HIV interventions are organized as network and community organizations (e.g. HIV support groups, gay/lesbian groups, and in South Africa – most visibly – the Treatment Action Campaign), few investigations have been conducted on the association between social capital and adolescent sexual experiences and HIV vulnerability in sub-Saharan Africa. The few studies that have focused on voluntary membership in community groups have not examined the effects of community social cohesion on sexual behaviour.

Although their experiences and social circumstances are not directly comparable, the evidence from young people living in urban settings in the United States is informative, nonetheless. Significant relationships between social capital and adolescent HIV and sexual health risk behaviours have been documented. Crosby et al. (2003) assessed the effects of social capital, poverty and income inequality on adolescent sexual risk behaviours using the national 1999 Youth Risk Behaviour Surveillance Survey. In multivariate analysis, only social capital (social networks and interactions) was significant and was inversely correlated with sexual risk behaviours and positively correlated with protective behaviours. Gold et al. (2002), using path analysis, investigated the hypothesis that the causal link between income inequality and poor health is through social capital. According to this hypothesis, income inequality undermines social cohesion, civic engagement and mutual trust in the community. Using data from thirty-nine US states, they found that both poverty and income inequality were associated with higher teen birth rates, with the effect of the latter being primarily through its impact on social capital. Browning et al. (2004) studied the effects of community cohesion on adolescent sexual behaviours using multilevel data from Chicago. This study reveals that higher levels of neighbourhood trust and reciprocity – referred to by the authors as 'collective efficacy' – contributed to the delay of sexual onset among adolescents. The reasoning was that neighbourhood structural disadvantage (economic insecurity, insecure housing tenure and a high proportion of recent immigrants) inhibits the formation of social capital, which in turn reduces the ability of local residents to mobilize around neighbourhood goals, including the effective supervision and socialization of children and teenagers. Although the authors control for gender in their multivariate analysis, they do not disaggregate by gender and therefore cannot assess the impact of collective efficacy on girls versus boys. Yet another hypothesis, borne out in the poor slums of Bogota, Colombia, is that low levels of community social cohesion can reduce the utilization of social, health and other types of services and facilities by adolescents – especially girls (Harpham et al., 2005).

The studies in sub-Saharan Africa that associate social capital and adolescent sexual experiences and HIV vulnerability concentrate on membership in community groups – although a handful have looked at the extent to which community safety, as perceived by adolescents, is associated with sexual and reproductive health behaviours by gender (Brady, 2003; Kenworthy et al., 2008). Some of the impacts of group membership are similar to those found in the United States, but in other instances, they differ. Gregson et al. (2004) showed that among young Zimbabwean women aged between 15 and 24, membership in various types of voluntary community groups had a range of associations with being HIV sero-negative. Controlling for other factors, young women with secondary education who belong to a community group they describe as well-functioning were more successful in having avoided HIV infection than those who did not belong to such a group; this was particularly the case for membership in youth, women's and church groups. For women without any secondary education, on the other hand, HIV avoidance was positively related to youth group membership and negatively related to membership in political parties. In KwaZulu-Natal, Kaufman et al. (2004) analyse the effect of community characteristics and own-club membership (sports, religious and an aggregated 'other types' category) on whether 14–24-year-olds had had sex in the year before the survey, and if they had sex during that time, whether a condom was used at the last encounter. The authors find that in communities where young people had high rates of participation in sports activities, girls had decreased odds of recent sexual activity, but boys had significantly lower chances of having used a condom at last sex. In a different part of South Africa, Campbell et al. (2002) examined the association between adult and adolescent membership in voluntary organizations and three HIV-related risk behaviours (having casual sexual partners, condom use with casual partners and alcohol consumption) and HIV sero-status. Using multivariate analysis of variance, they find a range of significant results that varied by age and gender, and not all of the associations were what had been expected beforehand. Among those who belonged to sports clubs, young men and young women were less likely to be HIV-positive, and young women were more likely to use condoms with casual partners than non-members. However, among those belonging to *stokvels* (voluntary savings clubs that include social activities), young men were more likely to be HIV-positive, women of all ages were more likely to have a casual partner, and both young men and young women were more likely to drink alcohol than non-members. Finally, Camlin and Snow (2008) use the Cape Area Panel Study to assess the effects of club membership and parental investment on condom use at first sex and condom use at most recent sex among 14–22-year-olds in Cape Town. The authors use an indicator for any club membership, but unfortunately, their analysis is not disaggregated by gender. Controlling for other factors their multivariate results reveal that club membership is positively associated with condom use at both first and last sex.

Two studies among adults in the region are also worth mentioning. Kohler et al. (2007) use longitudinal survey data from rural Kenya and Malawi to test the hypothesis that social interactions – specifically the extent to which members of social networks perceive themselves to be at risk – exert causal influences on adult respondents' risk perceptions, prevention approaches and communication about the threat of HIV infection to spouses and children. Their study found that social networks have significant and substantial effects on risk perceptions and the adoption of new behaviours, even after observed and unobserved factors are controlled for. In rural South Africa, Pronyk et al. (2005) found community structural factors associated with higher HIV prevalence among adults. For both men and women, these included easier access to a trading centre, higher proportions of short-term residents and lower levels of social capital. HIV prevalence was higher in settings where the social order had broken down or had never been established in the first place. Among men, higher HIV prevalence was also observed in communities with easier access to a local mine, a higher density and activity of local bars, higher numbers of sex workers per village and lower proportions of out-migrants. Pronyk et al. (2006), on the other hand, found that targeted HIV community information and education campaigns together with microcredit for women decreased intimate-partner violence.

While these results are instructive, there is still a lack of evidence on the effects of both individual group membership and community-level trust and reciprocity on the gendered sexual health behaviours of adolescents in sub-Saharan Africa. This is especially salient in contexts in which there are high and gendered levels of HIV prevalence, changing and overstressed family configurations due to AIDS, a history of migrant seasonal labour, and shifting social relations and norms. This chapter assesses the effects of these two forms of social capital on adolescent sexual and HIV risk experiences and behaviours in KwaZulu-Natal, South Africa.

Data and methods

The analysis in this chapter uses data from the 2001 survey *Transitions to Adulthood in the Context of AIDS in South Africa* conducted in KwaZulu-Natal (Magnani et al., 2005; Rutenberg et al., 2001). The survey included interviews with young people aged between 14 and 24 and covered many aspects of the passage from childhood to adulthood, with questions being directed to adolescents themselves in one-on-one interviews with same sex, race and native language enumerators on topics such as schooling; paid and unpaid work; sexual and reproductive health and HIV and AIDS knowledge, attitudes and behaviours; child-bearing; marriage; individual membership in voluntary community groups; and individual perceptions of community reciprocity and trust. This section uses the subsample of adolescents aged between 14 and 18.

Variables

An individual-level social inclusion indicator was constructed based on the work of Morrison et al. (2005) and Harpham et al. (2005). Each adolescent was asked about own-friendship networks; perceptions of community trust, cohesion and reciprocity; perceived levels of community crime and safety; and if s/he would be happier if s/he lived in a different community. Specifically, the variable is constructed by summing the responses to the five questions and then defining a binary indicator of 'less connected', for those with scores below the median value of 3, and 'more connected', for those with scores equal to or above the median value. A voluntary community group involvement measure was constructed based on the research of Haddad and Maluccio (2003) in South

Africa and Campbell et al. (2002) in South Africa. Affirmative responses to membership in nine types of groups were assessed; unfortunately, membership in HIV-related groups was not assessed during the survey because of privacy and stigma-related concerns.

The key behavioural and experiential outcomes examined for girls and boys were: (1) whether the adolescent had ever had vaginal and/or anal sex; (2) if they answered 'yes' to the first question, they were asked whether s/he was or was not a 'willing' party in the first sex act; (3) whether s/he ever experienced non-consensual sex; (4) whether s/he had ever received money, goods or favours in exchange for sex; (5) if they had sex in the twelve months before the survey, did they use a condom at the last sex act; and (6) if they had sex, did they have multiple sexual partners in the twelve months before the survey. Regrettably, the timing and conditions around receiving items in exchange for sex are not available in the survey. In general there are currently few examples of standardized questions on the topic of HIV and reproductive health in developing countries.

Findings

Results show that boys tend to report feeling more 'included' in their communities than girls (P ≤ .001) and are more likely to report having many friends (see Table 1). They are likely to report that they feel safe moving about in the community and that trust between neighbours is high. The one exception is that more boys than girls felt they would be happier living elsewhere. This is likely to be correlated with the greater degree of mobility that adolescent males have relative to females (Kenworthy et al., 2008), as well as historical labour patterns.

Boys were more likely than girls to belong to voluntary groups (see Table 2). One third of female and one fourth of male respondents did not belong to any group. Males were most likely to belong to a sports group, whereas female involvement was greatest in religious groups – both indications of gendered social role norms during adolescence (Mensch et al., 1998). Boys and girls were equally likely to belong to music and dance groups. Few young people reported belonging to groups related to livelihood security. *Stokvels* and other savings schemes and products have historically been the territory of adults and not young people (Piprek et al., 2004), and community garden and sewing groups did not exist to any great extent in the area where the survey was conducted.

Table 1. Adolescent-reported community social cohesion (14–18-year-olds)

	GIRLS	BOYS
'I have many friends in this community' (1=agree; 0=disagree)	57%	81%
'I feel safe walking around in my neighbourhood during the day' (1=agree; 0=disagree)	85%	93%
'There is a lot of crime in my neighbourhood' (0=agree; 1=disagree)*	54%	53%
'I would be happier living in a different community' (0=agree; 1=disagree)*	50%	60%
'People in this neighbourhood trust each other' (1=agree; 0=disagree)	54%	66%
Mean number of 'agree' responses	2.93	3.26

*These are negative questions, so response codes were reversed. This transformation was performed in order to make all items in the index positive and hence consistent.

Table 2. Group membership (14–18-year-olds)

	GIRLS	BOYS
Savings group or *stokvel*	5%	4%
Community garden group	1%	2%
Sewing group	1%	0%
Sports group	22%	56%
Study group	14%	25%
Dancing, singing, music or choir group	18%	18%
Religious group	41%	26%
Other type of group	19%	15%
Mean number of groups affiliated with	1.19	1.48
Percentage with any group affiliation	66%	77%

Table 3. Sexual experience by social capital, males and females aged 14–18 years (proportion): means of outcome measures

	FEMALES			MALES		
	Mean	More cohesive community	Less cohesive community	Mean	More cohesive community	Less cohesive community
Ever had sex (entire sample)	0.31	0.29	0.33	0.43	0.42	0.44
First sex was unwilling (sexually debuted)	0.46	0.44	0.50	0.06	0.05	0.10
Ever experienced non-consensual sex (entire sample)	0.16	0.15*	0.19*	0.04	0.04	0.05
Ever traded sex for money, goods or favours (entire sample)	0.02	0.02	0.02	0.01	0.01	0.00
Used a condom at last sex (those who had sex in 12 months before survey)	0.58	0.59	0.56	0.69	0.71	0.62
Multiple partners in 12 months before survey (sexually debuted)	0.09	0.09	0.07	0.36	0.35	0.40

	Mean	Belongs to a voluntary community group	Does not belong to any voluntary community group	Mean	Belongs to a voluntary community group	Does not belong to any voluntary community group
Ever had sex (entire sample)	0.31	0.26 ***	0.39 ***	0.43	0.44 *	0.37 *
First sex was unwilling (sexually debuted)	0.46	0.45	0.47	0.06	0.07	0.04
Ever experienced non-consensual sex (entire sample)	0.16	0.14 **	0.20 **	0.04	0.04	0.03
Ever traded sex for money, goods or favours (entire sample)	0.02	0.02	0.02	0.01	0.02	0.00
Used a condom at last sex (those who had sex in 12 months before survey)	0.58	0.65 **	0.50 **	0.69	0.70	0.64
Multiple partners in 12 months before survey (sexually debuted)	0.09	0.08	0.09	0.36	0.37	0.31

Significance of within gender differences in outcomes by social capital status: ***$P \leq .001$, **$P \leq .01$, *$P \leq .05$.

With regard to sexual behaviours/experiences (see Table 3), males are much more likely to be sexually experienced, consistent with findings from all recent South African youth surveys: around 43 per cent of males versus 31 per cent of females. Among those who are sexually experienced, females are approximately six times more likely than males to report their first encounter as unwilling (16 per cent versus 6 per cent), in line with other population-based surveys from South Africa and globally (Jejeebhoy and Bott, 2003). For all young people, the proportion of females who have ever experienced non-consensual sex is four times greater than the proportion of males, at 16 per cent versus 4 per cent. Due to the sensitive nature of questions on non-consensual sex, the research team chose not to ask for further information about the person involved or the setting where such episodes occurred. Reports of ever having exchanged sex for money, goods or favours were low at 2 per cent of females and 1 per cent of males. This may be due both to the young age of this subsample (less overall sexual experience) and to social desirability bias (under-reporting of socially stigmatized behaviours). Within the group that had had sex in the twelve months before the survey, reported condom use at last sexual encounter is relatively high for all respondents; males have higher levels than females (69 per cent versus 58 per cent). Over one-third of sexually experienced males had more than one sexual partner in the twelve months before the survey versus only 9 per cent of sexually experienced females.

Table 3 presents mean outcomes by the two constructed social capital indices: whether the adolescent resides in a more or less cohesive community (as defined previously) and membership in any voluntary community group. Girls in more cohesive communities appear able to practise safer behaviours relative to girls who reside in less cohesive communities. Most of the differences, however, are not statistically significant, with the exception of the outcome 'ever experienced non-consensual sex', which is significant at the p ≤ .05 level. Among males, differences by degree of community cohesiveness are also in the hypothesized direction, but none are statistically significant.

Outcomes vary by involvement in at least one voluntary community group. Among females, group membership is correlated with more protective behaviours, and three of the five outcome variables differ significantly at the p ≤ .01 level or greater. Girls involved in any group were much less likely to have ever had sex or to have ever experienced non-consensual sex and more likely to have used a condom at last sex. Among males, voluntary group involvement is associated with a greater likelihood of having sexually debuted. In fact, for all outcomes studied, males who belonged to community groups had

Table 4. Adjusted odds ratios on social capital indices, aged 14–18: regression results

	FEMALES		MALES	
	More (vs. less) cohesive community	Membership in any (vs. no) community group	More (vs. less) cohesive community	Membership in any (vs. no) community group
Ever had sex (entire sample)	1.270	0.537 ***	0.903	0.837
First sex was unwilling (sexually debuted)	0.802	0.373	0.188 *	1.158
Ever experienced non-consensual sex (entire sample)	0.922	0.358 ***	--	--
Ever traded sex for money, goods or favours (entire sample)	--	--	--	--
Used a condom at last sex (those who had sex in 12 months before survey)	1.255	1.754	2.118	1.624
Multiple partners in 12 months before survey (sexually debuted)	3.678	2.189	0.807	0.999

Note: Each gender-disaggregated regression controls for social capital, socio-economic status, orphanhood status, age, race, urban versus rural residence, grade attainment, household size, education level of the household head, residence in female-headed household, relationship of adolescent to the household head and region of residence.

--: Less than 5 per cent had affirmative responses to this outcome, resulting in an unstable statistical model.
***$P \le .001$, **$P \le .01$, *$P \le .05$.

higher levels of risk behaviours, even though most of the differences were not statistically significant.

Multivariate results are presented in the next series of tables. It should be noted that one gender-separate regression was run for each dependent variable, implying that all factors of interest are controlled for simultaneously. In cases where the prevalence of the dependent variable was less than 1 per cent, multivariate analysis was not undertaken because the models would have been too unstable to obtain meaningful results. Therefore, the outcomes 'ever traded sex for money, goods or favours' among the unconditional samples of girls and boys are not presented.

Table 4 presents adjusted odds ratios for the two social capital indicators, namely: residing in a more (versus less) cohesive community (e.g. above or below the median value of the distribution); and membership in a community group (as opposed to not being a member). After controlling for other factors, the community cohesion index did not yield statistically significant results for females. Among males, first sex being unwilling is significantly negatively correlated with residing in a more tight-knit community. The indicator for membership in any voluntary community group, on the other hand, has significant impacts on girls but not boys. Girls who are members of groups are less likely to have sexually debuted and are less likely to have ever experienced a non-consensual sexual encounter. Among boys, the relationships between voluntary community group membership and protective behaviours are positive or neutral, but none of the adjusted odds ratios are statistically significant.

A second set of regressions was then run where the two social capital indices are replaced with their individual components. Tables 5 and 6 present the impacts of the individually reported community cohesion factors for females and males, respectively. Among girls, there were some significant protective effects of perceived community cohesion and no significant negative results. Girls residing in communities where neighbours are perceived to trust one another were less likely to have sexually debuted at the time of the survey; this factor is also associated with girls being less apt to have ever experienced a non-consensual sexual encounter. Girls who reported they would be happier living in a different community were significantly more likely to have had multiple sexual partners in the twelve months before the survey. Among boys, perceived community cohesiveness was correlated statistically with two outcomes: having many friends in the community reduced the odds of male first sex being non-consensual; and high perceived levels of crime were associated with having more sexual partners in the twelve months before the survey.

Tables 7 and 8 present results on the effects of membership in specific types of groups for females and males, respectively. Among females, group membership is generally associated with a more protective environment. The delay of sexual debut among females is correlated with membership in most group types, with the effects of sports, study and religious groups being statistically significant. Controlling for household economic status, membership in a savings group/*stokvel* or a religious group predicts lower odds of a girl's first sexual experience being unwilling. Non-consensual sex is negatively and significantly related to membership in a sports group. Membership of girls in athletic groups also appears to greatly increase their chances of having used a condom at last sex. Having multiple sexual partners in the twelve months before the survey was not associated with community group membership for girls. The findings in Table 8 for boys show that the impacts of group membership are not as large as they are for girls, they are more mixed in direction with regard to safeness of behaviours, and only one is marginally significant statistically – boys in dance, music and choir groups are more likely to have sexually debuted relative to boys who are not members of such groups.

Discussion

This research has investigated the associations between gendered adolescent sexual behaviours/experiences and two dimensions of social capital: community social cohesion and individual membership in community groups. A handful of recent studies from sub-Saharan Africa have examined the impacts of individual membership in community groups on HIV risks for young people. None, however, has examined associations with social cohesion (trust and reciprocity among community members). Moreover, most research on this topic does not disaggregate by gender or includes only females. In a setting where gendered economic and social inequalities underlie many of the norms and behaviours that render young women and men vulnerable to HIV in differing ways, the gendered effects of structural factors deserve more full investigation.

Social cohesion was measured using responses to questions posed to each adolescent about her/his perceptions of trust and reciprocity in her/his community. An index, and then the individual components of that index, was used alternatively in separate regression specifications where community voluntary group membership was also controlled for. With the index, a more cohesive

Table 5. Adjusted odds ratios on community cohesion elements, females aged 14–18

	I have many friends in this community	I feel safe walking during the day	There is a lot of crime in this community	I would be happier if I lived elsewhere	Neighbours here trust each other
Ever had sex (entire sample)	1.30	1.32	0.95	1.29	0.74**
First sex was unwilling (sexually debuted)	0.98	0.69	0.45	0.75	0.64
Ever experienced non-consensual sex (entire sample)	1.03	1.12	0.63	1.50	0.60**
Ever traded sex for money, goods or favours (entire sample)	--	--	--	--	--
Used a condom at last sex (those who had sex in 12 months before survey)	0.63	0.62	1.54	0.88	0.83
Multiple partners in 12 months before survey (sexually debuted)	2.38	0.89	3.52	6.33**	0.35

Note: Each gender-disaggregated regression controls for social capital, socio-economic status, age, race, urban versus rural residence, grade attainment, household size, education level of the household head, residence in female-headed household, relationship of adolescent to the household head and region of residence.

--: Less than 5 per cent had affirmative responses to this outcome, resulting in an unstable statistical model.
***P≤.001, **P≤.01, *P≤.05.

Table 6. Adjusted odds ratios on community cohesion elements, males aged 14–18

	I have many friends in this community	I feel safe walking during the day	There is a lot of crime in this community	I would be happier if I lived elsewhere	Neighbours here trust each other
Ever had sex (entire sample)	0.97	0.79	1.15	0.87	0.93
First sex was unwilling (sexually debuted)	0.13**	9.65	1.41	0.39	0.39
Ever experienced non-consensual sex (entire sample)	0.75	2.90	2.34	1.74	1.26
Ever traded sex for money, goods or favours (entire sample)	--	--	--	--	--
Used a condom at last sex (those who had sex in 12 months before survey)	0.97	0.59	1.60	1.72	2.12
Multiple partners in 12 months before survey (sexually debuted)	0.71	2.02	2.59*	0.93	1.19

Note: Each gender-disaggregated regression controls for social capital, socio-economic status, orphanhood status, age, race, urban versus rural residence, grade attainment, household size, education level of the household head, residence in female-headed household, relationship of adolescent to the household head and region of residence.

--Less than 5 per cent had affirmative responses to this outcome, resulting in an unstable statistical model.

***P≤.001, **P≤.01, *P≤.05.

Table 7. Adjusted odds ratios on group membership type, females aged 14–18

	Savings Group/ *Stokvel*	Sports group	Study group	Dance, music, choir	Religious group	Other group
Ever had sex (entire sample)	1.282	0.562***	0.513*	0.856	0.741**	0.662
First sex was unwilling (sexually debuted)	0.049*	1.100	2.059	0.717	0.311**	2.039
Ever experienced non-consensual sex (entire sample)	0.572	0.377*	0.827	--	--	--
Ever traded sex for money, goods or favours (entire sample)	--	--	--	--	--	--
Used a condom at last sex (those who had sex in 12 months before survey)	0.328	11.324**	1.728	1.796	0.963	4.300
Multiple partners in 12 months before survey (sexually debuted)	0.651	0.145	xx	0.385	2.217	xx

Note: Each gender-disaggregated regression controls for social capital, socio-economic status, orphanhood status, age, race, urban versus rural residence, grade attainment, household size, education level of the household head, residence in female-headed household, relationship of adolescent to the household head and region of residence.

--: Less than 5 per cent had affirmative responses to this outcome, resulting in an unstable statistical model.
xx: regressor dropped due to predicting failure of outcome perfectly.
***P≤.001, **P≤.01, *P≤.05.

Table 8. Adjusted odds ratios on group membership type, males aged 14–18

	Savings Group/ *Stokvel*	Sports group	Study group	Dance, music, choir	Religious group	Other group
Ever had sex (entire sample)	0.759	0.882	1.166	1.401 *	0.761	1.100
First sex was unwilling (sexually debuted)	xx	2.854	0.350	0.926	1.835	3.523
Ever experienced non-consensual sex (entire sample)	--	--	--	--	--	--
Ever traded sex for money, goods or favours (entire sample)	--	--	--	--	--	--
Used a condom at last sex (those who had sex in 12 months before survey)	0.572	1.244	1.622	0.556	0.917	1.091
Multiple partners in 12 months before survey (sexually debuted)	1.763	1.097	1.288	1.101	0.692	0.727

Note: Each gender-disaggregated regression controls for social capital, socio-economic status, orphanhood status, age, race, urban versus rural residence, grade attainment, household size, education level of the household head, residence in female-headed household, relationship of adolescent to the household head and region of residence.

--: Less than 5 per cent had affirmative responses to this outcome, resulting in an unstable statistical model.
xx: regressor dropped due to predicting failure of outcome perfectly.
***P≤.001, **P≤.01, *P≤.05.

71

community was associated with lower chances of male first sexual experience being coerced; there were not significant effects on female sexual experiences. When the individual components of the index were entered as separate determinants, having more friends was associated with lower odds of male first sex being coerced (most likely through protection from coercion by older males), whereas higher perceived levels of crime were associated with greater odds of males having multiple sexual partners in the year before the survey. Higher perceived trust among neighbours was associated with a slimmer probability of females having had sex or experiencing coerced sex, whereas girls who wished they lived in a different community were more likely to have had multiple sexual partners in the year before the survey.

Using a similar set of questions to form an index, Browning et al. (2004) found in a gender-pooled analysis that trust and reciprocity within the community independently contributes to delay in the onset of sexual debut among youths in the Chicago area. Youngblade et al. (2006) found that community investment in social capital predicted lower levels of risky sexual behaviours among adolescents in Florida. It was not possible to compare these results directly to ours since the American studies did not disaggregate by gender; however trust among neighbours in both settings appears to delay sexual onset.

Belonging to any voluntary community group also had more effects on girls than boys. Multivariate results indicate this factor, even after controlling for the social reciprocity variables discussed above, is significantly associated with delayed sexual onset and lowered odds of coerced ever sex among females and coerced first sex among males. By group type, girls in sports, study and religious groups had later age of sexual onset, whereas those in sports groups were less likely to have experienced non-consensual sex and had eleven times the chances of using a condom at last sex than girls that did not form part of a sports group. The only significant group results for males were membership in a dance, music or choir group, and these were associated with *greater* odds of sexual debut.

Kaufman et al. (2004) found that sports group membership among 14–24-year-olds in KwaZulu-Natal reduced the odds of sexual debut among females but lowered the odds of males having used a condom at last sex. Results from Campbell et al. (2002) in Carletonville, South Africa, show that for 15–24-year-olds membership in sports groups and burial societies was linked with greater chances of female condom use with recent casual sex partners and that females in sports and youth groups had lower chances of being HIV-positive. In Zimbabwe, Gregson et al. (2004) found that group membership overall is associated with lower chances of females living with HIV and that well-functioning groups are more strongly associated with protection than poorly functioning groups. They also found that females with secondary education are more likely to benefit from well-functioning groups than females who do not have secondary education.

Both types of social capital measures – community social cohesion and voluntary group membership – had significant impacts on the environment in which adolescent sexual lives commence in KwaZulu-Natal. Each is important and statistically significant even when the other is controlled for: greater trust and reciprocity among community members appears to protect both male and female adolescents from the threat of non-consensual sex and to reduce the number of reported sexual partners in the year before the survey. Belonging to a voluntary community group itself also reduces the chances of non-consensual sex among both sexes; sports groups are highly associated with protection for girls. Music and dance group membership on the other hand appeared to reduce the age of sexual debut among boys.

If only one set of these social capital measures (either community social cohesion or voluntary group membership) were controlled for, the effect of the unmeasured one would be mistakenly attributed to the one that was measured and included in the regression – leading to the possibility of less than fully informed policy recommendations. Moreover, since voluntary group membership is a decision that is much more subject to individual choice than is community social cohesion, it may be much more amenable to change by programs designed to affect individual behaviours – but with the caveat that many past studies may have in fact overstated its impacts as most past research does not simultaneously control for the community social environment in which these policies are to be enacted.

According to these results programme planners and policy-makers should consider the following when designing HIV prevention programs for adolescent males and females in South Africa: First, communities perceived by adolescents to be crime-ridden and unsafe appear to increase the number of concurrent sexual partners among both males and females – perhaps this emanates from a sense of needing to experience safe and meaningful personal relationships within a turbulent and dynamic environment. Second, communities where adolescents report having trusted friends and/or neighbours seem to be associated with lower chances of reported non-consensual sexual experiences among both sexes. Being surrounded by trusted friends and/or adults may deter socially vulnerable adolescents from entering into relationships with individuals who have less than altruistic motives. It may be particularly constructive for community authorities and decision-makers to work to reduce social crime and violence and make concerted attempts to create safe social spaces where adolescent males and females can grow friendship networks and trust among same-age, same-sex peers and among older positive role models and mentors. Such safe social spaces can also be used as platforms to deliver health and livelihood skills and training to adolescents (see Bruce and Hallman, 2008). Third, voluntary community groups that were particularly associated with protection for females included study, religious and sports groups; belonging to a sports group was especially associated with a high number of positive outcomes for girls. While the effects were not statistically significant, study groups were positively correlated with boys having fewer non-consensual sexual experiences and greater chances of using condoms during their most recent sexual encounter.

Overall, the study results indicate that socially excluded adolescents – a group that constitutes a growing percentage of sub-Saharan Africa's population – were not being reached at the time of the survey with effective programmes. The majority of programming in this region consists of: (a) mitigation approaches for young orphaned children (housing, food and education assistance), which do not pay attention to sexual health and development (Foster et al., 2005); and (b) HIV prevention programmes for adolescents that focus on individual behaviour control and change. Neither of these is context-specific nor well-targeted to the subpopulations most in need. As emphasized by Hunter (2002), 'At fault here, and more broadly in many well-intentioned but often disappointedly ineffective AIDS "education" campaigns, is a fundamental conceptual weakness: the abstraction of sexual relations from social relations and historically rooted dynamics and practices'. Interventions must adopt a more ecological approach and focus on the gendered economic, social, political and cultural determinants of sexual practices. They must recognize that behaviours associated with negative health consequences over the long term frequently have great psychological, social and economic benefits in the short term and are natural elements of the transition to adulthood (Balmer et al., 1995; DiClemente et al., 2005; Dixon-Mueller, 1993; Varga, 1997; Worth, 1989). Adolescent programming intended to address HIV risk should therefore offer stronger forms of social support in order to build individual, family and community resilience for responding to HIV and AIDS, including coping with the loss of a parent or other key adults (Campbell et al., 2005; Hsu et al., 2002). Such interventions should be tailored not only to the specific sociocultural setting but also to the differential needs of young males and females (Stephenson and Allen, 2007).

Acknowledgements

The author would like to thank Hannah Carter-Menn for research and editorial assistance and Emmanuelle St. Jean and Eva Roca for research assistance. Helpful comments were provided by Jennifer Klot, Vinh-Kim Nguyen, the Fourth Wave editorial committee and participants in the Fourth Wave authors seminar held in October 2007 at UNESCO Headquarters in Paris. Susan Lee-Rife is thanked for fruitful discussions on the topic. The work was supported by grants from the Hewlett Foundation and the UK Department for International Development (DFID) through the Addressing the Balance of the Burden of AIDS Research Program Consortium (ABBA RPC). The views expressed are not necessarily those of Hewlett or DFID.

References

Balmer, D. H., Gikundi, E., Kanyotu, M. and Waithaka, R. 1995. The negotiating strategies determining coitus in stable heterosexual relationships. *Health Transition Review,* Vol. 5, pp. 85–95.

Baum, F. 1999. Social capital: Is it good for your health? *Journal of Epidemiological and Community Health,* Vol. 53, pp. 195–96.

Baylies, C. 2000. Perspectives on gender and AIDS in Africa. C. Baylies and J. Bujra (eds), *AIDS, Sexuality and Gender in Africa: Collective Strategies and Struggles in Tanzania and Zambia.* London/New York, Routledge, pp. 1–24.

Brady, M. 2003. Safe spaces for adolescent girls. UNFPA and Population Council (eds), *Adolescent and Youth Sexual and Reproductive Health: Charting Directions for a Second Generation of Programming* (background documents). New York, UNFPA, pp. 155–76.

Browning, C. R., Leventhal, T. and Brooks-Gunn, J. 2004. Neighbourhood context and racial differences in early adolescent sexual activity. *Demography,* Vol. 41, No. 4, pp. 697–720.

Bruce, J. and Hallman, K. 2008. Reaching the girls left behind. *Gender & Development,* Vol. 16, No. 2, pp. 227–45.

Camlin, C. S. and Snow, R. C. 2008. Parental investment, club membership and youth sexual behaviour in Cape Town. *Health Education and Behaviour,* Vol. 35, No. 4, pp. 522–40.

Campbell, C., Foulis, C. A., Maimane, S., and Sibiya, Z. 2005. The impact of social environments on the effectiveness of youth prevention: A South African case study. *AIDS Care,* Vol. 17, No. 4, pp. 471–78.

Campbell, C., Williams, B. and Gilgen, D. 2002. Is social capital a useful conceptual tool for exploring community level influences on HIV infection? An exploratory case study from South Africa. *AIDS Care,* Vol. 14, No. 1, pp. 41–54.

Campbell, C., Wood, R. and Kelly, M. 1999. *Social Capital and Health.* London, Health Education Authority.

Cohen, D. 1998. Poverty and HIV/AIDS in sub-Saharan Africa. *UNDP HIV and Development Programme.* New York, UNDP. (Issues Paper No. 27.)

Crosby, R. A., Holtgrave, D. R., DiClemente, R. J., Wingood, G. M. and Gayle, J. A. 2003. Social capital as a predictor of adolescents' sexual risk behaviour: A state-level exploratory study. *AIDS Behaviour,* Vol. 7, No. 3, pp. 245–52.

DiClemente, R. J., Salazar, L. F., Crosby, R. A. and Rosenthal, S. L. 2005. Prevention and control of sexually transmitted infections among adolescents: The importance of a socio-ecological perspective – a commentary. *Public Health,* Vol. 119, No. 9, pp. 825–36.

Dixon-Mueller, R. 1993. The sexuality connection in reproductive health. *Studies in Family Planning*, Vol. 24, No. 5, pp. 269–82.

Erkut, S. and Tracy, A. J. 2000. *Protective Effects of Sports Participation on Girls' Sexual Behaviour*. Wellesley, Mass., Wellesley Centers for Women. (Working Paper No. 301.)

Foster, G., Levine, C. and Williamson, J. (eds). 2005. *A Generation at Risk: The Global Impact of HIV/AIDS on Orphans and Vulnerable Children*. New York, Cambridge University Press.

Gold, R., Kennedy, B., Connell, F. and Kawachi, I. 2002. Teen births, income inequality, and social capital: Developing an understanding of the causal pathway. *Health and Place*, Vol. 8, No. 2, pp. 77–83.

Gregson, S., Terceira, N., Mushati, P., Nyamukapa, C. and Campbell, C. 2004. Community group participation: Can it help young women to avoid HIV? An exploratory study of social capital and school education in rural Zimbabwe. *Social Science and Medicine*, Vol. 58, No. 11, pp. 2119–132.

Haddad, L. J. and Maluccio, J. A. 2003. Trust, membership in groups, and household welfare: Evidence from KwaZulu-Natal, South Africa. *Economic Development and Cultural Change*, Vol. 51, No. 3, pp. 573–601.

Harpham, T., Snoxell, S., Grant, E. and Rodriguez, C. 2005. Common mental disorders in a young urban population in Colombia. *British Journal of Psychiatry*, Vol. 187, No. 2, pp. 161–67.

Hartell, C. G. and Chabilall, J. A. 2005. HIV/AIDS in South Africa: A study of the socio-educational development of adolescents orphaned by AIDS in child-headed households. *International Journal of Adolescence and Youth*, Vol. 12, No. 3, pp. 213–29.

Hsu, L., du Guerny, J. and Marco, M. 2002. *Communities Facing the HIV/AIDS Challenge: From Crisis to Opportunity, From Community Vulnerability to Community Resilience*. Bangkok, UNDP, South East Asia HIV and Development Programme.

Hunter, M. 2002. The materiality of everyday sex: Thinking beyond 'prostitution'. *African Studies*, Vol. 61, No. 1, pp. 99–120.

Jejeebhoy, S. J. and Bott, S. 2003. *Non-consensual Sexual Experiences of Young People: A Review of the Evidence from Developing Countries*. New Delhi, Population Council. (Regional Working Papers No. 16.)

Kaufman, C. E., Clark, S., Manzini, N. and May, J. 2004. Communities, opportunities, and adolescents' sexual behaviour in KwaZulu-Natal, South Africa. *Studies in Family Planning*, Vol. 35, No. 4, pp. 261–74.

Kawachi, I. and Kennedy, B. P. 1997. Socio-economic determinants of health: Health and social cohesion: Why care about income inequality? *British Medical Journal,* Vol. 314, No. 7086, p. 1037.

Kenworthy, N., Hallman, K. and Diers, J. 2008. *Identifying Sources of Adolescent Exclusion Due to Violence: Participatory Mapping in South Africa.* New York, Population Council. (Promoting Healthy, Safe, and Productive Transitions to Adulthood Brief No. 30.) http://www.popcouncil.org/gfd/TA_Briefs_List.html

Kohler, H. P., Behrman, J. R. and Watkins, S. C. 2007. Social networks and HIV/AIDS risk perceptions. *Demography,* Vol. 44, No. 1, pp. 1–33.

Latkin, C. A. and Knowlton, A. R. 2005. Micro-social structural approaches to HIV prevention: A social ecological perspective. *AIDS Care,* Vol. 17, No. 4, Suppl. 1, pp. 102–13.

Lehman, S. J. and Koerner, S. S. 2004. Adolescent women's sports involvement and sexual behaviour/health: A process-level investigation. *Journal of Youth and Adolescence,* Vol. 33, No. 5, pp. 443–55

Lester, P., Rotheram-Borus, M. J., Lee, S., Comulada, S. et al. 2006. Rates and predictors of anxiety and depressive disorders in adolescents of parents with HIV. *Vulnerable Children and Youth Studies,* Vol. 1, No. 1, pp. 81–101.

Magnani, R., MacIntyre, K., Karim, A. M., Brown, L., Hutchinson, P. and the Transitions Study Team (Kaufman, C., Rutenburg, N., Hallman, K., May, J. and Dallimore, A.). 2005. The impact of life skills education on adolescent sexual risk behaviours in KwaZulu-Natal, South Africa. *Journal of Adolescent Health,* Vol. 36, pp. 289–304.

Mensch, B. S., Bruce, J. and Greene, M. E. 1998. *The Uncharted Passage: Girls' Adolescence in the Developing World.* New York, Population Council.

Miller, K. E., Sabo, D. F., Farrell, M. P., Barnes, G. M. and Melnick, M. J. 1998. Athletic participation and sexual behaviour: The different worlds of boys and girls. *Journal of Health and Social Behaviour,* Vol. 39, No. 2, pp. 108–23.

——. 1999. Sports, sexual behaviour, contraceptive use, and pregnancy among female and male high school students: Testing cultural resource theory. *Sociology of Sport Journal,* Vol. 16, No. 4, pp. 366–87.

Morrison, S. D., Howard, R., Hardy, C. and Stinson, B. 2005. Social capital, health and HIV awareness of girls in a rural Caribbean community. *International Electronic Journal of Health Education,* Vol. 8, pp. 135–45.

Piprek, G., Dlamini, P. and Coetzee, G. 2004. *FinMark Trust: Financial Literacy Scoping Study and Strategy Project (Final Report).* Woodmead, South Africa, ECIAfrica.

Pronyk, P. M., Hargreaves, J. R., Kim, J. C., Morison, L. A. et al. 2006. Effect of a structural intervention for the prevention of intimate-partner violence and HIV in rural South Africa: A cluster randomised trial. *Lancet,* Vol. 368, pp. 1973–983.

Pronyk, P. M., Morison, L.A., Euripidou, R., Phetla, G. et al. 2005. Why do some communities have more HIV than others? The association between structural factors and HIV prevalence in rural South Africa. Durban, 2nd South African AIDS Conference, abstract.

Putnam, R. D. 1993. The Prosperous Community: Social Capital and Public Life. *American Prospect,* No. 13, pp. 35–42.

——. 1995. Bowling Alone: America's Declining Social Capital. *Journal of Democracy,* Vol. 6, No. 1, pp. 65–78.

——. 2000. *Bowling Alone: The Collapse and Revival of American Community.* New York, Simon and Schuster.

Rutenberg, N., Kehus-Alons, C., Brown, L., Macintyre, K. et al. 2001. *Transition to Adulthood in the Context of AIDS in South Africa: Report of Wave 1.* New York, Population Council.

Sabo, D. F., Miller, K. E., Farrell, M. P., Melnick, M. J. and Barnes, G. M. 1999. High school athletic participation, sexual behaviour and adolescent pregnancy: A regional study. *Journal of Adolescent Health,* Vol. 25, No. 3, pp. 207–16.

Shisana, O, Rehle, T. M., Simbayi, L. C., Parker, W. et al. 2005. *South African National HIV Prevalence, HIV Incidence, Behaviour and Communication Survey, 2005.* Cape Town, HSRC Press.

Stephenson, R. and Allen, S. 2007. Community influences on young people's sexual behaviour in three African countries. Presented at the Population Association of America 2007 Annual Meeting, New York, 29–31 March.

Tawil, O., Vester, A. and O'Reilly, K. R. 1995. Enabling approaches for HIV/AIDS prevention: Can we modify the environment and minimize the risk? *AIDS,* Vol. 9, pp. 1299–306.

UNAIDS (Joint United Nations Programme on HIV/AIDS). 2006. *Report on the Global AIDS Epidemic: A UNAIDS 10th Anniversary Special Edition.* Geneva, UNAIDS.

Varga, C. A. 1997. Sexual decision-making and negotiation in the midst of AIDS: Youth in KwaZulu-Natal, South Africa. *Health Transition Review,* Vol. 7, Suppl. 3, pp. 45–67.

Wood, K., Chase, E. and Aggleton, P. 2006. 'Telling the truth is the best thing': Teenage orphans' experiences of parental AIDS-related illness and bereavement in Zimbabwe. *Social Science and Medicine,* Vol. 63, No. 7, pp. 1923–933.

Worth, D. 1989. Sexual decision-making and AIDS: Why condom promotion is likely to fail. *Studies in Family Planning,* Vol. 20, No. 6, pp. 297–307.

Youngblade, L. M., Curry, L. A., Novak, M., Vogel, B. and Shenkman, E. A. 2006. The impact of community risks and resources on adolescent risky behaviour and health care expenditures. *Journal of Adolescent Health,* Vol. 38, No. 5, pp. 486–94.

CHAPTER 3

HIV, male labour migration and female risk environments in the southern Caucasus

Cynthia J. Buckley

Evidence from 'first wave' countries clearly demonstrates the importance of migration in accelerating and widening the spread of HIV infection. Labour migrants, the displaced and the trafficked occupy marginalized social, economic and political positions, which tend to increase the likelihood that they will engage in risk-related behaviour. Across the former Soviet Union, the general rise in HIV infections and massive temporary labour migration from less HIV-prevalent countries in the southern regions to more HIV-prevalent countries in the north highlight the critical importance of understanding how migration shapes the terrain of risk of HIV exposure. What are the direct and indirect effects of large-scale labour migration within the region on HIV risk–related behaviour? Can understanding the sociocultural context of the region extend and expand our understanding of the ways in which male out-migration directly and indirectly alters the risks faced by migrant families generally and the wives of male migrants specifically? How can we better understand gendered patterns of risk and reliance by focusing on migrant families rather than on individual migrants?

Three specific issues, unresolved in existing examinations of the links between migration and HIV, are especially relevant in the countries of the former Soviet Union. First, our limited capacity to precisely quantify HIV prevalence or the number of labour migrants hampers our ability to assess the regional importance of either issue and, more importantly, understand the relationship between them. The under-registration of both HIV infection and labour

The designations employed and the presentation of material throughout this publication do not imply the expression of any opinion whatsoever on the part of UNESCO concerning the legal status of any country, territory or area or of its authorities, or concerning the delimitation of its frontiers or boundaries.
The ideas and opinions expressed in this publication are those of the authors and do not necessarily reflect the views of UNESCO and its Member States.

migration, which is in part due to cultural and legal factors, prevents us from knowing the prevalence of either. In addition, most existing sources tend to focus on the characteristics of individual migrants and people living with HIV (PLHIV) rather than their spouses or family networks. Secondly, across the former Soviet Union shifting social, political and economic institutions generate a context of instability and uncertainty, complicating individual decision-making (both health- and migration-related) and placing greater strains upon families for support. Lastly, examining the relationship between HIV transmission and migration provides us with valuable insight into gendered norms and sexual relations. In this region, HIV transmission via sexual contact is increasing, and the proportion of women among those registered as HIV-positive is rising. Much of the discussion on HIV and AIDS in the region focuses on women's exposure in the context of the risk-increasing behaviour of their husbands. Less emphasis has been placed on issues touching upon sexual health knowledge, the context of women's behavioural choices, communication and negotiation within couples, or how any of these factors can be altered by temporary labour migration. The ways in which temporary labour migration, a predominantly male phenomenon in the southern Caucasus, alters economic security, gender roles and health practices within families remain poorly understood.

The discussions on HIV and migration that follow examine temporary male migration flows out of the southern Caucasus in order to better assess their influence on transmission pathways and the growth trajectory of HIV prevalence in Georgia, Azerbaijan and Armenia. Male labour migration into the Russian Federation and Ukraine – a common phenomenon throughout the Soviet era – continues to provide a socially acceptable and historically reliable route for survival during economically challenging times. Both migrants and their family members experience significant changes in their life situations, socio-economic status and decision-making opportunities during the migration process. These changes can alter behaviour and practices that increase the risk of HIV transmission. The relational and behavioural implications of temporary male labour migration for husbands, wives and children in the southern Caucasus are considered on the basis of interviews, ethnographic research and secondary statistics. Analysing the effects of labour out-migration on the spouses left behind can broaden our understanding of the complex relationship between HIV and migration, as well as provide insights into migration, family networks and HIV risk. More important, a detailed focus on the constraints and opportunities for health-related decision-making for women recasts women as active agents and deepens our understanding of how spousal migration affects HIV transmission.

The region of the southern Caucasus plays an increasingly important role in global energy markets, international labour flows and efforts to combat global narcotic trafficking (German, 2008; Ivankhnyuk, 2006). Located between the Black Sea and the Caspian Sea and bordering the Russian Federation to the north and Turkey and the Islamic Republic of Iran to the south, the region struggles with persistent poverty, socio-economic instability, collapsing public health systems, ethnic hostilities and significant concerns over the porous nature of its borders. Some economic and political developments, such as the opening of the Baku-Tbilisi-Ceyhan oil pipeline in 2005 and Georgia's 'Rose Revolution' in 2004, led to optimistic global assessments of the region's development possibilities. More recently, continued concerns over political corruption, rising socio-economic inequality, persistent strife over issues of local autonomy, limited tax collection capabilities and persistent inadequacies in social service provision have damped projections of development in the region. The eruption of violent military conflict between Russia and Georgia in August of 2008 over authority in South Ossetia clearly underscores the contentious nature of regional autonomy, the continued role of Russia within the southern Caucasus and the socio-political fragility of the region.

The socio-political instability and barriers to economic development in the southern Caucasus amplify the challenges presented by marked increases in HIV incidence. Prior to the 2008 meeting of the International AIDS Society in Mexico City, UNAIDS director Peter Piot remarked, 'I'm still very pessimistic about what is going on in Russia and Eastern Europe. That's the region of the world where there's the least progress' (Sulaiman, 2008). Competing security and development priorities and the need to maintain a level of social stability are testing the state capacities in Armenia, Azerbaijan and Georgia, leaving scant resources for HIV prevention efforts. The scale of the challenges facing these countries and the limited capacity of their respective states to address them are impeding prevention efforts, limiting the ability to monitor the development of the pandemic and amplifying the social, economic and political threats posed by the spread of HIV and AIDS.

Raising the importance of HIV and AIDS in public policy debates is further challenged by the relatively modest official prevalence levels. Based on evaluations of officially registered cases, Georgia, Armenia and Azerbaijan are all experiencing a highly concentrated epidemic, with prevalence over 1 per cent only among sex workers and injecting drug users. However, there are clear causes for concern, including recent steep increases in newly reported HIV infections, an alleged shift in transmission modes (from injecting drug use to sexual transmission), and rapidly increasing proportions of women among PLHIV. As of late 2008, there were 4,167 officially registered cases of individuals living with HIV in the region, approximately 30 per cent of whom are classified as having acquired the virus through heterosexual contact.[1] In line with developments in other 'second wave' countries, officially registered cases are likely to represent a significant underestimation of actual prevalence. At the close of 2007, UNAIDS estimated the number of HIV-positive individuals in the region at 12,900 (low estimate of 8,000 and high estimate of 25,600) (UNAIDS, 2008). Few women were registered as living with HIV in the 1990s, but by the end of 2006 they accounted for 16.4 per cent of all cases in Azerbaijan, 25.5 per cent of all cases in Armenia and 24.7 per cent in Georgia.[2] While present prevalence appear modest, the recent rise of HIV infection rates in Ukraine and the Russian Federation illustrates both the rapidity with which HIV infection can spread within national populations and the potential importance of labour migration as an important transmission mechanism in the southern Caucasus.

Hundreds of thousands of migrants, mostly men, continue to travel from the southern Caucasus to countries such as Ukraine and the Russian Federation as temporary labourers. As regionally produced reports in the southern Caucasus often stress, many of the people living with HIV are believed to have contracted HIV during a stay in Ukraine or the Russian Federation.[3] The National AIDS Centers of Azerbaijan and Armenia specifically note the high proportion of cases related to travel in Ukraine and the Russian Federation. Such claims add to the perception of HIV and AIDS as an 'outsiders' disease, contributing to hostilities towards Russia, especially in Armenia and Georgia. With hundreds of thousands of men from the region engaged in temporary labour migration to higher prevalence regions, such as Russia and Ukraine, migrants do represent an important potential pathway of transmission. Yet, to date, few of the existing regional programmes have specifically targeted labour migrants or their families in terms of HIV education, prevention or testing.

Understanding the historical and cultural context of labour migration movements in the southern Caucasus can help to clarify the influence of migration on HIV transmission pathways; identify the potential growth trajectory of HIV infections in Georgia, Azerbaijan and Armenia; and contribute to the development of programme interventions. In order to contextualize the links between migration and HIV and AIDS in the southern Caucasus, this chapter presents four interrelated sections. Section 1 provides an overview of the HIV and AIDS pandemic in the region, focusing on the difficulties in tracking HIV prevalence, indications of changes in transmission routes and key populations over time, and the regionally specific cultural and social norms underpinning actions linked to HIV exposure. Section 2 examines regional labour out-migration. Section 3 expands the theoretical framing of the links between behaviours that increase the risk of HIV infection and migration and assesses migration and HIV using the family as the core unit of analysis, thereby expanding our appreciation of the complex decision-making context of migrant wives. Section 4 discusses intervention opportunities targeting migrant families in the region, advocates the targeting of migrant families and emphasizes the importance of shaping interventions to the specific sociocultural context of the southern Caucasus.

1. HIV and AIDS in the southern Caucasus

Public discussion of AIDS (and the first registered cases of HIV) emerged in the southern Caucasus during the 1980s, and as in other regions of the former Soviet Union, mandatory testing regimes were established across Armenia, Azerbaijan and Georgia during the early 1990s. All pregnant women, surgery patients and men enlisting in the armed forces were subject to mandatory testing. As seen in Figure 1, the number of registered cases remained very low until the late 1990s.

The World Health Organization (WHO) reports that the number of registered HIV-positive adults per 100,000 population was 2.6 in Azerbaijan, 5.8 in Georgia and 2.3 in Armenia at the end of 2006. In contrast, comparable adult rates in the Russian Federation were 27.51 and 28.83 in Ukraine. As in most other countries of the former Soviet Union, people living with HIV in the southern Caucasus tend to be young, urban and male, but the number of women living with HIV is growing rapidly. Official statistics identify 321 AIDS-related deaths in the region at the end of 2006, but the number of individuals officially registered as living with AIDS in the region rose from 14 in 1996 to 833 in 2006 (WHO, 2008). Transmission patterns, originally tightly concentrated within the injecting drug user (IDU) community and specific groups of sex workers, are now expanding well beyond these communities. Patterns of increasing co-morbidity with tuberculosis and hepatitis C – two diseases that amplify infection potential and have high prevalence in the region – are also a source of concern. Concurrently, social and political instability present difficulties for epidemiological monitoring, prevention programmes and treatment efforts.

The most important transmission route for the spread of HIV infection in the southern Caucasus continues to be through injecting drug use by men,

Figure 1. Cumulative registered HIV infections, southern Caucasus, 1996–2006

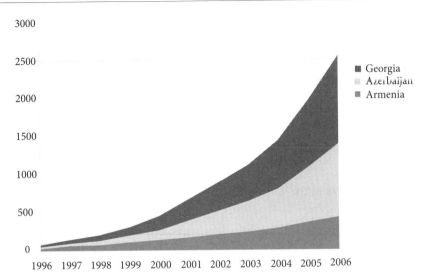

Source: WHO, Computerized Information System for Infectious Disease (http://data.euro.who.int/cisid/?TabID=39145).

but different transmission routes can now be discerned. Most reported sexual transmission of HIV is classified as heterosexual, with recent trends suggesting a slight decline in the proportions of transmission attributed to sex workers. While the accuracy of transmission attribution is often questionable, increasing numbers of new HIV infections attributed to heterosexual transmission do indicate that IDUs are serving as a bridge population and propagating wider sexual transmission of HIV – a phenomenon that is eerily similar to the experience of Ukraine in its earliest period of rapid growth of HIV infections. The growing importance of sexual transmission marks an expansion beyond the previous core key populations in the region: sex workers and IDUs.[4] Based on data for cumulative reported infections in 2006, 25 per cent of cases in Azerbaijan are attributed to heterosexual transmission, compared to 32 per cent in Georgia and 39 per cent in Armenia. As sexual transmission of HIV gains importance, infection rates are likely to grow rapidly for men and even more rapidly among women.

As in many countries with relatively low HIV prevalence, precise estimates are very difficult to obtain. The highly stigmatized nature of HIV, low knowledge levels of treatment options and declining confidence in health services across the southern Caucasus are likely to deter people from seeking tests.

As in many 'second wave' countries, reported figures are viewed as woeful underestimates of actual prevalence. In the case of the southern Caucasus, dire reports claim actual prevalence exceeds registered prevalence by a factor of ten, or even higher. Sentinel testing investigations in all three countries indicate very high rates of HIV infection among sex workers and IDUs. However, such small-scale, non-random investigations are difficult to extrapolate. The size of these targeted groups is not known and non-random results may not be representative of the overall group. Results from blood donor screenings, particularly in Georgia (where paid donations are the norm), are alarming. Thirty-five or more of every 100,000 blood donations were HIV-positive in 2004, a similar level to high-prevalence regions, such as the Russian Federation, Estonia and Moldova (EuroHIV, 2008). However, donor data is also difficult to extrapolate, as reagent shortages have precluded comprehensive screening of all donations and blood donors are not likely to be representative of the entire population. Although both the number of registered cases and data from antenatal clinics in the southern Caucasus indicate relatively low prevalence levels, shifting patterns of transmission and indications of significant under-registration point to the increasing importance of HIV.

Across the southern Caucasus, cultural practices, social norms and economic coping strategies create an enabling environment for both the transmission of HIV and the development of AIDS. Armenia, Georgia and Azerbaijan are culturally and religiously distinct, with each adhering to deeply ingrained norms regulating gender roles and sexuality. Sexual activity outside of marriage, increasingly common, is nonetheless strongly stigmatizing for women. Within marriage, men retain household authority and responsibility for material provision. In spite of significant strides made by women in educational attainment and employment outside the home during the Soviet era, the post-independence period has witnessed disproportionate unemployment levels among women. There is increasing emphasis on traditional gender norms and roles across the region, often supported by increasing religious identification and stress placed on ethnic traditions. Social norms discourage the discussion of sexual health, even within families. In spite of several attempts, the adoption of comprehensive sexual health education in schools has not occurred in any of the countries. To date, most pilot education programmes have been met with strong resistance from parents, teachers and religious groups. Young women are especially reluctant to seek out information on reproductive and sexual health. Survey data indicate that most young people are unaware of basic reproductive and sexual health issues at the time of sexual debut. Numerous national and regional studies centering on reproductive health have found extremely low levels of knowledge concerning the transmission, symptoms and treatment of HIV and AIDS and high levels of misconceptions regarding transmission.[5]

Overtaxed public health infrastructure, resource-constrained government budgets and widespread poverty are often cited as limitations on the capacity of Armenia, Azerbaijan and Georgia to unilaterally launch large-scale educational, prevention or treatment programmes targeting HIV and AIDS. Since independence in 1991, the systems of state-provided universal health care in these countries have crumbled. Private clinics have emerged across the health sector, but the cost of treatment in such clinics remains out of the reach of many citizens. Some state-run clinics are functioning, but the quality of care and reliance upon informal payments for services rendered put many out of the market for 'free' health care.[6] Additional state funds to bolster public health systems are not likely, given severely constrained national budgets. Potential future revenues from oil and gas in Azerbaijan and pipeline activities in Georgia are not altering this reality. Long-term investments in public health compete, often unsuccessfully, for limited state funds with security interests, public transfer programmes and economic development projects.

Widespread poverty in the southern Caucasus amplifies emergent regional public health concerns, one of the most publicized of which is HIV and AIDS. Estimated poverty rates vary dramatically according to the methodology employed, but most estimates indicate that between 40 per cent and 50 per cent of the populations live below the poverty threshold of the countries concerned. Poverty indirectly elevates the risk of becoming infected by decreasing access to health care, accentuating the negative physiological effects of stress and leading to increased rates of negative health behaviours, such as smoking, alcohol and drug use. Anecdotal evidence indicates a more direct link between financial hardship and risk of HIV infection as some women report to be engaging in sex work to financially support their families (Babayan, 2002). Severe economic dislocation and poverty have intensified reliance upon temporary labour out-migration as a family coping strategy. While there are some indications that the number of destination countries for migrants from the southern Caucasus has grown, most migration flows remain directed towards the Russian Federation and, to a lesser extent, Ukraine.[7] Based upon ample evidence indicating a link between migration and HIV transmission in other countries and contexts, migration will most likely play an important role in determining the trajectory of HIV transmission in the region (for examples, see Anarfi, 1993; Decosas et al., 1995; and Quinn, 1994).

2. Labour migration from the southern Caucasus

There is a longstanding tradition of temporary labour out-migration from the countries of the southern Caucasus. During the Soviet era, seasonal migrants from the region were often involved in trading fruits and vegetables across the northern Slavic regions of the USSR. Workers from the southern Caucasus were also actively engaged in construction projects in these regions.[8] Soviet-era 'labour brigades' composed of regional migrants, often specializing in seasonal construction work, lessened the negative effects of labour shortages in the then Russian Republic. This work provided important earning opportunities for migrants, who spent their earnings on weddings, home construction and small-scale investments. Economic hardships emerged across the successor states following the collapse of the Soviet Union in 1991, but labour market opportunities in the Russian Federation and Ukraine remained relatively attractive to people living in the southern Caucasus. Pre-existing network linkages and migration experiences served to diminish the uncertainty in deciding whether to migrate from the southern Caucasus to the Russian Federation.

Out-migration from the southern Caucasus has been especially high since the early 1990s. However the bulk of these population movements went unregistered, and estimates of their magnitude vary widely. Gagik Yeganyan, the director of the Department of Migration in Armenia, estimates that at least 800,000 Armenians left the country during the 1990s (Pope, 2001). The entire region continues to experience population loss through negative net migration. Attempts to measure migration have proven difficult as few migrants follow official registration channels for labour migration; typically, they leave their countries of origin as tourists and work at destination without legal registration or work permits. Structural incentives to avoid registration, either upon leaving the origin location or arriving at the destination, are significant. Individuals leaving a region are likely to maintain registration in their home countries in anticipation of return or in order to protect ownership rights to housing. Registration at destination can be costly or hindered by visa restrictions. Although the Russian Federation presently mandates the use of migration registration cards for migrants, it remains notoriously difficult to obtain legal registration, and the role of migrants in the economy is a source of heated debate in the country. Migration networks can assist individuals in either circumventing or engaging with legal requirements by providing information, assistance networks and social support during and after migration.[9] As in the Soviet era, strong pre-existing networks make countries such as the Russian Federation and Ukraine especially attractive destinations.

Although several scholars have noted the global international feminization of migration, migrants from the southern Caucasus remain predominantly male (Pedraza, 1991). Strong social and cultural norms emphasizing the importance of the role of men as the principal breadwinners continue to exist throughout the region, making men more likely to migrate to find worthwhile employment opportunities abroad. At the same time, women are less likely to migrate because of deeply rooted practices emphasizing female responsibility for the day-to-day needs of the family. Pre-existing networks within traditionally male occupations and significant labour market demands for physically demanding, low-skilled labour in the destination countries are perhaps of even greater importance in the gendering of migration. Studies estimate that between 65 per cent and 90 per cent of economic migrants from the region are male (Dersham and Khoperia, 2004). In addition, the International Organization for Migration (IOM) and UNICEF have found that the majority of these migrants leave their spouses and dependent children behind at their place of origin (Horvaty et al., 2006). As migration networks grow into regions with demand in traditionally female sectors of the labour market, such as care of the elderly and services-related work, the numbers of female migrants from the southern Caucasus may grow. However, migration from the region continues to be characterized by the image of men who migrate and families who wait.

Migrant remittances are extraordinarily important to the economies of Armenia, Azerbaijan and Georgia and reaffirm the ties that bind migrants to their families at home. Remittance levels are extremely difficult to determine because of the region's poor financial infrastructure and incentives to keep remittances unreported and untaxed. However, as the commercial banking sector and wire transfer services have undergone rapid development and expansion, remittance flows have become somewhat more visible. Still, informal observations and discussions with migrants in the region indicate that the bulk of remittance flows is transferred from hand to hand and therefore escapes capture in most remittance measurement approaches. Estimations based on financial transfers and survey data indicate that remittances from the Russian Federation to the southern Caucasus involve billions of US dollars (IOM, 2002; Mansoor and Quillan, 2006).

3. Migration, families and HIV and AIDS risk

A sizeable amount of literature exists linking the process and challenges of migration to various mechanisms leading to elevated risk of HIV transmission for migrants and, in some cases, their spouses. Adaptation is challenging due to the marginal social position of unregistered migrants and the challenges to labour market access at destination. These uncertainties, in turn, make the advance planning of migration duration nearly impossible. Existing literature tends to focus on the attitudinal and behavioural changes likely to occur among migrants. These approaches emphasize the adaptation of individual migrants to new socio-economic roles, decreased social control and altered social contexts, even while they maintain obligations to families and social networks in their home countries. Do the adaptation challenges associated with migration differ significantly for the families of migrants, who remain in their countries of origin? Spouses and children of migrants must also adapt to new roles, changing social control and altered social status. Family strategies for coping with the temporary absence of a migrant also vary according to the expected and experienced duration of migrant absence.

The adaptation choices made within migrant families remaining in the country of origin are likely to have direct and indirect implications for HIV-related risks, thereby reflecting and expanding the risks faced by individual migrants. Migration is clearly linked to an elevated individual risk of contracting HIV, for both men and women and across a number of socio-economic settings.[10] Recent research indicates that migrants actively renegotiate and reconstruct sexuality as they adapt to new socio-economic roles in the settlement process, as seen in the case of Ghana (see Arnafi, 1993). Evidence from India also indicates that decreased social monitoring and control can increase the likelihood that migrants will engage in sex work or employ professional sex workers (Mishra, 2004). As found in the Mexican case, migrants may have more sexual partners than non-migrants, reflecting exposure, altered social settings and decreased social monitoring (Magis-Rodriguez et al., 2004). Furthermore, studies focusing on migration within the countries of the former Soviet Union indicate that migrants may seek to diminish the stress of resettlement through alcohol or drug use. These types of coping mechanisms, at best, impede responsible decision-making and, at worst, directly expose migrants to HIV infection (CEEHRN, 2002).

In addition to these elevated behavioural risks, migrants typically exhibit lower levels of health care utilization and medical treatment, which may be linked to poor knowledge of available health services at destination, issues of expense and, among those unregistered, basic issues of access. The marginalization of migrants from health services decreases the likelihood of testing and treatment and also provides a potential barrier to awareness campaigns aimed at improving health knowledge. Migrants in the Russian Federation also have clear structural reasons for avoiding testing or treatment for HIV. Foreign nationals found to be HIV-positive are deported under a law promulgated in 1995 (Stanley, 1995).

The risks associated with migration for migrant partners are frequently discussed in academic and policy documents but primarily framed in terms of their secondary and passive exposure to HIV through their migrant partners. Discussions concerning effective policy interventions relating to migration and HIV in the region tend to focus on migrant communities at destination and are also aimed at individual migrants. Expanding our interpretations of 'who migrates?' to include members of migrant family networks enables a more comprehensive examination of sexual health risk factors within migrant-sending communities. Such approaches are particularly well suited to the context of the southern Caucasus, where migration of household members influences various indirect and direct behavioural and relational risk factors associated with HIV.

Members of migrant families face challenges similar to those of migrants in adjusting to changes in their respective cultural, social and economic contexts. This is especially true for migrant wives. In the context of widespread male labour migration, it is critically important to understand the influence of migration on women generally and more particularly on their vulnerability to HIV. The migration of household members, particularly partners or spouses, profoundly alters the likelihood of women contracting HIV as a result of their relationships to a migrant and their own behavioural choices. In terms of other household members, male labour migration may also influence the likelihood of discussions between parents and children on issues relating to sexual and reproductive health.

The trails and stresses associated with labour migration typically lead to changes in the lines of responsibilities within family systems and often challenge gender norms. Such renegotiation may be beneficial to female spouses and partners as male out-migration can be associated with increased autonomy for women. Although the permanence of such expanded autonomy after the return of male migrants remains questionable, increased autonomy during the absence of a spouse may expand the behavioural choices and family responsibilities of female partners during the migration process. The temporary labour migration of adult men leads to an increase in female-headed households, which are more vulnerable to a variety of social ills. This vulnerability may manifest itself indirectly through the fragile economic security provided by remittances. Reliance upon remittances is a precarious base on which to build economic stability for families. In addition to economic uncertainty, social vulnerabilities in the form of decreased community status, social marginalization and susceptibility to the control of male relatives or neighbours are also possible. Within the family, women maintaining migrant households in the country of origin shoulder an increased burden in terms of child-rearing and health education.

Standard approaches to migration as a contributing factor for vulnerability to HIV highlight the risks faced by migrants, viewing the risks for non-migrating spouses in terms of their dependence on the migrant. A non-migrating wife is subject to relational risk through her relationship to a migrating spouse or partner. Relational risk may operate directly through sexual contact with a migrating spouse or partner already living with HIV. Returning male migrants transfer their elevated risk to female spouses and partners, who for reasons relating to cultural norms, economic dependence and social practices are unlikely to question male fidelity or initiate condom negotiation. Relational risk also operates indirectly as the absence of a male spouse or partner can signify or amplify the relatively powerless position of women. Without a resident spouse or partner, women are potential targets for exploitation, either economically or sexually. In regions with high rates of temporary out-migration, women may band together in order to minimize opportunities for exploitation, but in areas in which female-headed households are hidden, or viewed as transgressing social norms, women may face increased risk of exploitation.

The appreciation of both direct and indirect relational risk factors is essential for understanding the ways in which male out-migration influences the risk of contracting HIV for female spouses and partners. However, in viewing women's social and economic context primarily in relation to male migration, relational risk approaches tend to minimize issues of female autonomy and agency. Migration is an inherently social process, altering the context for calculating priorities, the processes of decision-making and behaviour choices. As migration is best conceptualized as taking place within family systems, it is important to pay greater attention to the ways migration influences the decision-making capacity and the behaviour of women who remain in the country of origin. Expanding our understanding of the effects of migration on women within family systems to include behavioural risk factors can assist in highlighting issues of women's agency and extend our understanding of the links between migration and HIV risk. Women within migrant households may elevate their likelihood of contracting HIV directly, through the pursuit of risk-related behaviours, or indirectly, by prioritizing health care for others, investments in the household and the education of children over their own health care needs. In response to the challenges presented by migration, female partners of male migrants may turn to behaviours, such as alcohol or drug use, that increase the risk of HIV infection. The absence of a spouse may also signal a decline in social monitoring and control, leading to increased opportunities to pursue a variety of these risk-related coping strategies. Long-term spousal absence may also be associated with additional sexual partners for women. While throughout the region, professed sexual mores for women are quite restrictive, national surveys and expert interviews indicate that a growing number of women are sexually active prior to marriage as well as outside of marriage. Patterns of non-marital sexual activity are poorly understood, and further research is needed in order to incorporate the behavioural choices of the non-migrating spouse or partner into the analysis of HIV infection risk within family migrant networks.

Within migrant families, the decision-making processes women employ regarding health care utilization can influence the access to health-related information and the health status of the entire family system. Throughout the southern Caucasus, women are traditionally responsible not only for their health but also their children's welfare. However, they do not always possess the prerequisite economic authority to invest in health care. The precarious economic support represented by remittances can lead to uncertain household budgets, thereby limiting the scope of health-related choices. Many migrant wives view seeking costly medical care for themselves as an expense that is best avoided. Even when care is needed, questions regarding economic authority or constrained resources diminish the likelihood that women in migrant families will seek health care, especially for themselves. Women's decision-making regarding their own health care takes on added importance as studies have shown an association between diminished access to health care and increased risk of poor sexual health in the region (Doliashvili and Buckley, 2007).

Finally, parental responsibility within households changes during the process of temporary labour migration. Male labour migration changes the context for making health education decisions concerning young adults. When, as in the southern Caucasus, labour migration tends to be predominantly male, de facto female-headed households face increased burdens relating to child care and child-rearing. This can decrease the social monitoring of young adults, enabling a variety of potentially risk-related behaviour. In addition, male labour migration hinders the transmission of reproductive and sexual health information to young men within family units. In the absence of national reproductive and sexual health education programmes in the region, the transmission of information within families can provide a potentially effective means of communicating information to young adults. Recent surveys indicate that few young adults receive sexual health information from their parents. When discussions regarding sexual health do take place within the family, they are strongly gender-specific. Mothers and sisters discuss reproductive and sexual health with daughters, and fathers or brothers with sons. Migrant families, due to gendered norms regarding the transmission of information, are less able to rely upon family channels for information on sexual or reproductive health issues. Migrant wives report that social and cultural norms make it all but impossible for them to discuss sexual health issues with their sons. These patterns increase the likelihood that overall sexual health knowledge levels in the region will remain low, again elevating the risk of contracting HIV.

4. Implications and discussion

In assessing the relationship between migration and HIV, the example of the southern Caucasus clearly indicates that focusing on migrant families, specifically women and children, provides a promising entry point. Labour migration flows from the southern Caucasus have been sizable, predominantly male and directed towards regions such as the Russian Federation, with its substantially higher HIV prevalence. While the HIV and AIDS pandemic has only recently emerged in the southern Caucasus as an issue of widespread social importance, increasing prevalence, low knowledge levels and shifting transmission patterns from IDUs to sexual transmission combine with these migration patterns to raise serious concerns regarding the future spread of HIV and AIDS in the region. Temporary labour migration will influence risk patterns and behaviour associated with elevated HIV-associated risk, including potential relational and behavioural risks experienced by the female spouses and partners of migrants. The effect of migration on families alters the decision-making context for women who remain in the country of origin. The influences of migration shape the social, behavioural and economic decisions of these women, who often act as heads of households, but may also increase autonomy and agency – a fact that is often masked by approaches that focus on relational risk alone. Examining women's actions and adjustments around temporary labour migration can lend insight into how family networks cope and how these coping mechanisms relate to potential HIV-related risk.

Increased efforts to increase sexual health knowledge and to monitor HIV prevalence as well as migration processes and the well-being of migrant families are clearly needed in the southern Caucasus. Significant under-registration of both HIV and labour migration conceals the true levels and trajectories involved, hindering the development of evidence-based policy interventions. Focusing only on migrants has also concealed the importance of migration in understanding the behavioural and relational risks for migrant wives. Attempts to both improve the quality of information available on HIV and AIDS and migration and expand analytical frames to incorporate the experiences of adaptation strategies of migrant-sending families are sorely needed and justified in this context.

Programmatic efforts, including increased education, targeting individual migrants can be effective but fail to address the needs of women who head migrant families living in sending regions. Increased efforts to address the needs of migrant families by targeting remittance transfer points, post offices and international telephone exchanges can be effective in moving towards addressing the needs of both migrants and their families. Attempts to improve family transmission of information on sexual and reproductive health may be of great assistance to some young adults but will fail to address the needs of young men in migrant families, who may need alternative interventions and heightened attention.

An increased appreciation of the relational and behavioural risks of women in migrant families is vital. Migration scholars have increasingly shifted analytical frames away from standard neoclassical evaluations of individual migrants towards a greater appreciation of, and reliance upon, families and migration. These approaches have reframed the answer to the question 'Who migrates?' beyond individual experiences in order to include the direct and indirect influences migration exerts within networks, such as family systems. To clarify the influence of migration and gender on the risk of HIV transmission, our analytical focus should be on capturing the influence of migration upon both those actors who physically move and those who experience significant alterations in their life situations, contexts and decision-making opportunities due to their relationship to the person who migrates. Put another way, in societies with strong familial bonds, as is the case in the southern Caucasus, it is not only individuals that migrate but family networks as well.

Acknowledgements

This research was supported by the National Council for East European and Eurasian Research, the International Research Exchange and a Special Initiatives Grant from the American Councils. An earlier version of a related paper was presented at the American Sociological Association Annual Meeting in 2007.

Notes

1. As of 1 December 2008, Armenia had 656 cases of individuals living with HIV (www.armaids.am, accessed 1 December 2008). As of 1 November 2008, Azerbaijan registered 1,708 (www.gfund.az, accessed 1 December 2008), and by 19 December 2008, Georgia reported 1,803 total registered cases of individuals living with HIV (www.aidscenter.ge, accessed 1 December 2008).

2. See National AIDS Center website listed in note 3.

3. In noting the large number of male IDUs among those living with HIV in Armenia, the website for the Armenian National AIDS Center states that 'as a matter of fact, some of them temporarily inhabited in the Russian Federation (Moscow, St. Petersburg, Irkoutsk, Rostov, Surgut etc.) and the Ukraine (Odessa, Kiev, Mareupol etc.) and were probably infected with HIV there' (http://www.armaids.am/HIVStatistics.html, accessed 1 December 2008). See also Buckley (2005).

4. As men who have sex with men (MSM) remain highly stigmatized in the region, non-heterosexual identities are typically kept secret. To date, reported MSM transmissions account for less than 1 per cent of all registered cases.

5. Additional details can be found in Buckley (2005).

6. Numerous studies have investigated the collapse of public health in the region. For details see Lewis (2000) and Asian Development Bank (2007).

7. The recent tense relations between the Russian Federation and Georgia have influenced destination choice, but pre-existing networks and linguistic, geographic and cultural ties link the southern Caucasus to the Russian Federation and Ukraine. In 2003, an estimated 1.5 million migrants from Georgia, Azerbaijan and Armenia lived in the Russian Federation. See Dimitriev and Pradukhov (2005).

8. For additional information on Soviet-era migration patterns, see Shabanova (1991).

9. On the importance of migration networks, see Massey et al. (1998).

10. For a general overview, see UNAIDS/IOM (1998).

References

Adeleja, T. 2007. No one Russian is knocking at the door. *Moscow Times,* 31 January, p. 1.

Anarfi, J. 1993. Sexuality, AIDS and Migration in Ghana. *Health Transitions Review,* Vol. 4 (Suppl.), pp. 273–95.

Asian Development Bank. 2007. *MDCs in Central Asia and the southern Caucasus: An Overview.* (ADB Technical Report.)

Babayan, K. 2002. Armenia: Reducing sexually transmitted infections among commercial sex workers. *Entre Nous,* Vol. 14, No. 53.

Buckley, C. 2005. The socio-cultural correlates of HIV/AIDS in the Southern Caucasus. *The Social and Cultural Context of HIV/AIDS in the Caucasus.* Paris, UNESCO, pp. 11–33.

CEEHRN (Central and Eastern European Harm Reduction Network). 2002. *Injecting Drug Users, HIV/AIDS Treatment and Primary Care in Central and Eastern Europe and the Former Soviet Union.* Vilnius, CEEHRN.

Decosas, J., Kane, F., Anarfi, J., Sodji, K. and Wagner, H. 1995. Migration and AIDS. *Lancet,* Vol. 23, No. 346, Issue 8978, pp. 826–28.

Dersham, L. and Khoperia, T. 2004. *The Status of Households in Georgia, 2004.* Tbilisi, Save the Children/USAID/Institute for Polling and Marketing.

Dmitriev, A. and Piadukhov, G. 2005. Ethnic groups, and conflicts in the enclave labour markets. *Sotsiologicheskie Issledovannie,* Vol. 31, No. 8, pp. 90–100. (In Russian.)

Doliashvili, K. and Buckley, C. 2007. Women's sexual and reproductive health in post-socialist Georgia: Does internal displacement matter? *International Family Planning Perspectives,* Vol. 34, No. 1, pp. 21–29.

EuroHIV. 2008. *HIV/AIDS Surveillance in Europe: Mid-year Report 2007.* Saint Maurice, France, Institut de Veille Sanitaire, p. 39.

German, T. 2008. Corridor of power: The Caucasus and energy security. *Caucasian Review of International Affairs,* Vol. 2, No. 2, pp. 1–9.

Horvaty, G., Gollob, A., Daita, S. and Carbollo, M. 2006. *Migration in Central Asia and the southern Caucasus: Its Implications for Women and Children.* Geneva, International Center for Migration and Health.

IOM (International Organization for Migration). 2002. *The Return and Re-integration of Migrants to the Southern Caucasus: An Exploratory Study.* Geneva, IOM.

Ivankhnyuk, I. 2006. Migration in the CIS region: Common problems and mutual benefits. Paper presented at the International Symposium on International Migration and Development, Ruin, Italy, June. http://www.un.org/esa/population/migration/turin/Symposium_Turin_files/P10_SYMP_Ivakhniouk.pdf (Accessed 10 December 2008.)

Lewis, M. 2000. *Who is Paying for Health Care in Eastern Europe and Central Asia.* Washington DC, World Bank.

Lutz, H. 2004. Life in the twilight zone: Migration, transnationality and gender in the private household. *Journal of Contemporary European Studies,* Vol.12, No. 1, pp. 47–55.

Magis-Rodriguez, C., Gayet, C., Negroni, M., Leyla, R., Brav-Garcia, E., Uribe, P. and Bronfman, M. 2004. Migration and AIDS in Mexico: An overview based on recent evidence. *Journal of Acquired Immune Deficiency Syndromes,* Vol. 37, No. 4, pp. S215–S226.

Mansoor, A. and Quillan, B. 2006. M*igration and Remittances: Eastern Europe and the Former Soviet Union.* Washington DC, World Bank.

Massey, D., Arango, J., Hugo, G., Kourouci, A., Pellegrino, A. and Taylor, J. 1998. *Worlds in Motion.* Oxford, United Kingdom, Clarendon Press.

Mishra, A. 2004. Risk of sexually transmitted infections among migrating men: Findings from a survey in Delhi. *Asian and Pacific Migration Journal,* Vol. 13, No.1, pp. 89–105.

Pedraza, S. 1991. Women and migration: The social consequences of gender. *Annual Review of Sociology,* Vol. 17, No. 1, pp. 303–25.

Pope, H. 2001. Armenia, after a decade of statehood, suffers rapid loss of human capital. *Wall Street Journal, 6* July, p. 4.

Quinn, T. 1994. Population migration and the spread of Types 1 and 2 Human Immunodeficiency Viruses. *Proceedings of the National Academy of Science, USA,* Vol. 91, No. 4, pp. 2407–414.

Shabanova, M. 1991. *Sezonnaya i postoyannaia migratsiia naseleniia v sel'skom raione* [Seasonal and permanent population migration into a rural region]. Novosibirsk, Russian Federation, Nauka.

Southern Caucasus Anti-Drug Programme of the United National Development Programme and the European Union. http://scadprogramme.org/ (Accessed 10 December 2008.)

Stanley, A. 1995. Russian AIDS law requires testing for most foreigners. *New York Times,* 4 April, A4.

Sulaiman, T. 2008. UNAIDS chief concerned about Russia, Eastern Europe. *Agence France Presse,* 29 July. http://www.cabsa.co.za/newsite/DisplayPage. asp?Id=415#Russia (Accessed 10 December 2008.)

UNAIDS (Joint United Nations Programme on HIV/AIDS). 2008. *2008 Report on the Global AIDS Epidemic.* Geneva, UNAIDS, p. 220.

UNAIDS/IOM (Joint United Nations Programme on HIV/AIDS/International Organization for Migration). 1998. Migration and AIDS. *International Migration,* Vol. 36, No. 4, pp. 445–68.

WHO (World Health Organization). 2008. Computerized Information System for Infectious Disease. http://data.euro.who.int/cisid (Accessed 30 December 2008.)

CHAPTER 4

HIV, sexual violence and exploitation during post-conflict transitions: The case of Sierra Leone

Johannes John-Langba

Introduction

This chapter explores the links between sexual violence and exploitation (SVE) and the vulnerability of women to HIV and AIDS. Specifically, it examines the nature and extent of SVE in conflict and post-conflict Sierra Leone in order to better understand the relationship between SVE and HIV and AIDS. The study is based on in-depth interviews and focus group discussions conducted in four rural and urban communities that were chosen on the basis of data from the National Population-based HIV Seroprevalence Survey of Sierra Leone (Sierra Leone National HIV/AIDS Secretariat, 2005). The study examines the causes and consequences of SVE and highlights how gender inequalities have contributed to the vulnerability of women to violence and, by extension, to sexually transmitted infections, including HIV. The chapter ends with policy recommendations for national HIV and AIDS initiatives in post-conflict Sierra Leone.

The interviews and focus group discussions held with women, men, boys and girls explored the nature and extent of SVE in Sierra Leone and the physical, psychological, social and reproductive health consequences of sexual violence. The discussions also focused on the cultural norms and pressures that shape the roles, rights, responsibilities and social conditioning of men and women, including community views and perceptions about the causes and consequences of SVE and HIV and AIDS. Key informant interviews were also conducted with community leaders, health care workers and policy-makers.

The designations employed and the presentation of material throughout this publication do not imply the expression of any opinion whatsoever on the part of UNESCO concerning the legal status of any country, territory or area or of its authorities, or concerning the delimitation of its frontiers or boundaries.
The ideas and opinions expressed in this publication are those of the authors and do not necessarily reflect the views of UNESCO and its Member States.

Prevalence and correlates of HIV in Sierra Leone

According to official figures, the prevalence of HIV among adults in Sierra Leone is 1.53 per cent (Sierra Leone NAS, 2006). About 48,000 people are thought to be living with AIDS in Sierra Leone, 43,000 of whom are adolescent girls and women aged 15 and above. It is estimated that about 4,600 people die every year of AIDS-related diseases or complications (UNAIDS, 2008).

The first seroprevalence survey was conducted in 2002 by the US Centers for Disease Control and Prevention, in collaboration with the Government of Sierra Leone. The survey reported HIV prevalence at 0.9 per cent (2.1 per cent in Freetown and 0.7 per cent in the provinces). These estimates excluded the areas that had been the worst affected by the war. A subsequent survey conducted in 2004 in antenatal clinics reported a HIV prevalence of 2.9 per cent based on the findings of eight sentinel testing sites (Sierra Leone NAS, 2006, p. 2). A National Population-based HIV Sero-Prevalence Survey conducted in 2005 with a nationally representative sample of households reported a national HIV prevalence of 1.53 per cent with no significant difference in prevalence between males (1.5 per cent) and females (1.6 per cent). As shown in Figure 1, among women, those aged between 20 and 24 had the highest prevalence (2.0 per cent), whereas for men, those aged between 35 and 39 years had the highest prevalence (3.5 per cent). Females aged between 15 and 24 years had a higher prevalence (1.9 per cent) than older females aged between 25 and 49 years (1.2 per cent) (Sierra Leone NAS, 2005).

Prevalence in urban areas was significantly higher (2.1 per cent) when compared to rural areas (1.3 per cent). There was no difference in the prevalence between males and females in rural areas; however, in urban areas, prevalence was higher among females (2.2 per cent) than males (1.9 per cent). As can be seen in Figure 2, the prevalence by districts ranged from a low of 0.5 per cent in Tonkolili District to a high of 3 per cent in Koinadugu District. The lowest prevalence for females was in Tonkolili (0.3 per cent), and the highest in Koinadugu (3 per cent) (Sierra Leone NAS, 2005).

Knowledge levels on HIV and AIDS were generally low, especially in rural areas. Only 59 per cent of respondents said that condom use can prevent transmission of HIV; about 40 per cent believed that HIV could be transmitted through mosquito bites, and 32 per cent thought that it could be contracted by sharing a meal with an infected person. Close to half (49 per cent) said that people living with HIV and AIDS should not be allowed to work, whereas 36 per cent indicated that they would not be willing to look after a person living with

Figure 1. HIV Prevalence by age group and sex

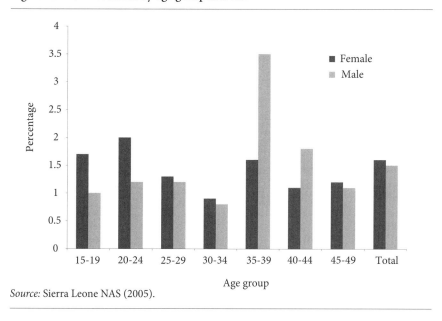

Source: Sierra Leone NAS (2005).

Figure 2. Adult HIV prevalence in Sierra Leone, by district

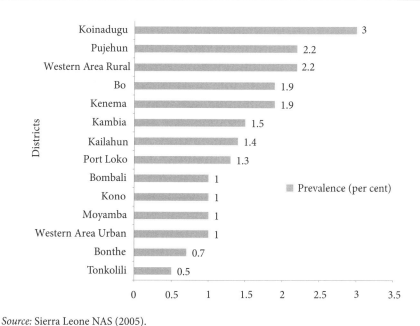

Source: Sierra Leone NAS (2005).

HIV and AIDS. In terms of educational level and HIV status, the highest prevalence (3.8 per cent) was found among people who had completed some form of tertiary education, as compared to 1.2 per cent among individuals with no formal education. Further disaggregation by educational level and sex revealed the highest prevalence (4.8 per cent) among women with basic formal education. This is significantly higher than men with a similar educational background, whose prevalence was 1.8 per cent (Sierra Leone NAS, 2005).

Condom use is relatively low at 9 per cent; urban dwellers (16 per cent) reported higher condom use than those living in rural areas (4.4 per cent). The survey indicated that higher levels of education are related to higher rates of condom use and HIV testing. Among those with tertiary education, 35.4 per cent knew their HIV status and had a condom use rate of 34.4 per cent. Only 3.1 per cent of those with little or no formal education reported having an HIV test, and only 4 per cent of them had used condoms (Sierra Leon NAS, 2005).

Although HIV prevalence is generally low in Sierra Leone, consecutive surveys have shown that infection rates are rising gradually and raising an alarm among health professionals, who are seeing the beginnings of an HIV epidemic in Sierra Leone among high-risk and key populations, such as soldiers, truck drivers and sex workers (Sahr et al., 2008; Women's Commission for Refugee Women and Children, 2008).

Sexual violence and exploitation during the conflict

The conflict in Sierra Leone began in March 1991 when the rebels from the Revolutionary United Front (RUF) launched an attack in the east of the country aimed at overthrowing the government. By the time a peace agreement was signed between the government and the rebels in July 1999 in Lome, there was ample evidence that all parties to the conflict had perpetrated war crimes against Sierra Leonean women and girls. The crimes consisted of rape, sexual slavery, forced pregnancy, abduction, enslavement, torture, forced labour and induction as child soldiers. An estimated 250,000 women and girls (33 per cent of the total female population) were subjected to SVE (Amnesty International, 2007; Human Rights Watch, 2003; Physicians for Human Rights, 2002). Many women, together with their families and community members, lost their lives or limbs or were forced to witness or engage in horrendous acts, including killing members of their own family. Thousands of women and girls were abducted and forced to become sexual slaves, or 'marry' rebel husbands; they were also repeatedly raped (sometimes with foreign objects, such as fuelwood or firearms), tortured and forced to work for the rebels. During the invasion of Freetown in January 1999, rebels deliberately targeted virgins, and many women and girls were subjected to egregious forms of sexual violence. Pregnant women were not spared from the violence, and reports exist of forced pregnancies and miscarriages (Human Rights Watch, 2003).

The Armed Forces Revolutionary Council (AFRC) also allegedly committed atrocities similar to those carried out by the RUF rebels. After the Lome Peace Agreement in 1999, the RUF joined forces with an AFRC splinter group known as the West Side Boys and unleashed a new wave of violence, which included killings, abductions, deliberate mutilations and rape (US Department of State, 2001). The Government's human rights record was also brought into question. There were reports that forces belonging to the Government and the Military Observer Group of the Economic Community of West African States (ECOMOG) committed extrajudicial killings of suspected rebels and their collaborators. Human Rights Watch (2003) has documented incidences of SVE carried out by the United Nations Mission in Sierra Leone (UNAMISIL) and ECOMOG, the two multinational forces mandated to keep the peace in the country. These incidents included rape, sexual exploitation of women and solicitation of child prostitutes (US Department of State, 2001). The Civil Defense Force (CDF) was also guilty of inducting child soldiers and conducting summary executions and killing civilians, including women and children, in attacks on rebel-controlled areas (Physicians for Human Rights, 2002; US Department of State, 2001, pp. 2–11). Unlike the RUF and other warring parties, CDF forces did not engage in widespread acts of sexual violence, and only isolated cases of rape were reported (Human Rights Watch, 2003, pp. 27, 46–48).

Many women and girls suffered serious reproductive health problems as a result of the sexual violence they had been subjected to. These included unwanted pregnancy, prolapsed uterus, vesico-vaginal and vesico-rectal fistula, and sexually transmitted infection (STI), including HIV (Barnes et al., 2007, p. 13). Women and girls also suffered from mental health problems, including depression, anxiety and post-traumatic stress disorder, as a result of the violence. Given the poor state of the health care system, most of the victims had very limited access to medical care, including counselling.

The social implications of the violence that took place also proved to be damaging, not just to the victims themselves, but also to communities at large. Historically, women and girls in Sierra Leone have had relatively little control over their sexuality. Thus, for instance, virginity was highly prized. The widespread rape and sexual violence meted against women and girls during the war challenged some of the norms associated with virginity and women's sexuality, especially since much of the sexual violence was perpetrated in front of the victim's family or community members. The devastating result was that many victims of sexual violence were stigmatized and rejected by their families and communities, and many chose to remain silent about the abuses they suffered, leading to 'double victimization' (Barnes, et al., 2007, p. 13). Unable to access a support system and alienated from their families and communities, many of the victims were forced to survive by exposing themselves to further acts of sexual exploitation, thereby increasing the risk of contracting HIV and other STIs.

The marginalization of victims of sexual violence, the lax attitude adopted in the face of such serious crimes and the general impunity enjoyed by those who perpetrated these acts have made it difficult to change attitudes and practices towards sexual violence and exploitation in post-conflict Sierra Leone. Recognizing this, the former United Nations Special Rapporteur on Violence Against Women, Radhika Coomaraswamy, notes that 'the failure to investigate, prosecute and punish those responsible for rape and other forms of gender-based violence has contributed to an environment of impunity that perpetuates violence against women in Sierra Leone, including rape and domestic violence' (United Nations Commission on Human Rights, 2002).

Sexual violence and exploitation in post-conflict Sierra Leone: Trends and causes

SVE in post-conflict Sierra Leone is believed to be concentrated in particular communities and, in most instances, occurs in situations where there are acute differential power relations between men and women. Occurrence of SVE is now less widespread than during the war, but interviews with health care providers and community leaders indicate that levels remain high. The main perpetrators of SVE against women and girls are family members, elderly wealthy men, teachers and lecturers. As a key informant describes:

> Yes, SVE is a problem. People use their position to exploit people. Rape is a crime, but the perpetrator is usually a member of the family. Rape is widespread, especially of underaged girls. Some people force their children into prostitution. (Key informant interview, health worker, Freetown)

Reliable statistical data on the frequency of SVE in post-conflict Sierra Leone is limited due to inadequate monitoring and reporting systems. According to some community leaders, SVE is on the rise in rural communities in Sierra Leone, particularly after the war. 'SVE is a problem in my community, and levels are rising once again,' reported a community leader in Goderich, near Freetown. However, some reproductive health service providers disagreed and claimed that:

> Rape was common two years ago, but it is now uncommon because of the presence of sex workers. The prevalence of forced marriages is also low, and domestic violence has been declining because of government intervention after the conflict. (Key informant interview, health service provider, Freetown)

As SVE occurs in private settings and away from the public eye, it is difficult to obtain an accurate picture of SVE trends in post-conflict Sierra Leone. As a health worker in Freetown described, 'SVE mostly happens secretly. It is common knowledge that someone who wants to obtain a good score in an exam or a job may be obliged to grant sexual favours. These "secret" transactions, and the obvious reluctance of parties to talk about them, make it especially difficult to assess the scale and nature of SVE.'

The vulnerability of women and girls to SVE in post-conflict Sierra Leone is influenced by various factors, including the absence of relevant knowledge on reproductive health and how HIV is transmitted. According to an NGO (nongovernmental organization) providing health services in Freetown:

> Women in particular generally have low self-risk perceptions to both SVE and HIV. Knowledge gaps on important issues about HIV/AIDS, limited community dialogue on sex, sexuality and HIV and AIDS, gender inequalities at all levels, religious beliefs, harmful cultural and sexual beliefs and practices, and drug use increase a woman's or a girl's chances of experiencing SVE. (Key informant interview, Freetown)

Focus group discussions with women revealed widespread misconceptions about HIV and AIDS. Some women, for example, believed that 'small peppers called "toch" can be used as medicine for HIV' and that 'HIV is a chronic illness caused when your bladder bursts' and that 'girls who do not change their clothing after bathing can become infected.' This lack of knowledge about HIV and AIDS is facilitated by high female illiteracy rates – rates that are significantly higher than for males, mainly as a result of lower school enrolment, higher drop-out rates, early marriages, higher household demand for female labour, and teenage pregnancies. According to the United Nations Development Programme, the adult female literacy rate in Sierra Leone is 24.2 per cent, as compared to 46.7 per cent for males. Females account for only 38 per cent of the combined primary, secondary and tertiary gross enrolment ratio, as compared with males, who account for 52 per cent (UNDP, 2007).

The lack of knowledge on HIV and AIDS often leads people to deny that it even exists. A group of girls taking part in a focus discussion group said they did not believe AIDS existed as they had never seen or met anyone living with HIV and AIDS or any patients suffering from AIDS-related diseases. Students attending a college in Freetown also claimed that there was no proof that HIV and AIDS existed, and their claims were supported by a college lecturer who said, 'AIDS does not exist; claims about its existence are just a way of getting money from donors.' A community health worker and key informant in Freetown thought that 'the majority of sexually active people do not believe AIDS exists. They say that AIDS is an American invention to discourage sex and to reduce birth rates.'

Poverty also has an impact on women's vulnerability to SVE. According to the World Bank Group (2008), 70 per cent of the population in Sierra Leone lives below the poverty line. The UNDP *Human Development Report 2007* ranks Sierra Leone as one of the poorest countries in the world. This poverty increases women's vulnerability to casual sex, multiple sexual partners for economic gains and early sexual relationships, which, in turn, exposes women and girls to a higher risk of SVE and contracting STIs, including HIV. In focus discussion groups with community leaders, interviewees frequently linked poverty to the probability of women and girls experiencing SVE. As one participant in a focus discussion group in Freetown remarked, 'Women sell themselves because they are poor; they have sex with fishermen in order to get fish.'

With limited access to formal sector employment, many women fall back on petty trading and food production, where income levels are generally low. This places them at a higher risk of exposure to SVE as they are forced to prostitute themselves or exchange sexual favours to meet basic needs. Girls who do not have caregivers are especially vulnerable. 'In some areas in the community, sex with children can be bought for Le 4,000/5,000 [approximately US $1.50]' reported an adult participant during a focus group discussion in the Goderich area. 'Some of the young women, including girls who have lost their parents or husbands, have their body as their only commodity. They also have no one to protect them,' reiterated a programme coordinator working with HIV/AIDS Care and Support Association (HACSA) in Freetown.

Women constitute about 80 per cent of the labour force in rural areas and are mostly engaged in subsistence farming. However, they have little control over land or property as this is often in the hands of men. When not involved in subsistence farming, women invariably become petty traders or make soap or dye textiles, but this work generates a low income. Thus, women tend to rely heavily on their husbands for economic survival. In urban areas, there are very few opportunities for remunerated work for women. A policy paper by the Ministry of Social Welfare, Gender and Children's Affairs indicates that women make up only 40 per cent of clerical staff and just 8 per cent of the administrative and managerial workforce (Sierra Leone Ministry of Social Welfare, Gender and Children's Affairs, 2000, p. 3).

Women's vulnerability to poverty in Sierra Leone is exacerbated by discriminatory property and inheritance laws. Land tenureship and property rights generally favour males, thereby denying women access to a vital source of financial security. This is particularly true of the plight of female-headed households. After the war, many single mothers and widows tried to return to their homes but were denied access to their land or property because of their gender. As a result, many of them resorted to petty trading in order to survive and slipped deeper into poverty, thus increasing their vulnerability to SVE.

Other legal provisions also contribute to women's vulnerability to SVE. Whereas it is generally agreed that SVE is a serious crime, the punishment meted out to perpetrators is often too lenient, and in some cases scandalously low. Most key informants claimed that SVE exists within a culture of silence and impunity. The justice system is perceived to be too ill-equipped, or unwilling, to address the issue of gender-based sexual violence. A number of respondents said that existing laws needed to be enforced; however, there is limited knowledge of which laws are applicable and what the sanctions are for people who commit crimes of a sexual nature. The general sentiment is that there are no laws that cover SVE and that perpetrators are not adequately punished for the crimes they commit against women and girls. Perpetrators of SVE generally get away with their crimes, in part because victims rarely report them. The air of secrecy and stigma is made worse by some customary laws and cultural practices, which are deeply discriminatory against women and girls. For instance, under customary law, the consent of a minor for sex is not required. In Sierra Leone, it is still widely believed that a man is only liable to prosecution if he rapes a virgin, and not any other woman. Marital rape is not recognized under Sierra Leonean law. It is therefore not surprising that the first successful prosecution of a rape case in Sierra Leone did not occur until 1999 (Human Rights Watch, 2003, p. 24).

Cases of rape and sexual violence are usually settled directly between the rapist or aggressor and the parents or guardians of the girl child, without the victim having a say in the matter. In some cases, monetary compensation is offered, or the offender is forced to marry his victim. As a community leader in Kabala explained, 'Cases of sexual violence that are brought before the courts are eventually settled privately because the perpetrators are often neighbours or family members ... and because laws are seldom enforced.'

Cultural notions of masculinity also contribute to gender-based sexual violence. Under customary law, the position of a woman is secondary to that of a man; she is always under the guardianship of a male relative, and her status rises in the eyes of society and within polygamous households with each child she bears (Joko Smart, 1983, p. 108). Many households are polygamous, and men can marry as many wives as they want. Sixty per cent of the population is Muslim, and Islamic law allows men to marry up to four wives. 'Most cases of SVE happen because of masculinity,' a participant in a focus group discussion stated. Sierra Leonean culture is patriarchal and emphasizes the superiority of men over women, encouraging them to exercise their authority over women. As a result, men affirm their masculinity by, among other things, engaging in irresponsible sexual behaviour and domestic violence. 'Most men demonstrate their superiority by forcing women to yield to their sexual desires; men are generally better off and can coerce women into sex by paying for it. Culturally, a woman has no right to refuse having sex with her husband or partner,' explained a health programme coordinator in Freetown.

While there is widespread community consensus that women need to be protected from SVE, our research showed that misconceptions about the causes of SVE are high. A cross-section of focus group participants, ranging from religious and community leaders to people involved in community-based organizations, shared strikingly similar views about the causes of SVE. For example, they all concurred that the high incidence of SVE was due to 'the manner in which women and girls dressed.'

Conclusion

Women and girls in post-conflict Sierra Leone are particularly vulnerable to HIV and AIDS as they are deliberately targeted for rape, torture, sexual slavery, trafficking and forced marriages, thereby increasing their risk of contracting sexually transmitted infections, including HIV and AIDS (Benjamin, 2001).

In addition, as traditional custodians of the family, women are forced to adopt coping mechanisms, such as selling sex, to secure basic necessities for the survival of their families, thus increasing the risks of being exposed to gender-based sexual violence and to HIV and AIDS. This is reflected in the high HIV prevalence among young women aged between 15 and 24 years.

The effective implementation of gender laws that enable women to claim their inheritance rights can help to reduce SVE and prevalence of HIV. These gender-sensitive laws should also address effective forms of redress against men involved in sexual violence against women. The current legal system needs to be reformed so that offenders are brought to justice and can no longer enjoy impunity.

On the economic front, new programmes are needed that specifically focus on reducing poverty among women. Livelihood opportunities are needed to allow women to become more autonomous. The fishing sector is one obvious sector where more jobs could be created for women, particularly as poverty forces women to engage in sexual transactions in order to survive.

From a policy standpoint, greater efforts should be made to change perceptions of HIV and AIDS in Sierra Leone in order to encourage voluntary testing and counselling and reduce high-risk behaviour. Likewise, greater political will and commitment are needed to effectively prevent HIV and mitigate the impacts of HIV and AIDS in the country. Sensitization and awareness-raising programmes are key to improving knowledge on HIV and AIDS among women and girls.

Acknowledgements

I wish to thank Vivian Nasaka Makunda, Charles Saidu Bangura and Adama Thorlie for their assistance in preparing this study, as well as focus group discussion participants and key informants in Sierra Leone, who shared their invaluable insights and experiences.

References

Amnesty International. 2007. *Sierra Leone: Getting Reparations Right for Survivors of Sexual Violence*. New York, Amnesty International.

Barnes K., Albrecht P. and Olson M. 2007. *Addressing Gender-Based Violence in Sierra Leone: Mapping Challenges, Responses and Future Entry Points*. Limerick, Ireland, Irish Aid.

Benjamin, J. 2001. *Women, War and HIV/AIDS*. Washington DC, Population Reference Bureau.

Human Rights Watch. 2003. *We'll Kill You If You Cry: Sexual Violence in the Sierra Leone Conflict*. New York, Human Rights Watch.

Joko Smart, H. M. 1983. *Sierra Leone Customary Family Law*. Freetown, Fourah Bay College Bookshop Limited.

Physicians for Human Rights. 2002. *War-related Sexual Violence in Sierra Leone: A Population-based Assessment*. Boston, Mass., Physicians for Human Rights.

Sahr, F., Jalloh, M. I., Kargbo, B. and Gbakima, A. A. 2008. Prevalence of HIV and other sexually transmitted infections in the Republic of Sierra Leone Armed Forces. *African Journal of Science and Technology*, Vol. 9, No. 1, pp. 1–9.

Sierra Leone Ministry of Social Welfare, Gender and Children's Affairs. 2000. *National Policy on Gender Mainstreaming*. Freetown, Ministry of Social Welfare, Gender and Children's Affairs.

Sierra Leone NAS (National HIV/AIDS Secretariat). 2005. *National Population-based HIV Seroprevalence Survey of Sierra Leone*. Freetown, NAS.

——. 2006. *Sierra Leone HIV/AIDS National Strategic Plan (2006–2010)*. Freetown, NAS.

Truth and Reconciliation Commission of Sierra Leone. 2004. Women and armed conflict in Sierra Leone. *Witness to Truth: Report of the Truth and Reconciliation Commission of Sierra Leone*, Vol. III B, Chap. 3. Freetown, Liberia, Truth and Reconciliation Commission of Sierra Leone.

UNAIDS (Joint United Nations Programme on HIV/AIDS). 2008. *Country Report on Declaration of Commitment to HIV and AIDS (2006–2007)*. Geneva, UNAIDS. http://www.unaids.org/en/CountryResponses/Countries/sierraleone.asp

UNDP (United Nations Development Programme). 2007. *Human Development Report 2007*. http://hdr.undp.org/en/statistics

United Nations Commission on Human Rights. 2002. *Report of the Special Rapporteur on Violence Against Women, Its Causes and Consequences*. New York, UN Economic and Social Council. (E/CN.4/2002/83/Add.2.)

US Department of State. 2001. *Sierra Leone, Country Reports on Human Rights Practices–2000*. Washington DC, Bureau of Democracy, Human Rights, and Labor, pp. 2–11. http://www.state.gov/g/drl/rls/hrrpt/2000/af/755.htm

Women's Commission for Refugee Women and Children. 2008. *Country at a Crossroads: Challenges Facing Young People in Sierra Leone Six Years after the War*. New York, Women's Refugee Commission.

World Bank Group. 2008. *Sierra Leone at a Glance*. http://devdata.worldbank.org/AAG/sle_aag.pdf

CHAPTER 5

The price of liberation:
Economy, gender and HIV and AIDS in China

Shao Jing

Sex, condoms and clients

On the eve of World AIDS Day on 1 December 2007, the Ministry of Health of China released new epidemiological figures placing, for the first time, heterosexual sex (44.7 per cent) ahead of injecting drug use (42 per cent) as the main route of transmission of HIV in China. Including HIV infection among men who have sex with men (12.2 per cent), sexual transmission accounted for well over half (56.9 per cent) of the estimated 50,000 new cases of HIV in 2007. These new figures carry a clear message: the HIV epidemic in China is now poised to break free from the 'marginal cells' of previously scrutinized 'high risk groups', that is, key populations at higher risk, and permeate China's mainstream population through sex, one of the most difficult human behaviours to regulate.

The most common line of defence promoted by international organizations and national governments for combating a generalized outbreak is the use of condoms by individuals, who are to be made aware of the immanence of the danger they face and who are exhorted to take responsibility for protecting themselves and the larger society. Somewhat in line with this common approach, China's national government's 2007 campaign formed part of an aggressive, public move to fight the epidemic. The government's response was prompted in part by a recognition of an alarming convergence of several epidemiological factors (Qian et al., 2005): a well-established, though technically

The designations employed and the presentation of material throughout this publication do not imply the expression of any opinion whatsoever on the part of UNESCO concerning the legal status of any country, territory or area or of its authorities, or concerning the delimitation of its frontiers or boundaries.
The ideas and opinions expressed in this publication are those of the authors and do not necessarily reflect the views of UNESCO and its Member States.

illegal, sex industry across China both in urban and rural areas (Smith, 2005; Xia and Yang, 2005; Yang et al., 2007); increasing spread of drug use; huge internal migration of labour; and a raging 'sexual revolution' leading to a rising prevalence of sexually transmitted infections (Parish et al., 2003; Parish et al., 2007; Qu et al., 2002; Wong et al., 2007; Zhang and Li, 1999). As new public service advertisements make clear, the target of intervention of government programmes has now been expanded to include the most sexually active groups in the general population, namely, those aged between 20 and 39.

Oddly enough, while sex has now become a prominent target in intervention programmes aimed at checking the spread of HIV, attention to issues related to women and gender has been conspicuously absent. One explanation for this could be that women and gender as a topic has already received considerable attention as the theme chosen for World AIDS Day in China in 2004 was 'Women and HIV/AIDS'. We are here alerted to the fact that even though there is heightened awareness of sex as a route of transmission, gender remains a token category in China's, and the international community's, response to the problem. More important, consideration of the role of gender in shaping the contours of the epidemic needs to extend beyond the current narrow focus on sex and sex work and instead focus on broad social, economic and political forces powerfully inflected by gender in its many manifestations.

An examination of the trajectory of China's response to the epidemic can be instructive in this connection. In the early days of the epidemic, few in China anticipated its tenacity. It was seen as a curse, brought on by decadence, that was foreign and capitalist in its origin and could be easily kept at arm's length.[1] Today, however, Chinese political leaders and policy-makers are far more pragmatic and less bashful about the social problems emerging in the wake of economic liberalization in China. Lessons from experiences with the epidemic in other countries, such as Thailand, Brazil and the United States, have contributed to the dramatic change in the political thinking on the issue, which has in recent years resulted in a shift towards strategies derived from 'scientific evidence,' that is, interventions that have been shown to have statistically reduced the rate of infection among high-risk populations (Wu et al., 2007). The influx of international aid to fight the epidemic has been also persuasive in shaping China's response, which has adopted the language, protocols and above all the display of openness demanded by international funding agencies. Prominent among these funding agencies are the United Kingdom Department for International Development (DFID), the Global Fund to Fight AIDS, Tuberculosis and Malaria, and the Ford Foundation. The shift in public policy also means that policies are increasingly being guided by epidemiological expertise rather than 'conservative, moralistic attitudes'. Important 'sub-populations' (Qian et al., 2005) are managed medically and also ideologically through regimens of punishment, isolation and re-education. Methadone maintenance, needles and syringes, for example, are now provided for injecting heroin users for harm reduction (Sullivan and Wu, 2007). Likewise for sex workers, behavioural modification has become the mainstay of intervention (see, for example, Lin et al., 2007).

This intervention approach argues strongly in favour of an epidemiological examination of factors close to the site of transmission in order to determine the population distribution of the disease. In the case of the spread of HIV, two such risk factors are most frequently singled out: use of non-sterile injecting equipment among injecting drug users (IDUs) and sex without a condom. Individuals who engage in such activities are considered to be at risk of contracting the virus and transmitting it to others. Once duly informed of the risks involved, it is argued that reasonable individuals will wish to shy away from 'harmful behaviours'. The logic behind this type of intervention model is clear and forceful. Unfortunately, it has also served to blind us to less proximate but no less fundamental factors, including the role of gender – with all its dimensions and not readily recognized and analysed manifestations – in shaping the diverse social geographies of the HIV epidemic in China and elsewhere in the world.

Most surveys of sex workers in China, for example, incorporate at least two measures: knowledge about how the use of condoms can reduce the risk of HIV infection, and the rate of condom use. The responses in these surveys are alarming and reflect the probable threat posed by this potential bridge population and the need for epidemiological scrutiny. Education programmes serving this population often produce the happy result of demonstrable increase in both sets of measures (Foss et al., 2007).[2] However, without knowing the actual post-intervention rates of condom use, which are much harder to ascertain, the impact of knowledge on behaviour cannot be assumed.

What some epidemiologists find particularly troubling is the fact that sex workers tend to negotiate condom use far less frequently in their private lives than in their sex work. A possible explanation for this can be found in the implicit but only rarely openly acknowledged gendered assignment of responsibility in the surveys. In other words, these surveys investigate rates of *male* condom use by *female* sex workers when selling *female* sex. Moreover, it is the skills of these *female* workers that are found most lacking when they have to negotiate with their *male* clients to convince them to accept *male* condoms in the transaction.[3] This gendered assignment of responsibility, and by impli-cation, blame, in the realm of sex work, however, is consistent with broader gender-derived inequalities, control and motivations. Moreover, while condom use is considered applicable to sex between strangers, it does not seem to apply to sexual activity in the context of a close social relationship. As a Chinese so-ciologist observed bluntly, 'Fidelity and love are natural predators of condoms' (Shuiming, 2007). This antagonism is further borne out in the fact that the po-lice in China often use possession of condoms as evidence when arresting and fining sex workers and their clients (Jeffreys, 2006; Ren, 1999). The focus on sex in the recent Chinese efforts to curb the spread of HIV thus serves both to conceal and perpetuate gender-based inequalities and patterns of vulnerability to HIV infection.

Here we are confronted with what appears to be a cultural, though by no means uniquely Chinese, classification of sexual relations that are considered most relevant with regard to condom use. In the case of sexual activity in the context of a close social relationship, behavioural interventions are not easily applied. The classification of sexual relations that are deemed relevant for con-dom use is also having an impact more widely in China than just among sex workers and their clients. Avoidance of condom use in sex between spouses or regular, stable partners can be a profession of trust; on the other hand, the use of condoms is seen as indicating that one party may have something to hide.

In the context of sex work, one study probed the 'negative attitudes to-ward condom use' among sex workers in Shanghai and found them statistically significant in accounting for inconsistent condom use. Among statements that the researchers used to measure attitudes are: 'condom use is troublesome; con-dom use can destroy the natural feelings of sex; and you cannot give yourself completely to your partner if a condom is used' (Yang and Xia, 2006). The statements assume the voice of sex workers, but the viewpoints are clearly not theirs. If anything, these statements should be used to measure the extent to which sex workers have come to view the quality of their services from the perspective of male clients. Sometimes, an element in the perceived quality of purchased sex, paradoxically, is the simulation of social affinity that conceals the very fact of a purchase. Often this gesture towards concealing the fact of a commercial transaction results in a higher price. In this market, the buyer's power to purchase dominates and ironically can unify the goals of the gendered parties in the transaction. Nonetheless, the duty of protection against harm is still assigned to the seller, who is often not in a position to fulfill it, as reflected in the epidemiological literature that informs policies.

The expansion of the current campaign to promote condom use to include the local population, and by implication the far less well defined and studied but nonetheless crucially significant population group of *clients* of sex work, reveals the ineffectiveness of previous efforts targeting sellers and may suffer from the same limitations unless important questions about the role of gender-related social and cultural factors in shaping behaviour and the epidemic are addressed. In what follows, I will focus on what has been set aside in the epidemiological literature as a 'separate epidemic', one that is often excluded from the narrative used to describe the overall HIV and AIDS scenario in China. Sex did not figure as a route of transmission in this 'separate epidemic.' Yet, both in terms of the large number of women infected and the depth and devastation of the affected communities, it has a profile characteristic of advanced stages of HIV epidemic not yet found elsewhere in China. This outbreak demonstrates that gender can remain a crucial issue under radically different epidemiological circumstances and calls for interventions to halt further gender-derived suffering in the aftermath of an infectious outbreak of massive proportions.

The poverty of epidemiology

Barely mentioned in the current season of heightened national alert is the regional outbreak early in the 1990s, which led to HIV infection among large numbers of commercial plasma donors in rural central China, most notably in the Province of Henan. The outbreak had been kept a secret for years, not only from the public at large, but also from those who had been infected. When finally brought to light in the new millennium by waves of deaths from a 'strange disease' in the most severely affected villages, now widely known as 'AIDS villages', the epidemic was the source of serious political embarrassment for the Chinese Government. According to conservative estimates released by the provincial Government of Henan, more than 30,000 people in this province alone were infected as a result of plasma donation.[4] Among donors in dozens of villages, which are referred to in Chinese epidemiological reports as 'lesion sites', the prevalence of HIV infection is alarmingly high.[5] Much has since been done by the government to alleviate the suffering of those infected, as well as to regulate the supply of blood and plasma to prevent transmission of HIV through blood donations. But this outbreak deserves a second look because it reveals the dynamic interplay between economic forces and social and cultural factors in giving the epidemic its unique profile. This was also an outbreak that defied the well-recognized pattern of progression, particularly in terms of the male-to-female ratio of the infected; from the start, it claimed both men and women as victims in equal numbers, but by a transmission route that was far more efficient than sex.

The mechanics of transmission for this outbreak were starkly simple. Infection occurred when contaminated blood cells were returned to the donor after the whole blood was centrifuged to allow the harvesting of plasma. Sources of contamination in the manual method of plasma collection used at the time include unsterile implements and breakage of plastic blood bags loaded in the centrifuge. With deadly efficiency, the epidemic rapidly established itself over a wide swathe of several central provinces. This situation does not make for startling epidemiological discoveries, but it does compel us to examine determinants that are not usually included in conventional epidemiology.

Attempts to include 'larger social determinants' for the spread of HIV and other bloodborne diseases in rural China (e.g. Mastro and Yip, 2006; Tucker and Lin, 2006) have pointed to generic poverty as a root cause. This vague explanation is not only insufficient but highlights the frequent 'poverty' of epidemiological studies, as well as exemplifying how inaccurate and misleading information is sometimes used to support a conventional political agenda. A few years ago, a querulous search for culprits followed the media exposure of the outbreak. For the government, the villains are the 'blood heads' who acted as human agents for the spread of the virus; they recruited donors and sent them from one collection centre to another and introduced illegal plasma harvesting to the villages. A few audacious activists have pointed the finger at the biggest 'blood head' of all, the head of the Bureau of Health in Henan, who personally promoted commercial plasma collection in the province.[6] Using evidence from molecular epidemiology (Zhang, 2004), some have also blamed IDUs from border provinces in the southwest for contaminating the pristine pool of donors in China's central province. Everyone now agrees that poverty, resulting specifically from overpopulation and increasingly scarce agricultural land, was the ultimate cause of this tragedy.

Poverty alone, however, defined either by absolute standard of living or comparatively, does not explain the two most salient and related aspects of the outbreak. The donors and the infected are not uniformly poor but rather predominantly 'rural residents' in general. Secondly, this epidemic was concentrated in the agricultural heartland of China, not in the western provinces, which have the highest levels of poverty. Both 'rural-ness' and poverty deserve a closer look.

Labour, blood and HIV and AIDS

The term 'rural resident', often included as a demographic variant in Chinese epidemiological literature, is a bureaucratic category designating the less powerful and disenfranchised, but far more numerous rural people whose place of residence is determined by one of the legacies of the socialist era – the household registration system. This structure of inequality has survived even the most radical eradication of socialist institutions to ensure that rural migrants provide a vast source of cheap labour through their exclusion from basic social services in urban areas. This resource is a crucial element of much of China's recent economic growth.

What contributed to the vulnerability to HIV infection of 'rural residents' in the central provinces, ironically, was the fact they had initially benefited most from China's economic liberalization that began three decades ago in the agricultural sector. The introduction of the 'household responsibility system' (Oi, 1999) to replace the previous collective system of production has been widely credited for the rapid agricultural growth experienced during the initial phase of the reform from 1979 to 1984, as it was believed to have provided incentives to agricultural producers to improve productivity by 'linking remuneration to output' (Ash, 1988). This economic logic became the template for liberalization in other sectors of the Chinese economy, including health care.

The impact of decollectivization on agricultural growth (as well as on health care), however, should be more carefully examined. First, the substantial increase in income for agricultural producers in the early years of reform was clearly a result of the massive redistribution of capital by central planners, rather than the fruit of entrepreneurial activity (Gates, 1996). As if to purchase the certainty of success for an ideologically dubious economic experiment, the government significantly raised its procurement prices for agricultural products from 1979 to 1984 but kept retail prices low for urban consumers. Farmers received more money for their produce and improved their standard of living dramatically. Cutting in the opposite direction, the 'price scissors' that had been used to extract agricultural surplus to build socialist industrialization soon cut a sizeable hole in the state budget (Knight, 1995; Sah and Stiglitz, 1984). The slowdown in the rate of income increase in the years that followed can be clearly linked to the government's decision in 1985 to withdraw this significant 'subsidy' for agriculture, ostensibly to allow the market to play a greater role in regulating the prices of agricultural products (Ash, 1992; Hsu, 1984; Lin, 1992).

Second, a regional pattern of rural income disparity emerged in the later years of agricultural reform. From 1985 to 1990, for example, the heavily agricultural provinces in central China, including Henan, suffered a decline in rural income levels, whereas the coastal provinces in south-east China enjoyed rising income. This disparity suggests that the expansion of rural industry was becoming the primary source of rising income levels in the coastal provinces (Rozelle, 1996).

Third, the sharp increase in the use of chemical fertilizers contributed substantially to the accelerated growth in agricultural output early in the reform period (Lin, 1992). Many of the 'developments in agricultural technology' necessary for manufactured fertilizers to have an impact on crop yield, for example through effective irrigation and 'high yielding fertilizer responsive [seed] varieties', had already been deployed in the pre-reform era of collective agriculture (Stone, 1988). The improved provision of chemical fertilizers at the beginning of the reform period, it seems, was designed to allow China's agricultural producers to reap the benefits of a long-planned 'green revolution'.

But the benefits for farmers turned out to be elusive. Individual farming households are much less capable of absorbing the impact of price fluctuations in the market, both for what they produce and for their inputs. They have also become more vulnerable to changes in weather conditions in recent years because of the decrease in effectively irrigated areas resulting from the exhaustion of water resources and the lack of maintenance of public irrigation works built during the socialist period. In the context of economic liberalization, technological developments have only facilitated the transformation of traditional labour-intensive agricultural systems into capital-intensive enterprises. The capital input in each cycle of agricultural production often would have purchased more grains than the increase in yields brought about by the 'green revolution'. The value of agricultural labour had thus become increasingly dubious, a surplus with no profit.

Under these conditions, 'rural residents' in the heavily agricultural central provinces were compelled to convert their surplus labour into cash, either by migrating to urban and coastal industrial centers to look for work or by selling their blood. When plasma collection began, it was perceived as an attractive way of generating revenue as it seemed to only take the insubstantial part of their blood, the part not essential to their vitality, physical strength and force. Many HIV-infected women have reported that they began selling their plasma much earlier than their husbands did, and sold far more frequently, because they wanted to protect their husbands' physical strength. As women, they reasoned, they had to 'waste' blood every month anyway because of their monthly periods. Many of these women had in fact returned from working in manufacturing in the cities. They worked for several years to build dowries. They returned, got married and raised their children in their home villages. Selling plasma gave them an opportunity to continue supporting their families by bringing in cash that could no longer be obtained through out-migration.[7] This gendered understanding of selling blood or plasma should be understood, on the one hand, as resulting from the promotion of gender equality under socialism, which ironically had expanded women's 'responsibility' in the household economy in the era of economic liberalization that followed, and on the other hand, in terms of the naturalization of persistent gendered inequalities. In fact, before plasma collection became widespread in the region, rural women far outnumbered men in selling whole blood to supplement household income.

To fault poverty per se for the outbreak of HIV infection among rural plasma donors is thus not particularly revealing and does not completely remove the moral censure on an apparently 'blameless population' (Cao et al., 2006). Poverty has also been viewed as a symptom of a moral defect attributed to these twice-liberated agricultural producers. Liberated first by the Communist revolution from the fetters of a 'feudal society' in 1949 and then again from collective agriculture with the return of a market economy in 1978, they had nonetheless chosen what was considered a most 'unnatural route' to wealth. Many villagers were resentful of purportedly sympathetic stories in the media of how some had gotten rich and built new houses with their blood money only to be struck down by AIDS in the end. The moral censure that these stories imply is clear: poverty comes from a lack of industry and a willingness to sell one's blood for money.

It is important to understand that the exchange between people and land, as between labour and food, has now become irreversibly mediated by money and goods that have to be purchased with money. Increasingly, money has replaced and displaced labour itself and rendered the people in the exchange redundant. To maintain the exchange between people and land, the displaced labour has to be liquidated in the market, despite all its uncertainties. When the agricultural producers, bypassing the fruits of their labour on the land, alienate the liquid part of their blood in the market, liquidation becomes immediate and literal. Plasma in a cash-starved agricultural economy becomes cash by virtue of the demand for albumin in a health industry hungry for 'volume expansion'.[8]

The wealth of health

The market for blood products, principally albumin, was created by economic reform in China's health sector launched in the mid-1980s. Public hospitals and other health care facilities, which previously had been supported by state subsidies, now had to compete in the market and generate revenue, largely through the services they provided and the drugs they sold in their in-house pharmacies. 'Production quotas' were set for each clinical department in a manner similar to the 'household responsibility system' in the agricultural reforms, and the personal income levels of staff members fluctuated with how well quotas were met and how much above-quota income they could distribute among themselves. This arrangement encouraged serious conflicts of interest in health care. More expensive treatment alternatives were always promoted to patients, and the prices of the drugs became a bogus measure of their efficacy. In this context, albumin quickly became a favourite drug at hospitals, prescribed often in the absence of any specific indications to patients who were convinced of its restorative efficacy and could afford to pay for this luxury (Shao, 2006).

The fledgling plasma fractionation industry in China was boosted by a ban on all imported blood products, issued by the Ministry of Health in 1985, aimed at keeping HIV and AIDS outside China's borders (see China Ministry of Health, 1984, 1986). The ministry also promised to build the capacity of China's own fractionation industry so that it could meet any shortfalls created by the ban. The industry grew quickly in the decade following the ban on foreign blood products. Many newcomers to the industry were companies formed by individuals who had previously worked for the ministry's institutes but decided to give up the security of state employment for the prospect of greater rewards as entrepreneurs. As demand for 'source plasma' grew, new collection centers mushroomed in the central provinces, particularly in Henan, with the encouragement of the head of the province's health bureau, who saw an opportunity to profit from the province's high population levels. In addition to exporting labour to the coastal and urban industrial centres, then, the province could benefit more directly by supplying them source plasma. Plasma collection moved in exactly the opposite direction of labour migration: many of the earliest plasma collection centres had, in fact, been set up in rural coastal areas near Shanghai, but by the time this region began to attract migrants from the central provinces, plasma collection had disappeared completely from this area and re-emerged inland (see Liu and Ji, 1989; Rozelle, 1996).

The plasma fractionation industry suffered a brief setback when the government shut down all the plasma collection operations and banned manual collection methods in Henan Province in 1995 when news filtered out on the scale of HIV infections. Since this move was made without alerting collectors and donors about the risk of HIV infection, plasma collection went underground and continued for nearly a year, expanding significantly the scope of the epidemic. With plasma collection prohibited but a ready plasma processing capacity in place, Henan Province then became a major importer of source plasma. Collection moved to provinces in the south-west, primarily Guizhou and Guangxi, according to the allocation of collection quotas established by the Ministry of Health in 2004. Rural residents in the mountainous parts of these provinces were thought to be 'safer' donors because they tended to live in more isolated areas and were less likely to travel. They were also the most impoverished and thus more likely to see plasma donation as an attractive source of income. This reasoning, however, seems remarkably similar to the initial rationale for collecting source plasma in the central provinces.

The industry's resilience can only be explained by the continued high demand in the health industry for blood products. For years, serum albumin has remained among the most prescribed drugs in hospitals in cash value. A recent market analysis of 2003–2005 data puts albumin consumption at the top of the category of 'nutritional drugs' prescribed by hospitals sampled in ten major Chinese cities. Among the over thirty fractionation plants currently licensed in China, the five leading plants, based in Henan, Sichuan and Shanghai, processed as much as two-thirds of all plasma collected in 2004, whereas the rest are much smaller in scale, and many will surely be pushed out of the industry in the fierce competition for access to capital, raw material and market share (Cai, 2007). The survival of a fractionation plant now depends on how successfully it can pursue the strategy of 'volume expansion', an image frequently invoked by industry analysts. In other words, the capacity for processing large volumes of plasma and the ability to derive more marketable products from the same raw material are key factors for profitability. Both of these, however, require heavy capital investment for high-capacity and state-of-the-art technology. To ensure the performance of the money raised in the capital market for this investment, fractionation plants have to procure sufficient amounts of source plasma to keep equipment running at full capacity. Any sign of 'shock' (to extend the analogy between blood and capital) caused by an insufficient supply of plasma can quickly lead to capital flight and business failure.

A few fractionation plants have gone public in the past few years and have issued shares to raise capital to expand further. Invariably they have presented the industry's tremendous potential for growth by arguing that China, in its current state of underdevelopment, is an albumin-starved nation. From the industry's perspective, it seems that the nation's gross domestic albumin consumption has somehow acquired a GDP-like quality, capable of measuring the nation's health and wealth at the same time. Sadly, associating albumin consumption with health and wealth has not helped those plasma donors who were infected with HIV: two such donors I encountered in Henan Province fell deeply into debt in order to purchase albumin as 'nutrition shots' in the months before they died.

Pathways of pathology

Three concurrent historical processes have been presented in the course of this chapter: the economic reform in the agricultural sector, the economic reform of health care, and the emergence of a plasma fractionation industry. The value and utility of labour and blood, as well as plasma, have been reviewed in gendered terms. When examined separately, each of these forms a realm of purely economic activities, guided by the same ideological conviction in the liberating power of a 'socialist market' that could not be delivered under the earlier socialist 'model'. Separately, none of these historical processes created the necessary conditions for the outbreak of the HIV epidemic. The necessary condition was the introduction of HIV into the pool of plasma donors, specifically the viral subtype that dominated the infected injecting heroin users in Yunnan Province close to the Gold Triangle, as recent research in molecular epidemiology confirms (Zhang et al., 2004). But the pathological confluence of these historical processes determined the geography and demography of the HIV epidemic among plasma donors in rural central China.

This analysis confirms the long recognized connections, both causal and reciprocal, between distribution of disease and 'fundamental' conditions (Link and Phelan, 1995) variously theorized as 'socio-economic disparity' (House, 2001, 2005), 'structural violence' (Farmer, 1996, 2004), 'inequality' (Fassin, 2003; Nguyen and Peshard, 2003) or 'political economy' (Baer, 1982; Morgan, 1987; Singer, 1998). A further step of critical importance is to identify and act upon pathways of pathology in historically, socially and culturally specific contexts.

In the current atmosphere of overwhelming attention to curbing the spread of HIV into the local population, it is easy to forget that the same social and political conditions and cultural logic that have led to the epidemic in central China continue to shape the experience of the disease of those already infected. Among the earliest symptoms of the progression of HIV disease, and the one most keenly felt by these hardworking villagers, is fatigue. When they had allowed their blood to be borrowed and returned through a process locally referred to as 'blood transfusion',[9] they had been told that they were making money out of a useless part of their blood, which was renewable and inexhaustible like well-water. The beer-coloured plasma does not even bear any resemblance to real blood, as many collectors would not hesitate to point out in an effort to allay anxieties over permanent health damage from frequent donations. The irreversible loss of their labour power due to HIV infection was a shocking price to pay for money they had made selling plasma years before.

The technical and temporal gap between HIV infection and AIDS is all too easily obliterated if those infected with the virus are condemned to social death before they develop the disease syndrome itself. In the midst of intensifying media attention on the AIDS-related deaths in a few villages in Henan, the government hastily rolled out a free antiretroviral (ARV) treatment early in 2003. This limited programme distributed ARV drugs but without adequate medical services to provide testing or clinical staging to initiate and monitor the treatment, deal with side effects and ensure adherence. With uncharacteristic modesty, the government claimed, as a measure of the programme's success, a three-year survival rate of only 50 per cent (Zhang, 2004) – a survival rate that is no better than the rate without any treatment at all. Thus, there was speculation among many villagers, alarmed by the violent side effects that some experienced after initiating the therapy, that the free ARV drugs were part of a conspiracy to hasten their deaths and thereby eliminate a problem that the government had been forced to deal with. Nausea and vomiting were among the most common side effects of the ARV regimen in the free government treatment programme, resulting in appetite loss or inability to keep anything down, as well as dizziness and sore muscles, which further weakened their bodies. These common side effects were experienced as life threatening by these agricultural producers, exactly because they seemed to assault the most essential dimensions of their lives: food and labour. Often they would not give the treatment enough time for some of the short-term side effects to subside before they would cut their doses or stop taking the drugs altogether (Shao, 2006).

The lack of comprehensive treatment delivery, a symptom of the collapse of the rural health care system during the reform era, however, is only part of the reason for the failure of the programme. The villages that saw the greatest decline in participation and adherence were all well-known 'AIDS villages,' favoured not only by journalists, AIDS activists and NGOs but also by pharmaceutical manufacturers and an army of traditional medicine practitioners chasing lucrative dreams of finding a cure for 'the plague of the millennium'. Major research hospitals recruited clinical trial subjects from these villages to fill their purchase orders from pharmaceutical developers. In these villages, government supplied ARV drugs, which promised only the suppression but not the eradication of the disease, competed poorly with the plethora of free samples of hope represented by remedies of uncertain efficacy that are far more easily ingested without the pain of the dreaded side effects, especially when the recruited clinical trial subjects were rewarded with free trips to Beijing to have their blood samples taken, provided with free meals and even given small sums of money.

The diseased bodies of HIV-infected villagers are now brought into economic circulation, resulting in greater morbidity and mortality in high-profile 'AIDS villages' where recruitment for clinical trial subjects is the most intense. This epidemiological pattern makes a mockery of the compassion and hope that highly active antiretroviral therapy, or HAART, is meant to inspire. The parallels that one could draw between the circuits of value relating to the out-migration of rural labour, 'source plasma' collection and clinical trials are stunning. Construction companies relied on 'labour contractors' from the villages for their supply of workers; plasma collection centers used the help of 'blood heads' to recruit and transport donors. The Chinese character for 'head' appears in both these terms. Likewise, infectious disease hospitals supplied clinical trial data on drugs under development with the assistance of the same cast of intermediaries living among HIV-positive villagers.

In one of the villages, I came to know a 55-year-old grandmother who was herself infected, as were her husband, their two daughters and one granddaughter. The daughters returned to the village to live with their parents after their own husbands died of AIDS-related illness. The grandmother had started taking the government-supplied ARV drugs early but had given up several times because she could not tolerate the side effects, which made it impossible to work in the field and cook at home. She had finally managed to restart the treatment and stay on the medication long enough for its side effects to subside when I saw her for the last time. A few weeks after I left, someone in the village called to tell me that she had been hit by a truck near a tollbooth and had died instantly. Upon my return, I inquired about the accident, and the villager who helped negotiate a settlement told me it happened near the exit from the toll station. My suspicions were immediately aroused that she had intended to risk injury (not death) in search of monetary compensation because I knew that the trucks leaving the toll station could not possibly be going very fast. On another occasion, I asked this same villager about the size of the settlement for her death. After giving a figure, he added, 'Not bad!' The villagers were living with the awareness of premature death, an inevitability that strips the enterprise from their lives. Taking a quick exit while leaving behind a useful amount of money for her family was perhaps really 'not bad'.

This sad and poignant story compels us to understand the price that China's 'rural residents' have had to pay for their multiple experiences of 'liberation'. A price has also been paid by women, particularly among rural communities, for their even more dubious liberation. The majority of the epidemiological subpopulation categorized as 'commercial sex workers' are also 'rural to urban migrants', yet another epidemiological label. Their entry into China's booming sex industry is aided by that industry's ubiquity and its many disguises, operating as it does in illegality behind a bewildering variety of service and entertainment outlets. The high turnover of those who work in this industry and their extreme mobility are both significant. Freed to sell sex, for a period of time, with anonymity and perhaps impunity, away from the social world to which they hope to return, very much as they would after working in factories, as wives and mothers, the population of 'commercial sex workers' is difficult to identify and track. Risk-taking, often despite knowledge, motivation and skills, is then not simply a behaviour but integral to the temporal nature of the work itself in its local context. Sexually transmitted infections that compromise their capacity to earn, and the resultant infertility that blocks their return to 'proper' gender roles, are sometimes far more feared as the liabilities of their work. Epidemiologically informed behavioural inventions have not yet adequately addressed this seeming irrationality of risk perception.

How do we, then, effectively block the pathways of pathology? The answer can come from quite unexpected quarters. In 2006, the Chinese Government abolished all agricultural taxes, which, over a period of decades, had been an indispensable revenue source for the government. A little more than a year later, hospitals all over China ran out of coagulating factors that haemophilic patients relied upon; in the face of this situation, these patients launched a vocal lobby for the government to lift the ban on imported blood products, which has remained in place since it was first issued almost twenty years ago. Many hospitals also suffered from shortages of albumin. This time, the shortfall was directly caused by the modest amount of money the government now gives to rural residents, which has made selling plasma less attractive and less necessary. An unintended but happy outcome of this shift in economic and social policy is the reduction of the risk of HIV infection among plasma donors and blood product users.

Notes

1. This confidence was seen most clearly in the text of the ban on imported blood products that was issued in 1985.

2. A student group at my university proposed one such programme for sex workers in Nanjing. The programme had a modest budget, primarily aimed at the purchase of bananas as props to teach condom use. I suspect that most sex workers had already been educated by the city's health officials and were probably more knowledgeable about condoms and how to use them than the students themselves.

3. Less ironic but equally problematic are female condoms or vaginal microbicides.

4. A survey conducted in 2004 of over 280,000 former rural commercial blood/plasma donors in Henan, nine years after the provincial government banned commercial blood and plasma collection in the province, found over 25,000 tested positive for HIV (see http://news.xinhuanet.com/newscenter/2004-09/10/content_1967309.htm, accessed 10 August 2006). According to an earlier official document by the Health Bureau of Henan Province quoted in Yu (2003), the number of donors infected with HIV was estimated to be between 23,100 and 33,500. For further information regarding this document, see Liu (2004) and Pomfred (2003).

5. One study, Zheng et al. (2000), shows that the rate of HIV infection among former commercial blood and plasma donors in a county in Henan is 17 per cent. In a more recent study, Xue (2006) reports a prevalence of 17.39 per cent among 4,351 former donors in another county in Henan, pointing out however that the majority of the HIV-infected donors are concentrated in a small number of villages. The official document quoted in Yu (2003) indicates that a sampling of the former donors in high-prevalence villages in 2000 resulted in prevalence between 16 per cent and 48 per cent.

6. Wan Yanhai, a prominent activist, for example, called for in 2001 criminal investigation into this official's possible role in the HIV outbreak among blood and plasma donors in Henan (see http://www.aizhi.org/shyx/lxx.txt, accessed 21 December 2007).

7. These comments are based upon the author's ethnographic field research and interviews in Henan Province, 2004–2007.

8. See Anagnost (2006); Erwin (2006); Rosenthal (2000); Shao (2006); Wu et al. (2001); and Wu et al. (2004).

9. 'Blood transfusion' (*shuxue*) proper has now come to be referred to as 'blood supplementation' (*buxue*) as a result. The term supplementation here is closely

associated with a therapeutic approach (*zhifa*) in traditional Chinese medicine in which the body is seen as an economy of dynamic components that need to be kept in balance. The popularity of plasma-derived albumin and immune globulin in China, ironically, can be largely explained by the popular understanding of their potency in 'supplementation' in this traditional sense.

References

Anagnost, A. 2006. Strange circulations: Blood economy in rural China. *Economy and Society,* Vol. 35, No. 4, pp. 509–29.

Ash, R. F. 1988. The evolution of agricultural policy. *China Quarterly,* Vol. 116, pp. 529–55.

——. 1992. The agricultural sector in China: Performance and policy dilemmas during the 1990s. *China Quarterly,* Vol. 131, Special Issue: The Chinese Economy in the 1990s, pp. 545–76.

Baer, H. A. 1982. On the political economy of health. *Medical Anthropology Newsletter,* Vol. 14, No. 1, pp. 1–2, 13–17.

Cai, D. 2007. Yinyang yao chunfeng deyi [Nutritional drugs are selling well]. Yiyao jingji bao *[Bulletin of Pharmaceutical Market],* 2 May. (In Chinese.)

Cao, X., Sullivan, S. G., Xu, J. and Wu, Z. 2006.Understanding HIV-related stigma and discrimination in a 'blameless' population. *AIDS Education and Prevention,* Vol. 18, No. 6, pp. 518–28.

China Ministry of Health. 1984. Guanyu xianzhi jinkou xueye zhipin fangzhi AIDS jinru woguo de lianhe tongzhi [Notification regarding limiting blood products importation to prevent AIDS from coming into our country]. (In Chinese.) http://www.fm120.com/zt/law/laws/1/YPJCKGL/YPJCKGL1034.htm (Accessed 9 June 2005.)

——. 1986. Guanyu jinzhi jinkou VIII yinzi zhiji deng xueye zhipin de tonggao [Announcement regarding the prohibition of importation of factor VIII preparations and some other blood products]. http://www.fm120.com/zt/law/laws/1/YPJCKGL/YPJCKGL1022.htm (Accessed 9 June 2005.)

Erwin, K. 2006. The circulatory system: Blood procurement, AIDS, and the social body in China. *Medical Anthropology Quarterly,* Vol. 20, No. 2, pp. 139–59.

Farmer, P. 1996. Social inequalities and emerging infectious diseases. *Emerging Infectious Diseases,* Vol. 2, No. 4, pp. 259–69.

——. 2004. An anthropology of structural violence. *Current Anthropology,* Vol. 45, No. 3, pp. 305–25.

Fassin, D. 2003. The embodiment of inequality: AIDS as a social condition and the historical experience in South Africa. *EMBO reports,* Vol. 4, Suppl., pp. S7–S9.

Foss, A. M., Hossain, M., Vickerman, P. T. and Watts, C. H. 2007. A systematic review of published evidence on intervention impact on condom use in sub-Saharan Africa and Asia. *Sexually Transmitted Infections,* Vol. 83, No. 7, pp. 510–16.

Gates, H. 1996. *China's Motor.* Ithaca, NY, Cornell University Press.

House, J. S. 2001. Relating social inequalities in health and income. *Journal of Health Politics, Policy and Law*, Vol. 26, No. 3, pp. 523.

——. 2005. Social disparities in health: An Anglo-European perspective. *Health Affairs*, Vol. 24, No. 2, pp. 559–61.

Hsu, R. 1984. Grain procurement and distribution in China's rural areas: Post-Mao policies and problems. *Asian Survey*, Vol. 24, No. 12, pp. 1229–246.

Jeffreys, E. 2006. Governing buyers of sex in the People's Republic of China. *Economy and Society*, Vol. 35, No. 4, pp. 571–93.

Knight, J. 1995. Price scissors and intersectoral resource transfers: Who paid for industrialization in China? *Oxford Economic Papers*, Vol. 47, No. 1, pp. 117–35.

Lin, J. Y. 1992. Rural reforms and agricultural growth in China. *The American Economic Review*, Vol. 82, No. 1, pp. 34–51.

Lin, K., McElmurry, B. J. and Christiansen, C. 2007. Women and HIV/AIDS in China: Gender and vulnerability. *Health Care Women International*, Vol. 28, No. 8, pp. 680–99.

Link, B. G., and Phelan, J. 1995. Social conditions as fundamental causes of disease. *Journal of Health and Social Behavior*, Vol. 35, pp. 80–94.

Liu, J. X., and Ji, Y. C. (eds). 1989. *Dancai Xuejiang Shu Shouche [Handbook for Plasmapheresis]*. Beijing, Renmin Weisheng Chubanshe [People's Health Publisher]. (In Chinese.)

Liu, Z. M. 2004. Ma Shiwen: kending yao youren zuochu xisheng [Ma Shiwen: someone has to make a sacrifice]. *Nanfang Renwu Zhoukan [Southen People Weekly]*, 1 December. (In Chinese.) http://www.nanfangdaily.com.cn/rwzk/20041201/fmrw/200412130013.asp (Accessed 15 December 2007.)

Mastro, T. D. and Yip, R. 2006. The legacy of unhygienic plasma collection in China. *AIDS*, Vol. 20, No. 10, pp. 1451–452.

Morgan, L. M. 1987. Dependency theory in the political economy of health: An anthropological critique. *Medical Anthropology Quarterly*, Vol. 1, No. 2, pp. 131–54.

Nguyen, V. K. and Peshard, K. 2003. Anthropology, inequality, and disease: A Review. *Annual Review of Anthropology*, Vol. 32, pp. 447–74.

Oi, J. C. 1999. Two decades of rural reform in China: An overview and assessment. *China Quarterly*, Vol. 159, pp. 616–28.

Parish, W. L., Laumann, E. O., Cohen, M. S., Pan, S. et al. 2003. Population-based study of chlamydial infection in China: A hidden epidemic. *JAMA*, Vol. 289, No. 10, pp. 1265–273.

Parish, W. L., Laumann, E. O. and Mojola, S. A. 2007. Sexual behavior in China: Trends and comparisons. *Population and Development Review*, Vol. 33, No. 4, pp. 729–56.

Parish, W. L., Luo, Y., Laumann, E. O., Ken, M. and Yu, Z. 2007. Unwanted sexual activity among married women in urban China. *Journal of Sex Research*, Vol. 44, No. 2, pp. 158–71.

Pomfred, J. 2003. China detains health official for publicizing AIDS coverup. *Washington Post*, 8 October 2003, p. A23.

Qian, Z. H., Vermund, S. H. and Wang, N. 2005. Risk of HIV/AIDS in China: Subpopulations of special importance. *Sexually Transmitted Infections*, Vol. 81, No. 6, pp. 442–47.

Qu, S., Liu, W., Choi, K., Li, R., Jiang, D. et al. 2002. The potential for rapid sexual transmission of HIV in China: Sexually transmitted diseases and condom failure highly prevalent among female sex workers. *AIDS and Behavior*, Vol. 6, No. 3, pp. 267–75.

Ren, X. 1999. Prostitution and economic modernization in China. *Violence Against Women*, Vol. 5, No. 12, pp. 1411–436.

Rosenthal, E. 2000. In rural China, a steep price of poverty: Dying of AIDS. *New York Times*, 28 October.

Rozelle, S. 1996. Stagnation without equity: Patterns of growth and inequality in China's rural economy. *China Journal*, Vol. 35, pp. 63–92.

Sah, R. K. and Stiglitz, J. E. 1984. The economics of price scissors. *American Economic Review*, Vol. 74, No. 1, pp. 125–38.

Shao, J. 2006. Fluid labor and blood money: The economy of HIV/AIDS in rural central China. *Cultural Anthropology*, Vol. 21, No. 4, pp. 535–69.

Shuiming, P. 2007. *Male Clients in the Sex Industry: A Preliminary Investigation* [*Xing Chaiye Zhong De Nanke: Chubu Tansuo*] Beijing, Renmin University of China, Institute of Sexuality and Gender. (In Chinese.) http://www.sexstudy.org/english/article.php?id=2402 (Accessed 6 December 2008.)

Singer, M. 1998. Forging a political economy of AIDS. M. Singer (ed.), *The Political Economy of AIDS*. Amityville, NY, Baywood Publishing.

Smith, C. J. 2005. Social geography of sexually transmitted diseases in China: Exploring the role of migration and urbanisation. *Asia Pacific Viewpoint*, Vol. 46, No. 1, pp. 65–80.

Stone, B. 1988. Developments in agricultural technology. *China Quarterly*, Vol. 116, pp. 767–822.

Sullivan, S. G. and Wu, Z. 2007. Rapid scale up of harm reduction in China. *International Journal of Drug Policy*, Vol. 18, No. 2, pp. 118–28.

Tucker, J. D. and Lin, C. C. 2006. Poverty and the spread of bloodborne disease in central China. *Journal of Infectious Diseases*, Vol. 193, No. 6, pp. 902–03.

Wong, S. P. Y., Yin, Y. P., Gao, X., Wei, W. H., Shi, M. Q. et al. 2007. Risk of syphilis in STI clinic patients: A cross-sectional study of 11 500 cases in Guangxi, China. *Sexually Transmitted Infections,* Vol. 83, No. 5, pp. 351–56.

Wu, Z., Rou, K. and Cui, H. 2004. The HIV/AIDS epidemic in China: History, current strategies and future challenges. *AIDS Education and Prevention,* Vol. 16, Suppl. A, pp. 7–17.

Wu, Z., Rou, K. and Detels, R. 2001. Prevalence of HIV infection among former commercial plasma donors in rural eastern China. *Health Policy and Planning,* Vol. 16, No. 1, p. 41.

Wu, Z., Sullivan, S. G., Wang, Y., Rotheram-Borus, M. J. and Detels, R. 2007. Evolution of China's response to HIV/AIDS. *Lancet,* Vol. 369, No. 9562, pp. 679–90.

Xia, G. and Yang, X. 2005. Risky sexual behavior among female entertainment workers in China: Implications for HIV/STD prevention intervention. *AIDS Education and Prevention,* Vol. 17, No. 2, pp. 143–56.

Xue, F. H. 2006. Moudi jiwang youchang gongxue renyuan HIV ganran liuxingbingxue fengxi [Epidemiological survey and analysis of HIV prevalence among former paid blood donors in a certain district of southeast of Henan]. *Shiyong Yufang Yixue [Practical Preventive Medicine],* Vol. 13, No. 3, pp. 617–18. (In Chinese.)

Yang, X., Derlega, V. J. and Luo, H. 2007. Migration, behaviour change and HIV/STD risks in China. *AIDS Care,* Vol. 19, No. 2, pp. 282–88.

Yang, X. and Xia, G. 2006. Gender, work, and HIV Risk: Determinants of risky sexual behavior among female entertainment workers in China. *AIDS Education and Prevention,* Vol. 18, No. 4, pp. 333–47.

Yu, C. 2003. Henan weisheng guanyuan xielou 'aizhijimi' ruyu [Henan health official arrested for leaking 'AIDS secrets']. *Fenghuang Zhougan [Phoenix Weekly],* No. 129, pp. 26–27. (In Chinese.)

Zhang, F. 2004. *Manual for Free Government Antiretroviral Therapy [Guojia Mianfei Kangbingdu zhiliao Shouce].* Beijing, Chinese Center for Disease Control. (In Chinese.)

Zhang, K. and Li, D. 1999. Changing sexual attitudes and behaviour in China: Implications for the spread of HIV. *AIDS Care,* Vol. 11, No. 5, pp. 581.

Zhang, L. et al. 2004. Molecular characterization of human immunodeficiency virus type 1 and hepatitis C virus in paid blood donors and injection drug users in China. *Journal of Virology,* Vol. 78, No. 24, pp. 13591–3599.

Zheng X. et al. 2000. Zhongguo mouxian youchang xianxueyuan aizibing bingdu ganran liuxingbingxue yanjiu [The epidemiological study of HIV infection among paid blood donors in one county of China]. *Zhonghua Liuxingbingxue Zazhi [Chinese Journal of Epidemiology],* Vol. 21, No. 4, pp. 253–55. (In Chinese.)

CHAPTER 6

Masculinity + HIV = risk: Exploring the relationship between masculinities, education and HIV in the Caribbean

David Plummer

Introduction

Recent decades have seen important changes in educational outcomes for both boys and girls in the English-speaking Caribbean. These changes are a cause for both celebration and concern.

On the one hand, educational outcomes for girls have improved markedly. Girls now constitute the majority of secondary school enrolments in the region (Reddock, 2004) and girls' school attendance and retention rates exceed those for boys for all age cohorts (Chevannes, 1999). These improvements for young women are in evidence at the tertiary level too. More women than men now graduate each year from the University of the West Indies[1] (Figueroa, 2004; Reddock, 2004). The number of women graduates has been growing consistently over the past few decades: By 1974 female enrolments at the Jamaican campus passed the 50 per cent mark for the first time, and by 1982 they exceeded 50 per cent for all campuses. By late 1992, 70 per cent of all graduates from the Jamaican campus were female (Reddock, 2004). And by 2007, according to internal university statistics, 83 per cent of the student intake in Jamaica were female and only 17 per cent were male. Not surprisingly, this has not always been the case. Between 1948 and 1972 the reverse situation prevailed, with males occupying a sizeable majority (over 60 per cent) of places at the university (Figueroa, 2004).

The designations employed and the presentation of material throughout this publication do not imply the expression of any opinion whatsoever on the part of UNESCO concerning the legal status of any country, territory or area or of its authorities, or concerning the delimitation of its frontiers or boundaries.
The ideas and opinions expressed in this publication are those of the authors and do not necessarily reflect the views of UNESCO and its Member States.

Of course, it is possible that these changes simply reflect changes in the types of courses being offered. Figueroa does note that the gender balance varies by discipline. For example, in Jamaica 54 per cent of law enrolments are female; for agriculture this figure drops to 33 per cent; and only few women – 10 per cent – enroll in engineering classes (Figueroa, 2004). Nevertheless, it is now evident that male students no longer dominate many courses that they once did (including medicine, the law and the sciences).

So while we must celebrate and promote the achievements of Caribbean women, we also need to direct our attention to what is happening with Caribbean men. This chapter uses the quantitative data mentioned above as the starting point for an exploration of the meanings and explanations that underpin these shifts in gendered educational outcomes. It also looks at the consequences of those changes on men's lives (and by implication, on women), including in their interpersonal relationships, sex lives and attendant HIV risks.

This chapter argues that gender taboos mean that opportunities for a boy to secure his gender identity have increasingly become focused away from educational achievements and towards physical dominance, including hard, physical, risk-taking, hyper-masculine activities, such as bullying, harassment, crime, violence and sexual risk. Boys who achieve in intellectual pursuits are vulnerable to being considered 'suspect' by their peers. For example, boys who use 'standard English' or show a preference for reading regularly report homophobic criticism, perhaps the deepest masculine taboo of all. Likewise, through the twin mechanisms of masculine obligation and taboo, a wide range of risks, including HIV risks, have become resiliently embedded in the social fabric and are, as a result, extremely resistant to change. This phenomenon, which I call 'social embedding', exerts its effect via gender roles, peer group dynamics, taboo and stigma, and socio-economic inequalities.

Methods

This chapter aims to make sense of the accumulating quantitative evidence concerning the education and well-being of Caribbean boys. To do this, two sources of qualitative data are examined: first, data reported by other Caribbean researchers on education enrolment and retention, and second, findings from our own ongoing research into Caribbean masculinities (the Caribbean Masculinities Project), which documents the experiences of young men in their late teens and early twenties at school and among their peer groups. To date, 138 detailed interviews have been conducted in eight Caribbean countries: Guyana, Trinidad and Tobago, Grenada, St Vincent and the Grenadines, St Lucia, St Kitts and Nevis, Anguilla and Jamaica. Further interviews are planned with full transcription and more detailed analyses. Nevertheless, these findings, along with cumulative evidence from other researchers, build a compelling case that academic achievement is indeed becoming taboo, at least for some Caribbean boys, whereas risk-taking has virtually become a compulsory 'rite of passage'.

Policing masculinity: The central role of peers

Data from the Caribbean Masculinities Project confirms that establishing a gendered identity and being able to convincingly project yourself as masculine take centre stage as boys mature. Boys aspire to achieving masculine status, and their behaviour is policed to ensure that it conforms to the prevailing standards of acceptable masculinity. Central to this surveillance and policing process is the peer group, which emerges as the chief arbiter of masculine achievement and as a formidable force in boys' lives, particularly during adolescence. Indeed, the present research reveals that for many teenaged boys peer group authority competes with and frequently overrides adult authority. In that respect the data corroborates the words of Barry Chevannes (1999, p. 30) who says:

> The peer group virtually replaces mother and father as the controlling agents or, if not entirely a substitute, a countervailing force.

So while it is popular to ascribe blame to parents, teachers and the media for boys' adverse outcomes, the pre-eminent influence of the peer group is often greatly underestimated and may well exceed any of the above. As we will see shortly, this peer group influence has wide-ranging ramifications from educational achievement through to crime and HIV.

Of course peer groups can exert a powerful positive influence, but under certain conditions they can also be extremely bad. The present research found strong linkages between peer groups and gang development. Because of this, a core concern emerged from the project: at what point does a peer group become a gang? It seems as if in the absence of sufficient restraint, for example where there is lack of adult supervision or a 'power vacuum', the male peer group readily fills that vacuum and asserts its authority. Often this occurs on the streets, where peer groups readily dominate (for instance, see Bailey et al., 1998).

A question that is often asked is: where do these adverse influences on male peer groups come from? The question implies that boys learn these adverse behaviours from outside influences, such as significant adults and the media. The answer, however, is somewhat paradoxical.

On the one hand, it is the case that the rules of masculinity are comprehensively coded into our cultures and that boys start learning the codes of hegemonic masculinity from birth. Moreover, parents, teachers and adult 'role models', including women, contribute significantly to setting the standards that boys emulate. Crichlow (2004, p. 193) reports that his mother placed him in a 'very rigid hyper-male gender prison', and when he acted out the hard masculinities that were instilled in him, he notes that

> these activities demonstrated 'power' to parents, women, teachers and friends, who were proud to see that a young man was not a buller, a sissy or a coward.

Note here that the term 'buller' is used in Trinidad and Barbados to denote a homosexual (the equivalent of 'faggot' in the United States or 'poofter' in Britain). We will return to the significance of homophobia shortly.

On the other hand, concerning the responsibility of some external influence for producing anti-social behaviours (such as aggression, violence and crime), the research found that boys are not simply cultural sponges but that peer groups themselves are able to actively fashion and create new forms of dominant masculinity, which can include acting out the above behaviours. In the following quote from Barry Chevannes (1999), we see hints of the powerful influence that the peer group can wield ('exact an affinity', 'loyalty as sacred', 'as strong as … religion') plus evidence for the culture generating and transmitting role that these groups have:

> An adolescent boy's friends exact an affinity and a loyalty as sacred as the bond of kinship as strong as the sentiment of religion. They socialise one another, the older members of the group acting as the transmitters of what passes as knowledge, invent new values and meanings.

The phenomenon of transmitting peer group codes along generations of boys I refer to elsewhere as 'rolling peer pressure' (Plummer, 2005, p. 226). This concept helps to explain how the cultures that adolescent boys immerse themselves in can operate semi-autonomously from the adult world and can effectively take on a 'life of their own'. Codes and standards are continually passed down the chain from older to younger boys, usually in play and recreation areas, often out of sight of adults. As a result, peer groups have a culture-transmitting and culture-generating role that is, on reflection, highly evident in most modern societies, that is, as generators of linguistic expressions, fashion styles, jewellery, musical trends and so on. It also means that neither parents, nor teachers nor the media can be held primarily responsible for social movements that emanate from youth culture, including the problems that accompany them. On the contrary, the most important thing that adults can do to empower these trends is to be absent – the peer group will do the rest.

Aspiring to be bad: Peer group obligations and the rise of hard masculinity

The constant 'policing' of masculinity becomes a straitjacket for most adolescent boys. Young men find themselves confined to a narrow space of authorized masculinity while at the same time being cut off from great swathes of social life that are rendered taboo by the very masculine standards the boys are obliged to conform to. The descriptions by the young men of the powerful influence of peers provide revealing insights into the standards against which boys are judged and the price to be paid for failing to meet peer group expectations. At the forefront of these standards is the importance of conforming to hard, physical, narrow, polarized masculinity. As Bailey et al. (1998, p. 82) note:

> younger teenaged boys had embraced, in the most uncompromising way, the [prevailing] male gender ideology.

Boys are subjected to a relentless policing of 'manliness', which the data reveals is particularly intense from peers. As a result, they learn to choose their styles carefully and to craft an image that reflects both their own personality and their allegiance to the prevailing standards of masculinity as endorsed by youth culture. Clothing, designer labels, wearing 'bling' (male jewellery), styles of speech, and how to strike a 'cool' pose are all governed by elaborate codes of conduct authorized by peers. For many boys image is everything – it sustains their masculine reputation.

Image is also very much about performance. Masculine status and a boy's position in the 'pecking order' are strongly influenced by displays of sexual prowess, physical toughness and social dominance. Moreover, the consequences of legitimizing hard and risky masculinities are far reaching and constitute the very foundation of some of our most profound social problems. There is strong pressure to resist adult authority, to earn status by taking risks and to display masculine credentials in hard, physical and sometimes anti-social ways. As Crichlow (2004, p. 200) describes:

> In an attempt to temporarily secure my masculinity or hyper-masculinity and hegemonic heterosexuality, I participated in events such as stealing ... breaking bottles with slingshots or stones on the street, engaging in physical fights, and 'hanging on the block' with boys until late at night.

It is here that the links between the prevailing standards of masculinity and crime start to emerge. From the young male's perspective, far from being a disgrace, crime is the ultimate expression of masculinity – it stems from boys emulating the ways 'real men' are supposed to act according to the culture they grew up in and are immersed in:

> The so-called inner-city don is a role model not only because of his ability to command and dispense largesse, but also because he is a living source of power: the power over life and death, the ultimate man ... Among the youth, a common word for penis was rifle. (Chevannes, 1999, p. 29)

The phallocentric reference in this quote is a blunt reminder of the close linkage that exists in boys' minds between power, violence, gender and sexuality.

The importance of sexual prowess

The social pressures that boys experience, from a young age, to conform to complex gender-based obligations and taboos in order to be a 'man' imply – and indeed, almost require – sexual behaviour that is associated with HIV risk. In the words of Bailey and colleagues (1998, p. 53):

> By the age of 10 ... boys began to realise that toughness, physical strength and sexual dominance, all features of traditional masculinity, were expected of them.

Moreover, while it is commonly asserted that there are strong prohibitions against speaking about sexuality in Caribbean society, this silence does not extend to young people themselves. On the contrary, their environment is saturated with sexual references:

Sex then was very much in the environment of the young boys and girls … they did pick up a great deal of information from observing their environment and from listening to 'people', particularly the age group just older than themselves. (Bailey et al., 1998, p. 29)

By way of contrast, adults are notable for their silence on these issues with the result that

Boys are expected to obtain virtually all their sexual preparation on the street and secondarily from school. (Brown and Chevannes, 1998, p. 23)

Clearly young people teach themselves about sexual practice and the gender roles that should accompany that practice, largely with inputs from older peers and youth culture. Against the vacuum of adult influence is the reality that all societies demand that boys achieve a culturally acceptable gender identity. The combination of adults being largely absent from sex education and the ceding of sex education to young people themselves has profound implications for this achievement. Sexuality and gender are tightly intertwined, and accomplishing a masculine (gendered) reputation is tightly linked to adolescent discourses, peer group dynamics and sexual accomplishments. Barry Chevannes explains:

Manhood is demonstrated by sexual prowess … it is usually measured by the number of female sexual partners. (Brown and Chevannes, 1998, p. 23)

Moreover, in circumstances where having multiple partners is a public affirmation of one's masculine status, even being faithful to a single partner can result in scorn and loss of face:

For males, multiple partnerships could become also a matter of status. … The term 'one burner' applied to a faithful male in some Jamaican communities was a phrase of derision. (Bailey et al., 1998, p. 65–66)

Indeed, the importance attached to having multiple female sexual partners is tied to one of the deepest male social taboos, homophobia, as the following quotation suggests:

Someone who did not have as many women as they did was 'sick', 'suspected as a 'buller' or not 'the average young black male'. (Crichlow, 2004, p. 206).

Furthermore, the consequences of these gender expectations reach far beyond sexual practice. A combination of obligation and taboo profoundly configures the quality of young people's relationships too – often adversely so. The basis for this impact stems from equating successful masculinity with physical strength, being emotionally withholding and social dominance; consequently there are taboos around weakness, tenderness and commitment. Not only do these taboos impact on relationships between men and women, but they set men up to have adversarial relationships with each other.

The social and peer group codes that govern the sexual practices of young men have profound implications for HIV. Being a 'stud', developing a reputation for sexual prowess and being known for having multiple female partners are widely valued in youth culture and are emphasized by those who matter most to boys: their peers. This is because they are all public symbols of status – of having achieved the ultimate goal of being a 'real man'. Failure to fulfil those expectations in the quest for manhood threatens to dishonour the boy and damage his reputation (possibly irreparably) by invoking the combined taboos of emasculation, feminization, peer group betrayal and taboos against homosexuality. Combining these deep taboos with risky sexual obligations sets the scene for HIV risk and for resistance to prevention messages: it is not considered 'cool' for a 'hot-blooded' young male to be overly concerned with safety.

Masculine taboos – enforcing 'no-go' zones

Almost as noticeable as the symbols of masculinity that are widely flaunted are the human qualities that go 'missing in action'. An early casualty is the ability to cry, which although not actually lost, is steadfastly suppressed in public. The rest of a boy's emotional repertoire soon succumbs to the same constraints, especially emotions that denote tenderness. However, some emotions are not suppressed. For example, aggression and anger are actively cultivated precisely because they symbolize masculine strength.

In the following quote, Brown and Chevannes (1998, p. 30) describe how boys use aggressive acts as a substitute for other emotions that have since been banished:

> Boys greet each other with clenched fists and backslaps, and often use
> other forms of aggression to express their feelings.

Of course, there are always two sides to binary phenomena: aggression is both an expression of masculinity and a simultaneous public disavowal of tenderness. Here is Morgan's perspective:

> Our fights usually indicated an 'overt disdain for anything that might appear soft or wet – more a taboo on tenderness than a celebration of violence'. (Morgan quoted in Crichlow, 2004, p. 200)

It becomes increasingly clear from the present research and from the cumulative findings of other Caribbean researchers that much of the 'macho' acting out among boys and young men is indicative of their allegiance to prevailing standards of masculinity while at the same time proclaiming their rejection of 'failed' masculinities, defined as soft, feminizing, infantile and castrating. According to Bailey et al. (2002, p. 8):

> The culture demanded physical responses from boys and made toughness the hallmark of the real male. Young boys knew that if they performed outside the expected, traditional roles they would be ridiculed and labelled 'sissy' by boys and girls.

Is boys' education a casualty of the rise of hard masculinity?

The powerful social pressures on boys to embrace hard, risk-taking, often anti-social 'hyper-masculinities' puts their lives in danger: on the road, in the gang and in bed. By disenfranchising boys from activities that have been rendered taboo by their own codes of masculinity, boys are denying themselves access to considerable longer-term social benefits. For example, if being safe is considered 'sissy', then driving small, low-powered cars at a safe speed potentially comes at a cost to one's reputation. Likewise, if dominant masculinity is defined by risk-taking and sexual potency, then safety is implicitly feminizing, and there will be entrenched barriers to HIV prevention – including condoms, being faithful and abstinence. Many men therefore opt to place themselves (and others) at risk in order to affirm their masculine status.

Similarly, if educational achievement is associated with emasculation or homophobic taboos, then a 'real man' will go to great lengths not to engage in education. Chevannes (1999, p. 26) documents this attitude in an interview with an 8-year-old inner-city Jamaican boy:

> School is girl stuff!

Similarly, the following quote illustrates both homophobic and misogynistic taboos undermining the educational aspirations of boys:

> Many young men in Trinidad argue that academic subjects, such as mathematics, physics and English are for bullers and women, while trades are for men. (Crichlow, 2004, p. 206)

From Mark Figueroa (2004, p. 152), we see misogynistic prejudice underwriting contempt for education by boys:

> There is evidence that boys actually actively assert their maleness by resisting school. This is particularly true with respect to certain subjects that are seen as 'feminine'. Male-child subculture therefore exerts considerable peer pressure on boys to be disruptive in school and to underrate certain subjects.

In the work of Odette Parry (2004, p. 179), we find these taboos reinforcing an anti-academic ethos of contemporary Caribbean masculinity, as well as a self-defeating role that adults sometimes play, including school staff:

> The homophobic fears expressed by staff and the resulting censure of attitudes and behaviours which were felt to be 'effeminate', 'girlish', 'sissy like' and 'nerdish' reinforce a masculine gender identity which rejects many aspects of schooling as all of the above.

Discussion

The progress made by Caribbean women in education is an important success story that warrants celebration. Unfortunately, this progress is on the verge of being overshadowed by developments that, by and large, show that male educational achievements are compromised. Many commentators make the assumption that these changes are linked, that is, that the price of progress by girls is a decline in the standards for boys. This assumption has such profound implications that a critical analysis is essential.

In 1986, Errol Miller published his work titled *The Marginalisation of the Black Male: Insights from the Development of the Teaching Profession*. Miller's thesis – that Caribbean men were being marginalized by (racialized) social forces largely beyond their control – struck a chord that continues to reverberate two decades later, especially in popular culture. Likewise Miller's thesis stimulated vigorous debate in academic circles and has been the subject of many academic critiques over the years. Chevannes (1999, p. 33), for example, is unconvinced by Miller's thesis about 'male marginalisation' and asks:

> Are males being marginalized? Certainly not if the main factor being considered is power.

Mark Figueroa (2004) took the argument further by suggesting that instead of being a reflection of marginalization, recent changes in male educational outcomes are in fact a paradoxical effect of traditional male privilege. According to Figueroa, males traditionally enjoyed privileged access to public space, which they dominated, whereas women were largely restricted to the private domestic sphere, where they are better placed to study. This privileging of public space meant that boys spent more time outdoors, on the playing field and on 'the street' during the school years, which ultimately worked against men's academic development.

While Figueroa's (2004, p. 159) thesis reconfigures the debate from male marginalization to privilege, it nevertheless perpetuates the cross-linking between the progress that Caribbean girls are making and the difficulties that boys are experiencing:

> Increasingly, as women 'take over' [sic] so-called male academic subjects, the options for boys will be more and more limited. Ultimately, there will be little that boys can safely do without threatening their masculinity.

However, Figueroa's argument does not explain why boys are vacating this aspect of traditional male privilege (education) so readily, especially given that academic pursuits were privileged male domains in the past too. Nevertheless, data from the present research reaffirms the findings of other researchers cited here that the development of masculine identity is linked to boys' physicality and their affinity with public space, especially 'the street'. Moreover, in contemporary Caribbean settings, hard, aggressive, dominant masculinity occupies the 'privileged' status of being the epitome of manhood, and increasingly so in recent years. Certainly, gang culture and music laced with violent allusions have become more prominent in the Caribbean in the course of the past few decades. But the present research adds a further piece of the puzzle. Data from the Caribbean Masculinities Project expose the role that masculine taboos play in creating social 'no-go' zones for young men – one of which increasingly appears to be education, which is positioned as the counterpoint of 'true' physical masculinity.

A surprising, but nonetheless important, finding is the role that homo-phobia plays in stigmatizing boys who are academically inclined. Instead of being a peripheral issue, this stands out as a consistent and deep-seated phe-nomenon. Although the role of homophobia might seem difficult to account for in this situation, recent research has shown that homophobic abuse is regu-larly used as a mechanism for policing manhood and to enforce the 'pecking order', especially among adolescent male peer groups. It turns out that most homophobia is only secondarily and indirectly concerned with sexual prac-tice (Plummer, 2005). In other words, boys who fail to conform to the gender expectations of their peer group are 'suspects' and are vulnerable to being tar-geted. In this sense, as a repository for 'failed manhood' and as a mechanism for policing the standards of masculinity, homophobia is rightly seen as being a gender prejudice – one that fundamentally impinges on the lives of all men.

So where does this leave the 'male marginalization' thesis? The conclu-sion from the present research is that if marginalization of boys is occurring, then it seems likely that they are actively absenting themselves in order to es-cape the discrediting stigma of prevailing masculine taboos. The process of developing male identity involves adopting and displaying shared symbols of masculinity while simultaneously disavowing any hint of 'failed' manhood. In recent years, education has become increasingly associated with feminizing and homophobic taboos, which serve to alienate boys from large areas of social life that they would be much better off having access to. A consequence is that education is positioned as a negative binary counterpoint to physical mascu-linity, which is valorized, encouraged and promoted. This shift may well have coincided with the progress made by girls in education, but there seems to be no reason why this has to be the case: greater access by women to education does not explain why males should have less access – that is, of course, unless education has become taboo for men. Another consequence is that these same misogynistic and homophobic taboos reinforce masculine identity formation and drive men towards dangerous, exaggerated 'hyper-masculinities'.

A question to consider is whether the data offer any clues as to ways for-ward (see Table 1). First, while associations have been made by some commenta-tors between girls' educational accomplishments and boys' underachievements, it is important to recognize that these do not have to be linked. The problem clearly lies with the prejudices indoctrinated into men and boys rather than with girls and women. Indeed, girls are just as victimized by these prejudices as are boys, but in different ways. But for as long as these biases play a role in the development of young male identity, they will impact on the social performance of masculinity, including educational outcomes. On the other hand, if those taboos can be alleviated, then boys will find it much easier to engage with the education system, and in more constructive ways – because engagement will not come at the expense of their masculine reputation. At least this particular social domain (education) will no longer be seen as belonging to one gender or the other, but as a site where both sexes can develop in fulfilling and meaningful ways. Girls' accomplishments in education need to be celebrated and sustained, and we need to take a much more strategic approach to promoting boys' education. The assumption of an inverse relationship between girls' and boys' achievements needs to be exposed as both unnecessary and harmful.

Table 1. The way forward

- Celebrate girls' educational successes

- Take a more strategic approach to promoting boys' achievements

- De-link girls' successes from boys' difficulties

- Recognize that contemporary dominant masculinities are problematic

- Resist hard, narrow, polarized masculinity

- Create greater opportunities for adult involvement in boys' lives

- Counterbalance hard, physical, narrow masculinities with well-rounded, diverse male role models

- Embrace diverse masculinities and alternative male role models

- Reassociate masculinity with education and academic prowess

- Engage more fully with peer group dynamics

- Confront the taboos that cause boys to turn their backs on educational pursuits and retreat to hard, physical masculinity

- Reject homophobic and misogynist prejudices

- Support research into masculinities, masculine taboos and peer group dynamics

Moreover, men need to realize that the prevailing contemporary masculinities, which promote both narrow and hard role models, are leading young men into difficulties and putting them at risk. It is masculinity that is at the root of many of boys' educational problems: hard, narrow, polarized masculinities. These forms of masculinity must therefore be resisted. Well-rounded, diverse male role models need to be visible and accessible. Notions of masculinity need to be reconnected with intellectual achievement. The complex and powerful role of male peer groups needs to be carefully studied and sophisticated strategies developed to intervene in their anti-social potential. The unrestrained power of peer groups needs to be countered by greater involvement of adults in boy's lives, including mentoring and providing diverse role models. Taboos have to be confronted if progress is to be possible. Based on the evidence from the present research and corroboration with the findings of other Caribbean researchers, this necessarily includes addressing misogyny and homophobia.

Finally, I want to highlight some conclusions about the relationship between this research and HIV. This chapter explores the social context that underwrites a sustained epidemic of HIV by promoting male gender roles during boys' development that drive risk and resist safety. The present research highlights the role of peer groups in policing the crucial process of masculine identity formation. This process rests on prevailing cultural notions of what manhood is and sets the benchmark against which boys judge their achievements. Boys who 'fail' run the risk of ostracism and of being targeted with sanctions and violence. In the current social order there are heavy pressures for boys to subordinate intellectual development, which is no longer considered to embody 'true' manhood, in favour of prevalent ideologies that emphasize physical strength, risk-taking and displays of sexual prowess.

When masculinity is defined in terms of heterosexual prowess and risk-taking, then even the best-intended HIV prevention campaigns will be compromised because notions of safety have come to be associated with deep masculine taboos around sexual inadequacy, feminization and homophobia. This can apply to condoms, partner restriction or abstinence. These pressures also create the dangerous twin paradox of: (1) gay men feeling pressured to conceal their sexuality and to form seemingly heterosexual 'down-low' relationships, whereas (2) all men experience homophobic pressure to publicly prove themselves, most readily by having unprotected sex with multiple women and producing offspring. The combination of masculine obligation and taboo puts boys in danger when they simply do what society apparently expects of them: achieve and prove their manhood. These pressures weigh heavily even before we start to consider other important factors, such as desire, lust, love, individual variation, personal agency and positive peer pressure (which can sometimes have an important mitigating effect).

To conclude: gender roles drive the HIV epidemic. To better prevent HIV and to manage the consequences of the epidemic, we have no choice but to engage with these roles at fundamental levels in sophisticated ways. This chapter finds that gender roles can create a trap that disadvantages both men and women. Through the twin mechanisms of obligation and taboo, a wide range of risks, including sexual risks, have become resiliently embedded in the social fabric and are therefore highly resistant to change. I call this phenomenon 'social embedding'. But there is cause for optimism: Research has shown that gender roles are in a constant state of flux and dominant masculinities have changed radically over time and vary across cultures. Gender roles are clearly amenable to remodelling. The way forward, then, is to realize that individual behaviour change interventions will inevitably have limited outcomes due to the way that risk is socially embedded (in gender roles, peer pressure and taboos). Instead, we need to look towards producing grassroots social change that is more readily compatible with healthy behaviours which can be readily and comfortably embedded as a result. These are much more likely to produce widespread, sustained impacts on HIV.

Acknowledgements

Thanks to the participants who generously gave their time to inform this research. Thanks to the University of the West Indies for supporting this research and to the Commonwealth Secretariat and UNESCO for funding the early stages. Special thanks to my research assistant, Joel Simpson; also to Arden McLean, Vidyartha Kissoon, Nigel Mathlin, Egbert Felix, Brian-Paul Welsh, Robert Carr, Novlet Reid, Ian McKnight, Civilla Kentish and Kevin Farara for their superb support; and to Sharon Reddock, Cheryl Gomez, Elvis Philip and Dwayne Carruthers for their skilled transcribing. Thanks as well to the Society Against Sexual Orientation Discrimination, Guyana (SASOD), the Grenada Caribbean HIV/AIDS Partnership (GrenCHAP), the St Vincent and the Grenadines Caribbean HIV/AIDS Partnership (VincyCHAP), the St Kitts and Nevis HIV/AIDS Group, the Caribbean Vulnerable Communities Coalition (CVC), Jamaica AIDS Support for Life (JAS), and Children and Community for Change, Jamaica. This chapter is based on a paper originally given at the

Academy for Educational Development (AED) in Washington DC as part of a symposium titled Tailoring the Education Message: A Diversity of Settings and Needs, which was held under the aegis of the UNAIDS Inter-Agency Task Team on Education on 14 May 2007 and jointly hosted by AED, the American Institute of Research, and the Education Development Center.

Notes

1. The University of the West Indies is the oldest and largest university in the English-speaking Caribbean, with major campuses in Jamaica, Trinidad and Barbados and an Open Campus with facilities in twelve other countries and territories.

References

Bailey, W. (ed.). 1998. *Gender and the Family in the Caribbean*. Mona, Jamaica, Institute of Social and Economic Research.

Bailey, W., Branche, C. and Henry-Lee, A. 2002. *Gender, Contest and Conflict in the Caribbean*. Mona, Jamaica, Sir Arthur Lewis Institute of Social and Economic Studies.

Bailey, W., Branche, C., McGarrity, G. and Stuart, S. 1998. *Family and the Quality of Gender Relations in the Caribbean*. Mona, Jamaica, Institute of Social and Economic Research.

Brown, J. and Chevannes, B. 1998. *Why Man Stay So – Tie the Heifer and Loose the Bull: An Examination of Gender Socialisation in the Caribbean*. Mona, Jamaica, University of the West Indies Press.

Chevannes, B. 1999. *What We Sow and What We Reap – Problems in the Cultivation of Male Identity in Jamaica*. Kingston, Jamaica, Grace Kennedy Foundation.

Crichlow, W. 2004. History, (re)memory, testimony and biomythography: Charting a buller man's Trinidadian past. R.E. Reddock (ed.), *Interrogating Caribbean Masculinities*. Mona, Jamaica, University of the West Indies Press, pp. 185–222.

Figueroa, M. 2004. Male privileging and male academic underperformance in Jamaica. R. E. Reddock (ed.), *Interrogating Caribbean Masculinities*. Mona, Jamaica, University of the West Indies Press.

Miller, E. 1986. *The Marginalization of the Black Male: Insights from the Development of the Teaching Profession*. Kingston, Jamaica, Institute of Social and Economic Research.

Parry, O. 2000. *Male Underachievement in High School Education*. Mona, Jamaica, Canoe Press.

Plummer, D. 2005. Crimes against manhood: Homophobia as the penalty for betraying hegemonic masculinity. G. Hawkes and J. Scott (eds), *Perspectives in Human Sexuality*. Melbourne, Australia, Oxford University Press.

Reddock, R. (ed.). 2004. *Interrogating Caribbean Masculinities*. Mona, Jamaica, University of the West Indies Press.

Section II: Cultures of Intervention

Introductory Essay

Didier Fassin

Since the beginning of the epidemic, HIV and AIDS interventions have been inscribed in a dual cultural framework. On the one hand, they fit within the traditional culture of public health, with its prejudices and paradigms, its insistence on behaviours and on blaming victims, its preference for technical solutions and its fascination for 'magic bullet' approaches. On the other, these interventions can create an innovative culture that invents new rules in medicine and new roles for patients, disrupts the usual precautions and proposes unusual procedures, mobilizes the media on a massive scale and shifts legal frontiers. This combination of tradition and innovation makes the epidemic exceptional in the long history of public health – a history that can conversely contribute to understanding the way HIV and AIDS are dealt with on the international as well as the local scale. Particularly relevant are comparisons with the reactions to and management of syphilis in Europe in the late nineteenth century and in Africa in the early twentieth century. These interventions, which include relating to crucial gender and sexual issues, combine the stigmatization of so-called key populations with the transformation of norms and values.

These gender and sexuality issues differ widely in Western and in developing countries, especially in Africa. In Western countries, where the epidemic initially affected men who have sex with men, interventions were rapidly dominated both by the epidemiological paradigm of risk and by the social mobilization of activists who were directly and personally affected by the disease. In developing countries, the epidemic often disproportionately affects women

The designations employed and the presentation of material throughout this publication do not imply the expression of any opinion whatsoever on the part of UNESCO concerning the legal status of any country, territory or area or of its authorities, or concerning the delimitation of its frontiers or boundaries.
The ideas and opinions expressed in this publication are those of the authors and do not necessarily reflect the views of UNESCO and its Member States.

infected through heterosexual intercourse. Here, interventions have been made within a moral framework that opposes promiscuity and vulnerability, whereas activism has primarily been undertaken by Western non-governmental organizations. The interpretative framework oscillates between assumptions of sexual promiscuity supposedly specific to African cultures where multiple partnerships are taken to be common and a less judgmental approach that insists on the vulnerability of women in terms of their socio-economic positions and their exposure to sexual violence by men. The public health response therefore combined health education to change harmful behaviours and social empowerment to help women resist male domination.

Women have thus been considered both endangering and endangered. Moral assumption about them straddles that of gay men and drug users, who are stigmatized as being personally responsible for their disease, and haemophiliacs and children, who are seen as innocent victims. In this conception, women are simultaneously vulnerable to sexual abuse by men and potential transmitters of the virus, either as supposedly promiscuous or as mothers. This epidemiological ambivalence and moral ambiguity have served to impede the development of effective prevention programmes for women. Resistance to the prescription and implementation of antiretroviral treatment regimes for women who have been raped is a tragic illustration of this peculiar gender configuration.

International policies to combat the epidemic also suffer from these tensions between normative and emancipatory discourses and practices. However, human rights and gender considerations have been included in early prevention plans to a greater extent than in responses to previous epidemics, often due to pressure by global activists and, to a lesser degree, by local organizations. Yet global action is contradictory; UNAIDS has actively engaged in defending sexual rights, including the protection of women, while PEPFAR (US President's Emergency Plan for AIDS Relief) has operated in favour of traditional methods, like abstinence, that can contribute to the stigmatization of sexuality. At the same time, the financial involvement of Western countries through their governments, non-governmental organizations and international agencies has been significant, especially in terms of treatment provision, which not only has curative effects but can also increase positive social consequences by giving patients a form of dignity. On this global scene, Lisa Ann Richey describes an innovative manner of raising funds that merges commercial and charitable benefits: the rock star Bono's marketing strategy of selling products that are labeled 'humanitarian' has gained support not only from celebrities and the media but also from scientists and doctors. The price of this campaign, however, is the production of simplified and dramatized images of Africans – and particularly African women – that reinforce prejudices about the endemic misfortune of the continent and the powerlessness of female victims. Indeed, international aid policies have often tended to reproduce at the symbolic level the global inequalities they seek to remedy through their concrete actions.

It has long been clear that the same standards are not applicable in the North and in the South in terms of access to antiretroviral drugs. Not only are the prices of these medicines far beyond the economic capacities of most poor countries – especially given the number of patients to be treated on the African continent, for example – but the management of drug regimes often exceeds the professional competences and technical resources available in many health systems in the South. While efforts have been made to lower the cost of treatment and improve access, antiretroviral drug provision remains extremely unequal. In this context, the discovery of the efficacy of a protocol using a single dose product, nevirapine, was hailed by many public health specialists as a great step towards generalized prevention of mother-to-child transmission. Complex multitherapy clinical trials were conducted in rich countries, but this simplified and cheap treatment was intended for poor countries – or, rather, for poor patients in poor countries. However, as Alton Philips shows, it was known from the outset that the therapy might have harmful consequences, the most likely and serious being the development of resistance to the whole antiretroviral family of nevirapine among all mothers who receive the drugs and the few children for whom prevention fails. While uncertainty and the urgent need for action can explain this ethical failure, this is only one episode in a long history of protecting children at the risk of endangering mothers' lives. Women's vulnerability here is iatrogenic – that is, provoked by medical intervention.

Current policies are often the result of interactions and even confrontations between international actors, whether states or agencies, and national actors, including governments and activists. Many African countries, for example, have shown signs of ideological resistance to the reality of the epidemic, as well as to the interventions of foreign institutions. Claims to have invented antiretroviral drugs, such as MM1 in the Democratic Republic of the Congo, Kemron in Kenya, Virodene in South Africa and Therastim in the Côte d'Ivoire, constitute a specific form of therapeutic nationalism. At the same time, some countries have demonstrated unexpected capacities to combat the epidemic. The most famous example is Brazil, which is often presented as a model of government collaboration with non-governmental organizations. However, as Inês Dourado, Vera Paiva and Francisco Bastos suggest, the Brazilian policy of generalized access to antiretroviral drugs requires a larger reform of the health system and social protection that aims towards equity, including for women. The Brazilian success story must therefore be put into context, since the country's economic inequalities, which rank among the highest in the world, continue to have negative impacts on the results of its exemplary policy. This case study provides a useful reminder that the most effective but also most difficult – intervention to prevent HIV transmission is the broad reduction of social inequalities, including gender inequalities.

Sexual violence is often – and relevantly – presented as the central issue in terms of women's specific vulnerability to HIV infection. However, the question of what is meant by sexual violence from an epidemiological point of view remains. This is not merely a theoretical question but one that is crucial in deciding the types of prevention measures to be implemented. Health specialists and policy-makers have tended to focus on the most extreme forms of violence. Judy El-Bushra discusses this trend on the basis of available knowledge about situations of war, such as that in the Great Lakes area. She shows that, contrary to general belief, gang rape committed by militia and soldiers probably does not account for the majority of infections in women. Rather, they can be attributed to ordinary forms of sexual violence exerted by ordinary men, often civilians, in these conflict contexts. Many programmes ignore this complexity and focus only on violence directly related to war, thus neglecting many women in need of psychological support and medical assistance. This observation can be applied beyond the context of conflict, as the programmatic focus on rape has led to the neglect of the effects of everyday sexual violence. In South Africa, for instance, more women are infected by self-defined violent intercourse with their usual partner than by being raped by a stranger. Shifting our understanding of sexual violence from the 'exceptional' to the 'ordinary' is an important challenge for the cultures of intervention.

The four chapters in this section demonstrate how gender and sexual issues, which must be taken into account in HIV and AIDS interventions, are deeply embedded in social determinants, logics and processes. The widespread representations of problems and their solutions – culturalizing and caricaturing issues; depicting women solely as victims; focusing on 'magic bullet' approaches; concentrating exclusively on access to drugs; emphasizing exceptional situations – have biased many interventions. This has contributed to the avoidance of more complex and painful questions about the ubiquity of gendered and other social inequalities. It is important to recall this lesson, almost three decades after the beginning of the epidemic.

CHAPTER 7

Representations of African women and AIDS in Bono's (PRODUCT) RED

Lisa Ann Richey

Introduction

(PRODUCT) RED was launched by Bono at the World Economic Forum in 2006 to raise awareness and money for the Global Fund to Fight AIDS, Tuberculosis and Malaria. Under this initiative, iconic brands, such as American Express, Apple, Converse, Gap, Emporio Armani, Hallmark, Motorola, and now Dell, Microsoft, and Starbucks, have teamed up to produce RED-branded products and encourage customers to 'do good by dressing well'. The advent of 'Brand Aid' explicitly links international development assistance to commerce and not philanthropy (see Ponte, Richey and Baab, 2009). The RED initiative is an example of a cause-related marketing[1] strategy to finance international development aid. Like Western philanthropy in general, RED has its origins in nineteenth century Christian charities' scepticism about the ability of market mechanisms to reduce human misery caused by unchecked capitalist growth (Di Leonardo, 2008). However, unlike other contemporary mergers between shopping and helping, such as the Oxfam charity shops or the many plastic armband campaigns, RED co-brands with 'iconic brands' and emphasizes commerce, not charity. RED relies on stereotypically gendered representations to sell products and 'save lives.'

RED has both material and symbolic consequences for its target group, 'women and children with AIDS in Africa'. In other work, we have conducted a materialist critique of the ways that RED engages business in corporate social

The designations employed and the presentation of material throughout this publication do not imply the expression of any opinion whatsoever on the part of UNESCO concerning the legal status of any country, territory or area or of its authorities, or concerning the delimitation of its frontiers or boundaries.
The ideas and opinions expressed in this publication are those of the authors and do not necessarily reflect the views of UNESCO and its Member States.

responsibility (CSR). RED both corporatizes aid relations and limits the scope of CSR (Ponte et al., 2008). In RED, CSR is limited to combating problems that are outside the 'normal' functioning of business, and the beneficiaries of RED are distant others, not those living in communities where the RED corporations source their labour or those where they sell their products. At the (PRODUCT) RED launch Bono explicitly stated that labour issues are of secondary importance to people dying with AIDS: 'We do not think that trade is bad. We are for labour issues. Labour issues are very serious, but six and a half thousand Africans dying every day, in my opinion, is more serious'.[2] At the same time, in RED, Bono is the totem of 'compassionate consumption,' steering attention away from the causes of poverty, such as the inequities of systems of production and trade, by focusing on one of the outcomes, HIV and AIDS. This chapter will engage with the representational side of the RED campaign, arguing that these effects must be taken seriously when considering the impact that RED might have on Africans living with HIV and AIDS.

Reputable 'aid celebrities' like Bono negotiate the interface between shopping and helping, yet it is the pivotal role of the consumer that distinguishes Brand Aid from previous modalities of financing development assistance. A 'rock star's burden' – imagined in terms of familiar constructs of sex, gender, race and place – frames Africans as the 'distant others' to be saved. At the same time, RED depicts consumer-citizens as fashion-conscious yet actively engaged and ethically reflective. Brand Aid creates the image of a world in which it is possible to buy as much as you want while at the same time helping others.

The possibility of 'saving' Africans with AIDS through your choice of sunglasses is constituted by the virtualism of ARV (antiretroviral) treatment in RED. In RED, ARV treatment must be distanced from other important social, economic, psychological or medical factors affecting the lives of the Africans to be 'saved.' The RED promotional materials on the internet and in print media emphasize the link between saving lives and the provision of ARV pills. This 'dis-embedding' or 'decontextualizing' of AIDS treatment activities creates virtualisms of treatment. Karl Polanyi (1957, cited in Carrier, 1998, p. 2) describes dis-embedding in relation to economics as the extrication of economic activities from the social and other relationships in which they occurred and the subsequent conducting of those activities in contexts in which the only important relationships are those defined by the economic activities themselves. Re-embedding such an activity in its own self-referential context creates a virtualism. In reliance on James Carrier's (1998) usage of the term, Dan Brockington (2009) describes virtualisms of Africa as 'collections of images, ideas, discourses and values that reproduce the material world according to the ways that they imagine it to be'.

The representations of ARV treatment in (PRODUCT) RED's campaign abstract the economic accessibility of antiretrovirals (if there was simply more money for more pills, the people who need those pills would get them and their lives would be saved) from their social, psychological and political relationships and then reinscribe this distilled 'reality' into imagined relationships. The virtualism created relies on what Westerners 'know' about Africans with AIDS and as such perpetuates narrow imaginaries of the 'Other' (Spivak, 1985). Boltanski (1993) and others (for example, Butt, 2002; Kleinman and Kleinman, 1996; and Littler, 2008) have theorized the importance of understanding the meaning of bringing suffering at a distance close up through mediated images. RED produces a virtualism of AIDS treatment that relies on the proximity and distance of Western consumers and African sufferers.

However, describing the use of AIDS treatment in RED as a virtualism does not mean that this chapter is arguing that ARVs do not work in 'real bodies'. Antiretroviral drugs are an essential part of AIDS treatment for patients all over the world whose Human Immunodeficiency Virus has become strong enough to diminish their immune system and help prevent vertical transmission of the virus. However, drugs are not the only significant component of a system of AIDS treatment. Saving lives in Africa begins with the actions and beliefs of the people whose lives are to be saved and interacts with social, spiritual, medical and political relationships. These power relationships involve local and global points of both solidarity and conflict. RED's depiction of ARVs as sufficient for saving lives produces a virtualism in which treatment becomes understood only in terms of providing the necessary drugs, and thus, interventions are put into place only to provide drugs. This neglects many of the other important aspects of AIDS care and treatment, of overall health care for Africans who may or may not have AIDS, and of non-medical needs for maintaining the social as well as the biological life of a human being.

This chapter analyses the RED initiative not only as an example of cause-related marketing, or consumer-driven philanthropy, but also as a meaningful player in representing HIV and AIDS and Africa to external audiences. The United Nations (UN) (2008, p. 25) recently pointed to 'the unequal relationships between men and women, as well as gender stereotypes, [that] fuel the spread of HIV'. These stereotypes are, of course, not simply a gender problem for societies that receive international development assistance and philanthropic donations but also part of the constitution and representations of aid and giving. Colleen O'Manique's contribution in this volume demonstrates how our gendered constructions of the African woman have limited the necessary multifaceted critique of structural power.

Drawing on Paula Treichler's (1999) work, which argues that the manner in which AIDS is represented is critical for shaping the possibilities for understanding, responding to and living with the disease, this chapter will interrogate how RED constitutes images and stereotypes of African women and children. First, the (PRODUCT) RED initiative is introduced as a manifestation of a new international funding template that combines business with aid to address the HIV and AIDS pandemic in Africa. The next section briefly introduces the Global Fund, (PRODUCT) RED's beneficiary and the modality through which shoppers are meant to engage. Then, the chapter moves on to critique the Africa issue of *Vanity Fair,* examining the ways in which the RED initiative constitutes gender and race relations within the context of 'helping' Africans with AIDS. The discussion focuses on an analysis of the use of representations of 'The Lazarus Effect' and argues that these images constitute a virtualism of AIDS treatment. Finally, the chapter concludes with links that (PRODUCT) RED has with other types of global emergency responses. Throughout the analysis, I will highlight how RED, through its selective focus on glamour and consumerism, provides highly gendered representations of the epidemic. Analysing these gendered representations can yield insights into the expanding number of other initiatives that use consumer-driven philanthropy to support international development interventions.

(PRODUCT) RED

In stories in the mass media and press releases, RED is depicted as the brainchild of the aid celebrity extraordinaire, Bono.[3] His first foray in awareness raising, advocacy and fundraising began with DATA (Debt, AIDS, Trade, Africa), a non-governmental organization launched in 2002, along with activists from the Jubilee 2000 campaign. RED is described as the outcome of Bono's conviction that a less 'misty-eyed, bleeding-heart' approach needed to be adopted to help the poor. Accordingly, worthy causes should be marketed in the same way as 'a sports-shoe company does, or dare I say it, a cigarette company does' (Bishop, 2006).

At the RED launch, Bono declared: 'Philanthropy is like hippy music, holding hands. Red is more like punk rock, hip hop, this should feel like hard commerce' (Weber, 2006). A popular media report declared that 'the real surprise is that Bono turns out to be a card-carrying capitalist. He wants companies selling RED products to make a profit by helping the poor – doing well by doing good' (Bishop, 2006). Despite the prominence of pessimistic discourse about aid, the premises of 1950s modernization theory in which the poor needed a push to help them 'take off,' after which they were destined to become affluent and 'modern like the rest of us' still underpin most development aid. Brand Aid brings modernization theory into postmodern times as consumption becomes a mechanism for compassion.

Giorgio Armani was most explicit in his recognition of the capitalist bottom line with his speech launching the RED Armani sunglasses at Davos: 'One of the main reasons why I like this formula that Bono and Bobby have thought of is the fact that the word "trade" does no longer have a negative connotation.'[4] Bono explicitly rejected the suggestion that he was being used by companies to restore their reputations,[5] and refuted the idea that the Global Fund was endorsing products. On the contrary, Bono claimed, 'We are not endorsing their products, these products endorse us' (Weber, 2006).

HIV and AIDS provides the quintessential cause as the focus of Brand Aid's 'hard commerce' approach to doing good because, like fashion, rock music or celebrity, it is about money, power and sex. Furthermore, the distance between RED and its recipients obscures the contradictions between an initiative embedded in privileged, heterosexist frameworks and the actual gendered struggles of preventing and living with HIV and AIDS in Africa. Western consumers are encouraged to express their sexuality, their attractiveness and their desire through consumer choices. RED never connects this to the exchange of sexual services for consumer goods within its recipient societies most affected by HIV.[6]

As described in the UK's *Sunday Times,* 'the sex appeal of red' comes also from stars such as Scarlett Johansson, 'the sizzling face of Bono's new ethical brand': 'Johansson is peeling off her clothes in a photographic studio in LA, in preparation for becoming the pin-up for Bono's new plan.' Johansson's interpretation of why the new product is called RED is: 'It's a sexy, hot colour that's vibrant and attention-grabbing. It has been since the 1940s, such a time of high glamour and red lipstick and red nails. That's probably why they chose it for this campaign – glamour!' (Darke, 2006). The use of stereotypical imagery of sexy, scantily clad women to sell products to consumers is perhaps too commonplace to merit mention; however, using these images to raise funds for international development efforts to respond to AIDS in Africa is distinctive.

Ironically, at the same time that many HIV and AIDS campaigns seek to dismantle gendered stereotypes that potentially disempower women, RED seems to reinforce the very stereotypes that other campaigns fight against.

The media hype surrounding celebrities and the crass consumerism of RED makes it difficult to address it as a serious contribution to international aid funding or to the global response to HIV and AIDS. However, RED cannot be so easily dismissed. Another RED product, launched on 5 August 2006, was a special issue of the prestigious international medical journal, the *Lancet* – specially entitled *(The Lancet)*[RED]. As the journal's editorial (*Lancet,* 2006) for that issue explained:

> For the first time in its 183 year history, this week's issue of The Lancet is black and white and RED all over. The journal also contains, rather unusually, advertisements for a Motorola mobile phone, an American Express card, and clothing by GAP. This is because The Lancet has joined (PRODUCT) RED. ... The Lancet is taking part in this exciting initiative and is contributing US$30,000 to (PRODUCT) RED in support of this important project. We hope that other medical and scientific journals and publishers will join this cause.[7]

The *Lancet's* explicit endorsement of RED may also be read as providing an implicit endorsement of the private sector's response to HIV and AIDS. Furthermore, it suggests an important epistemic shift, inasmuch as what we understand about the epidemic is increasingly being shaped by the private sector.[8] RED explicitly links private business with public health.

The Global Fund

(PRODUCT) RED's beneficiary, the Global Fund, is an independent, private foundation governed by an international board that works in partnership with governments, NGOs, civil society organizations and the private sector. It limits its activities to funding projects rather than implementing them. The Global Fund differs from bilateral initiatives in its governance structure and has a more balanced decision-making process that aims to include representatives from a broad range of donor and recipient constituencies, including developing country governments, people living with HIV and AIDS, and so on. The Global Fund is financed primarily by governments but also by foundations and individuals, and thus commitments are not legally binding under international law. One of the largest contributors to the Global Fund, the US Government, is not permitted to contribute more than 33 per cent of the total paid-in funding in order to minimize disproportionate contribution and control over the institution.

(PRODUCT) RED seeks to give the impression that the activities it funds around HIV and AIDS are innovative, not burdened by the same bureaucratic mire associated with development aid, and driven by individuals. Yet, the Global Fund receives most of its revenue from donor governments or traditional philanthropy, not from young fashionistas, as shown in Table 1. As of November 2008, a total of US$18.9 billion had been pledged by donors, of which US$11.8 billion was actually disbursed: 95 per cent of disbursed funds came from 'traditional' bilateral donors. The rest came from private sources. Within private sources, 'traditional' philanthropy provided the bulk of the money (the Gates Foundation alone provided 72 per cent of all private funding). RED is actually the second source of private funding, with US$115 million disbursed as of November 2008 – or 1 per cent of total disbursements (public and private). Note that there is no RED entry into pledges because RED contributions depend on the volume of RED product sales. Given the high level of transparency in reporting in the Global Fund, it is surprising that no breakdown is provided to show the contributions by each RED co-branded company, nor the disbursements by year (only a grand total to date is provided). Even though all (PRODUCT) RED corporate partners have made multiyear commitments supporting the initiative, the Global Fund cannot bank on RED as contributions are dependent on profits. Nonetheless, the power of RED lies not in its effectiveness as a funding modality but in its innovative characterization of the relation between consumption and donation.

With (PRODUCT) RED, it is the first time that the Global Fund has publicly permitted donations to be channelled to support particular types of grants (the best-performing AIDS programs benefiting women and children in Africa) rather than the Fund's overall activities. This may have more fundamental repercussions on the Global Fund as donors decide the priorities of the Fund on the basis of the areas to which they will mandate that their contributions be channelled. In-house management of the RED campaign is almost the exclusive focus of the Global Fund's budget for private sector support (Global Fund, 2007, p. 20).

The Global Fund has been criticized for its insufficient attention to gender issues. One review noted the lack of gender-disaggregated data in Fund monitoring and reporting and an absence of programmes addressing women's vulnerability to HIV infection and gender inequality or targeting gender

Table 1. The Global Fund to Fight AIDS, Tuberculosis and Malaria:
Pledges (US$ '000, nominal prices)

DONOR	PLEDGE (US$ '000)	YEAR	TOTAL PAID TO DATE (US$ '000)
Countries			
Australia	158 127	2004–2010	95 669
Belgium	111 992	2001–2010	78 542
Brazil	200	2003–2004, 2006–2007	200
Brunei Darussalam	50	2007	
Cameroon	125	2003, 2007	
Canada	100 000	2002–2004	100 006
	709 419	2005–2010	373 887
China	16 000	2003–2010	12 000
Denmark	208 781	2002–2010	148 091
European Commission	1 178 009	2001–2010	789 911
Finland	15 419	2006–2009	10 892
France	2 399 470	2002–2010	1 396 882
Germany	1 232 784	2002–2010	715 319
Greece	788	2005–2007	788
Hungary	45	2004–2006, 2008	45
Iceland	421	2004–2005	421
	700	2006–2008	700
India	11 000	2006–2010	3 000
Ireland	219 176	2002–2010	135 088
Italy	200 000	2002–2003	215 160
	1 130 453	2004–2010	793 101
Japan	1 406 120	2002–2008, 2009	846 520
Korea (Republic of)	11 000	2004–2009	4 000

DONOR	PLEDGE (US$ '000)	YEAR	TOTAL PAID TO DATE (US$ '000)
Kuwait	2 000	2003, 2008	2 000
Latvia	10	2008	
Liechtenstein	425	2002, 2005–2008	425
	117	2004, 2006	117
Luxembourg	24 015	2002–2010	17 546
Mexico	200	2003, 2005	200
Netherlands	619 098	2002–2010	321 556
New Zealand	2 169	2003–2005	2 169
Nigeria	20 000	2002–2003, 2006	9 081
Norway	340 369	2002–2010	170 480
Poland	50	2003–2006	50
Portugal	15 500	2003–2010	7 500
Romania	436	2007	436
Russia	254 500	2002–2010	154 854
Saudi Arabia	28 000	2003–2006, 2008–2010	16 000
Singapore	1 000	2004–2008	1 000
Slovenia	28	2004–2006	28
	44	2007	44
South Africa	10 000	2003–2008	8 000
	231	2006, 2008	131
Spain	751 547	2003–2005, 2007–2010	304 307
	63 900	2006	63 900
Gen. Catalunya/Spain	7 579	2005–2008	5 639
Sweden	539 232	2002–2010	378 297
Switzerland	10 000	2002–2003	10 000

DONOR	PLEDGE (US$ '000)	YEAR	TOTAL PAID TO DATE (US$ '000)
	35 341	2004–2010	16 920
Thailand	10 000	2003–2012	6 000
Uganda	2 000	2004–2007	1 500
United Kingdom	2 313 811	2001–2015	674 644
United States	4 028 356	2001–2008	3 328 837
Other Countries	2 750	2001–2004	1 675
Total	18 192 787		11 223 558
Other			
Bill & Melinda Gates Foundation	650 000	2002–2004, 2006–2010	450 000
Communitas Foundation	3 000	2007–2009	2 000
Debt2Health – Germany, of which realized as restricted contribution from:			
Indonesia	33 879	2008–2012	8 006
UNITAID	52 500	2007	38 692
CPEF (Idol Gives Back)	6 000	2007–2008	5 500
(PRODUCT) RED™ and Partners			115 292
The United Nations Foundation (UNF) and its donors:			
Hottokenai Campaign (G-CAP Coalition Japan)	250	2006	250
Other UNF Donors	4 022	Various	6 510
Other Donors		Various	12
Total	749 651		626 262
Grand Total	18 942 438		11 849 820

Source: Elaboration from Global Fund data (Global Fund, 2008).

violence (ICRW, 2004). Also, the innovative country coordinating mechanisms (CCMs) could potentially provide spaces for the political empowerment and recognition of women in the political process of AIDS governance. Yet, so far, participation in the CCMs has been gender-biased in all regions, and only 32 per cent or fewer of the CCM members in sub-Saharan Africa are women. Furthermore, the lack of integration between the Global Fund's projects and sexual and reproductive health services has been documented as draining staff and worsening a human resource crisis in some African contexts (Hanefeld et al., 2007, pp. 25–26). If RED is in fact so concerned with women and children, it should advocate better gender monitoring, representation and integration of programmes within the Global Fund.

Africa and our global family in *Vanity Fair*

In its first two years of operation, RED donated US$100 million to the Global Fund's best-performing programmes for HIV and AIDS in Africa – so far, funds have gone to Rwanda, Swaziland, Lesotho and Ghana. As described above, this is the first time that a contributor has been allowed to 'hand pick' successes from the Global Fund's repertoire of programs. RED chooses recipients that are both 'successful' and 'African.' That (PRODUCT) RED's beneficiaries are African is not coincidental, as reimagining Africa is part of the effect produced by RED. Mbembe (2001) has argued that the real and the imaginary are interwoven in the category of 'Africa.' Ferguson (2006) takes this further by suggesting that 'Africa' has a particular place in 'globalization,' a 'place' understood as both a location in space and a rank in a system of social categories. The 'forcefully imposed position in the contemporary world – is easily visible if we notice how fantasies of a categorical "Africa" (normally "sub-Saharan" Africa) and "real" political-economic processes on the continent are interrelated' (Ferguson, 2006, p. 6). Africa seems the obvious 'place' where RED money could buy pills to save women and children living with HIV and AIDS and where the constructions of donor and recipient would not be challenged, as Africa's 'place' in the hierarchy of development is well-established.

Global AIDS has been described as an 'epidemic of signification' (Treichler, 1998, 1999) in which the representations of the infection are intrinsically related to the ways in which the infection is perceived and managed at all levels. Within global AIDS, Africa has been depicted as a dark zone, 'a dark, untamed continent from which devastating viruses emerge to threaten the

West' (Kitzinger and Miller, 1992, cited in Bancroft, 2001, p. 96). Photographic images play a particular and significant role in representations of AIDS in Africa, serving as 'visual quotations' (Bleiker and Kay, 2007, p. 140; Sontag, 2003). In an analysis of photographic representations of African AIDS, Bleiker and Kay (2007) argue: 'At a time when we are saturated with information stemming from multiple media sources, images are well suited to capture issues in succinct and mesmerizing ways.' From the Live Aid concerts onwards, the dominant images of the AIDS pandemic in Africa have been ones of suffering, aimed at generating pity more than compassion; these images have portrayed Africans as victims with no agency, living in circumstances that are far removed from those in developed countries. Yet RED's Africa is not full of suffering; in fact, the only images that could give cause for concern are clearly staged as 'before' pictures in a 'before' and 'after' scenario.

(PRODUCT) RED seeks to bring 'Africa' to the minds of the idle rich, thus providing an opportunity for them to 'help'. This was epitomized by its recent engagement with *Vanity Fair,* which is a monthly magazine featuring reviews, celebrity interviews and trend stories. The magazine usually contains at least one highbrow feature with literary ambitions dealing with a serious issue, like the Iraq War, women's prisons, or AIDS. But typically, much of what *Vanity Fair* depicts is the chasing of 'cool'. In July 2007, Bono was the guest editor of a special issue of the magazine that aimed to 'rebrand Africa' (Carr, 2007). Given the legacy of slavery and colonialism and the extraction of mineral resources and supply of armaments to the continent, it is difficult to imagine a time when the rich have not been interested in Africa. Bono (2007), however, tried to encapsulate a special appeal of the (PRODUCT) RED intervention in his promotional video for the issue: 'That's what this issue of *Vanity Fair* is all about ... trying to bring some sex appeal to the idea of wanting to change the world'. Assuming that Africa is far from the minds, lives and income sources of its (comparatively rich) readers, *Vanity Fair* contributes to the myth that there is no real linkage between rich and poor, between entrepreneurs and Africa or between capitalism and disease.

With no indications that this was intentional irony, the UK version of the Africa issue came bundled with a 78-page insert advertising, of all things, diamonds (Shaffir, 2007).[9] While the topic of focus is explicitly Africa there are recurrent reminders that this is Africa from a neoliberal, American perspective. The inability to think beyond the world as constituted by American foreign policy is illustrated first by the issue's editor's letter justifying the choice of 'Africa' as a topic. The editor sets the time-frame as 'sometime after 9/11'.[10] The editor of *Vanity Fair* is reminding readers that after the fall of the Twin Towers in New York, Africa's strategic importance dropped considerably (see Comaroff, 2007); thus a justification is necessary for a focus on Africa.[11] After dividing the world into geopolitical time units, the editorial then makes reference to the place 'in what is now Ghana' and describes how 'there was once a mini-empire called Bono, ruled by kings called Bonohene.' There is a marked and skilful shift in time-perspective from the contemporary and urgent referent to New York to the timeless and ahistorical referent to 'Africa.' The less than oblique imagined history of Bono as the mini-emperor of Africa stands in for the complex history of the independent country that has been called 'Ghana' for half a century but places well into a virtualism of a continent plagued with suffering where Western celebrities and consumers have a responsibility to intervene.

RED relies on coexisting notions of familiarity and distance between the shoppers it tries to engage and the beneficiaries it tries to help. A few examples from the magazine reflect this: The masthead of *Vanity Fair's* contributors to this issue is annotated with each staff member's 'haplogroup'. A text-box explains: 'Thanks to minor genetic mutations that have occurred over tens of thousands of years of human history and are shared by large groups of people, scientists can trace the migrations of early human beings from Africa to the far corners of the world'. Spatial imagery is interesting here, representing Africa as a space from which everyone has moved. From this we learn that Bono's matrilineal ancestry is linked to the same African mother as that of the magazine's London editor and his patriline pairs with that of the editor of the US edition, Graydon Carter. Such a genetic map tracing contributors back to their 'African roots' reinforces a notion of primordial, genetic identity while also fundamentally destabilizing notions of who is the African. There is no action or sentiment required, no claims to be made or fulfilled, but a community is imagined, and everyone simply is part of it in a truly cosmopolitan sense. This creates a relation described by Fadlalla (2008, p. 210) as 'familial globality.' With no claim to culture or place, genetic Africans are everywhere. Thus, we are all so close to Africa that we are actually African. A cosmopolitan call for compassion to help suffering others in faraway places recreates our own agency and limits the possibility for activism by those slotted as 'helpless'. Magubane (2008, p. 102.22) describes how 'people living on the Continent today, must simply sit and wait, with the hope that someone will take pity on them and write them into history. This is Sontag's "applied Hegelianism" taken to the extreme. The Other completely ceases to exist except insofar as a tiny remnant of her survives in us. The Other is not even a memory, she is only the vaguest genetic trace'.

The Lazarus Effect and virtual salvation

Between stereotypical gender notions of bourgeois feminine beauty and wild adventure-seeking masculinity (an article profiling the first 'woman of colour' to be named as 'the Face of Estee Lauder' and one entitled 'Congo from the Cockpit'), *Vanity Fair* published a story entitled 'The Lazarus Effect' (Shoumatoff, 2007). Two African women and two African men, all aged between 24 and 34, were shown in paired 'before' and 'after' photographs 'showing how ARV treatment has allowed them to resume their lives' (Shoumatoff, 2007, p. 160). This 'Lazarus Effect' was chronicled, perhaps in allusion to yet another Biblical analogy, in two images taken forty days apart in Lusaka. The article begins with the heading 'A population on the mend', but the text refers not to urban Zambia, as one might expect from photographs taken in Lusaka, but to a health centre in Kigali, Rwanda. One of our contentions in this chapter is that the slippage between two countries bordering the Democratic Republic of the Congo is not merely a lack of professional attention to detail by one of the world's most successful magazines but a rudimentary marker of the effacement of Africans with HIV and AIDS into one smooth, global subjectivity in which there is no great difference between being a Rwandan or a Zambian. Of the two, only Rwandans have so far received any money from the RED contributions to the Global Fund.

The faces of AIDS are shown in dramatic black and white photographs; three of the subjects are partially unclothed so that the viewer cannot fail to identify the contours of their collar and rib bones. These photographs, intimate and pleading to illicit pity from the readers (see Bleiker and Kay, 2007), are quite unusual in the RED campaign. In fact, in the entire *Vanity Fair* Africa issue, only these images of the four Zambians living with AIDS before they began taking ARVs refer to suffering.[12]

The 'after' photographs show colour images of a young mother, Silvia, with her toddler and Nancy holding a head of cabbage in front of a cement house with a small plot in the background. They also show one young man, Elimas, sitting with his wife. Another young father, Nigel, poses with his wife and three small children. All four 'after' photographs are smiling representations of a return to domestic productive and reproductive life. In this depiction, we are led to believe that conjugal marriages involving caring spouses and healthy children are part and parcel of the Lazarus Effect of ARVs.[13] From these images, it is difficult to understand the relationships, or disease vectors, between the people in the photographs. It would be difficult to speculate on whether or not the partners and children of these families had been tested for HIV or whether they also were on treatment, or needed it. However, the transformative focus of treatment is on the domestic self, the husband, mother or father, or home gardener. We do not know if Nancy will find a market for her produce or even if she has access to land. Nor do we know which, if any, of Nigel's three small girls have the virus or how many other siblings they have.

Still, we are also left somehow with visual finality, a sense of completion and closure that the domestic transformation is finished. Yet, Zambians live in a culture that values child-bearing and fertility. So, it could be likely that those photographed might want to have more children when they have regained their health, but that would open up a difficult and complicated story about the possibility of reproducing while on AIDS treatment (see Richey, 2008; Richey, forthcoming; and Smith and Mbakwem, 2007). Finally, we do not know how these four individuals were persuaded to be photographed while they were so obviously ill. The imagined closure in stereotypical gendered terms firmly re-instates a fiction of economically stable, heterosexual, monogamous life that distracts the viewer from questions of how gender inequalities have fuelled the transmission of HIV and constrained the treatment of AIDS.

Also, it is quite difficult to identify with much specificity the background of the photographs. What is the likely social or economic situation of these people? A stone-brick house with windows and plants in pots appears decid-edly middle class, whereas a straw mat over a stone floor seems less prosperous. But these are only guesses at best. And how do we know that the large, wooden framed mirror into which Elimas gazes forlornly at himself in his 'before' shot is actually part of his home's interior design, rather than a prop brought along by the photographer? These may appear as petty or irrelevant questions, but these images illustrate the point that the representations of AIDS treatment, like the representations of AIDS suffering before it, are bound up with the iden-tities and expectations of the producers and consumers of these images and have little to teach us about the lived experiences of Africans who are managing treatment.

The same photographs of Silvia, Nigel and Elimas from *Vanity Fair* also provide the only video imagery for a YouTube video from (PRODUCT) RED (2007*a*) entitled 'The Lazarus Effect'. This video's message in thirty seconds is as follows: Written text fills the screen with '4,400 people die every day of AIDS in sub-Saharan Africa'. This slide is followed by the words 'treatment exists'. And Silvia's 'before' photograph fills the screen as an American female voice explains, 'In about sixty days, an HIV patient in Africa can go from here [Silvia before] to here [Silvia after]. We call this transformation "the Lazarus Effect". The voice continues as Nigel's and then Elimas's before and after photos fill the screen: 'It's the result of two pills a day taken by an HIV/AIDS patient for about sixty days. Learn more about how you can help give people this chance at life at joinrcd.com'.

Why would the promotional video for (PRODUCT) RED rely on the same six photographs that had already been disseminated to a popular audience in the *Vanity Fair* magazine months before? Surely of the 1.4 million people living with AIDS receiving ARVs provided by the Global Fund since September 2007, according to the RED website, there are other subjects who could represent the Lazarus Effect – perhaps even those living in the countries where RED's support is channelled (as opposed to Zambia, where it is not). This chapter suggests that RED's Lazarus Effect is a virtualism: it is a prescriptive demonstration of reality that relies on the replication of iconic images. The power of these images comes from their framing and sense to their viewers that they feel real.

When the Lazarus Effect images are compared to other RED photographs, their claims to authenticity are even more marked. One could argue that the image that most closely resembles the bodily emaciation, the shadow-like framing and the claims of urgency of the 'before' photos of AIDS victims is in fact the cover of the RED edition of the *Independent*, which shows not an African living with AIDS but supermodel Kate Moss in blackface titled 'Not a Fashion Statement'.[14]

In this 'blackface' cover of the RED *Independent*, 'skin is used as a means of invoking the experience of an African woman by performing a surface-level transformation of an iconic British supermodel' (Sarna-Wojcicki, 2008, p. 19). In a competing British newspaper, the *Guardian*, Hannah Pool (2006) writes of the Moss cover:

> I suppose it is meant to be subversive, but what does it say about race today when a quality newspaper decides that its readers will only relate to Africa through a blacked-up white model rather than a real-life black woman? What does it say about the fight against HIV/Aids if that is the only way to make us care?

RED is about redeeming sex and stylizing gender relations. Percy Hintzen's (2008, p.79) detailed critique of the text in the *Vanity Fair* Africa issue describes how both its features and its product advertisements draw out the appeal of racialized sexuality of Africa. He argues 'that the targeted "modern sophisticated consumer" is to be enticed by sexual desire produced by "stunning photography" to create "demand." This is to be accomplished through "popular dialogue" and "social commentary." It is the very (stunning but unsurprising) template evident in the juxtaposition of Bono's plea for Africa with the "stunning photography" of sexual desire'. Of course, the racialization of sexuality long pre-dates contemporary initiatives like RED, but RED puts a new spin on it to allow the West to reclaim sex as healthy. The sexy blacked-up body of a supermodel is able to stand in for the African woman dying from sex. We as viewers do not need to actually confront literal images or experiences of suffering; we can have the virtual mediation of a familiar translator. As other critical scholars have also noted, RED has not taken onboard any of the central messages of feminist scholars of development, and 'a Hollywood standard of heterosexual sexiness prevails, which may be good marketing but fails to provoke deeper analysis of broadly viable models of sexuality' (Cameron and Haanstra, 2008, p. 1485). Still, this argument must be pushed further because the RED images also constitute a 'familial globality,' as described earlier, that actively reinforces, rather than destabilizes, notions of sexualized distant others.

Conclusion

This chapter does not argue that the RED representations are purposefully misleading, distorted or lying; whether or not this is the case is in fact beside the point. There are always implications of relying on representations as 'truth,' and RED must be understood within the existing history of selling images of AIDS in Africa. We must also consider the meaning of using images of suffering to sell products. W. J. T. Mitchell (2005, p. 105) describes images such as the RED visuals: 'As objects of surplus value, of simultaneous over- and underestimation, these stand at the interface of the most fundamental social conflicts'. This statement is integral to the focus of this chapter on representations of AIDS, gender and domesticity by a co-branding, cause-related marketing initiative.

Within the possible parameters of corporate engagement in ethical interventions, such as corporate social responsibility, the scope of the RED initiative is limited to helping distant others in a way that does not challenge normal business practices. Shoppers are able to 'save African women and children' through the power of their purchases. The beauty of this celebrity simplification is that it provides the possibility that everyday people can engage in low-cost heroism. As an American Express RED ad states, it provides 'the union of consumerism and conscience, demonstrating how something as simple as everyday shopping can now help to eliminate AIDS in Africa'. Only through celebrity diplomacy could such a quick fix be given a sort of legitimacy. As explained by Andrew Cooper, 'that's the beauty of celebrity diplomacy – they don't know all the details' (Dalton, 2006). The reduction of a complex disease of biology and economy into 'fragmented knowledge ... packaged in oversimplified moral categories' (Fadlalla, 2008, p. 209) resembles most closely perhaps the contemporary 'Save Darfur' campaign in its creation of the helpless African and the compassionate Western helper (see Flint and DeWaal, 2005). Mobilizing an army of shoppers is even easier when the fight is against a disease, something that no one could actually be 'for'.

Branded philanthropy is taking on an increasingly important role in the responses to HIV and AIDS by 'concerned strangers'. According to Fadlalla (2008, p. 227), 'Instituting humanitarianism as the only strategy for eliminating poverty and suffering also reproduces a colonialist narrative of modernity and progress within which the privileged/West is compassionate and agentive and the "third world" is only helpless'. Bono states, 'I represent a lot of [African] people who have no voice at all ... They haven't asked me to represent them. It's clearly cheeky but I hope they're glad I do' (Iley, 2005, cited in Hume, 2005; Harrison, 2006). The rock star's burden shows how aid celebrities like Bono are shaping the AIDS agenda in ways to suggest how wealthy Western consumers should shop to the aid of their less fortunate global citizens.

While (PRODUCT) RED explicitly claims to link development goals with capitalist methods, to constitute shopping 'at home' as an effective means of combating AIDS in Africa, the gendered and racial tensions that underpin such an approach tap into traditional discourses of power. In an interview with the *New York Times,* Bono said that 'Africa is sexy and people need to know that' (Carr, 2007). While (PRODUCT) RED's aid celebrities redeem sex in 'sexy' Africa, they never challenge the global inequities of masculinity, the racialization of sexuality or the social hierarchy where cool, rich, white men save poor African women and children. The aid celebrities make it possible for Western shoppers to feel empowered through the purchase of RED products. All of this is managed within a discourse of concern, care and ethics. Public, Western, and masculine agency is called forth to save intimate, African and feminine beneficiaries. Subtle, yet stereotypical depictions of gender relations throughout the campaign, particularly the framing of 'African women and children' as passive yet worthy recipients and aid celebrities as powerful and effective, does nothing to thwart the existing 'unequal relationships between men and women' or the 'gender stereotypes' to which the international community returns when continuing to try to understand HIV and AIDS (see UN, 2008). The proximity and distance of (PRODUCT) RED's virtualism of AIDS treatment distracts our attention from critical issues of gender relations in both African recipient societies and Western consumption ones. In the biggest global health initiative in history – providing AIDS treatment to Africans – we still know very little about who is living or who is dying, or why.

Notes

1.   Cause-related marketing links the promotion of a brand, company, product or service directly to a social cause, most often with a portion of sales revenue going to support the cause.

2.   Initially shown in the RED product launch at Davos video, viewed from www. joinred.com. Can now be accessed only in audio form from http://streamstudio. world-television.com/gaia/wef/worldeconomicforum_annualmeeting2006/ podcast/press1.mp3, last accessed 13 March 2009.

3.   However, RED may be less attributable to celebrity genius and more to advanced international fundraising strategies. The Global Fund's marketing and media campaign, which began in 2004, includes 'co-branded product tie-ins' as part of a priority of 'engaging consumer audiences in key donor markets' (Global Fund, n.d.).

4.   We use the English version spoken by the translator in the audio of spoken words in Italian. Initially shown in the RED product launch at Davos video, viewed from www.joinred.com. Can now be accessed only in audio form from http://streamstudio.world-television.com/gaia/wef/worldeconomicforum_ annualmeeting2006/podcast/press1.mp3, last accessed 13 March 2009.

5.   For example, Converse is owned by Nike, a company accused in the past of using sweatshop labour in developing countries.

6.   See Hunter (2002) for one of the best discussions of the materiality of sexual exchanges in Africa. This article avoids stereotypes of 'sugar daddies' and 'prostitutes' while maintaining a loyal and thorough material analysis of sexuality. See also Campbell et al. (2006) for a frank and engaged discussion of these topics.

7.   Note that Motorola joined RED after the launch of the four original RED products.

8.   We appreciate the anonymous reviewer who brought this to our attention.

9.   There were no articles on the diamond trade in Africa, which might have been expected given Leonardo DiCaprio's awareness raising of the topic of 'blood diamonds' and its prevalence in popular media.

10. The focus of the first column of the piece involves the earnestness of the work done by Graydon Carter, the magazine editor, and Bono, his guest editor for the RED issue. However, the piece details how the actual work seemed to have been done by 'Aimee' and 'Sheila' (no last names given), their respective deputies. Framing the accomplishments of *Vanity Fair* as the result of 'big men' instead of the fruit of the labour of nearly anonymous women perpetuates gender-biased

thinking about production and accomplishment. We see a similar parallel with the depiction of RED as the brainchild of Bono, instead of the result of an ongoing collaborative effort.

11. The cultural angst of the West brought forth by 9/11 may have increased interest in Africa, both as an outlet for charitable impulses and as a preventive strategy against poverty-induced terrorism (Magubane, 2007).

12. There is a tiny aerial shot of the Mathare Valley Slum, but only rooftops are visible. So one would have to know that this is the largest slum in Nairobi to have any sense that this photograph represented suffering.

13. Ferguson's (1999) work on the abjection of Zambians from the promises of neoliberal modernity places insightful emphasis on how 'expectations of domesticity' left unfulfilled create particularly painful repercussions for familial and conjugal life.

14. On 21 September 2007 the *Independent* published its second RED edition, this one edited by Giorgio Armani. It included articles by Leonardo DiCaprio, George Clooney, Bill Gates and Beyonce.

References

Bancroft, A. 2001. Globalisation and HIV/AIDS: Inequality and the boundaries of a symbolic epidemic. *Health, Risk and Society*, Vol. 3, No. 1, pp. 89–98.

Bishop, M. 2006. View from Davos: Bono marketing his red badge of virtue. *Daily Telegraph*, 27 January. http://www.telegraph.co.uk/finance/2930938/View-from-Davos-Bono-marketing-his-red-badge-of-virtue.html (Accessed 15 October 2008.)

Bleiker, R. and Kay, A. 2007. Representing HIV/AIDS in Africa: Pluralist photography and local empowerment. *International Studies Quarterly*, Vol. 51, No. 1, pp. 139–63.

Boltanski, L. 1993. *La Souffrance à Distance*. Paris, Métailié. (In French.)

Bono. 2007. *Bono Brings Africa to Vanity Fair*. http://www.youtube.com/watch?v=D7srZjpCTaI (Accessed 15 October 2008.)

Brockington, D. 2009. *Celebrity and the Environment: Fame, Wealth and Power in Conservation*. London, Zed Books.

Butt, L. 2002. The suffering stranger medical anthropology and international morality. *Medical Anthropology*, Vol. 21, No. 1, pp. 1–24.

Cameron, J. and Haanstra, A. 2008. Development made sexy: How it happened and what it means. *Third World Quarterly*, Vol. 29, No. 8, pp. 1475–489.

Campbell, C., Nair, Y. and Maimane, S. 2006. AIDS stigma, sexual moralities and the policing of women and youth in South Africa. *Feminist Review*, Vol. 83, pp. 132–38.

Carr, David. 2007. Citizen Bono brings Africa to idle rich. *New York Times*, 5 March. http://www.nytimes.com/2007/03/05/business/media/05carr.html?ex=1330750800&en=a49746a2935ab3e9&ei=5088&partner=rssnyt&emc=rss (Accessed 15 October 2008.)

Carrier, J. G. 1998. Introduction. J. G. Carrier and D. Miller (eds), *Virtualism: A New Political Economy*. Oxford, United Kingdom, Berg, pp. 1–24.

Carter, G. 2007. Editor's letter: Annie get your passport. *Vanity Fair*, 1 July.

Chesler, E. 2005. Introduction. W. Chavkin and E. Chesler (eds), *Where Human Rights Begin: Health, Sexuality and Women in the New Millenium*. New Brunswick, NJ, Rutgers University Press, pp. 1–34.

Comaroff, J. 2007. Beyond bare life: AIDS, (bio)politics, and the neoliberal order. *Public Culture*, Vol. 19, No. 1, pp. 197–220.

Dalton, M. 2006. Local professor welcomes 'Bono-ization' of diplomacy. *The Record*, 13 September. http://www.atu2.com/news/article.src?ID=4349&Key=&Year=&Cat=14 (Accessed 15 October 2008.)

Darke, T. 2006.The sex appeal of red. *Sunday Times,* 26 February. http://women. timesonline.co.uk/tol/life_and_style/women/beauty/article732241.ece (Accessed 15 October 2008.)

di Leonardo, M. 2008. Introduction: New global and American landscapes of inequality. J. L. Collins, M. di Leonardo and B. Williams (eds), *New Landscapes of Inequality: Neoliberalism and the Erosion of Democracy in America.* Santa Fe, NM, School for Advanced Research Press, pp. 3–19. http://sarpress.sarweb.org/sarpress/images/ pdf/sarpress_108.pdf (Accessed 15 October 2008.)

Fadlalla, A. H. 2008. The neoliberalization of compassion: Darfur and the mediation of American faith, fear and terror. J. L. Collins, M. di Leonardo and B. Williams (eds), *New Landscapes of Inequality: Neoliberalism and the Erosion of Democracy in America.* Santa Fe, NM, School for Advanced Research Press, pp. 209–28.

Ferguson, J. 1999. *Expectations of Modernity: Myths and Meanings of Urban Life on the Zambian Copperbelt.* Berkeley, Calif., University of California Press.

——. 2006. *Global Shadows: Africa in the Neoliberal World Order.* Durham, NC, Duke University Press.

Flint, J. and de Waal, A. 2005. *Darfur: A Short History of a Long War.* New York, Zed Books.

Frazier, M. 2007. Bono & Co. spend up to $100 million on marketing, incur watchdogs' wrath. *Advertising Age,* 5 March. http://adage.com/article?article_id=115287 (Accessed 15 October 2008.)

Global Fund. 2004. Confirmation of U.S. pledge for 2004 boosts Global Fund resources for fourth proposal round to $900 Million. Press release, 26 February. http://www. theglobalfund.org/en/media_center/press/pr_040226.asp (Accessed 15 October 2008.)

——. 2007. *Report of the Global Fund Task Team on Resource Mobilization.* Geneva, Global Fund.

——. 2008. *Monthly Progress Update – 24 April 2008.* Geneva, Global Fund. http://www. theglobalfund.org/en/files/publications/basics/progress_update/progressupdate. pdf (Accessed 15 October 2008.)

——. n.d. *Marketing and Media Opportunities.* Geneva, Global Fund. http://www. theglobalfund.org/en/files/factsheets/marketing_media.pdf (Accessed 15 October 2008.)

Hanefeld, J., Spicer, N., Brugha, R. and Walt, G. 2007. How have global health initiatives impacted on health equity? What strategies can be put in place to enhance their positive impact and mitigate against negative impacts? A literature review commissioned by the Health Systems Knowledge Network WHO Commission on the Social Determinants of Health. http://www.who.int/social_determinants/ resources/csdh_media/global_health_initiatives_2007_en.pdf

Harrison, G. 2006. Sovereignty, poverty, history: 2005 and western moralities of intervention. Paper presented at the African Studies Association of the UK, London, 11–13 September.

Hintzen, P. C. 2008. Desire and the enrapture of capitalist consumption: Product Red, Africa, and the crisis of sustainability. *Journal of Pan African Studies,* Vol. 2, No. 6, pp. 77–91.

Hume, M. 2005. Africa: A stage for political poseurs. *spiked,* 10 June. http://www. spiked-online.com/index.php?/site/printable/329 (Accessed 15 October 2008.)

Hunter, M. 2002. The Materiality of Everyday Sex: Thinking Beyond Prostitution. *African Studies,* Vol. 61, No. 1, pp. 99–120.

ICRW (International Center for Research on Women). 2004. *Civil Society Participation in Global Fund Governance: What Difference does it Make?* Geneva, Global Fund.

Iley, C. 2005. Why Africa needs U2. *Evening Standard,* 10 June. http://www.thisislondon. co.uk/music/article-19222312-details/Why+Africa+needs+U2/article.do (Accessed 15 October 2008.)

Kitzinger, J. and Miller, D. 1992. 'African AIDS': The media and audience beliefs. P. Aggleton, P. Davies and G. Hart (eds), *AIDS: Rights, Risk and Reason.* London, Falmer Press, pp. 28–52.

Kleinman, A. and Kleinman, J. 1996. The appeal of experience; the dismay of images: Cultural appropriations of suffering in our times. *Daedalus,* pp. 1–24.

Lancet. 2006. Editorial: The business of HIV/AIDS. *Lancet,* Vol. 368, No. 9534 (5 August), p. 423. http://download.thelancet.com/pdfs/journals/0140-6736/ PIIS0140673606691241.pdf (Accessed 15 October 2008.)

Littler, J. 2008. 'I feel your pain': Cosmopolitan charity and the public fashioning of the celebrity soul. *Social Semiotics,* Vol. 18, No. 2, pp. 237–51.

Magubane, Z. 2007. Africa script needs rewrite. *Zelaza Post,* 13 June. http://zeleza.com

——. 2008. The (Product) Red man's burden: Charity, celebrity and the contradictions of coevalness. *Journal of Pan African Studies,* Vol. 2, No. 6, pp. 102.1–102.25.

Mbembe, A. 2001. *On the Postcolony.* Berkeley, Calif., University of California Press.

Mitchell, W. J. T. 2005. *What Do Pictures Want? The Lives and Loves of Images.* Chicago Ill., University of Chicago Press.

PEPFAR (US President's Emergency Plan for AIDS Relief). 2007a. President Bush announces five-year, $30 billion HIV/AIDS plan. http://www.pepfar.gov/85811. htm (Accessed 15 October 2008.)

——. 2007b. *Technical Support to Global Fund Grants.* Washington, DC, US Global AIDS Coordinator and the Bureau of Public Affairs, US State Department. http://www. pepfar.gov/documents/organization/91500.pdf (Accessed 15 October 2008).

Polanyi, K. 1957. Aristotle discovers the economy. K. Polanyi, C. M. Arensberg and H. W. Pearson (eds), *Trade and Market in Early Empires: Economies in History and Theory.* Glencoe, Ill., Free Press, pp. 64–94.

Ponte, S., Richey, L. and Baab, M. 2009. Bono's Product (RED) initiative: Corporate social responsibility that solves the problems of 'distant others'. *Third World Quarterly,* Vol. 30, No. 2., pp. 301–317.

Pool, H. 2006. Return to the Dark Ages. *Guardian* (UK), 22 September.

(PRODUCT) RED. 2007*a. The Lazarus Effect.* http://www.youtube.com/watch?v= ZwRXF6r5tL0, http://www.youtube.com/watch?v=W82SoRp9Au4 (Accessed 15 October 2008.)

——. 2007*b. RED Ambassador Christy Turlington in Africa.* http://www.youtube.com/ watch?v=v-jZeiC8EUw (Accessed 15 October 2008).

Richey, L. A. 2008. *Population Politics and Development: From the Policies to the Clinics.* New York/London, Palgrave MacMillan.

——. forthcoming. Gendering the therapeutic citizen in reproduction. C. H. Browner and C. F. Sargent (eds), *Globalization and the State.* Durham, NC, Duke University Press.

Richey L. A. and Ponte, S. 2008. Better RED Than Dead? From 'Band Aid' to 'Brand Aid'. *Third World Quarterly,* Vol. 29, No. 4, pp. 711–29.

Sarna-Wojcicki, M. 2008. Refigu(red): Talking Africa and AIDS in 'causumer' culture. *Journal of Pan African Studies,* Vol. 2, No. 6, pp. 14–31.

Shafrir, D. 2007. *Vanity Fair* wants you to love diamonds and Africa. *Gawker,* 14 June. http://gawker.com/news/diamonds-are-a-magazine.s-best-friend/vanity-fair-wants-you-to-love-diamonds-and-africa-268830.php (Accessed 15 October 2008.)

Shoumatoff, A. 2007. The Lazarus Effect. *Vanity Fair,* 1 July, pp. 156–61.

Smith, D. J. and Mbakwem, B. C. 2007. Life projects and therapeutic itineraries: Marriage, fertility, and antiretroviral therapy in Nigeria. *AIDS,* Vol. 21, Suppl. 5, S37–41.

Sontag, S. 2003. *Regarding the Pain of Others.* New York, Farrar, Straus and Giroux.

Spivak, G. 1985. Can the subaltern speak? Speculations on widow sacrifice. *Wedge,* Vol. 7, No. 8, pp. 120–30.

Stillwaggon, E. 2003. Racial metaphors: Interpreting sex and AIDS in Africa. *Development and Change,* Vol. 34, No. 5, pp. 809–32.

——. 2005. *AIDS and the Ecology of Poverty.* Oxford, United Kingdom, Oxford University Press.

Treichler, P. A. 1998. AIDS, homophobia, and biomedical discourse: An epidemic of significance. R. Parker and P. Aggleton (eds), *Culture, Society and Sexuality: A Reader.* London, Routledge, pp. 357–86.

——. 1999. *How to Have Theory in an Epidemic: Cultural Chronicles of AIDS.* Durham, NC, Duke University Press.

UN (United Nations). 2000. *United Nations Millennium Declaration.* New York, UN. http://www.un.org/millennium/declaration/ares552e.pdf (Accessed 15 October 2008.) (A/res/55/2.)

——. 2008. *Declaration of Commitment on HIV/AIDS and Political Declaration on HIV/AIDS: Midway to the Millennium Development Goals.* Report of the Secretary-General, 1 April. New York, UN. http://data.unaids.org/pub/Report/2008/20080429_sg_progress_report_en.pdf (Accessed 15 October 2008.) (A/62/780.)

Weber, T. 2006. Bono bets on Red to battle AIDS. *BBC News,* 26 January. http://news.bbc.co.uk/2/hi/business/4650024.stm (Accessed 15 October 2008.)

CHAPTER 8

The life course of nevirapine and the culture of response to the global HIV & AIDS pandemic: Travelling in an emergency

Alton Phillips

Introduction: Travelling in an emergency

Single-dose nevirapine (sdNVP) has been lauded as a 'magic bullet' to prevent mother-to-child transmission (PMTCT) of the HIV virus (Timberg, 2004). Without any preventive intervention, approximately 15 per cent to 30 per cent of babies born to HIV-positive women will be infected with the virus during pregnancy or delivery, and an additional 5 per cent to 20 per cent through breastfeeding (De Cock et al., 2000). A single dose of nevirapine given to both mother and child has been shown to reduce transmission to the child by about half (Guay et al., 1999; Moodley et al., 2000). Yet single-dose nevirapine has also faced a tumultuous history with concerns about it accelerating drug re-sistance and complicating future treatment (Arrive et al., 2007; Cuningham et al., 2002; Eshleman et al., 2001a, 2001b, 2004, 2005; Jackson et al., 2000; Johnson et al., 2005; Jourdain et al., 2004; Lockman, 2007; WHO, 2000). And, despite the availability of more effective PMTCT regimens (Connor et al., 1994; Moodley et al., 2000; WHO, 2001), many of which use combinations of anti-retrovirals (ARVs) not plagued by similar concerns about resistance, single-dose nevirapine has been lauded as an ideal intervention in developing coun-tries (Garnett, 2000) and continues to be recommended by the World Health Organization (2006b) for use in resource-constrained settings. In changes made to the WHO recommendations in November 2009, single-dose nevi-rapine continues to be recommended during pregnancy as part of an ongoing

The designations employed and the presentation of material throughout this publication do not imply the expression of any opinion whatsoever on the part of UNESCO concerning the legal status of any country, territory or area or of its authorities, or concerning the delimitation of its frontiers or boundaries.
The ideas and opinions expressed in this publication are those of the authors and do not necessarily reflect the views of UNESCO and its Member States.

regime of ARVs, with continued consideration to emergencies and limited resource capacity.

To understand how a seemingly suboptimal regimen became the treatment option of choice in developing countries, this chapter traces the life course of nevirapine as it travels from clinical trials through webs of donor regulations and ultimately into the supply chains that distribute nevirapine and other ARVs to HIV treatment programmes. According to UNAIDS, an estimated US$10 billion was available globally in 2007 for the response to HIV and AIDS. While this represents a six-fold increase from funding in 2001, it is still $8.1 billion short of the amount estimated to meet global prevention and treatment needs (UNAIDS, 2007). This rapid scale-up of resources has been undertaken by a loose, heterogeneous conglomeration of entities working to address the HIV and AIDS pandemic and its effects. The network includes local communities and organizations, as well as national, international and transnational funding agencies, regulatory bodies, corporations and non-governmental organizations (NGOs). It is a network occasionally referred to critically as 'the AIDS Industry.'

The story of nevirapine reveals a culture of response to the global HIV and AIDS pandemic produced by this network that frequently frames the pandemic as an emergency. Understanding the pandemic as an emergency encourages and justifies particular types of action and particular strategies for intervention that have often proved optimal neither in the immediate nor the longer term. While the impact of an 'emergency' frame is often cited in relation to the US President's Emergency Plan for AIDS Relief (PEPFAR) specifically (e.g. Bass, 2005), the deployment of sdNVP for PMTCT shows how this kind of thinking is more widespread than a single donor programme. There is little doubt the HIV and AIDS pandemic is a vital global public health concern. However, as we will see, approaching it as an emergency can skew interventions in ways that diminish their efficacy, especially over longer time spans. An emergency frame narrows decision-making horizons, encourages rapid and immediate action and focuses attention on the exceptional nature of the pandemic, instead of examining how negative outcomes may, in part, be heightened by prevailing political, economic and cultural norms like gender. In the words of noted American social theorist Craig Calhoun (2006, p. 5):

'Emergency,' thus, is a way of grasping problematic events, a way of imagining them that emphasizes their apparent unpredictability, abnormality and brevity, and that carries the corollary that response – intervention – is necessary. The international emergency, it is implied, both can and should be managed. But the managerial response to an emergency focuses on restoring the existing order, not changing it.

As a result, understandings of the pandemic as a 'long-wave' event and interventions framed around longer time spans often take second place to approaches that emphasize rapid intervention and strategies designed to achieve results quickly (Barnett, 2006).

In an emergency mindset, 'magic bullet' solutions like single-dose nevirapine are ideal interventions – simple, inexpensive and relatively easy to implement, and promising an agile and rapid response. Single-dose nevirapine presents the opportunity to save a child's life for a few US dollars compared to spending hundreds or thousands of dollars a year when treating an HIV-positive mother with highly active antiretroviral therapy (HAART). However, the cost-effectiveness and feasibility of sdNVP come at the cost of increased risk of maternal drug resistance and less effective future treatment to save their children. Such approaches unwittingly privilege the child's life over the mother's and may fail to consider the economic and cultural costs associated with women's caregiving and orphanhood. Further, the same emergency mindset is used to justify development strategies for the scale-up of PMTCT and other HIV treatment programmes that prioritize expedience over programme sustainability and that have the unintended consequence of further weakening many local health systems.

Yet the emergency frame is not without contestation. While the emergency frame often trumps gender and longer-term concerns in ways that hinder the efficacy of interventions, it is also challenged by those who believe it should be subsumed to other objectives, the pursuit of economic liberalization in particular. Some of the same players that use a sense of emergency to support expedient development strategies have also implemented procurement regulations that prioritize economic liberalization over cost-effectiveness and that retard programme scale-up. By cutting through what might otherwise appear to be a disparate set of issues – clinical trials, procurement regulations and programme scale-up strategies – the story of nevirapine reveals both consistency and contestation in the cultures of response emerging to confront the global HIV and AIDS pandemic. Tracing the life course of nevirapine provides insight into the competing priorities in the cultures of response, the bureaucratic maneuvering around them, and, in so doing, illustrates opportunities to make future interventions more effective.

Clinical trials: Printing tickets

Our story with nevirapine begins with the clinical trials that determined the safety and efficacy of sdNVP for PMTCT. Clinical trials provide the permission slip for regulatory agencies to approve a drug's widespread sale and use. They are an integral step in the production of pharmaceutical knowledge and are supposed to ensure that treatment is safe and effective. Nevirapine was developed by research teams at Boehringer Ingelheim, a pharmaceutical firm headquartered in Ingelheim, Germany. The research and development of nevirapine was conducted in Boehringer Ingelheim's labs in Ridgefield, Connecticut, US, and Biberach, Germany. In 1996, the United States Food and Drug Administration (FDA) approved nevirapine to treat HIV-1 in adults, but only if prescribed in combination with other ARVs; approvals in Europe came the following year.

Before single-dose nevirapine could be used for PMTCT, however, it needed to undergo a further series of trials to demonstrate its safety and efficacy. In the late 1990s, researchers from the Department of Pathology at Johns Hopkins University in Maryland, US, and Makerere University in Kampala, Uganda, carried out trials in Uganda (referred to as 'HIVNET 006') that concluded that the regime was well tolerated with no serious adverse events (Musoke et al., 1999). The same research team carried out further trials between 1997 and 1999 (HIVNET 012) to compare the efficacy of sdNVP with the ACTG076 regimen of zidovudine (AZT), the standard PMTCT regimen at the time. The HIVNET 012 trial showed that sdNVP reduced the transmission of HIV from mother to child by about half (Guay et al., 1999). Another randomized trial, the South African Intrapartum Nevirapine Trial (SAINT), carried out by the University of Natal in South Africa from 1999 to 2000 compared sdNVP to a zidovudine and lamivudine combination regimen (AZT + 3TC); however, unlike HIVNET 012, the protocol indicated a second dose of nevirapine to be administered to the mother twenty-four to seventy-two hours after delivery to reduce the risk of transmission from breastfeeding. The study concluded that both regimens were effective. Single-dose nevirapine again reduced transmission, by about half to 12.3 per cent. The AZT+3TC combination regimen, however, was significantly more effective, reducing transmission to only 9.3 per cent (Moodley et al., 2000).

While beneficial, from the beginning sdNVP was not the most effective regimen for PMTCT. The original ACTG076 AZT regimen had been shown by Connor et al. (1994) to be more effective than sdNVP or AZT+3TC, reducing transmission 68 per cent after eighteen months in non-breastfeeding populations. However, the ACTG076 regimen needed to begin at the early stages of pregnancy, a situation not considered practical in resource-constrained environments. In 2001, the World Health Organization (WHO) carried out a meta-analysis of data from clinical trials of various PMTCT regimens and again confirmed sdNVP was not the most effective treatment option available. Despite this, sdNVP soon became one of the most common treatment regimens used in developing countries.

Speaking at the US National Institutes of Health on 17 February 2000, Dr J. Brooks Jackson, one of the authors of the HIVNET 012 study, summed up part of the rationale for rolling out sdNVP in developing countries. He noted the success of AZT regimens and combination therapy for PMTCT:

> While very successful here [in the US], it's very difficult for governments in developing countries to afford an $800 regimen, where health-care expenditures are typically $3 to $10 per person. … We think the nevirapine is safe and will be effective in preventing perinatal transmission, and it is deliverable in sub-Saharan Africa and other resource-poor settings, but it does need to be translated into public health policy. (Garnett, 2000)

Despite the benefits of sdNVP's ease of implementation and low cost, concerns about the suboptimal efficacy of sdNVP were compounded by evidence of drug resistance that began with the earliest clinical trials (Arrive et al., 2007; Cuningham, 2002; Eshleman 2001*a*, 2001*b*, 2004, 2005; Jackson et al., 2000; Johnson et al., 2005; WHO, 2000). A single mutation (K103N) can make the Human Immunodeficiency Virus resistant to the entire class of drugs that nevirapine belongs to, that is, non-nucleoside reverse transcriptase inhibitors, or NNRTIs. Resistance to nevirapine means patients need to be switched to a regimen containing an entirely different class of drugs, protease inhibitors (Hirsch et al., 2003; Jourdain et al., 2004). However, drugs in this class are significantly more expensive. They are difficult to produce, and few are available as generics, making their use in resource-constrained environments particularly challenging.

Plasma analyses conducted after the HIVNET 006 clinical trial found evidence of resistance in 20 per cent of samples six weeks after the administration of nevirapine (Jackson et al., 2000). In response, a World Health Organization *Review of Reported Drug Resistance* was released on 24 March 2000 (WHO, 2000). The report noted that NVP-only treatment in adults showed rapid emergence of resistance (Havlir et al., 1996) and concluded that while the report from the HIVNET 006 trial did not justify halting the use of sdNVP in research settings and pilot programmes, more research was needed before the regimen could be approved for general clinical practice:

> There is currently insufficient information to recommend wide-scale implementation of NVP for MTCT-prevention. Long-term follow-up of mothers and children exposed to NVP or other antiretrovirals for the prevention of MTCT is required. Research should in addition explore options to reduce transmission through breastmilk, and potent and affordable long-term combination therapies. (WHO, 2000)

This additional research came from the two trials discussed above, HIVNET 012 and SAINT. While both studies confirmed the efficacy of sdNVP, they only raised more questions and concerns about drug resistance. Research published after the original HIVNET 012 results found NNRTI-resistant strains of HIV in 19 per cent of mothers and 46 per cent of infants who participated in HIVNET 012 but noted that resistant strains faded from detection over time (Eshleman et al., 2001b). The SAINT trial found even higher rates of resistance to nevirapine; at 4–6 weeks after treatment, resistance was detected in 67 per cent of mothers and was maintained in 22 per cent at 9–12 months resistance (Sullivan, 2002).

Results from HIVNET 012 and SAINT were presented at the 13th Annual International AIDS Conference, held in Durban, South Africa, from 9 to 14 July 2000. However, on 7 July 2000, two days before the Durban conference opened, Boehringer Ingelheim, the manufacturer and patent holder for nevirapine, issued a press release announcing a programme to provide free sdNVP for PMTCT in developing countries, even though the WHO had yet to approve sdNVP for general clinical practice. Citing demographic modelling, the release presented the potential benefits from low-level use of ARVs in South Africa, including short-course PMTCT regimens, such as sdNVP (Wood et al., 2000). The release cites the results of HIVNET 012 (Guay et al., 1999) to establish the efficacy of sdNVP for PMTCT, noting, 'While there are still scientific questions to be answered, the overwhelming opinion of experts is strongly in favour of treatment.' The release also mentions two 'critical' areas in need of further research – HIV transmission during breastfeeding and the development of drug resistance – also cited in the WHO review of March 2000.

Shortly after the Durban conference, on 13 October 2000, another WHO consultation was held. The panel ultimately recommended that short-course regimens, including sdNVP, should no longer be restricted to research settings, thereby reversing their March 2000 decision. While concerns about resistance remained, the roll-out of sdNVP for PMTCT moved forward. As Dr Andrea Kovacs, associate professor of pediatrics and pathology at the University of Southern California Medical School, concluded, 'In the setting of sub-Saharan Africa, the benefit of a 50 per cent reduction in transmission [from mother to child] greatly outweighs the risk of resistance' (Kovacs, 2000).

This type of cost-benefit analysis highlights the focus on short-term benefits central to an emergency mindset. On the one hand, the 'magic bullet' of sdNVP holds the promise of halving the number of HIV-positive children born to HIV-infected mothers. It can accomplish this for relatively small amounts of money, as Dr Jackson highlighted speaking about sdNVP at the US National Institutes of Health, and with a simple regimen that is an advantage in settings with limited health system capacity. However, these benefits come at a cost. At the time these decisions were being made, there was clear evidence that sdNVP increased drug resistance in mothers who received treatment. Such resistance would mean decreased efficacy of NNRTI-containing, first-line regimens among people receiving sdNVP. In 2000, the annual cost of adult ART was still thousands of dollars, and there was limited availability of ARVs in developing countries. The effective result of the policy decision to roll-out sdNVP meant saving the life of a child at low cost was prioritized over longer-term risks to maternal health from drug resistance or to the child's health from orphanhood. The logic of such an intervention overlooks the import of the caregiving activities of women. It also raises the question of whether decision-makers presumed the cost of adult ARV treatment would remain prohibitive for most people in developing countries, meaning mothers would die soon anyway, mitigating the longer-term risks to their health.

In the rush to act, part of what gets ignored is how the logic that justifies the use of sdNVP for PMTCT picks up and reproduces a well-worn idea about gender and women's caregiving in particular. There is a long history of neglect of the economic and cultural value of contributions made by women through caregiving (Orloff, 2001, 2002). By not weighing the potential costs of losing that labour against the cost-effectiveness and feasibility of the intervention, advocates for sdNVP reproduce the idea that women's caregiving has no value. Further, this logic also signals an acceptance of and yielding to the trade policies that made ARVs unaffordable in much of the developing world. Were ARVs thought to soon be made affordable and available throughout the developing world, would people have been as willing to accept a risk that could diminish the efficacy of one of only three major classes of ARVs? Or was that risk thought acceptable only because it was presumed adult ART was not coming to the developing world any time soon and the mothers were going to die anyway? As we will see in the following sections, allegiance to trade policy, and in particular the norms of economic liberalization that guide it, is one of the few issues that appears to trump concerns about emergency, immediate action and short-term results in the cultures of response.

Concerns about the development of resistance from the use of sdNVP and the potential impact on future treatment came to a head in 2004 during the 15th Annual International AIDS Conference, held in Bangkok, Thailand. A month before the conference, the South African Medicine Control Council presented data on the use of sdNVP for PMTCT to the South African Ministry of Health that raised some 'challenges' around the development of resistance. After the presentation, the Ministry of Health issued a press release noting that while no recommendation to review PMTCT protocols was made, a meeting to discuss nevirapine resistance would be scheduled after the Bangkok conference (SAMOH, 2004a). A further press release was issued after a speech given by the South African Minister of Health announcing that the Medicine Control Council now recommended against using sdNVP for PMTCT. Noting resistance, the press release stated that 'the risk-benefit profile of nevirapine monotherapy has changed and therefore no longer recommends its use for the prevention of mother to child transmission (PMTCT) of HIV' (SAMOH, 2004c).

In response, UNAIDS, UNICEF and the Elizabeth Glaser Pediatric AIDS Foundation (2004) issued a joint statement that expressed 'strong concern about the South African Medicine Control Council's decision to discontinue use of single-dose nevirapine for prevention of mother to child transmission.' The statement reiterated the revised WHO guidelines for PMTCT, also released in Bangkok, which recommended the use of a number of PMTCT regimens, including sdNVP. Addressing concerns about resistance from sdNVP directly, the separate press release for the new guidelines reads:

> Drug resistance linked to short-course regimens to prevent mother to child transmission that do not fully suppress the virus has been known since early 2000. Programmes to prevent mother to child transmission and treat AIDS are rapidly expanding and antenatal clinics are able to identify more women who are HIV positive. Since these women are all expected to eventually require treatment, potential resistance has become a far greater concern. However, concerns about resistance

need to be balanced with the simplicity and practicality of delivering single-dose nevirapine compared with other regimens. Antiretroviral prophylaxis using single-dose maternal and infant nevirapine remains a practical alternative when provision of more effective regimens is not feasible. Progress in implementing programmes to prevent mother to child transmission based on single-dose maternal and infant nevirapine or other short course regimens should not be undermined. (WHO, 2004)

The South African Ministry of Health later clarified that it had intended to continue the sdNVP programme while at the same time looking into new approaches involving multidrug cocktails (Stent, 2004). (The new approach was ultimately announced in late 2007.) In the end, further debate around resistance in 2004 came to the same conclusion reached by the WHO in 2000. Despite evidence of resistance, its potential effect on future treatment and the efficacy of other regimens, the short-term feasibility and cost-effectiveness of sdNVP were again seen to justify the use of a suboptimal regimen that places mothers at higher risk.

Resistance was not the only controversy to beset nevirapine. Controversy flared yet again in 2005 with media reports of concerns at the US National Institutes of Health about the conduct of the HIVNET 012 trial in Uganda. The concerns centered largely on documentation procedures during the trial and the reporting of adverse effects. A review carried out by the Institute of Medicine (IOM, 2005) ultimately concluded that the trial results showing that sdNVP reduces the probability of mother-to-child transmission of HIV were valid. Despite this, the revelations around the conduct of HIVNET 012 raised further concerns about whether the 'emergency' response to the pandemic resulted in weakening the rigorous standards for the conduct of clinical trials in the name of immediate action. Unfortunately, some of the coverage of HIVNET 012 incorporated legitimate concerns over the conduct of the trial with the rhetoric of AIDS denialism, which claims that HIV does not cause AIDS. There is a clear scientific consensus that HIV causes AIDS, and the denialist position rests largely on outdated research and a selective reading of the available scientific data. In many ways, the debate about AIDS denialism detracted from a legitimate and necessary conversation about the oversight of these trials and the possibility that a lower standard for conduct exists considering the 'emergency' situation in which they occur.

To date, another study in addition to Jourdain et al.'s (2004) has since shown that women starting NNRTI-containing therapy within six months of sdNVP have worse response rates than those who did not take the regimen (Lockman et al., 2007). Further studies have shown no adverse effect if treatment is started six months or more after sdNVP (Coovadia et al., 2006, Lockman et al., 2007; Zijenah et al., 2006). Another two studies have also shown that sdNVP is effective for a second pregnancy (Eure et al., 2006; Martinson et al., 2006; McConnell et al., 2007). When the decision to approve sdNVP was made, however, these data had yet to be published, and all that was known was that resistance occurred. As evidence of adverse consequences accumulated, the use of sdNVP continued. The questions that the controversy over the use of sdNVP raises are not about whether it reduces the transmission of HIV – significant evidence even outside of HIVNET 012 and SAINT confirms it does – or even what, in the end, the consequences of resistance for mothers are. The question the story of single-dose nevirapine raises is whether framing the pandemic as an emergency meant focusing so much on short-term results that longer-term risks to maternal health and, in turn, the well-being of the child were neglected. At the time of writing, the longer-term risk of resistance having an adverse impact appears to be confined only to the six months following sdNVP. At the time these decisions were made, however, for what was known, the impact of resistance could have lasted much longer, and its consequences could have been much more severe. Between a willingness to trade suboptimal efficacy for cost-effectiveness and feasibility and the acceptability of long-term health risks for the mother to save her children, the use of sdNVP for PMTCT raises questions about whether a persistent short-term focus threatens to handicap our ability to successfully respond to the pandemic.

Regulatory regimes: Moving through the air

The cultures of response are not without contestation, and 'emergency' is not the only dominant trope. When we begin to untangle the web of regulations that must be navigated to procure ARVs like nevirapine with donor money, it becomes clear that in some cases the emergency focus on short-term results is subsumed to other concerns. Comparing the procurement regulations of the Global Fund to Fight AIDS, Tuberculosis and Malaria to those of PEPFAR, the requirement of FDA approval for PEFAR-funded antiretroviral procurements indicates a concern for something other than getting as many ARVs to as many patients as quickly as possible. What we see in US actions around intellectual property (IP), trade policy and procurement regulations is the importance of economic liberalization in shaping the response of a number of key players in the 'AIDS industry.' These cases where an emergency frame is overcome by another concern shed more light on the nature of the cultures of response. It sets the stage for a key area of contestation in a response, a fault line between those who believe the emergency nature of the pandemic should trump concerns over IP and trade policy and those who do not.

Two major donor programmes currently facilitate the purchase and distribution of nevirapine and other ARVs in developing countries – PEPFAR and the Global Fund. While both programmes aim to increase access to ARVs while adhering to World Trade Organization (WTO) rules, each programme has its own regulatory pathways through which nevirapine and other ARVs must travel before they arrive at an HIV treatment programme. The Global Fund requires drugs bought with its grants to have approval from the WHO Prequalification Project, which allows generics to be approved by demonstrating their bioequivalence to the original formulation. In contrast, PEPFAR requires approval by the US FDA. By requiring FDA approval, the US government effectively ties PEPFAR to US trade and IP policy. It allows the US a mechanism to require that drugs bought with PEPFAR money or through the PEPFAR Supply Chain Management System (SCMS) be produced according not only to WTO regulations but also to stricter US rules, such as those in US bilateral and regional free trade agreements (FTAs).

The production and procurement of nevirapine and other ARVs, as is the case for pharmaceuticals in general, is determined in large part by WTO policy, specifically the Agreement on Trade-Related Aspects of Intellectual Property Rights (TRIPS). However, bilateral and regional trade agreements, between the United States and other parties in particular, are also playing an increasingly important role in regulating the production and distribution of pharmaceuticals. TRIPS was intended to bring a degree of standardization to intellectual property laws by stipulating minimal levels of protection to be granted between WTO members – twenty years for both products and processes. Under TRIPS, WTO members were required to introduce the regulations into law within their own countries. The implementation of these regulations, in many cases, has impacted not only prices but also innovation.

For example, India's patent laws before the introduction of TRIPS legislation in 2005 only applied to the process through which a pharmaceutical was manufactured, not to the actual pharmaceutical compound itself. This allowed

India's generics industry to flourish. Generic drugs are generally available at a significantly lower cost than brand-name equivalents, and India has been one of the biggest producers of generic ARVs, in part because it produces many raw materials that are exported to manufacture brand-name pharmaceuticals. The pre-TRIPS regulatory regime in India allowed for the innovation of fixed-dose combinations, such as Duovir-N and Triomune, which contain drugs under patent to a number of different companies. Fixed-dose combinations have since become a valuable tool in the response to HIV. They are often the cheapest formulations available (Martínez-Jones and Anyama, 2002), and because they simplify dosing regimens, they are associated with higher rates of adherence (Connor et al., 2004) and are frequently the regimen of choice in resource-limited settings.

Civil society pressure against TRIPS regulations, led by Oxfam and Médecins Sans Frontières (MSF) in particular, mounted in response to the soaring costs of ARVs in developing countries and the TRIPS ruling against making a generic version of a drug still under patent. However, during the Doha Ministerial Conference held from 9 to 14 November 2001, exceptions were allowed for the protection of public health. Exemptions on introducing pharmaceutical patent protections were extended until 2016 for least developed countries. The agreement also allowed for drugs patented before 1995 to be made generically even if they were still under patent and created a system of compulsory licensing for drugs patented after 1995. While patent holders may grant voluntary licenses to allow other companies to produce a patented drug generically, compulsory licenses could be granted by a government if a patent holder abuses their rights, either by not offering a product on the market or by offering it at an unaffordable price.

Compulsory licensing theoretically provides a tool for governments to help provide lower-cost ARVs; however, compulsory licensing has presented a number of difficulties for the governments concerned. Beyond the bureaucratic difficulty in setting them up, they come with a risk of retribution from companies and countries holding the original patents. This became clear when Thailand announced in January 2007 that it would issue a compulsory license for Kaletra, an antiretroviral drug produced by Abbott Laboratories. At the time the license was issued the per-patient-year cost of Kaletra in Thailand was US$2,200, or 80 per cent of per capita gross domestic product (GDP). Abbott responded that as a result of the compulsory license, it would no longer register new drugs for sale in Thailand. The US Trade Representative placed Thailand on its 'Special 301' Priority Watch List to monitor the adequacy of its intellectual property protections, noting 'further indications of a weakening respect for patents.' In addition, the US pharmaceutical industry, under the guise of 'USA for Innovation,' launched an aggressive public-relations campaign, including advertisements in local newspapers and a website (http://www.thaimyths.com) intended to debunk the government's rationale for issuing the compulsory license.

Throughout the ongoing negotiation and renegotiation of IP regulations since the original TRIPS agreement, the US has consistently pushed for stricter intellectual property rules and has also negotiated stronger protections into numerous bilateral and regional trade agreements as part of a strategy of 'competitive liberalization.' This strategy has been pursued by the United States more aggressively in the wake of the 2001 Doha agreement and development of the G20 bloc of developing countries at the 5th WTO Ministerial Conference in Cancun in 2003. A 2003 letter to David M. Walker, the Comptroller of the United States, from Robert B. Zoellick, the then US Trade Representative and now head of the World Bank, summarizes the US strategy:

> At its most basic level, the competitive liberalization strategy simply means that America expands and strengthens its options. If free trade progress becomes stalled globally – where any one of 148 economies in the WTO has veto power – then we can move ahead regionally and bilaterally. If our hemispheric talks are progressing stage-by-stage, we can point to more ambitious possibilities through FTAs with individual countries and sub-regions. Having a strong bilateral or sub-regional option helps spur progress in the larger negotiations. The recent disappointment in Cancun [at the 5th WTO Ministerial Conference] provides a case in point. A number of the "won't do" countries that frustrated the "can do" spirit of Doha are now rethinking the consequences as the US vigorously advances FTAs around the world. (Zoellick, 2003)

Examples of these additional, stronger protections, often called 'TRIPS-plus provisions,' include extending the life of drug patents, limiting exceptions to patent rules and allowing modifications to an already-patented drug to be granted new patents. Further, the United States has also pushed to handicap the generics industry by including five-year data exclusivity regulations. Data exclusivity protections delay when manufacturers of generic drugs can use the drug originator's data to demonstrate the safety and efficacy of their own drug, potentially delaying the availability of generic formulations on the market or through the WHO prequalification programme (Mayne, 2005). These provisions have raised concern in a number of countries negotiating free trade agreements with the United States, including those involved in the Andean-US regional FTA negotiations (ICTSD, 2005). Nonetheless these provisions are currently included in FTAs the United States has negotiated with Australia, Chile, Jordan, Morocco, Singapore and the six Central American countries participating in the Central American Free Trade Agreement (Chase and Lueck, 2004; OUSTR, 2007).

While the pharmaceutical industry claims it requires protection of this kind to fund research and development (R&D) of new pharmaceutical products, the industry's unwillingness to release financial data has made these claims difficult to verify. Civil society organizations, such as Oxfam and MSF, express skepticism about the need for these regulations, especially as they apply to developing countries. Analysis by the British-government-sponsored Commission on Intellectual Property Rights concluded that IP rights played little role in stimulating R&D for tropical diseases in the developing world (Sands, 2005).

Because PEPFAR regulations require that ARVs be approved by both the US Food and Drug Administration and the national drug regulator, the programme functions as a tool of US trade and intellectual property policy. Effectively, this has meant that only branded formulations or generics manufactured under voluntary licensing agreements with the patent holder are approved. Originally, PEPFAR regulations excluded the purchase of generic formulations with PEPFAR entirely, but this quickly became the source of much criticism. According to the US Government Accountability Office (USGAO, 2005), the net effect of these regulations was that the US was paying significantly higher than market-average prices for ARVs supplied through the PEPFAR programme. As US Representative Henry Waxman of California wrote in a 2003 letter to US President Bush:

> I strongly oppose the efforts to block the use of low-cost generic drugs through the imposition of unnecessary and onerous drug approval standards. … It is no secret that U.S. pharmaceutical companies, which make brand-name drugs, do not want funds to flow to generic drug companies in India. (Ismail, 2006)

In response to this pressure, instead of moving to the WHO prequalification programme, in May 2004, the US FDA set up its own new system to give 'tentative' approval to generic drugs for use in PEPFAR. According to Ambassador Tobias, drugs approved through this process could be bought with PEPFAR money 'where international patent agreements permit them to be purchased' (USHHS, 2004).

The first generic drugs were able to be purchased with PEPFAR money in December of 2004 (OGAC, 2005*b*); however, the purchase of generic 3-in-1 fixed-dose combinations was not possible until July 2006 (McNeil, 2006). Only 10 per cent of PEPFAR-supported ARV purchases were for FDA-approved generics in fiscal year (FY) 2005, and 27 per cent in FY 2006 (OGAC, 2006*b*, 2007*b*). It was only in 2007 that generic drugs made up more than half of the drugs being bought with PEPFAR funds, reaching 73 per cent for FY 2007 (OGAC, 2008). In contrast, the WHO prequalification programme used by the Global Fund included generic fixed-dose combinations in 2002.

The FDA approval requirement was cited as the most significant impediment to the harmonization of PEPFAR with other HIV treatment programmes in developing countries according to the PEPFAR implementation review by the National Institute of Medicine (IOM, 2007). The review recommended the US Global AIDS Coordinator work with other donors to see that the WHO prequalification programme can sufficiently ensure the quality of generic medications and then transition PEPFAR away from the FDA approval requirement to WHO prequalification as quickly as feasible. It remains to be seen if this change will be implemented in the 2008 PEPFAR renewal, however. The version of the PEPFAR renewal being debated in the US House of Representatives (2008) at the time of writing calls only for PEPFAR 'to support efficient and effective drug approval and registration systems that allow expeditious access to safe and effective drugs'. Even if PEPFAR policy changes, the FTAs currently in place between the US and a number of other countries contain data exclusivity and other provisions that could delay the future availability of generic formulations even through the WHO prequalification programme.

The FDA approval requirement for PEPFAR-funded procurements represents one instance where longer-term considerations of economic liberalization are given priority over the short-term results that are usually the focus of an emergency mindset. Were the focus to be on short-term results, regulations that allow the fastest and cheapest procurements of ARVs would be favoured. However, with the launch of PEPFAR the US insisted on FDA approval, effectively blocking the procurement of lower-cost generics and more effective generic fixed-dose combinations. Faced with civil society pressure, instead of harmonizing regulation requirements with the WHO, the FDA set up a new system for 'tentative' approval of generic drugs. This compromise allowed the eventual approval of most relevant generic ARVs but allowed the US to maintain a mechanism that continues to slow the availability of new generic ARVs to PEPFAR programmes but ensures drugs not manufactured according to US trade policy are not bought with PEPFAR money. The subsumption of the emergency frame to economic liberalization in PEPFAR's procurement regulations is all the more compelling considering PEPFAR's use of the same emergency frame to justify its actions elsewhere, in particular its strategies for scaling up treatment programmes, as we will see in the following section.

Funding health infrastructures: Touching down

The final stage of our travels with nevirapine follows it through supply chains and into PMTCT and other HIV treatment programmes in developing countries. As with regulatory regimes, looking at how nevirapine moves through supply chains requires examining the drug along with the other pharmaceutical products and medical commodities that travel with it. The implementation of HIV treatment programmes requires achieving a difficult balance between the short-term scale-up and the long-term sustainability of projects. Comparing the different tactics used by the Global Fund and PEPFAR to fund programme scale-up exposes some significant differences in approach. As we will see, the emergency frame has meant some interventions, particularly those funded by PEPFAR, focus overwhelmingly on short-term goals, underutilizing local capacity and creating parallel systems in ways that may unintentionally weaken local health systems.

While PEPFAR and the Global Fund both provide funds to developing countries to buy ARVs, such as nevirapine, the principles and priorities that guide the pursuit of these goals differ significantly. The Global Fund is focused on financing nationally developed and implemented plans based on performance-based funding. As a result, the Global Fund works almost exclusively through national governments. In Uganda, for example, the Global Fund disburses funds exclusively to the Ministry of Finance, Planning and Economic Development. Critics charge funding can be slow, inconsistent and structured in such a way that developing sustainable health infrastructures with Global Fund money can be exceptionally challenging (Brugha, 2005; Oomman, 2007; WHO, 2007). 'Most of the financial resources that have been mobilized are tied to funding activities such as foreign technical assistance, information and education campaigns, and the provision of in-kind assistance in the form of condoms and antiretroviral drugs' (Poku, 2007, p. 188). In other words, the bulk of donor funding does not build capacity for large-scale, national responses involving, for example, health systems infrastructure and personnel. The WHO Secretariat's consultation on the Global Fund's funding of health system strengthening found that few proposals for health system strengthening were approved across the seven rounds of funding and that the Global Fund needed to do a better job of defining the scope and boundaries of proposals that it agreed to fund (WHO, 2007).

In contrast, PEPFAR's priority is to achieve its programmatic targets, such as the number of people on PEPFAR-funded treatment, and to fulfill its obligations to the US Congress. As a result, longer-term approaches that may be ultimately more sustainable are often de-emphasized in favour of partners and processes that can successfully meet the prevention and treatment goals. This has meant that PEPFAR also grants directly to organizations outside of the recipient country's national government, like the AIDS Support Organization in Uganda, a local NGO. Early on, most primary recipients of PEPFAR funding were US-based NGOs, such as the health care consultancy John Snow International (OGAC, 2005a). While the percentage of local organizations has increased with time (OGAC, 2006a; 2007a), this decentralization of funding distinguishes PEPFAR from many other development agencies, and critics argue that it can result in a lack of harmonization with national efforts, as well as the development of parallel capacities. While governments in target countries are often informed of PEPFAR activities and PEPFAR often works in some capacity with national coordinating committees, governments do not have direct oversight over projects, and the majority of PEPFAR funding is not channelled through government mechanisms in the countries concerned. Additionally, while PEPFAR's programme mandate calls for salaries to be pegged to local rates, this is not always observed, causing a brain drain from local- and state-run organizations. In Uganda specifically, PEPFAR has been criticized for drawing highly skilled doctors and nurses away from the public health system to work with PEPFAR-funded programmes (Oomman et al., 2007). As a result, while PEPFAR has been lauded for rapidly scaling up HIV treatment, it has been criticized for creating a 'parallel and unilateral initiative' with 'new and duplicative bureaucracy' (Africa Action, 2006) and for having minimal engagement with local actors and country-specific needs (Health GAP, 2005).

Speaking about the utilization of local partners and capacity, Agnes Binagwaho, the executive secretary of the Rwanda National AIDS Control Commission, pointed out that in Rwanda, local NGOs received a disproportionately low percentage of PEPFAR funding. Eighty-seven per cent of NGOs in Rwanda are local, but they receive only 30 per cent of the funding for HIV/AIDS under PEPFAR. Speaking at the HIV Implementers Meeting in Kampala, Uganda, she said that international NGOs that do receive the majority of funding often do not address the needs of African countries. Programming carried out by local NGOs, she said, is better attuned to local concerns and is more sustainable; international NGOs, in contrast, frequently implement programmes that are not in line with national development plans. 'We want an evaluation of the capacity of international NGOs to address our national needs' (Baguma, 2008b).

In Zambia, the Center for Global Development (CGD) notes that the PEPFAR programme has successfully increased the number of patients undergoing antiretroviral treatment, from 6,000 in 2003 to 81,000 at the end of 2006, and improved some infrastructure and equipment in public and private health facilities. Additionally, the high standards of PEPFAR programmes are cited as pressuring public systems to increase the quality of services provided. However, simultaneously the PEPFAR programme is criticized by advocacy organizations for circumventing national systems and other initiatives, creating parallel systems and weakening public health systems by drawing already limited health workers to better-funded PEPFAR facilities. CGD recommends that PEPFAR programmes be better integrated and harmonized with the Zambian government systems but notes that this would remove PEPFAR's current control over the management and use of funds, as well as the ability for the gains to be directly attributable to US assistance (Oomman et al., 2007). Notably, the PEPFAR review carried out by the National Institute of Medicine in 2007 makes a similar recommendation, proposing that PEPFAR must move beyond its 'emergency' phase and focus on achieving greater harmonization with local actors and programmes. It remains to be seen if and how these changes are implemented in PEPFAR's renewal. By focusing on short-term targets, PEPFAR has been successful in radically scaling up treatment, but at a cost of sustainability.

The PEPFAR Supply Chain Management System is another example of the distinctive strategy employed by the US to scale up PMTCT and HIV treatment in developing countries. Critics contend it is yet another example of how an emergency frame can produce a focus on short-term targets over longer-term sustainability of interventions. On 27 September 2005, USAID awarded the PEPFAR SCMS contract to a consortium of seventeen organizations, led by Management Sciences for Health and Boston-based consultancy John Snow Incorporated, that includes not-for-profit organizations, such as the International Dispensary Association and Affordable Medicines for Africa, and American defence contractors such as Northrop-Grumman and the Global Government and Defense Sector Division of UPS Supply Chain Solutions. The project is implemented by the USAID Division of Supply Chain Management in the Bureau of Global Health. SCMS is intended to deliver an uninterrupted flow of medicine and supplies to HIV/AIDS programmes. 'The project was created to improve the supply chain to deliver an uninterrupted supply of high-quality, affordable products. The project will focus on better forecasting to determine what drugs are really needed, aggregating demand and negotiating more affordable prices and improving systems for storage, transport and distribution' (SCMS, 2007).

While SCMS documentation repeatedly insists that part of its mission is to strengthen existing supply chains and to establish new ones, according to the Health Global Access Project and the Center for Health and Gender Equity (Health GAP, 2005), the focus of the programme to date has been on meeting its targets for the scale-up of prevention and treatment. As a result the programme has focused on working with partners that have the capacity to meet these targets and often partners who have existing relationships with USAID and are familiar with the required accounting procedures. This has meant that PEPFAR SCMS works largely with NGOs, many of which are based in the United States. SCMS has also been plagued by concerns about its adverse impacts on local supply chains and their sustainability and about the privatization of public sector capacity. The source, origin and nationality regulations imposed on medical commodities to ensure that goods and services financed by USAID 'provide benefit to the US economy' (USAID, n.d.), along with the aforementioned FDA regulations on ARVs, place significant limitations on which commodities can be made available through the SCMS. This creates an additional obstacle for the harmonization of PEPFAR programmes with existing capacity.

SCMS is touted as a 'one-stop shop' open to all PEPFAR, USAID and Global Fund grant recipients. However, indigenous supply chain capacity is composed of public, private and NGO networks and varies from country to country. While the SCMS contract is supposed to rely on and enhance this capacity, critics have been concerned that the focus of the contract is on building a global supply chain management system that creates efficiencies on the PEPFAR level versus a national level. The SCMS Statement of Work does not call for the involvement of local groups in the planning and implementation of the SCMS and instead focuses on the role of the international consortium in creating a new system. SCMS is structured to create operating efficiencies at the PEPFAR level and not at the country level, where it would increase national capacity. As a result, many local drug supply organizations that currently supply PEPFAR-funded programmes are concerned that they will be unable to compete with SCMS, meaning opportunities to enhance local capacities and economies will be usurped by SCMS (Health GAP, 2005). While PEPFAR purports that participation in and utilization of the SCMS by recipient countries is voluntary – 'PEPFAR-funded programmes can select services based on the needs of the country and programme. In countries where existing supply chains are working well, the SCMS project will be available as an option to "fill in the gaps" and monitor key steps in the supply chain process' (SCMS, 2007, p. 3) – these decisions will be made by the US country missions and not the recipients of the funds (Health GAP, 2005).

Further, an overall focus on short-term results can also obscure the role of gender in shaping outcomes of treatment programmes. Women, even despite their disproportionate infection rate, are overrepresented in HIV treatment programmes in Southern Africa (Muula et al., 2007). Men's aversion to seeking care may mean that a disproportionately low percentage of men avail themselves of services offered by these programmes (IRIN, 2005). Interventions should make note of a masculine aversion to care-seeking present in many cultures and design programming that seeks to draw men into care. Gender has a significant effect on the outcome of interventions; neglecting gender effects can skew the efficacy of an intervention in any number of ways. It can mean the devaluing of women's caregiving, which in the calculus of cost-benefit analyses can ultimately mean higher rates of acceptable risk for a mother. It can also mean that men's aversion to seeking care leaves fewer men in treatment programmes.

A successful response must consider that the pandemic is a long-wave event and focus on sustainable interventions. The implementation of PMTCT and HIV treatment programmes through PEPFAR has focused overwhelmingly on short-term scale-up over long-term capacity development and traded less sustainable interventions for immediate action. Interventions underutilize local capacity and end up duplicating capacity, thereby creating parallel systems that unintentionally weaken existing health systems. Interventions need to do a better job of utilizing local capacity and harmonizing their efforts with national development plans. Speaking about the Commission on HIV/AIDS and Governance's recent report *Securing Our Future,* the former prime minister of Mozambique, Pascal Mocumbi, noted that 'Donor assistance should be aligned with national policies so that funding supports country-owned AIDS strategies that are fully integrated within national development strategies' (allAfrica.com, 2008).

Conclusions

The story of the deployment of single-dose nevirapine for the prevention of mother-to-child transmission of HIV reveals both continuity and contestation in the prevailing cultures of response to the global HIV and AIDS pandemic. Repeatedly, over the life course of nevirapine, the use of an emergency frame justifies decisions that prioritize short-term gains over strategies to better equip the response over longer time-frames. At times, the pursuit of these immediate benefits has come at the cost of higher long-term risks to maternal health and the undermining of sustainable health infrastructures in developing countries through the creation of parallel capacities and the draining of resources from local health systems. A focus on short-term results is understandable to a point, however the cultures of response to the global HIV and AIDS pandemic must move out of an emergency mindset and focus instead on responding to the pandemic as the 'long-wave' event it is (Barnett, 2006). This means greater attention to longer-term outcomes is essential and should be prioritized. The response to the pandemic will not be successful if it is not sustainable, if it does not consider not only longer term political and economic factors (as we see some do with economic liberalization) but also social and cultural factors, like gender, which can have an equally profound effect on the outcome of interventions.

References

Africa Action. 2006. *Betraying Africa's Priorities: A Short Analysis of U.S. Policies on HIV/AIDS in Africa.* Washington DC, Africa Action.

allAfrica.com. 2008. Commission on HIV/AIDS and governance in Africa. http://allafrica.com/stories/200806101035.html (Accessed 10 June 2008.)

Arrive, E., Newell, M. L., Ekouevi, D. et al. 2007. Prevalence of resistance to nevirapine in mothers and children after single-dose exposure to prevent vertical transmission of HIV-1: A meta-analysis. *International Journal of Epidemiology,* Vol. 36, pp. 1009–021.

Baguma, R. 2008*a*. Donors could buy ARVs from country. *New Vision* (Kampala, Uganda), 6 June. http://allafrica.com/stories/200806090325.html (Accessed 9 June 2008.)

——. 2008*b*. Local NGOs want increased funding. *New Vision* (Kampala, Uganda), 8 June. http://allafrica.com/stories/200806090509.html (Accessed 9 June 2008.)

Barnett, T. 2006. A long-wave event. HIV/AIDS, politics, governance and 'security': sundering the intergenerational bond? *International Affairs,* Vol. 28, No. 2, pp. 297–314.

Bass, E. 2005. The two sides of PEPFAR in Uganda. *Lancet,* Vol. 365, No. 9477, pp. 2077–078.

Brink, A. 2005. The trouble with Nevirapine. http://www.virusmyth.net/aids/data/abnvp.htm (Accessed 4 December 2007.)

——. 2007. *The Trouble with Nevirapine.* Cape Town, Open Books.

Brugha, R., Donoghue, M., Starling, M. et al. 2005. The Global Fund: Managing great expectations. *Lancet,* Vol. 364, No. 3, pp. 95–100.

Calhoun, C. 2006. The emergency imaginary: Humanitarianism, states, and the limits of cosmopolitanism. Inaugural lecture, university professorship. New York University, 15 November.

Chase, M. and Lueck, S. 2004. In new trade pacts, U.S. seeks to limit reach of generic drugs. *Wall Street Journal.* 6 July, A1.

Connor, E. M., Sperling, R. S., Gelber, R. et al. 1994. Reduction of maternal-infant transmission of human immunodeficiency virus type I with zidovudine treatment. *New England Journal of Medicine,* Vol. 331, pp. 1173–180.

Connor, J., Rafter, N. and Rodgers, A. 2004. Do fixed-dose combination pills or unit-of-dose packaging improve adherence? A systematic review. *Bulletin of the World Health Organziation,* Vol. 82, pp. 935–39.

Coovadia A., Marais, B., Abrams, E. et al. 2006. Virologic responses to NNRTI treatment among women who took single-dose nevirapine 18 to 36 months earlier. Presented at the 13th Conference on Retroviruses and Opportunistic Infections, Denver, Colo.

Cunningham C. K., Chaix, M. L., Rekacewicz, C. et al. 2002. Development of resistance mutations in women receiving standard antiretroviral therapy who received intrapartum nevirapine to prevent perinatal human immunodeficiency virus type 1 transmission: A substudy of pediatric AIDS clinical trials group protocol 316. *Journal of Infectious Disease*, Vol. 186, pp.181–88.

De Cock, K. et al. 2000. Prevention of mother-to-child HIV transmission in resource-poor countries. *Journal of the American Medical Association*, Vol. 283, pp. 1175-182.

EPN (Ecumenical Pharmaceutical Network). 2006. A statement of the ecumenical pharmaceutical network (EPN) on the US President's Emergency Plan for AIDS Relief (PEPFAR) supply chain management system. Tuebingen, Germany, May.

Eshleman, S. H., Mracna, M., Guay, L. A. et al. 2001*a*. Selection and fading of resistance mutations in women and infants receiving nevirapine to prevent HIV-1 vertical transmission (HIVNET-012). *AIDS*, Vol. 15, pp. 1951–957.

Eshleman, S. H., Becker-Pergola, G., Deseyve, M. et al. 2001*b*. Impact of human immunodeficiency virus type 1 (hiv-1) subtype on women receiving single-dose nevirapine prophylaxis to prevent hiv-1 vertical transmission (hiv network for prevention trials 012 study). *Journal of Infectious Disease*, Vol. 184, No. 7, pp. 914–17.

Eshleman, S. H., Guay, L. A., Mwatha, A. et al. 2004. Comparison of nevirapine (NVP) resistance in Ugandan women 7 days vs. 6–8 weeks after single-dose nvp prophylaxis: HIVNET 012. *AIDS Research and Human Retroviruses*, Vol. 20, No. 6, pp. 595–99.

Eshleman, S. H., Hoover, D. R., Chen, S. et al. 2005. Resistance after single-dose nevirapine prophylaxis emerges in a high proportion of Malawian newborns. *AIDS*, Vol. 19, No. 18, pp. 2167–169.

Eure, C., Bakaki, P., McConnell, M. et al. 2006. Effectiveness of repeat single-dose nevirapinein subsequent pregnancies among Ugandan women. Presented at the 13th Conference on Retroviruses and Opportunistic Infections, Denver, Colo.

Farber, C. 2006. Out of control: AIDS and the corruption of medical science. *Harper's Magazine*, March.

Garnett, C. 2000. Infection rates rising in women: HIV/AIDS epidemic 'still advancing,' panel warns. *NIH Record*, Vol. 52, No. 7.

Guay, L. A., Musoke, P., Fleming, T. et al. 1999. Intrapartum and neonatal single-dose nevirapine compared with zidovudine for prevention of mother to child transmission of HIV-1 in Kampala, Uganda: HIV-1NET 012 randomised trial. *Lancet*, Vol. 354, pp. 795–802.

Havlir, D., McLaughlin, M. and Richman, D. 1996. Viral dynamics of HIV: Implications for drug development and therapeutic strategies. *Annals of Intern Medicine,* Vol. 124, p. 984–94.

Health GAP (Global Access Project). 2005. *Analysis of the U.S. Global AIDS Program and the PEPFAR Supply Chain Management System (SCMS).* New York, Center for Health and Gender Equity/Health GAP. (Briefing Series: SCMS.)

Hirsch, M. et al. 2003. Antiretroviral drug resistance testing in adults infected with Human Immunodeficiency Virus Type 1: 2003 Recommendations of an International AIDS Society–USA Panel. *Clinical Infectious Diseases,* Vol. 37, pp. 113–28.

ICTSD (International Centre for Trade and Sustainable Development). 2005. AG, IP hobble Andean-US free trade talks. *Bridges Weekly Trade News Digest,* Vol. 9, No. 41.

IOM (Institute of Medicine). 2005. *Review of the HIVNET 012 Perinatal HIV Prevention Study.* Washington DC, National Academies Press.

IOM (Institute of Medicine) (Committee for the Evaluation of the President's Emergency Plan for AIDS Relief). 2007. *PEPFAR Implementation: Progress and Promise.* Washington DC, National Academies Press.

IRIN (Integrated Regional Information Networks). 2005. South Africa: Men falling through the cracks. *PLUSNEWS* (Johannesburg) 25 July. http://www.aegis.com/news/irin/2005/IR050766.html (Accessed 6 March 2006.)

Ismail, M. A. 2006. *PEPFAR Policy Hinders Treatment in Generic Terms: Critics say FDA Approval Rule Has Meant Greater Use of High-Cost Drugs at Expense of Helping Fewer Patients.* Washington DC, Center for Public Integrity. http://www.publicintegrity.org/aids/report.aspx?aid=836 (Accessed 15 September 2007.)

Jackson, J. B., Becker-Pergola, G., Guay, L. A., et al. 2000. Identification of the K103N resistance mutation in Ugandan women receiving nevirapine to prevent HIV-1 vertical transmission. *AIDS,* Vol. 14, pp. F111–115.

Johnson, V. A., Brun-Vézinet, F., Clotet, B. et al. 2005. Update of the drug resistance mutations in HIV-1: Fall 2005. *Topics in HIV Medicine,* Vol. 13, pp. 125–31.

Jourdain, G., Ngo-Giang-Huong, N., Le Coeur, S. et al. 2004. Intrapartum exposure to nevirapine and subsequent maternal responses to nevirapine-based antiretroviral therapy. *New England Journal of Medicine,* Vol. 351, pp. 229–40.

Kovacs, A. 2000. Risk of resistance with single-dose nevirapine? *Medscape HIV/AIDS,* Vol. 6, No. 1. http://www.medscape.com/viewarticle/413345 (Accessed 1 December 2007.)

Lockman, S., Shapiro, R. L., Smeaton, L. M. et al. 2007. Response to antiretroviral therapy after a single, peripartum dose of nevirapine. *New England Journal of Medicine*, Vol. 356, No. 2, pp. 135–47.

Martínez-Jones, A. and Anyama, N. 2002. Access to antiretroviral therapy in Uganda. Kampala, Uganda, Oxfam GB.

Martinson, N., Ekouevi, D., Gray, G. et al. 2006. Effectiveness of single-dose nevirapine in consecutive pregnancies in Soweto and Abidjan. Presented at the 13th Conference on Retroviruses and Opportunistic Infections, Denver, Colo.

Mayne, R. 2005. Regionalism, bilateralism, and 'TRIP Plus' agreements: The threat to developing countries. Occasional paper, Human Development Report Office, United Nations Department of Peacekeeping.

McConnell, M., Stringer, J., Kourtis, A. et al. 2007. Use of single-dose nevirapine for the prevention of mother-to-child transmission of HIV-1: Does development of resistance matter? *American Journal of Obstetrics and Gynecology*, Vol. 197, No. 3, pp. S56–S63.

McNeil, G. 2006. F.D.A. approves new AIDS pill to treat people in poor countries. *New York Times Online*, 6 July. http://query.nytimes.com/gst/fullpage.html?sec=health &res=9D04E4DD1330F935A35754C0A9609C8B63 (Accessed 6 July 2006.)

Molotch, H. 2003. *Where Stuff Comes From*. New York, Routledge.

Moodley, D. on behalf of the SAINT Investigators Team. 2000. The SAINT trial: Nevirapine (NVP) versus zidovudine (ZVD) + lamivudine (3TC) in prevention of peripartum HIV transmission. Abstract LbOr2, 13th International AIDS Conference, Durban, South Africa, 9–14 July.

Moodley, D., Moodley, J., Coovadia, H. et al. 2003. A multicenter randomized controlled trial of nevirapine versus a combination of zidovudine and lamivudine to reduce intrapartum and early postpartum mother-to-child transmission of human immunodeficiency virus type 1. *Journal of Infectious Diseases,* Vol. 187, pp. 725–35.

Musoke, P., Guay, L. A., Bagenda, D. et al. 1999. A phase I/II study of the safety and pharmacokinetics of nevirapine in HIV-1-infected pregnant Ugandan women and their neonates (HIVNET 006). *AIDS*, Vol. 13, No. 4, pp. 479–86.

Muula, A., Ngulube, T., Siziya, S. et al. 2007. Gender distribution of adult patients on highly active antiretroviral therapy (HAART) in Southern Africa: A systematic review. *BMC Public Health,* Vol. 7, No. 63.

National Academy of Sciences. 2007. *PEPFAR Implementation: Progress and Promise.* Washington DC, National Academies Press.

OGAC (Office of the Global AIDS Coordinator). 2005a. *Fiscal Year 2005 Operational Plan.* Washington, DC, OGAC.

——. 2005b. *South African Generic Drug Eligible for Use in Emergency Plan.* Washington, DC, OGAC.

——. 2006a. *Emergency Plan for AIDS Relief – Fiscal Year 2006 Operational Plan.* Washington, DC, OGAC.

——. 2006b. *Action Today, A Foundation for Tomorrow: The President's Emergency Plan for AIDS Relief, Second Annual Report to Congress.* Washington, DC, OGAC.

——. 2007a. *Emergency Plan for AIDS Relief – Fiscal Year 2007 Operational Plan.* Washington, DC, OGAC.

——. 2007b. *The Power of Partnerships: Third Annual Report to Congress on PEPFAR.* Washington, DC, OGAC.

——. 2008. *The Power of Partnerships: Fourth Annual Report to Congress on PEPFAR.* Washington, DC, OGAC.

Oomman, N., Bernstein, M. and Rosenzweig, S. 2007. *Following the Funding for HIV/ AIDS: A Comparative Analysis of the Funding Practices of PEPFAR, the Global Fund and World Bank MAP in Mozambique, Uganda and Zambia.* Washington DC, Center for Global Development.

Orloff, A. S. 2001. Ending the entitlements of poor single mothers: Changing social policies, women's employment, and caregiving in the contemporary United States. N. J. Hirschmann and U. Liebert (eds), *Women and Welfare: Theory and Practice in the United States and Europe.* New Brunswick, NJ, Rutgers University Press, pp. 133–59.

——. 2002. *Women's Employment and Welfare Regimes: Globalization, Export Orientation and Social Policy in Europe and North America.* Geneva, United Nations Research Institute for Social Development. (Social Policy and Development Programme Paper Series, Paper Number 12.)

OUSTR (Office of the US Trade Representative). 2007. Bilateral Free Trade Agreements. http://www.ustr.gov/Trade_Agreements/Bilateral/Section_Index.html (Accessed 1 December 2007.)

Poku, N. 2007. A Case for Improving the Quality and Quantity of AIDS Financing. N. Poku et al. (eds), *AIDS and Governance.* Hampshire, United Kingdom, Ashgate.

Ready, T. 2005. WHO to Take on Nevirapine Resistance. Coverage of the 12th Conference on Retroviruses and Opportunistic Infections. *Medscape Medical News.* http://www.medscape.com/viewarticle/500316 (Accessed 4 December 2007.)

Rosenfield, A. and Maine, D. 1985. Maternal mortality – a neglected tragedy. Where is the M in MCH? *Lancet,* Vol. 2, pp. 83–85.

SAMOH (South African Ministry of Heath). 2004a. Resistance to nevirapine, 28 June. http://www.doh.gov.za/docs/news/2004/nz0628.html (Accessed 1 December 2007.)

——. 2004b. Speech by the Minister of Health at the opening of the South African HIV and AIDS stand at the Bangkok Conference, Thailand, 11 July. http://www.doh. gov.za/docs/sp/2004/sp0711.html (Accessed 1 December 2007.)

——. 2004c. Medicines Control Council changes its mind on nevirapine, 12 July. http://www.doh.gov.za/docs/news/2004/nz0712a.html (Accessed 1 December 2007.)

Sands, P. 2005. *Lawless World, America and the Making and Breaking of Global Rules.* London, Allen Lane/Penguin Books.

SCMS (Supply Chain Management System). 2007. *SCMS FAQ.* http://scms.pfscm.org/scms/about/faq (Accessed 1 April 2007.)

Stent, A. 2004. Single dose Nevirapine to stay. *Cape Argus,* 16 July. http://www.capeargus.co.za/index.php?fArticleId=2152734 (Accessed 1 December 2007.)

Sullivan, J. 2002. South African intrapartum nevirapine trial: Selection of resistance mutations. 16th International Conference on AIDS, Barcelona, Spain, 7–12 July. (Abstract no. LbPeB9024.)

Timberg, C. 2004. Long-sought HIV drug saving thousands of S. African babies. *Washington Post,* 9 June, A14.

UNAIDS (Joint United Nations Programme on HIV/AIDS). 2005. *AIDS in Africa: Three Scenarios to 2025.* Geneva, UNAIDS.

——. 2007. *Financial Resources Required to Achieve Universal Access to HIV Prevention, Treatment, Care and Support.* Geneva, UNAIDS.

UNAIDS, UNICEF and Elizabeth Glaser Pediatric AIDS Foundation. 2004. UNAIDS, UNICEF and EGPAF underscore importance of keeping single-dose nevirapine available to HIV-positive mothers. Press release, Bangkok, Thailand, 14 July.

USAID (US Agency for International Development). n.d. *USAID Policy Automated Directives System Series Chapter 310: Source, Origin and Nationality.* http://www.usaid.gov/policy/ads/300/310.pdf (Accessed 15 September 2007.)

USGAO (US Government Accountability Office). 2005. *Selection of Antiretroviral Medications Provided under U.S. Emergency Plan Is Limited.* Washington DC, January. (GAO-05-133.)

USHHS (US Dept of Health and Human Services). 2004. HHS proposes rapid process for review of fixed dose combination and co-packaged products. *HHS News Release,* 16 May.

US House of Representatives. 2008. *H.R. 5501.* A bill to authorize appropriations for fiscal years 2009 through 2013 to provide assistance to foreign countries to combat HIV/AIDS, tuberculosis, and malaria, and for other purposes. 110th Congress, 2nd Session.

WHO (World Health Organization). 2000. Use of nevirapine to reduce mother-to-child transmission of HIV (MTCT). *WHO Review of Reported Drug Resistance.* Geneva, WHO.

——. 2001. *Prevention of Mother-to-Child Transmission of HIV: Selection and Use of Nevirapine: Technical Notes.* Geneva, WHO.

——. 2004. WHO publishes new guidelines on preventing mother to child transmission of HIV. News release. http://www.who.int/mediacentre/news/releases/2004/pr50/en/ (Accessed 15 September 2007.)

——. 2006a. *Progress on Global Access to HIV Antiretroviral Therapy.* Geneva, WHO.

——. 2006b. *Antiretroviral Drugs for Treating Pregnant Women and Preventing HIV Infection in Infants: Towards Universal Access. Recommendations for a Public Health Approach.* Geneva, WHO.

——. 2007. *The Global Fund's Strategic Approach to Health System Strengthening – Background Note 4 for July 30–31 2007 Consultation.* Geneva, WHO.

Wood, R. on behalf of the 1090 Study Team. 2000. Sustained efficacy of nevirapine (NVP) in combination with two nucleosides in advanced, treatment – naïve HIV infected patients with high viral loads: A BI 1090 substudy. International Conference on AIDS, 2000, 9–14 July. (Abstract no. WeOrB604.)

Zijenah L, Kadzirange G, Rusakaniko S. et al. 2006. Community-based generic ART following single-dose nevirapine or short-course zidovudine in Zimbabwe. Presented at the 13th Conference on Retroviruses and Opportunistic Infections, Denver, Colo.

Zoellick, R. 2003. Appendix V: Letter from Robert B. Zoellick to David M. Walker. US Government Accountability Office, *International Trade: Intensifying Free Trade Negotiating Agenda Calls for Better Allocation of Staff and Resources.* http://www.gao.gov/htext/d04233.html (Accessed 1 December 2007.)

CHAPTER 9

Horizontal approaches: Social protection and the response to HIV in Brazil

Inês Dourado, Vera Paiva and Francisco Inácio Bastos

Introduction

Federal response to HIV and AIDS in Brazil was initiated in 1986 by the Ministry of Health in partnership with state and municipal health authorities and civil society, although other relevant initiatives had been implemented earlier at the state level, specifically in São Paulo State since 1983 (Galvao, 2002; Nunn, 2009). Different authors have pointed to the specific historical context that permitted the establishment and evolution of the concerted set of initiatives that make up the response (Bastos et al., 2006; Galvão, 2002; Teixeira, 2004). Alan Berkman et al. (2005, p. 1162) have noted that while the Brazilian programme is not necessarily a model that can be implemented by other nations due to the substantial differences between HIV epidemics in specific contexts and the deeply heterogeneous structure of health systems worldwide, examining this experience 'may be helpful to those grappling with their national realities'. The need to tailor responses to the dynamics of local epidemics and the structure of national health systems has been recently reviewed by Beck and Mays (2006).

A vigorous democratization process took place in Brazil in the early 1980s, after twenty years of military dictatorship. The process involved a number of highly committed activists, who helped to build a new social agenda, particularly in the areas of culture, health and education, which had been deeply affected under the old regime by censorship and the loss of a substantial number of highly qualified citizens to other countries.

The designations employed and the presentation of material throughout this publication do not imply the expression of any opinion whatsoever on the part of UNESCO concerning the legal status of any country, territory or area or of its authorities, or concerning the delimitation of its frontiers or boundaries.
The ideas and opinions expressed in this publication are those of the authors and do not necessarily reflect the views of UNESCO and its Member States.

Access to the public health system was established as a universal right of citizens and a responsibility of the state under the New Federal Constitution, which was adopted in 1988. The Unified Health System, known as the SUS (*Sistema Único de Saúde*), was built with the participation of health experts and members of the health reform movement and was conceived as a regionalized and decentralized network of health services with community and civil society participation, offering health care free at the point of delivery to the entire Brazilian population (Elias and Cohn, 2003). The core principles of the SUS – integrality (integrated prevention, treatment and care), equity, public accountability and funding – emerged out of a long period of advocacy for governmental responsibility for health promotion and have meant that the system is particularly appropriate for the comprehensive management of the HIV epidemic.

Berkman et al. (2005) claim that in Brazil, the response to the HIV/AIDS pandemic arose from initiatives in both civil society and the government and followed the process of democratization, which was a context with a strong orientation towards human rights. The response to the epidemic in Brazil was therefore implemented by a successful coalition between different levels of the government and civil society. Close cooperation with international leaders and institutions has added a third layer to the 'Brazilian model', which responds to the pressing need to integrate prevention, care and treatment to ensure the successful response that has been lauded worldwide.

The HIV epidemic has leveled out in Brazil in recent years, with stable incidence in the last five years and declining morbidity and mortality (Fonseca and Bastos, 2007). However, as has been discussed in detail by authors who analysed the epidemic dynamics over time and interpreted serial cross-sectional data (Ades, 1995), this stability may actually mask underlying changes, in terms both of the epidemic itself and of the broad sociodemographic dynamic. A stable epidemic should therefore not be understood as a frozen situation but rather as a stable sum of heterogeneous components that include harmonizing or conflicting trends. Such components must be assessed in detail before any definitive conclusion is drawn. The geographical dynamic described below and the changes in terms of the different populations affected by the epidemic in specific periods of time indicate an epidemic that is becoming endemic, like malaria and other tropical diseases, but remains dynamic. AIDS in Brazil is perhaps analogous to malaria in the Amazon: outbreaks of malaria have occurred in the Amazon region for decades but have affected different populations – in terms of age, gender, occupation, housing and micro-location – at different periods of time (Barbieri and Sawyer, 2007).

This chapter discusses the challenges faced by the response to the epidemic in Brazil, which is marked by social inequalities and the trends of 'heterosexualization', 'pauperization' and 'interiorization'. Since the mid-1990s, the epidemic has increasingly affected heterosexuals, who now comprise the largest subcategory within the broader category of those infected through sexual exposure. This trend is known as the 'heterosexualization' of the epidemic. HIV prevalence has also rapidly increased among women (the 'feminization' of the epidemic), which has required approaches that challenge gendered inequalities and link sexually transmitted infection (STI)/AIDS programmes with reproductive health programmes. The 'pauperization' (or impoverishment) and the 'interiorization' of the epidemic have also been observed (Fonseca et al., 2002, 2003). Pauperization refers to the increasing impact of the epidemic on the poor. It has typically been measured by taking education and occupation as proxies of socio-economic status. Interiorization refers to the spread of the epidemic to the 'interior' of the country, away from the vast majority of large cities, which are located in or near the coastal line.

Brazilian legislation on the funding and management of different health programmes, and specifically the response to HIV, has changed in parallel with the dynamic of the epidemic. Brazilian National AIDS Programme (NAP) initiatives are managed by a relatively sophisticated management structure and a cadre of highly qualified professionals. This contrasts, for instance, with the initiatives linked to the prevention, management and care of viral hepatitis B and C. Compared to the HIV programme, most other major Brazilian public health programmes are clearly underfunded and understaffed. However, this privileged situation will not last forever, not only because AIDS will become akin to a 'chronic' medical condition and the epidemic will be progressively 'endemicized', but also because of the progressive decentralization of the prevention, management and care initiatives for people living with HIV (PLHIV) in the context of the SUS.

In the context of the changing dynamics of the epidemic, a human rights framework has been critical in analyzing vulnerability to HIV at the individual, social and programmatic levels and in guiding the evaluation of services. A human rights framework has also been important for examining issues of gender, power inequalities, sexism, homophobia, racism and poverty, issues that are all reflected in the epidemic. In particular, the issues faced by children serve as a paradigm of the psychosocial and comprehensive care challenges involved in addressing HIV, stigma, discrimination and adherence.

A brief description of HIV epidemiology in Brazil

Brazil has approximately 192 million inhabitants in a territory of 8.5 million square kilometres. It is the world's fifth most populous country and the largest in Latin America. Brazil is the Latin American country most affected by the HIV epidemic in absolute numbers: it is estimated that 1.7 million people live with HIV in the region, and about 40 per cent of them are in Brazil. However, smaller countries, such as Guatemala, Honduras and Belize, have much higher HIV prevalences (UNAIDS, 2008). As of 30 June 2007, 474,273 AIDS cases have been reported in Brazil, with an incidence rate of 17.5 cases per 100,000 inhabitants in 2006 (Brazil, 2007*a*). National estimates of the number of people living with HIV range around 600,000 for the years 1998 (Szwarcwald and Castilho, 2000), 2000 (Szwarcwald and de Carvalho, 2001) and 2002 (Souza Jr et al., 2004).

AIDS cases have been reported in all twenty-six Brazilian states but are more prevalent in the south-east and the south (63 per cent and 18 per cent of all cases, respectively). Approximately 70 per cent of accumulated AIDS cases reported in Brazil until 2008 are related to sexual contact and 32.9 per cent of them have been reported among men having unprotected sex with men. This group accounted for the majority of cases in the first years of the epidemic. Transmission then increased among injecting drug users and, over the years, among people who acquired HIV through unprotected heterosexual intercourse.

Furthermore, the ratio of men to women infected has decreased from 18.9:1 in 1984 to 1.5:1 in 2005, a trend known as the 'feminization' of the epidemic (Brazil, 2007*a*). HIV prevalence has been higher among girls aged 13–19 years than boys of the same age since 1998, with ten HIV-positive girls for every six HIV-positive boys in 2005. The ongoing processes of heterosexualization and feminization seem to be closely linked to the prevailing machismo and the deep social and gender inequalities that compromise the capacity of women to make sexual and reproductive choices free of overt and powerful constraints. They are also linked to decades of prevention activities that targeted so-called vulnerable populations (gay men and injecting drug users) and the saturation (i.e. the slow spread or even a halt in the spread of HIV in a relatively small population after a large proportion of the susceptible individuals in that population have been infected) experienced by some of these populations, such as injecting drug users, in recent years (Bastos et al., 2005).

Less-educated and socio-economically underserved individuals tend to start sexual activities earlier, have a greater number of casual sexual partners and use condoms less, all of which are factors associated with greater vulnerability to HIV (Fonseca et al., 2007). The underlying reasons for these behaviours seem to be related to the deep gender and social inequality among less-educated and poorer people and to the 'compressed' life trajectory of those living in dire poverty. (The compressed life trajectory refers to the fact that life expectancy in Brazil can vary from over 70 years among affluent white women to less than 30 years for black men living in *favelas* [slums] in Rio de Janeiro [Waiselfisz, 2008].)

The process of 'interiorization' was described for the first time in the context of Brazil in two papers by Bastos and Barcellos (1995) and Barcellos and Bastos (1996). These papers assessed the spread of HIV in Brazil by following patterns of diffusion through both 'hierarchical jumps' over key commuting areas and 'spatial contagion' across neighbouring areas, as defined by the geographer Peter Gould (1993). Interiorization in Brazil combines the complicated effects of long-distance transportation by trucks, aerial transportation, circular movements between small municipalities and metropolitan areas, the opening up of new areas for farming and mining, and last but not least, the movement of people facing stigma (such as male transvestites) from small, traditional communities towards more tolerant environments in large cities (Kulick, 2008).

A national sentinel surveillance study in 2004 estimated a prevalence of 0.61 per cent among pregnant women who were between 15 and 49 years old. The rate of mother-to-child transmission has fallen in recent years, from 16 per cent in 1997 (Tess et al., 1998) to 7 per cent in 2001 (Menezes Succi, 2007). However, in poorer areas of the country, such as the north-east, the rate remained as high as 11 per cent due to a combination of different factors, including: uneven prenatal care by women facing a multitude of problems (such as unstable housing, high rates of unemployment and/or informal employment, expensive and scarce transportation from distant neighborhoods); excessive medical case loads managed by underpaid and unmotivated staff; and, last but not least, prejudice and discrimination against poor and marginalized people.

To the best of our knowledge, the effects of prejudice and discrimination in the specific context of prenatal and maternal care for women living with HIV have not been documented. However, discrimination against black women (compared to white women), women living in underserved neighborhoods (compared to those living in neighborhoods with basic infrastructure, such as regular garbage collection), single mothers (compared to those living in stable unions) and young mothers (those under 17 years old) has been demonstrated in maternity wards in hospitals in Rio de Janeiro, forcing vulnerable women to move from one facility to the next, sometimes visiting three different facilities before finding a place to deliver (Menezes et al., 2006).

In 2002, the Sentinel-Parturient study (Souza Jr et al., 2004) assessed a representative sample of pregnant women all over the country and showed rates of effective and timely detection of HIV infection during pregnancy of about 52 per cent for the country as a whole. Again, sociogeographic inequalities become obvious when comparing the country's north-eastern and southern regions, with significantly higher levels of detection of HIV infection in southern health facilities (71 per cent) compared to facilities located in the northeast (24 per cent). Similar patterns of inequality have been observed at the individual level: illiterate mothers were less likely to be tested for HIV (19 per cent) compared to those with eight or more years of education (64 per cent), whereas women who gave birth in small cities were half as likely to be tested as women who delivered in cities with over 500,000 inhabitants (37 per cent versus 66 per cent). In the country as a whole, 63 per cent of pregnant women knew their HIV status before giving birth, compared to only 31 per cent in the northeast (Souza Jr et al, 2004). Despite the clear trend towards a decrease in the number of AIDS pediatrics cases, there are significant delays in monitoring infection among those infants exposed to infected mothers, which may mask actual numbers.

Brazil was ranked sixty-ninth in the world according to the 2004 UNDP *Human Development Report* (UNDP, 2004). The poorest one-fifth of Brazil's 182 million people account for only a 2.2 per cent share of national income. Brazil is second only to South Africa in the global ranking of income inequality. More than one-quarter of the population lives on less than US$2 a day and 13 per cent lives on less than US$1 a day. The single largest concentration of rural poverty in Latin America is located in the north-east of Brazil (Brazil, 2007b). Thus, despite a relatively solid and diversified economy, social and economic inequality condemn a large proportion of Brazil's population to living conditions comparable to those prevailing in much poorer countries, such as those in sub-Saharan Africa (Rocha, 2007).

A temporal analysis of HIV incidence and mortality rates by gender shows different and somewhat conflicting trends in recent years. Incidence rates among men have slowed since 1999, with a slight growth in 2002, whereas they increased by 46 per cent among women between 1995 and 2005. Mortality rates among men decreased from 15.1 per 100,000 inhabitants in 1995 to around 8.8 per 100,000 in 2005. Among women, mortality rates have remained stable at around 4.0 per 100,000, with a highest rate of 4.8 per 100,000 in 1996 (Brazil, 2007a).

There are still people living with HIV who gain access to health services late and therefore have limited chances of benefiting from adequate therapy. A study by Brito et al. (2005) carried out in a north-eastern state showed that about half of people treated with highly active antiretroviral therapy (HAART) only learned their HIV status when they were hospitalized due to AIDS-related illness. In addition, those who did not know their HIV status were 50 per cent more likely to present AIDS-related symptoms at their first visit to a specialized HIV service than those who did.

A recent retrospective cohort study of patients treated at a reference centre in São Paulo between 1998 and 2002, which aimed to improve understanding of AIDS mortality, found that women began treatment in better clinical and laboratorial conditions than men but that female mortality was higher than male mortality over time. Multivariate analysis indicated that being a woman was a predictor of a shorter survival time and that women had a mortality risk 86 per cent higher than men, even when they had access to the same treatment. The authors discuss the hypothesis that contextual factors highlighted in research about HIV prevention – such as lower levels of education and information as well as the burden of care for partners and children – are usually underestimated by providers of services delivering care to women living with HIV (Braga et al., 2007).

However, these dramatic findings differ from most published studies on women and men living with HIV and receiving follow-up treatment at referral centers and major health units, as recently reviewed by Hacker et al. (2007). This suggests that the relationship between gender-based inequalities and other dimensions of social and economic inequality is complex and context-specific and highly affected by the nature of the patient-provider relationship and the heterogeneous infrastructure and staffing of the vast network of entities that dispense antiretroviral (ARV) drugs in Brazil (Nemes et al., 2004). Gender-based prejudice and stigmatization have been documented in Brazilian research about the management of different sexually transmitted infections (Giffin and Lowndes, 1999; Malta et al., 2007) and must be actively prevented and discouraged in the provision of all types of health care.

Some studies (Brito et al., 2005; Teixeira et al., 2004) have suggested that HIV incidence in Brazil is stabilizing. This process began in 1997 with the introduction of universal access to antiretroviral therapy (ART), perhaps because of the reduced infectivity of those under treatment (Porco et al., 2004) and the targeting of prevention strategies towards the most vulnerable populations. However, the stabilization of the epidemic has not been consistent throughout

Brazil. Dourado et al. (2006) have demonstrated that stabilization is mostly occurring in São Paulo (in the south-east), whereas rates are still increasing in the north-east and the north.

A brief overview of the management, care and prevention of HIV and AIDS in Brazil

Brazil was one of the first developing countries to ensure universal free access to highly active antiretroviral therapy through accredited public health units that are part of the SUS. This provision began in 1996, but people living with HIV had received treatment for opportunistic infections before this date and in 1991 started to receive AZT (the first antiretroviral medicine) through the public health system (Teixeira et al., 2004). An estimated 180,000 people are covered by the HAART programme, including all people living with HIV who are eligible for drug therapy, people who are at risk of HIV exposure due to their occupation and the newborn children of HIV-positive mothers. The National AIDS Programme expects to increase the number of people reached to 200,000 by the end of 2008.

A network of free public facilities for diagnosis, prevention, treatment and follow-up has been established, which includes anonymous testing sites, primary health care units, hospitals, day-care hospitals, home care and lymphocyte phenotyping, viral load and genotyping laboratories. People living with HIV with access to these public health services are entitled to receive, free of charge at the point of delivery, up to seventeen ARV drugs, eight of them locally produced, as well as drugs to treat and/or prevent comorbidity, such as with opportunistic infections (Greco and Simão, 2007).

A major strategy of the ARV access programme created by the NAP was the establishment of consensus recommendations about antiretroviral therapy, which are periodically updated by consulting committees. Universal access to ART is guaranteed by Federal Law 9.313, which was issued in 1996 (Brazil, 1996). The health care programme for PLHIV also includes other initiatives that aim to reduce hospital admissions by providing specialized outpatient care, day-care hospitals and home care.

All of these strategies aiming to halt the epidemic and to offer proper management and care for PLHIV benefit from the commitment of federal and state authorities, as well as from the active participation of civil society and the increasing involvement of local authorities. The NAP is therefore increasingly recognized as a successful example of an effective response to the HIV epidemic. But is this policy sustainable? A good discussion of this topic is presented by Grangeiro at al. (2006) and has recently been addressed in detail by Nunn et al. (2007). We will return to this subject in greater detail below.

In terms of prevention, national campaigns to promote condom use have debated the issue openly in the media. The proportion of Brazilians who agree with access to condoms for adolescents through health services (95 per cent) and at school (83.6 per cent) is high, with no differences between religious groups. Condom use during first sexual intercourse has increased significantly in both stable relationships (48.5 per cent in 1998 compared to 67.7 per cent in 2005) and casual relationships (47.2 per cent in 1998 versus 62.6 per cent in 2005) in almost all sections of the population (Paiva et al., 2006).

There has been a large increase in the number of condoms (primarily male condoms, plus a small number of female condoms) distributed by the government at various levels to different populations and communities. Data on condom sales have shown a substantial increase since 1990, with 87.2 million condoms sold in 1995, 170.8 million in 2000 and an estimate of 420 million in 2003 (Szwarcwald et al., 2004). More recently, serious efforts have been made to render Brazil self-sufficient in terms of condom provision. The recent opening of a pure rubber condom factory in the State of Acre (located in the Amazon rainforest) may represent a breakthrough initiative since it combines the sustainable development of an ecologically endangered area with increases in the dignity and employability of local communities of rubber workers and substantial decreases in the costs associated with condom importation (Duffy and Ferreira, 2008).

Numerous non-governmental organization (NGO) projects funded by the NAP have targeted key populations and others who have historically been excluded from Brazilian society and governmental programmes and who remain outside the reach of most official initiatives. Needle exchange programmes for injecting drug users have existed since 1990, and in 2006 there were 150 units throughout the country, mostly funded by the NAP (Fonseca et al., 2006).

Access to HIV testing has been expanded through the implementation of 329 voluntary counselling and testing (VCT) sites across the country and, more recently, rapid HIV tests in remote regions, such as the north (Paiva et al., 2006). In the Amazon rainforest in particular, such tests have been proposed as one way to contribute to the fully integrated delivery of care to hard-to-reach, stigmatized and/or marginalized populations.

The above-mentioned initiatives have had a similar impact to that in developed countries with regard to reducing HIV transmission, AIDS-related illness and mortality, opportunistic infections and hospital admissions. However, when the data are disaggregated and analysed in terms of the different regions of Brazil, it seems that these impacts are not evenly spread. Women in particular are affected by both social and gendered inequalities and do not benefit equally from these initiatives.

The increasing numbers of new AIDS cases in several Brazilian communities can be partially explained by the improved infrastructure for better detection, reporting and referral. The key elements that contribute to regional differences in the epidemic include: different epidemic courses, with a protracted dynamic in some remote locations; a heterogeneous coverage of preventive actions; asymmetric knowledge about HIV and AIDS (with lower levels of knowledge among poor, underserved and marginalized people); different levels of education; different levels of social participation; and differences in other socio-economic and cultural factors. The NAP should develop specific initiatives to target those populations living in poverty and remote areas because different epidemics, in different regions and among different populations, require tailored responses. One example of such a contextualized approach is the successful, visually attractive, cartoon-style educational material created by some NGOs in partnership with local health authorities to target young injecting drug users.

There is also a need to carefully review HIV surveillance in Brazil. Data are still scarce and frequently limited to the most accessible regions or networks of facilities. For instance, there must be an evaluation of whether initiatives, such as awareness campaigns and the implementation of VCT and rapid HIV testing in the north (the Amazon rainforest in particular), have effectively expanded access to HIV testing to the most vulnerable populations in different regions of Brazil.

Challenges to be addressed

Recent papers have addressed major challenges to the timely and optimal delivery of services in the context of management and care from the perspective of individuals (Kerrigan et al., 2006). Other studies have analysed such barriers from the broader perspective of the context of pervasive inequality, violence and lack of respect for human rights. This context includes impoverished communities in Rio de Janeiro or São Paulo, which live under a reign of terror imposed by drug dealers and corrupt policemen (Bastos et al., 2007), and the borders between Brazil and other Latin American countries, which are plagued by structural violence and corruption, drug trafficking, unstable housing and employment, and the insufficient accountability of public institutions (Lippman et al., 2007). This structural violence has meant that there is a pronounced increase in mortality in underserved communities relative to other populations, with young men overrepresented among the victims of the drug wars (de Lima et al., 2005; Soares et al., 1998). As a consequence, a growing number of households in the *favelas* (slums) are headed by single or widowed young women and these households are particularly affected by unemployment and food insecurity.

The process of redemocratization in Brazil in the 1980s placed a strong emphasis on respect for basic human rights and the rights of women and minorities. As mentioned above, this period roughly coincided with the emergence of the HIV epidemic and the initial response to the epidemic. These dynamics have, to a great extent, overlapped and cross-fertilized. Yet even in Brazil, where the human rights framework has guided the NAP since its inception, work on human rights in the context of the epidemic still suffers because most NAP initiatives have been implemented in an ad hoc fashion, as single-agency and reactive actions, when they should be strategic, multi-agency and proactive (Grangeiro et al., 2006).

Decentralization and the role of local contexts and forces

The 1988 Constitution and the establishment of the SUS have led to the decentralization of services and autonomy at the state and city levels in the provision of health services, a process known as 'municipalization'. This process started slowly in the 1980s but has speeded up significantly since 1993 (Pasche et al., 2006). Decentralization has had both positive and negative impacts. For example, patient care may be provided through sophisticated services, such as well-equipped university hospitals – or it may be provided through clinics or primary health care units without any laboratory support. Given Brazil's strong regional inequalities, the quality of care is not the same throughout the country (Schechter, 2007).

As we have recently shown (Fonseca and Bastos, 2007), local governance is particularly subject to the influence of local interest groups. Local policies designed to implement health and social programmes for people who are usually marginalized, such as injecting drug users, may therefore face strong opposition. Our analysis showed that the modest budgets and personnel of programmes aiming to reduce drug-related harm have decreased in recent years, when decentralization was more pronounced in key states such as Rio de Janeiro. The lack of interest, sometimes blended with subtle but firm opposition and combined with the manifold consequences of structural violence (Paiva et al., 2006), which compromises many of the initiatives targeting those most in need (such as injecting drug users who live in slums that are plagued by drug wars), means that these initiatives may be endangered. The same applies to initiatives targeting other marginalized groups, such as male and female sex workers, the success of which depends on local arrangements between sex workers, the local police, conservative and liberal political forces in each specific setting, community leaders, health professionals and policy-makers.

A recent evaluation (Grangeiro et al., 2006) of HIV and STI prevention measures indicates that most of these strategies are unevenly institutionalized. HIV prevention has been decentralized at the local level, and few state or city governments have any permanent staff dedicated to prevention initiatives. This makes it difficult to conduct critical evaluations and to adopt culturally sensitive approaches vis-à-vis the innumerable local, subjective, cultural and social dimensions that undergo changes over time and continuously (re)shape the behaviour of individuals and groups. Data on STIs other than HIV remain sparse and uncoordinated, as does the analysis of the quality of governmental prevention initiatives at the local level.

The exclusive focus on demand-driven initiatives and the paucity of evidence-based prevention knowledge, driven by a non-dialogical approach, has been criticized. This approach may not take into account local inequalities and different scenarios within which sexual behaviour takes place, the social organization of gender differences and different beliefs and religious affiliations. Moreover, 'ready-made' prevention strategies may construct individual participants as consumers of pre-formatted skills and behaviours rather than as sexual subjects and full citizens who can negotiate and tailor health discourses according to their own personal concepts, projects and choices (Paiva, 2005; Paiva et al., 2004).

The issue of the sustainability of the current response to HIV in Brazil is closely linked to that of decentralization. Decentralization involves a different way of partitioning funds and responsibilities. The 'mainstreaming' of HIV and AIDS care and management in Brazil will therefore primarily depend on the commitment of SUS health units to take on initiatives previously implemented through vertical programmes, with the support of the federal government.

The sustainability of current policies

The impacts of the different initiatives that aim to restrict and respond to the HIV epidemic in Brazil have been strong and consistent over time. The implementation of an integrated set of public policies has resulted in considerable public and private benefits, including: the reduction of new HIV infections and improved control of the epidemic; financial savings of approximately US$2 billion between 1997 and 2003 (Levi and Vitória, 2002); a dramatic increase in median survival time after diagnosis of HIV infection; and substantial improvements in the quality of life of PLHIV (Marins et al., 2003).

In the context of universal access to antiretroviral and prophylactic medicines through free distribution at the point of delivery to any Brazilian citizen, a key challenge is to maintain this expenditure – which is by far the most costly component of the Brazilian model – as part of the overall budget of the Brazilian Ministry of Health.

In the years up to 2005, the share of the federal budget allocated to the epidemic decreased due to a fortunate combination of decreasing costs associated with hospitalization and complex medical procedures – such as the intensive use of invasive diagnostic methods – and indirect benefits, such as the return of PLHIV to their jobs and therefore fewer disbursements in the form of pensions, social insurance and so on. However, since 2005 costs have been rising (Greco and Simão, 2007) in a context of declining prices worldwide. This is due to: increases in secondary resistance to ARVs, although far less than was predicted by some (in great part because of the prudent use of ARVs and the successful management of care and monitoring of PLHIV); shifts towards more sophisticated drug regimens, which almost invariably include medicines protected by patents, which are much more expensive, because patients live longer and, over time, face viral and clinical failures and increases in other conditions, such as co-infection (especially with hepatitis C) or metabolic and cardiovascular conditions, which become a major source of illness and morbidity (Pallela et al., 2006).

The most recent analysis of this subject documents contradictory trends (Nunn et al., 2007). The authors attribute the decline of costs over time to the systematic use of generic medicines and the substantial discounts obtained by the Brazilian Ministry of Health in its negotiations with international pharmaceutical companies. However, generic ARVs have become more expensive in Brazil (unlike other developing countries), and there is some uncertainty with regard to the recent compulsory licensing of Efavirenz due to the technological challenges involved in its domestic production and the need to procure large amounts of Efavirenz, a key component of antiretroviral regimens in Brazil (Costa et al., 2008; Nunn et al., 2007). Nunn et al. also attribute the more recent rise in the cost of generic ARVs to the increasing cost of the basic active principal ingredients, managerial problems and massive purchases by other countries and agencies that has resulted in scarcity and/or competition.

Throughout two decades of the response to HIV in Brazil, monitoring and initiatives led by civil society and NGOs have improved the accountability of public policies. At the same time, however, emphasis has been placed on specific issues linked to treatment (such as the availability of new medicines) instead of on a critical and comprehensive appraisal of management, care and prevention. Much remains to be achieved in most care and prevention settings in terms of equity and creating a user-friendly environment. HIV-related initiatives must narrow the gaps in terms of gender inequality (services are not tailored to the specific needs of women) and the marginalization of underserved and disenfranchised populations, such as the unemployed, the homeless, single mothers, drug-dependent individuals, children and adolescents living on the street and ethnic and sexual minorities.

How can a public health programme address social inequalities, such as those connected to gender and race, that are deeply rooted in Brazilian history and society? The next section attempts to address this issue.

Challenging inequalities through gendered approaches and the necessary link between STI and HIV programmes and reproductive health programmes

The Brazilian Secretary for Women's Policy, created in President Lula's Government in 2002, and the Ministry of Health recently developed a plan to tackle the feminization of the HIV epidemic (Brazil, 2007c). It recognizes important aspects of women's vulnerability to HIV, and in particular the unequal power balance between men and women, and considers strategic actions to address factors contributing to women's vulnerability. First, the plan suggests the control of STIs other than HIV, with an emphasis on primary care for major STIs, the elimination of congenital syphilis, the early detection of syphilis and HIV infection and the prevention of cervical cancer. Second and third, it suggests addressing domestic and sexual violence, through the strengthening of the Domestic and Sexual Violence Network for Women, and racial issues, to combat racism and foster racial equity. Fourth, it recommends addressing young people through health and prevention projects in schools. Fifth, it recommends addressing poverty-related issues through the integration of HIV control measures into the *Bolsa Família* programme, which targets those living in dire poverty, particularly women (90 per cent of the beneficiaries of *Bolsa Família* are women). Sixth, it suggests that drug-related harm be reduced or prevented. Seventh, it recommends that stigma and violations of human rights be combated and a culture of peace and tolerance promoted. The plan takes as its reference the reproductive rights framework proposed during the Cairo and Beijing Conferences and recently supported by a WHO document that stresses the sexual health and rights approach (WHO, 2006).

In 2004, the Joint United Nations Programme on HIV and AIDS (UNAIDS) and the United Nations Population Fund (UNFPA) acknowledged that the overwhelming majority of HIV infections worldwide are sexually transmitted or associated with pregnancy, childbirth and breastfeeding. In a document called *The New York Call to Commitment* (UNFPA, 2004), both agencies emphasized the need for sexual and reproductive health and HIV and AIDS initiatives to be mutually reinforcing. Although this call to commitment is less comprehensive than the above-mentioned Brazilian plan, it provides a central contribution to efforts to integrate HIV prevention and the broadest agenda of sexual and reproductive rights. In this context it is vital to analyse in detail the reproductive needs of men and women living with HIV in order to establish the extent to which these needs are being met by available health services and what challenges and obstacles exist at the programmatic and service delivery levels that might impair the fulfillment of the reproductive rights of PLHIV.

Access to ART may help to address the many factors that may prevent PLHIV from becoming parents, including stigma and discrimination. The plan outlined by the Brazilian Secretary for Women's Policy may enable the prioritization of ART provision related to parenthood. Furthermore, providing a continuum of care that includes sex education and primary health care for both women and men, as well as good antenatal, delivery and postpartum care services, may enable early interventions that aim to avoid new HIV infections and foster early engagement with treatment, particularly among highly vulnerable populations.

However, structural, social and cultural issues, as well as gaps in terms of policies and their translation into concrete initiatives, may affect the way opportunities that benefit men and women's rights to quality reproductive health care and to form a family are enhanced or missed. Denial, lack of leadership, illiteracy and women's increased vulnerability are all part of the 'complexities of plagues' in resource-limited settings (Kopelman and van Niekerk, 2002) – but they are not restricted to these settings. Men and women in countries, like Brazil, where ART is freely available may experience similar challenges in relation to HIV and AIDS, particularly with regard to discrimination related to sexual and reproductive health care. This discrimination may take the form of a lack of information regarding mother-to-child transmission and pregnancy, negative attitudes of health providers towards child-bearing by PLHIV and a lack of counselling about the need for PLHIV to sustain consistent condom use, as well as problems in accessing proper contraceptives or safe legal abortions (Paiva et al., 2003; UNAIDS/Guttmacher, 2006; UNFPA, 2004).

Across the world, various degrees of HIV-related stigma and discrimination constrain reproductive health and choices for women and men, particularly those living with HIV (Segurado and Paiva, 2007). This may be expressed through differences in service infrastructure and human resources and gaps in the availability of VCT or access to condoms, contraceptives, ART and other medication. Historical and cultural definitions of parenthood and reproduction as an exclusively female domain may also affect HIV and reproductive health services.

Gender differences should also be taken into account in sexual health promotion initiatives for young people in Brazil. A recent paper (Bassichetto et al., 2008) shows that young people in the city of São Paulo who visit VCT centres present disquietingly high rates of HIV infection. These rates probably reflect both an actual increase in HIV infection in this population and the fact that those in this age range who perceive themselves to be at risk do seek counselling and testing for HIV. Unfortunately, the paper does not provide further details about incidence disaggregated by age and gender.

Discussing topics related to sexuality with younger adolescents may still be difficult in Brazil, even though there is high public support for sex education for adolescents younger than 15 years old (Szwarcwald et al., 2004). Overall, 60.2 per cent of schools in Brazil provide STI/HIV prevention programmes, and the proportion of young people who used condoms during first sexual intercourse increased from 47.8 per cent in 1998 to 65.8 per cent, in 2005, with a higher proportion among boys (Paiva et al., 2005). The prioritizing of schooled

versus non-schooled youth and the prioritizing of high school students in relation to those in elementary school need to be reconsidered as it is known that
high school boys and girls represent Brazil's most protected group compared to
those not in school or in elementary school with regard to risks associated with
sexual activity and broad social vulnerability.

The impact of violence, particularly sexual violence and sexual abuse, on
all PLHIV (men, women and children) must be carefully assessed and prevented by the widest possible range of social institutions. The only national
study on violence against women was conducted in 2004 (Venturi et al., 2004)
and indicated that 43 per cent of Brazilian women reported at least one event
of violence perpetrated against them by a man: 33 per cent of those interviewed
reported physical violence, 13 per cent reported sexual abuse, and 27 per cent
reported psychological violence. Domestic and sexual violence have been related to health problems, especially in the context of HIV, with sexual abuse
associated with increased vulnerability to HIV infection (Segurado and Paiva,
2007). Violence has also been linked to stigma and to discrimination against
PLHIV and is perpetrated in the family, the neighbourhood and throughout
the health sector.

Children affected by HIV: A paradigm of psychosocial
and comprehensive care challenges

Brazil's support for the welfare of children affected by HIV is best demonstrated
by the country's success in dramatically reducing mother-to-child transmission.
This success can be attributed to Brazil's longstanding political commitment to
treatment, including the provision of ART to every HIV-positive person – adult
or child – in the country, which the country initiated over the objections of
international donors in 1996. Mothers and their babies have benefited from a
comprehensive set of initiatives, which include interventions at various stages
in child development, from prenatal care to the continuous monitoring of children born to HIV-positive women.

A growing challenge for HIV-related programmes throughout Brazil is
that of HIV-positive children who survive to adolescence because of their access to ART. This consideration needs to be incorporated into the psychosocial
and comprehensive care provided, which must include support for parents in
families affected by HIV, particularly in terms of the disclosure of HIV status
(IPAS, 2005).

Studies conducted among adolescents who were born with HIV or who acquired HIV after sexual exposure have highlighted important challenges that need to be addressed when linking HIV-related care with sexual and reproductive health (Ayres et al., 2006; IPAS, 2005; Marques et al., 2006). Boys and girls born to HIV-positive mothers tend to be overprotected, are not told their HIV status and lack basic information about sexuality and reproduction until late adolescence. Adolescents who are infected later in life through sexual intercourse suffer from stigma and discrimination at health care facilities, are disregarded in terms of adolescent developmental issues after the disclosure of their sero-status and, in the case of pregnant girls, are often ignored during regular visits to antenatal clinics. Adolescents living with HIV are very concerned about their bodies and the body image that is related to their health status; they are distressed by the emotional burden of keeping their HIV-positive status secret. They need psychosocial support in order to disclose their sero-status to friends and loved ones and to make plans for their future in terms of sexual relationships, building a family and having children.

Because ART is available in Brazil for all women at all stages of their lives and not only during pregnancy, maternal mortality rates are lower. Issues surrounding orphans and vulnerable children in Brazil have therefore not been as visible as in other developing countries. Brazil has many fewer orphans than sub-Saharan African countries, for example. However, a study conducted in Porto Alegre (Doring et al., 2005), the southern capital of Brazil, on the children of parents who died of AIDS-related illnesses between 1998 and 2001 and another conducted in the city of São Paulo (França Jr et al., 2006), which is the epicentre of the Brazilian epidemic, draw attention to certain aspects of the epidemic that should be incorporated into public policy. Both studies, based on household surveys of people who died of AIDS-related illnesses, found that for every 10 adult deaths, 8.8 children under 15 years old are orphaned, even though the profile of the epidemic is different in the two cities. Only a few of the orphans (5 per cent in Porto Alegre and 2 per cent in São Paulo) live in orphanages or public institutions. Half live with their extended families, and between 25 and 47 per cent live with the remaining parent; the remainder live with other relatives, friends and neighbours in informal arrangements. HIV prevalence is 9 per cent among orphans in Porto Alegre alone and 6 per cent among the orphans who have been tested in both Porto Alegre and São Paulo. Both studies indicated that orphans are more likely to come from lower social and economic strata. Both studies also suggest that informal networks of relatives and friends, who receive minimal or no support from the state, have been a fundamental component of support systems for orphans. The successful 'buffering' effect of these informal networks seems to be a consequence of the relatively small numbers of children orphaned by AIDS and the beneficial effects of broad social policies (such as the *Bolsa Família*).

In the city of São Paulo, male adolescent orphans are more likely than female orphans to be abandoned and, abandoned or not, to engage in unprotected sexual practices (Chongo, 2005). It is not entirely clear why girls are more likely to be adopted, but some anecdotal reports highlight the fact that girls are more likely to help their foster mothers carry out domestic work and less likely to consume illicit drugs, which is particularly valued in contexts where drug trafficking and extreme violence are rife (Weiselfisz, 2008). Forced sex or early marriage for girls were not visible issues in the study.

Prevenção positHiva (positive prevention): Fighting stigma and discrimination, and fostering adherence and comprehensive care for PLHIV

Prevenção positHiva (positive prevention), a concept originally coined by the American researcher Seth Kalichman to emphasize prevention among PLHIV, has been fully adopted by the Brazilian Ministry of Health and its network of health units. One must observe, however, that any initiative exclusively targeted at PLHIV may be damaging and increase stigma and discrimination if it does not stress that PLHIV have the same rights to prevention and care as non-infected people as well as the right to a consideration of their specific needs. Access to condoms and adherence to their use, as well as access to full information about sexuality and reproduction, should be regarded as just as relevant in HIV care settings as access and adherence to antiretroviral medication. Counselling about family care issues, family planning and STIs should also be part of comprehensive care initiatives. Unfortunately, the provision of proper information for PLHIV about vertical transmission, how pregnancy will affect disease progression, the future of children, the possibility that babies may also be infected and infant feeding has been a challenge (Segurado et al., 2003).

An extremely important issue relating to adherence is that of the changes in body fat composition that result from ART, which are known as lipodystrophy. It has been demonstrated that these changes, which may substantially alter the body shape and the face of the patient, have psychological impacts severe enough to affect patient adherence and to intensify the fear of stigmatization, especially among women and gay men (Santos et al., 2005). As in other countries, this experience has been compared in terms of stigma to the 'wasting syndrome' that was more prevalent in the first years of the epidemic (Martinez et al., 2001). It is an important issue within *Prevenção positHiva;* the NAP now provides plastic surgery within the SUS, offered for free at the point of delivery to both men and women (Brazil, 2004).

Final remarks

In addition to permanent government initiatives to respond to the HIV epidemic, the sustainability of the response depends on the expansion and enhancement of the SUS. One of its principles is transparency, or the accountability of public policies. NGOs working in the area of HIV and AIDS have been key to shaping the response to the epidemic in Brazil, although they have expended most of their efforts in fighting for access to care and the right to treatment. The right to prevention or to comprehensive high-quality psychosocial assistance for PLHIV is still rarely addressed by civil society and SUS entities. In other words, there is little activism for the 'right to prevention' – access to prevention materials (condoms and hypodermic needles) or to information, education or high-quality counseling – even where the interface with assistance services is higher, as is the case with access to quality STI treatment or prevention programmes for vertical transmission.

For reasons that cannot be fully elucidated in the space of this chapter, the fierce battles faced by different groups of activists, including feminist and gay movements and major NGOs, that campaign to protect and promote human, sexual and reproductive rights and/or for a full return to democracy in Brazil after more than two decades of dictatorship, are closely linked to urgent needs in terms of access to care, discrimination and rights violations. Activism and the formulation of AIDS public policies have been conducted within a human rights–based approach as part of the democratization process in Brazil. It has included: the control of blood banks by cartels exploiting commercial donations and the closure of these blood banks; access to ARVs and other life-saving medicines since the mid-1980s; and the permanent efforts to protect the domestic pharmaceutical industry (both state-owned and private) against litigation initiated (but later discontinued) by the US government and the permanent threat of sanctions by the World Trade Organization. Although such issues have been pivotal in a country where many other health needs (such as the care and management of hepatitis C) are far from being properly addressed, the focus on government-driven initiatives and a biomedical agenda may have narrowed the scope of social movements to achieve change.

On the academic front, we suggest that the gender, regional, racial and age inequalities discussed in this chapter will persist in the absence of research to monitor populations that are difficult to reach but highly vulnerable to HIV. Innovations in research have been attempted in recent years, including: more sophisticated methodologies (such as respondent-driven sampling) to assess hidden populations; large population-based studies of sexual and reproductive health; and cohort studies that address both vulnerable populations and people living with HIV.

Much has been achieved by Brazil's initiatives to respond to the epidemic, but much remains to be done in the context of one of the most heterogeneous and unequal societies in the world. The HIV response in Brazil is essentially a group of well-funded, well-managed initiatives under the umbrella of a renowned and visible federal programme. The years to come pose the renewed challenges of sustainability in the context of rising costs; equity, in terms of gender, class, sexual choice and so on; and 'horizontalization', or the full integration of AIDS initiatives into the daily operation of SUS health units.

References

Ades, A. E. 1995. Serial HIV seroprevalence surveys: interpretation, design, and role in HIV/AIDS prediction. *Journal of Acquired Immune Deficiency Syndromes and Human Retrovirology,* Vol. 15, No. 9, pp. 490–99.

Ayres, J. R., Paiva, V., França Jr, I., Silva, N, G., Lacerda, R., DellaNegra, M., Marques, H. S., Galano, E., Gutierrez, P. L. and Segurado, A. 2006. Vulnerability, human rights, and comprehensive health care needs of young people living with HIV/AIDS. *American Journal of Public Health,* Vol. 96, No. 6, pp. 1001–006.

Barbieri, A. F. and Sawyer D. O. 2007. Heterogeneity of malaria prevalence in alluvial gold mining areas in Northern Mato Grosso State, Brazil. *Cadernos de Saúde Pública,* Vol. 23, No. 12, pp. 2878–886.

Barcellos, C. and Bastos, F. I. 1996. Social networks and diffusion of AIDS in Brazil. *Boletín de la Oficina Sanitaria Panamericana,* Vol. 121, No. 1, pp. 11–24.

Bassichetto, K. C., Bergamaschi, D. P., Oliveira, S. M., Deienno, M. C., Bortolato, R., de Rezende, H. V., Arthur, T., Tomiyama, H., Watkins, C., Mesquita, F., Abbate, M. C. and Kallas, E. G. 2008. Elevated risk for HIV-1 infection in adolescents and young adults in São Paulo, Brazil. *PLoS ONE,* Vol. 9, No. 3, p. e1423.

Bastos, F. I. and Barcellos C. 1995. The social geography of AIDS in Brazil. *Revista de Saúde Pública,* Vol. 29, No. 1, pp. 52–62.

Bastos, F. I., Barcellos C., Lowndes, C. M and Friedman, S. R. 1999. Co-infection with malaria and HIV in injecting drug users in Brazil. A new challenge to public health? *Addiction,* Vol. 94, No. 8, pp. 1165–174.

Bastos, F. I., Bongertz, V., Teixeira, S. L, Morgado, M. G. and Hacker, M .A. 2005. Is human immunodeficiency virus/acquired immunodeficiency syndrome decreasing among Brazilian injection drug users? Recent findings and how to interpret them. *Memórias do Instituto Oswaldo Cruz,* Vol. 100, No. 1, pp. 91–96.

Bastos, F. I., Buchalla, C. M., Ayres, J. R. and Silva, L. J. 2006. Brazilian response to the HIV/AIDS epidemic, 2001–2005. *Revista de Saúde Pública,* Vol. 40, Suppl., pp. 1–2.

Bastos, F. I., Caiaffa, W., Rossi, D., Vila, M. and Malta, M. 2007. The children of mama coca: Coca, cocaine and the fate of harm reduction in South America. *International Journal of Drug Policy,* Vol. 18, No. 2, pp. 99–106.

Beck, E. J. and Mays, N. 2006. The HIV pandemic and health systems: An introduction. E. J. Beck, N. Mays, A. W. Whiteside and J. M. Zuniga (eds), *The HIV Pandemic: Local and Global Implications.* Oxford, United Kingdom, Oxford University Press, pp. 3–20.

Berkman, A., Garcia, J., Munoz-Laboy, M., Paiva, V. and Parker, R. 2005. A critical analysis of the Brazilian response to HIV/AIDS: Lessons learned for controlling and mitigating the epidemic in developing countries. *American Journal of Public Health,* Vol. 95, No. 7, pp. 1162–172.

Braga, P., Cardoso, M. R. and Segurado, A. 2007. Gender differences in survival in a HIV/AIDS cohort from São Paulo, Brasil. *AIDS Patient Care and STDs,* Vol. 21, No. 5, pp. 321–28.

Brazil. 1996. Dispõe sobre a distribuição gratuita de medicamentos aos portadores do HIV e doentes de AIDS. Vol. 13, 1996. Law 9313. http//www.aids.gov.br/assistencia/lei9313.htm (Accessed 18 April 2007.)

——. 2004. Portaria nº 2582/GM, de 02 de dezembro de 2004. Ministério da Saúde. http://www.aids.gov.br/data/Pages/LUMIS59BBE9C1PTBRIE.htm (Accessed 18 April 2007.)

——. 2005. *Boletim Epidemiológico AIDS e DST.* Brasília, Ministério da Saúde. Vol. 2, No. 1.

——. 2007a. *Boletim Epidemiológico AIDS e DST.* Vol. IV, No. 1. Brasília, Ministéria da Saúde. Health. http://www.aids.gov.br/data/documents/storedDocuments (Accessed 2 January 2008.)

——. 2007b. Brazil Country Brief. www.worldbank.org wbln0018.worldbank.org/LAC/LAC.nsf/ECADocByUnid/A220784F5BC3A1FB85256DB40070253B? Opendocument (Accessed 15 December 2007.)

——. 2007c. Plano Integrado de enfretamento da feminização da epidemia de Aids e outras DST. Ministry of Health, National Aids Programme. www.aids.gov.br (Accessed 15 December 2007.)

Brito, A. M., Castilho, E. A. and Szwarcwald, C. L. 2005. Regional patterns of the temporal evolution of the AIDS epidemic in Brazil following the introduction of antiretroviral therapy. *Brazilian Journal of Infectious Diseases,* Vol. 9, No. 1, pp. 9–19.

Chongo, L. S. 2005. Início da vida sexual de jovens órfãos por AIDS na cidade de São Paulo. Master of Public Health dissertation, Universidade de São Paulo, Brazil.

Costa, E., Santos da Costa, J. C. and Ferreira, H. P. 2008. Farmanguinhos, A experiência na produção pública de medicamentos. P. Buss, J. R. Carvalheiro and C. P. Romero Casas (eds), *Medicamentos no Brasil: Inovação e Acesso.* Rio de Janeiro, Editora Fiocruz.

De Bruyn M. 2005. *HIV/AIDS and Reproductive Health: Sensitive and Neglected Issues. A Review of the Literature: Recommendations for Action.* Chapel Hill, NC, IPAS. http://www.ipas.org/publications/en/HIVLITREV_E05_en.pdf (Accessed 1 April 2007.)

de Lima, M. L., Ximenes, R. A., Feitosa, C. L., de Souza, E. R., de Albuquerque, M. de F., Barros, M. D., de Souza, W. V. and Lapa, T. M. 2005. Violence clusters in Pernambuco, Brazil. *Revista Panamericana de Salud Pública,* Vol. 18, No. 2, pp. 122–28.

Doring, M., França Jr, I. and Stella, I. M. 2005. Factors associated with institutionalization of children orphaned by AIDS in a population-based survey in Porto Alegre, Brazil. *AIDS,* Vol. 19, No. 4, pp. S59–S63.

Dourado, I., Veras, M. A., Barreira, D. and de Brito, A. M. 2006. AIDS epidemic trends after the introduction of antiretroviral therapy in Brazil. *Revista de Saúde Pública,* Vol. 40, Suppl., pp. 9–17.

Duffy, G. and Ferreira, E. 2008. Jungle condoms Brasil. *Condomerie Nieuws News.* http://www.condomerie.com/news/nieuwsitem.php?id=67 (Accessed 16 February 2009.)

Elias, P. E. M. and Cohn, A. 2003. Health reform in Brazil: Lessons to consider. *American Journal of Public Health,* Vol. 93, No. 1, pp. 44–48.

Fonseca, E. M., Nunn, A., Souza Jr, P. B., Bastos, F. I. and Ribeiro, J. M. 2007. Decentralization, AIDS, and harm reduction: The implementation of public policies in Rio de Janeiro, Brazil. *Cadernos de Saúde Pública,* Vol. 23, No. 9, pp. 2134–144.

Fonseca, E. M., Ribeiro, J. M., Bertoni, N. and Bastos, F. I. 2006. Syringe exchange programs in Brazil: Preliminary assessment of 45 programs. *Cadernos de Saúde Pública,* Vol. 22, No. 4, pp. 761–70.

Fonseca, M. et al. 2003. Social distribution of AIDS in Brazil according to labor market participation, occupation and socioeconomic status of cases from 1987 to 1998. *Cad Saúde Pública,* Vol. 19, No. 5, pp. 1351-363.

Fonseca, M. G. P. and Bastos, F. I. 2007. Twenty-five years of the AIDS epidemic in Brazil: Principal epidemiological findings, 1980–2005. *Cadernos de Saúde Pública,* Vol. 3, No. 23, pp. s333–s344.

Fonseca, M. G. P., Szwarcwald, C. L. and Bastos, F. I. 2002. Análise sociodemográfica da epidemia de Aids no Brasil: 1989–1997. *Revista de Saúde Pública,* Vol. 36, No. 6, pp. 678–85.

França Jr, I., Doring, M. and Stelle, M. I. 2006. Orphans and vulnerable children affected by HIV/AIDS in Brazil: Where do we stand and where are we heading? *Revista de Saúde Pública,* Vol. 40, Suppl., pp. 23–30.

Galvão, J. 2002. Access to antiretroviral drugs in Brazil. *Lancet,* Vol. 360, No. 9348, pp. 1862–865.

Giffin, K. and Lowndes, C. M. 1999. Gender, sexuality, and the prevention of sexually transmissible diseases: A Brazilian study of clinical practice. *Social Science and Medicine,* Vol. 48, No. 3, pp. 283–92.

Gould, P. 1993. *The Slow Plague. A geography of the AIDS pandemic.* Oxford, United Kingdom/Cambridge, MA, Blackwell.

Grangeiro, A., Teixeira, L., Bastos, F. I. and Teixeira, P. 2006. Sustainability of Brazilian policy foraccess to antiretroviral drugs. *Revista de Saúde Pública,* Vol. 40, Suppl., pp. 60–69.

Greco, D. B. and Simão, M. 2007. Brazilian policy of universal access to AIDS treatment: Sustainability challenges and perspectives. *AIDS,* Vol. 21, No. 4, pp. s37–s45.

Hacker, M. A., Kaida A., Hogg, R. S. and Bastos, F. I. 2007. The first ten years: Achievements and challenges of the Brazilian program of universal access to HIV/AIDS, comprehensive management and care, 1996–2006. *Cadernos de Saúde Pública,* Vol. 23, No. 3, pp. s345–59.

IPAS. 2005. *Reproductive Rights for Women Affected by HIV/AIDS.* Chapel Hill, NC, IPAS. http://www.ipas.org/Publications/asset_upload_file904_2459.pdf (Accessed 16 February 2009.)

Kerrigan, D., Bastos, F. I., Malta, M., Carneiro-da-Cunha, C., Pilotto, J. H. and Strathdee, S. A. 2006. The search for social validation and the sexual behavior of people living with HIV in Rio de Janeiro, Brazil: Understanding the role of treatment optimism in context. *Social Science and Medicine,* Vol. 62, No. 10, pp. 2386–396.

Kopelman, L. M. and van Niekerk, A. A. 2002. AIDS and Africa: Introduction. *Journal of Medicine and Philosophy,* Vol. 27, No. 2, pp. 139–42.

Kulick, D. 2008. Travesti: Prostituição, sexo, gênero e cultura no Brasil. Rio de Janeiro, Brazil, Editora FIOCRUZ.

Levi, G. C. and Vitória, M. A. 2002. Fighting against AIDS: The Brazilian experience. *AIDS,* Vol. 6, No. 16, pp. 2373–383.

Lippman, S. A., Kerrigan, D., Chinaglia, M. and Diaz, J. 2007. Chaos, co-existence, and the potential for collective action: HIV-related vulnerability in Brazil's international borders. *Social Science and Medicine,* Vol. 64, No. 12, pp. 2464–475.

Malta, M., Bastos, F. I., Strathdee, S. A., Cunnigham, S. D., Pilotto, J. H. and Kerrigan, D. 2007. Knowledge, perceived stigma, and care-seeking experiences for sexually transmitted infections: A qualitative study from the perspective of public clinic attendees in Rio de Janeiro, Brazil. *BMC Public Health,* Vol. 1, No. 7, p. 18.

Marins, J. R., Jamal, L. F., Chen, S. Y., Barros, M. B., Hudes, E. S., Barbosa, A. A., Chequer, P., Teixeira, P. R. and Hearst, N. 2003. Dramatic improvement in survival among adult Brazilian AIDS patients. *AIDS,* Vol. 25, No. 17, pp. 1675–682.

Marques, H. H. S, Gravato da Silva, N., Gutierrez, P. L., Lacerda, R., Ayres, J. R. C. M., Della Negra, M., França Jr, I., Galano, E., Paiva, V., Segurado, A. A. C. and Silva, M. H. 2006. A revelação do diagnóstico na perspectiva dos adolescentes vivendo com HIV/AIDS e seus pais e cuidadores. *Cadernos de Saúde Pública*, Vol. 22, No. 3, pp. 619–29.

Martinez, E., Garcia-Viejo, M. A., Blanch, J. and Gatell, J. M. 2001. Lipodystrophy syndrome in patients with HIV infection: Quality of life issues. *Drug Safety*, Vol. 24, No. 3, pp. 157–66.

Menezes, D. C., Leite, I. C., Schramm, J. M. and Lcal, M. do C. 2006. Evaluation of antenatal peregrination in a sample of postpartum women in Rio de Janeiro, Brazil, 1999/2001. *Cadernos de Saúde Pública*, Vol. 22, No. 3, pp. 553–59.

Menezes Succi, R. C. 2007. Mother-to-child transmission of HIV in Brazil during the years 2000 and 2001: Results of a multi-centric study. *Cadernos de Saúde Pública* Vol. 23, Suppl. 3, pp. S379–89

Nemes, M. I., Carvalho, H. B. and Souza, M. F. 2004. Antiretroviral therapy adherence in Brazil. *AIDS*, Vol. 18, No. 3, pp. s15–s20.

Nunn, A. 2009. *The Politics and History of AIDS Treatment in Brazil*. New York, Springer.

Nunn, A., Fonseca, E. M., Bastos, F. I., Gruskin, S. and Salomon, J. 2007. Evolution of antiretroviral costs in Brazil in the context of free and universal access to AIDS treatment. *PLOS Medicine*, Vol. 13, No. 4, p. e305.

Paiva, V. 2005. Analysing sexual experiences through 'scenes':A framework for the evaluation of sexuality education. *Sex Education*, Vol. 5, No. 4, pp. 345–59.

Paiva, V., Aranha, F. and Bastos, F. I. 2008. Opinions and attitudes regarding sexuality: Brazilian national research, 2005. *Revista de Saúde Pública*, Vol. 42, Suppl. 1, pp. 54–64.

Paiva, V., Ayres, J. R. and Franca Jr, I. 2004. Expanding the flexibility of normative patterns in youth sexuality and prevention programs: Sexuality Research and Social policy. *Journal of NCRC*, Vol. 1, No. 1.

Paiva, V., Calazans, G., Venturi, G. and Dias, V. 2008. Age and condom use at first sexual intercourse among Brazilian adolescents. *Revista de Saúde Pública*, Vol. 42, Suppl. 1, pp. 43–53.

Paiva, V., Pupo, L. R. and Barboza, R. 2006. The right to prevention and the challenges of reducing vulnerability to HIV in Brazil. *Revista de Saúde Pública*, Vol. 40, Suppl., pp. 109–19.

Paiva, V., Santos, N., França Jr, I., Ventura-Filipe, E., Ayres, J. R. and Segurado, A. 2007. Desire to have children: Gender and reproductive rights of man and woman living with HIV: A challenge to health care in Brazil. *AIDS Patient Care and STDs*, Vol. 21, No. 4, pp. 268–77.

Paiva, V., Ventura-Felipe, E., Santos, N., Lima, T. and Segurado, A. 2003. The right to love: The desire for parenthood among men living with HIV. *Reproductive Health Matters*, Vol. 11, No. 22, pp. 91–100.

Palella Jr., F. J., Baker, R. K., Moorman, A. C., Chmiel, J. S., Wood, K. C., Brooks, J. T. and Holmberg, S. D. 2006. Mortality in the highly active antiretroviral therapy era: Changing causes of death and disease in the HIV outpatient study. *Journal of Acquired Immune Deficiency Syndrome,* Vol. 43, No. 1, pp. 27–34.

Pasche, D. F., Righi, L. B., Thomé, H. I. and Stolz, E. D. 2006. Paradoxes of health decentralization policies in Brazil. *Revista Panamericana de Salud Pública,* Vol. 20, No. 6, pp. 416–22.

Porco, T. C., Martin, J. N., Page-Shafer, K. A., Cheng, A., Charlebois, E., Grant, R. M. and Osmond, D. H. 2004. Decline in HIV infectivity following the introduction of highly active antiretroviral therapy. *AIDS,* Vol. 18, No. 1, pp. 81–88.

Rocha, M. G. 2007. Celso Furtado and the resumption of construction in Brazil: Structuralism as an alternative to neoliberalism. *Latin American Perspectives,* Vol. 34, No. 5, pp. 132–59.

Santos, C. P., Felipe, Y. X., Braga, P. E., Ramos, D., Lima, R. O. and Segurado, A. C. 2005. Self perception of body changes in persons living with HIV/AIDS: Prevalence and associated factors. *AIDS,* Vol. 19, No. 4, pp. S14–S21.

Schechter, M. 2007. Treatment at scale in Brazil: A physician's perspective. *AIDS,* Vol. 21, No. 4, pp. S31–S35.

Segurado, A. C., Batistella, E., Nascimento, V., Braga, P. E., Filipe, E., Santos, N. and Paiva, V. 2008. Sexual abuse victimization and perpetration in a cohort of men living with HIV/AIDS who have sex with women from São Paulo, Brazil. *AIDS Care,* Vol. 20, No. 1, pp. 15–20.

Segurado, A. C., Latorre, M. R., Pluciennik, A., França Jr, I., Ayres, J. R., Marques, H., Lacerda, R., Gravato, N., Miranda, S. and Paiva, V. 2003. Evaluation of the care of women living with HIV/AIDS. *AIDS Patient Care and STDs,* Vol. 17, No. 2, pp. 85–94.

Segurado, A. C. and Paiva, V. 2007. Rights of HIV-positive people to sexual and reproductive health: Parenthood. *Reproductive Health Matters,* Vol. 15, No. 29, Suppl. 1, pp. 27–45.

Soares, K. V., Blue, I., Cano, E. and Mari, J. de J. 1998. Violent death in young people in the city of São Paulo, 1991–1993. *Health and Place,* Vol. 4, No. 2, pp. 195–98.

Souza Jr, P. R. B., Szwarcwald, C. L., Barbosa Jr, A., Carvalho, M. F. and Castilho, E. A. 2004. Infecção pelo HIV durante a gestação: Estudo-Sentinela Parturiente, Brasil, 2002. *Revista de Saúde Pública,* Vol. 38, No. 6, pp. 764–72.

Souza Jr, P. R. B., Szwarcwald, C. L. and Castilho, E. A. 2007. Delay in introducing antiretroviral therapy in patients infected by HIV in Brazil, 2003–2006. *Clinics,* Vol. 62, No. 5, pp. 579–84.

Szwarcwald, C. L, Barbosa Jr, A., Souza Jr, P. R. and Pascom, A. R. and Esteves, M. A. 2004. Situação da Aids no Brasil: Uma análise de indicadores para o monitoramento da epidemia. Ministério da Saúde/SVS/PN-DST e Aids, *Monitoraids*. Brasília, DF. http://sistemas.aids.gov.br/monitoraids2/aidsi/frames.htm (Accessed 16 February 2009.)

Szwarcwald, C. L. and Castilho, E. A. 2000. Estimativa do número de pessoas de 15 a 49 anos infectadas pelo HIV, Brasil, 1998. *Cadernos de Saúde Pública*, Vol. 16, No. 1, pp 135–41.

Szwarcwald, C. L. and de Carvalho, M. F. 2001. Estimativa do número de indivíduos de 15 a 49 anos infectadas pelo HIV, Brasil, 2000. *Boletim Epidemiológico AIDS*, Vol. 14, No. 1, pp. SE1/1–13/1.

Teixeira, P. R., Vitória, M. A. and Barcarolo, J. 2004. Antiretroviral treatment in resource-poor settings: The Brazilian experience. *AIDS*, Vol. 18, No. 3, pp. S5–S7.

Tess, B. H., Rodrigues, L. C., Newell, M. L., Dunn, D. T. and Lago, T. D. 1998. Breastfeeding, genetic, obstetric and other risk factors associated with mother-to-child transmission of HIV-1 in São Paulo State, Brazil. *AIDS*, Vol. 26, No. 12, pp. 513–20.

UNAIDS (Joint United Nations Programme on HIV/AIDS). 2006. *Report on the Global AIDS Epidemic: A UNAIDS 10th Anniversary Special Edition*. Geneva, UNAIDS.

UNAIDS/Guttmacher Institute. 2006. Meeting the sexual and reproductive health needs of people living with HIV. *In Brief 2006 Series*, No. 6, pp. 1.

UNDP (United Nations Development Programme). 2004. *Human Development Report*. New York, UNDP. http://hdr.undp.org/reports/global/hdr2004 (Accessed 10 February 2007.)

UNFPA (United Nations Population Fund). 2004. *The New York Call to Commitment: Linking HIV/AIDS and Sexual and Reproductive Health*. New York, UNFPA. http://www.unfpa.org/publications/detail.cfm?ID=195&filterListType=2 (Accessed 16 February 2009.)

Venturi, G. 2004. M. Recaman and S. Oliveira (eds). *A mulher brasileira nos espaços público e privado*. São Paulo, Brazil, Editora Fundação Perseu Abramo.

Waiselfisz, P. P. 2008. *Mapa da violência dos municípios brasileiros 2008*. Brazil, Ministry of Health.

WHO (World Health Organization). 2006. *Defining Sexual Health: Report on Technical Consultation on Sexual Health, 2002*. Geneva, WHO. (Sexual Health Document Series.)

CHAPTER 10

How should we understand sexual violence and HIV and AIDS in conflict contexts?

Judy El-Bushra

Introduction

It has been assumed for many years that HIV transmission rates increase in situations of violent conflict. The principal explanation advanced for this increase is the presumed greater incidence of sexual violence during – and/or as a weapon of – war, with a secondary explanation being that violent conflict may exacerbate conditions known to favour high rates of HIV infection, such as poverty and population displacement. Evidence that a link exists between sexual violence and HIV infection at the individual level[1] has been supported by data about HIV prevalence among specific groups known to have suffered higher than usual incidences of sexual violence in wartime. For example, during the Rwanda genocide, 60 per cent to 80 per cent of victims of rape were estimated as being sero-positive, as against 13.5 per cent in the population at large (Nduwimana, 2004).

Recent studies, however, (for example, Anema et al., 2008; Mock et al., 2004; Spiegel et al., 2007) have challenged the assumption that violent conflict increases levels of HIV and AIDS by pointing out that the conditions prevalent during violent conflict can, paradoxically, both raise and lower transmission rates and that high prevalence for specific highly affected communities should not necessarily be extrapolated to whole populations. While accepting that the widespread individual incidences of sexual violence during conflict represent a humanitarian and human rights tragedy, they conclude that, at population level,

The designations employed and the presentation of material throughout this publication do not imply the expression of any opinion whatsoever on the part of UNESCO concerning the legal status of any country, territory or area or of its authorities, or concerning the delimitation of its frontiers or boundaries.
The ideas and opinions expressed in this publication are those of the authors and do not necessarily reflect the views of UNESCO and its Member States.

there is little empirical basis for the claim that violent conflict increases HIV prevalence. Moreover, Aranka Anema and her colleagues point to the existence of other types of behaviour, such as conducting concurrent relationships, that are believed by some to have a more tangible impact on rates of sero-positivity than sexual violence (Anema et al., 2008; Halperin and Epstein, 2004).

It may be more useful to focus on the meaning of 'sexual violence' and the different levels of risk associated with its different forms. We cannot assume one-off, opportunistic rape to be the only, or even the main, variety of sexual violence in the contexts under discussion. Indeed, sexual violence in war contexts often takes the form of violently enforced long-term sexual relationships, which may range from the 'sexual slavery' into which abducted girls may be taken as 'wives' to strategic and deliberate attempts at the destruction of the person by multiple attackers over periods of weeks or months. There could hardly be a more risky set of circumstances than these, combining the biological risks of violence and long-term exposure to multiple potentially HIV-positive partners with the social pressures commonly found in relationships based on extreme imbalances of power (WHO, 2004).

While respondents to the studies presented by Paul Spiegel and his collaborators on HIV prevalence have generally welcomed the call for greater rigour in interpreting data, some have also expressed the need for a broader approach to the interpersonal, social and political contexts in which infection takes place, and specifically to the interpretation of sexual violence in the context of violent conflict[2] (Jewkes, 2007; Spiegel, 2007). Indeed, there is a tendency within the broad thematic field of HIV and AIDS for an interest in the social context of HIV transmission to be seen as secondary to a concern with the medical and epidemiological features of the virus. Accordingly, there are important gaps in our understanding of the social context of HIV transmission (see, for example, Klot and DeLargy, 2007; Russell, 2007), and these gaps are arguably hindering our capacity to provide an effective response in situations of violent conflict.

A 'gender approach' would form part of the broader approach that Rachel Jewkes and others have called for. This approach would attempt to explore the social and cultural contexts in which relationships, including sexual relationships, are played out. This chapter aims to contribute towards such an approach. Specifically, it aims to explore the conflict-sexual violence–HIV and AIDS nexus from the perspective of gender relations, seeking to reclaim the notion that HIV and AIDS are nothing if not the products of an intimate relationship between individuals, played out within specific historical, geographical, social and cultural contexts. The chapter is framed by an overall conviction that understanding the social and cultural dimensions of sexual relations in conflict settings is a key step for effective prevention and that it moves beyond approaches that focus on the containment of sexual violence.

The chapter summarizes evidence about sexual violence and the international responses to it, using the Democratic Republic of the Congo, Burundi, Rwanda and Uganda in the Great Lakes region as examples and drawing on the experience of United Nations and non-governmental agencies working in those countries. Following that, it then assesses the strengths and weaknesses of current approaches and elaborates a revised approach, spelling out some initial questions for further research.

Sexual violence in conflict in the Great Lakes region

The Democratic Republic of the Congo (henceforth DRC), Burundi, Rwanda and Uganda have all experienced devastating civil war almost continuously for the last twenty years and more, although these wars have now mostly come to a formal end and the countries are in various stages of transition.[3] Both the wars and the sexual violence associated with them have taken different forms. For example, in Rwanda sexual violence has been primarily associated with the genocide of 1994, in which Hutu supremacist planners urged supporters to rape Tutsi women, although women's organizations have observed a recent resurgence of rape in the domestic context. In northern Uganda, the Ugandan People's Defence Force (the national army) is widely credited with having been the main perpetrator of the rapes of both men and women, whereas the rebel Lord's Resistance Army (LRA) is believed to have abducted tens of thousands of boys and girls to serve as camp followers, with the girls often undergoing forced marriage to officers and other soldiers. In the two DRC provinces of North and South Kivu, it is believed that thousands of women were raped by the army and other militias (Csete and Kippenberg, 2002; Human Rights Watch, 2003; International Alert et al., 2005), whereas large numbers of women joined rebel groups, often under various forms of coercion ranging from violent force to economic enticement, many experiencing sexual abuse over short or long periods. A similar pattern was in evidence in Burundi (Kandanga, 2007). Throughout the Great Lakes region there have been reports (generally anecdotal) of increased levels of sexual abuse of children (male and female) by neighbours and family members as well as strangers.

While patterns of sexual violence in the Great Lakes region have varied from context to context, a number of common features can nevertheless be observed. One is the sheer number of rapes: in one province of Burundi, for example, 90 per cent of women interviewed by CARE International reported that they had themselves been raped or knew someone who had (Zicherman, 2007). While firm statistics are hard to come by, it has been estimated that 2,000–5,000 children have been born of rapes that took place as part of the Rwandan genocide of 1994, that an average of forty women per day are even now being raped in the South Kivu Province of the DRC and that an estimated 20,000 – 30,000 children from northern Uganda were abducted by the LRA, of whom most of the girls were allocated to LRA cadres in forced marriage (Human Rights Watch, 2003).

A second feature of sexual violence in all four countries has been the extreme brutality of some of the sexual encounters concerned. International Alert and partners, for example, identified four types of rape based on interviews with 492 women and girls in South Kivu: individual rape, gang rape, rape in which victims are forced to rape each other and rape involving objects being inserted into the victim's genitals. In many cases, the victims were also tortured and/or murdered (International Alert et al., 2005). Françoise Nduwimana, in a report for Rights and Democracy, interviewed women in Rwanda who had been raped consistently by multiple attackers for up to sixty days (Nduwimana, 2004).

A further common feature is the widespread 'double violation' suffered by rape victims (especially adult women) who are ostracized by their communities and disowned by their husbands and families. In many cases this leaves them with no one to provide either moral or economic support, let alone medical or psychosocial care or assistance with the upkeep and care of the women's children, who may be rejected along with their mothers. There is some evidence that official duty-bearing agencies, such as the police and demobilization commissions, as well as service providers, including non-governmental assistance projects, may also discriminate against rape victims, especially those who have been abducted by militias and hence have spent time with them in the 'bush' (Aciro, 2007).

Finally, although there is evidence that at various times the main perpetrators have been soldiers (in national armies or rebel militias or both),[4] the end of formal hostilities has not led to a reduction in the numbers of rape cases being brought to the attention of service providers, and this has given rise to what has been described as a 'new' phenomenon, that of rape by civilians (Rodriguez, 2007). This point is picked up again below.

The international response

The prevalence of sexual violence in the Great Lakes region has been widely publicized internationally, and this has led to a large number of initiatives by both local and international agencies. Countries in the Great Lakes region have, as a result, benefited from substantial project funding for awareness-raising campaigns and for the delivery of support services to women victims of sexual violence. However, the quality of these interventions has given rise to criticism, including (notably in relation to the DRC) from within international agencies themselves. Many of the negative assessments have centred round the lack of effective coordination mechanisms, together with poor monitoring and regulation of standards (reported on by, for example, Bechler, 2008; and Rodriguez, 2007). However, a review of the record gives rise to several observations that require something more than a bureaucratic explanation.

A narrow range of solutions

Given the multifaceted impacts of sexual violence on the lives of the survivors, the response needs to be similarly all-encompassing; it should include not only specialized medical provision but also support in bringing cases to court, community sensitization and mediation, and support to victims in accessing independent economic opportunities. However, medical care dominates the field, and other forms of support are less in evidence. Projects offering psychosocial support are not uncommon, but questions linger about appropriate professional standards and the relevance of western psychotherapeutic approaches.[5] Nona Zicherman describes how a project run by CARE International in Burundi learned from experience that a holistic approach is essential: after eighteen months, the project found that it 'was unable to address the fundamental causes of the violence, including gender inequality and bad governance' (Zicherman, 2007, p. 49), a problem that it aimed to address in future programming through, for example, the integration of legal and economic as well as medical and psychosocial support. Many agencies, however, focus on one particular dimension of support, either because of the nature of their organization or as a result of funding constraints. General funding policies sometimes have the effect of excluding the provision of needed services, especially when the funding concerned is destined for 'emergency' projects.[6] Clearly, some support is better than none at all, but given that sexual violence initiatives in the Great

Lakes region tend to be well funded and politically supported, the patchiness in provision needs further explanation.

A narrow range of target beneficiaries

Services tend to focus on adult women survivors to the exclusion of others. While there can be little doubt that adult women form the majority of victims, the needs of other groups of sufferers are often sidelined. Marie-Josée Kandanga (2007) notes that in Burundi young women and girls who have spent time with armed groups (having been abducted, enticed, coerced or without other alternatives to survive, or having joined through political choice) tend to be excluded from internationally sponsored provision in favour of adult women.[7] International Alert's South Kivu partners providing refuges for abused women report that they are increasingly approached by male victims, for whose particular needs there is no special provision (Ndeye Sow, personal communication, 2006). This lack of capacity is confirmed by Wynne Russell (2007, p. 22), who points out that the phenomenon of sexual violence directed at men remains undocumented and poorly understood, despite helping 'to expose the broader phenomenon of conflict-related sexual violence, including against the women and girls who are the most numerous victims, for what it is: not "boys being boys" but an exercise in power and humiliation'.

Limited approaches to prevention

Approaches to the prevention of sexual violence tend to centre around advocacy and publicity campaigns (both local and international) to raise awareness and hence galvanize public censure of the perpetrators. For example, UN Action against Sexual Violence in Conflict (see http://www.stoprapenow.org) coordinates campaigns and other work for twelve UN agencies and a large number of international and local bodies. A less common approach to prevention is to curtail impunity through legal reform and the provision of legal assistance. The focus of prevention work is generally based on a normative human rights approach, in which other, more community-focused, initiatives are not always easily accommodated. Community-based prevention work is less common: examples that stand out are the CARE project in Burundi mentioned above, which seeks to enhance community-based prevention mechanisms by mobilizing local opinion in support of victims, and the work of International Alert's partners in South Kivu, combating prejudice against rape victims through conflict mediation. An approach which hardly appears at all is re-search into the motivations of perpetrators. International Alert's study in South Kivu sought, through interviews with survivors and other sources, including some perpetrators, to build up a picture of the context in which rapes took place with a view to understanding the factors that led to them (International Alert et al., 2005). Maria Erikson Baaz and Maria Stern (2008) interviewed military personnel in the DRC and documented their perspective on military ethics. These exceptions aside, there has been little work on prevention in the sense of seeking to understand the factors that lead to it as a preliminary to removing them.

Untested assumptions about the perpetrators of sexual violence

The impetus for much programming in this field (both victim-support proj-ects and advocacy work) is the assertion that there have been 'epidemics' of sexual violence in the Great Lakes region in recent years, the perpetrators of which have been army soldiers, other militias and supporters of violent move-ments, providing evidence for the use of rape as a 'weapon of war' (Csete and Kippenberg, 2002; Minzoni-Desroches, 2005). Such assertions have helped to put the issue of sexual violence high up on the advocacy agenda and have served to mobilize public opinion, locally and internationally, against the phenomenon. There can be no doubt that a great many perpetrators of sex-ual violence have been military (army or militias), and this is borne out by a large body of testimonial material from victims (see, for example, Ayoo, 2007; International Alert et al., 2005). Moreover, although there have been very few successful attempts to talk to perpetrators, evidence suggests that some soldiers may see sexual violence as being acceptable, under some circumstances, within military ethics (see Erikson Baaz and Stern, 2008, for interviews with the DRC army rank and file, both male and female).

However, there are two main reasons for recommending the careful in-terpretation of claims that sexual violence is used as a weapon of war. First, the phrase 'weapon of war' suggests that parties to conflict have adopted sex-ual violence as a conscious and deliberate military strategy. In the case of the Interahamwe Hutu nationalists, documentation does exist showing that their supremacist ideology was infused by a conscious gender analysis that fuelled hatred of Tutsi women and that as part of the genocide strategy Radio Mille Collines did incite supporters to rape Tutsi women (quoted in AVEGA, 1999: see also Nduwimana, 2004). Militia groups in the DRC do appear to have planned mass rapes as part of 'scorched earth' tactics for sowing terror and submission and for later demanding food and labour from the local population (Csete and Kippenberg, 2002, International Alert et al., 2005). However, evidence that sexual violence has been a deliberate military strategy in other contexts has been hard to come by.[8] The use of the phrase 'weapon of war' sometimes signals the writer's feelings about the severity of the impact of sexual violence rather than hard evidence of its deliberate and strategic use.

Secondly, there is some confusion surrounding the distinction between sexual violence by militias and that committed by 'ordinary' or 'civilian' men. As wars diminish in scale following peace agreements and demobilization, the threat from military personnel reduces, yet numbers of rapes do not necessarily go down. Indeed, they appear to continue at much the same levels: the CARE Burundi project, which saw a rough average of forty rape cases a month, began operating after the withdrawal of armed groups from the area concerned; perpetrators included neighbours, relatives and local burglars. In June 2008 in the DRC, two and a half years after the elections that brought in the current government and six months after the peace conference and ceasefire ending an outbreak of war in November 2007, there were reputed to have been over 2,000 cases of rape in North Kivu alone (Congo Advocacy Coalition, 2008). Workers in the field are often confused by this turn of events, so fundamentally unquestioned is the presumption that sexual violence in war is uniquely perpetrated by armed men as part and parcel of military strategy and ideology. However, a wide variety of explanations are possible, including – most significantly for our argument – the possibility that civilian men have been committing sexual violence all along without it having been adequately acknowledged or recorded. This point will be returned to below.

In summary, the response to the widespread sexual violence committed during and after civil war in the Great Lakes region has included strong policy advocacy and campaigning and increased levels of investment in practical support measures. However, the response has also been partial and has failed to fully take into account the diversity both of victims and of perpetrators, having been designed around untested assumptions about the nature of the problem. Moreover, the rather loose use of the concept of 'sexual violence as a weapon of war' in campaigns may inadvertently reduce the force of the argument. Most particularly, the response has failed to make a dent in levels of sexual violence, whether military or non-military. It cannot be said to resemble the 'comprehensive approach' called for by Rachel Jewkes (2007).

Discussion

To what extent might the roots of this insufficiency be found in the conceptual framing of the discourse around sexual violence? Does the model of 'sexual violence in conflict' current in mainstream policy discourse serve us well in building a transformative agenda? In this model, seen as a specific, natural product of armed conflict, the archetypal violent, aggressive male, encouraged by his participation in a predatory and uncontrolled military machine, seeks to destroy vulnerable womanhood as a key element in a strategy to bring down the enemy. Even if this model may indeed describe reality in many cases, it still does not constitute any form of explanation. Nor can we find in the model any clue as to how to explain other forms of sexual violence we have noted, such as the local violence that appears to continue after military confrontation has ended or the secondary violations experienced by raped women in the form of social rejection. Moreover, the fact that not all men behave in the same way is not addressed. This leaves us with some key questions about how violent, brutal masculinity is produced. Can we simply 'write off' perpetrators of sexual violence as being beyond the pale? Or should we view them as a phenomenon that demands analysis within a broader social context?

Looking outside the specificities of the Great Lakes region to the broader theoretical context, the 'archetypal aggressive male' model appears to be one of several subjects of increasing contestation around the gendered nature of violence in war. Lisa Kelly (2000) and Meredith Turshen (2001) have espoused the view that war is, in essence, 'war on women', an activity carried out by male militias with a view to acquiring both 'women's property' and 'women as property'. In this construction, rape in war takes on a variety of functions whose impact is, on the one hand, the inflicting of terror and humiliation on women as a means of fostering destabilization and social breakdown within the community of the enemy and, on the other hand, the enhancement of men's capacity to achieve these ends (Turshen, 1998). By contrast, however, a wide variety of literature on gender in the context of war suggests that the theorizing of gender and war needs to take account of a more complex reality. In this reality, men also suffer violence, including sexual violence and rape,[9] whereas women also perpetrate and provide various kinds of support to violence and war: taking part in combat itself, providing support services to other combatants as well as moral and practical support to war efforts, and through their role in socializing future generations (see, for example, Moser and Clark, 2001; Mukhta, 2000).

Assumptions are often made about how war does or does not have an impact on women's roles and on gender relations generally. However, a study for ACORD (Agency for Co-operation and Research in Development) based on case studies from five conflict-affected countries in Africa concluded that the impact of war is not consistent. While it is common for women to take on heavier economic and protection roles as a result of war, it does not follow that this will lead to greater control or decision-making power or to increased influence by women within community and political institutions. Indeed, at the level of underlying ideological values there is generally no change at all (El-Bushra and Sahl, 2005). Moreover, a number of writers have described the phenomenon of 'backlash' against the apparent gains that women have made during wartime (Pankhurst, 2007). This is certainly borne out in the Great Lakes region, where, in a preliminary study of women's political participation led by Ndeye Sow of International Alert, women parliamentarians and office-bearers described a consistent pattern of resistance – both overt and implicit, from both men and women (International Alert and EASSI, 2007). This suggests that underlying values that deny women a role in decision-making are firmly rooted, despite the fact that individuals may find ways of challenging them.

A hypothesis currently gaining ground among peacebuilding agencies is that structural inequality is a major factor in the generation of communal violence. The notion of 'cycles of violence', suggesting that the frustrations, resentments and learned behaviours of one generation can be carried over to the next ones, is relevant here and has some resonance in the Great Lakes region, where recent wars have been rooted in decades of history and where relationships based on violence of one sort or another have been replicated over generations. Further work towards understanding these relationships in greater depth in the Great Lakes context might build on work on gender, war and social change drawn from elsewhere that suggests that conflict dynamics and gender dynamics are intricately interconnected and will be drawn into interlocking and self-perpetuating cycles of violence unless the political will to create alternative dynamics can be mobilized (Cockburn and Zarkov, 2000; El-Bushra and Sahl, 2005).

Frustration at the narrowing of options may be an important factor in the generation of violence. Whereas individual men and women may respond to the crises generated by war with a wide range of adaptive strategies, some of which involve challenges to gendered norms of behaviour and role expectations, what they aspire to being remains relatively firm, even as the possibilities of living these aspirations fade (Dolan, 2002; El-Bushra and Sahl, 2005). The problem is not that society's values have been eroded by war but rather that these values continue to be critical to a person's sense of identity and self-esteem, with war narrowing the range of options through which these values can be lived.

Can this constraint legitimately be said to enhance violent sexual behaviour and contribute to ongoing cycles of violence? Some evidence suggests that this might be the case. Chris Dolan's (2002, p. 78) account of male violence in northern Uganda extends Henrietta Moore's (1994) notion of 'thwarting' to describe how the deprivations of the war have prevented men from attaining the ideal characteristics of manhood – the capacity to provide and protect, to marry and beget children, to provide responsible leadership and maintain respect – leading many to resort to various forms of abuse and self-harm, including alcoholism, domestic violence, and suicide. Violence, far from being a component of a masculine model, is the 'last resort of those who are unable to achieve "masculinity"'. Similarly, Maria Erikson Baaz and Maria Stern (2008, pp. 21–22), analysing interviews with rank and file soldiers in the DRC, describe how soldiers explain, if not excuse, coercive sex perpetrated by their fellow soldiers as being the result of desperation linked to their subordinate status within the military establishment: 'rape, poverty, frustration, power (having a "gun"), and the "craziness" of war are "all connected" ... the soldiers thus situated rape in a "general wish to destroy" which arises from "suffering" and "frustrations"'. Significantly, in their study such explanations are offered by female as well as male soldiers, raising the question of how men's violence can be supported by women, who arguably stand to lose as its potential victims.

This suggests the possibly controversial thought that perpetrators may themselves in some sense be victims, not only of the circumstances which have shaped their behaviour, but also of the mental health consequences to themselves of their own actions, consequences that can in turn lead to further violence on their part if they are not addressed. To cite a different but parallel case, evidence from International Alert's reconciliation programme in Rwanda suggests that genocide perpetrators, as well as survivors, may suffer trauma if not helped and that the majority of rank and file perpetrators – like many survivors – belong to groups that are socially and economically marginalized, a fact that limits opportunities for healing. The programme's experience so far is that cycles of deprivation, resentment and violence are difficult to break unless the psychological and economic needs of perpetrators, as well as survivors, are addressed (Gloriosa Bazigaga, personal communication, 2007). This experience may throw light on the issue of sexual violence: strategies aimed at alleviating the contextual factors that contribute to the phenomenon – that is, strategies that help the perpetrators – may also be to the advantage of potential victims and society more generally.

Returning to the question of why 'ordinary' men commit rape after the war is over, evidence from other contexts suggests that civilian violence in the period immediately following the end of a war is not uncommon. This phenomenon has given rise to surprise and confusion among workers in the field of sexual violence during conflict, and a wide variety of explanations have been offered, generally rather speculatively.[10] Rapes may be committed by demobilized militias returning to civilian life (facilitated by the continuing circulation of small arms, which enables ex-combatants to continue to impose their will by force); civilian men may use the cover of general lawlessness to settle old scores; militias may return home to a family situation to which it is difficult to adjust (wives may have left, had children with other men or, as in the case of Rwanda, have acquired increased rights through legal reform). For some workers in this field, the only possible explanation is that armed conflict must itself be to blame since it undermines the moral fabric of society.

It is less often suggested that improved reporting and increased access to information about affected populations might give the appearance of an increase in the incidence of sexual violence, whereas the truth may be that it has existed clandestinely all along. This may particularly be the case with the sexual abuse of children, awareness of which is nowadays on the increase. In fact, there is often little empirical basis for asserting that the level of sexual violence in the population at large has changed, in comparison with either pre-war or during-war levels. However, to the extent that levels of violence are indeed very high, the notions outlined above of 'thwarting' and 'cycles of violence' may have some explanatory power. It is arguable that rape by militias (whether as a weapon of war or not) and rape by non-military men might both arise out of similar sets of circumstances and hence be perfectly understandable in tandem. We might expect economic deprivation and political repression to be strong elements of these contexts. At the same time, the life experiences of individual men, also to be seen in context, might have an impact in the Great Lakes region, as it appears to elsewhere.[11] It is therefore important not to evaluate men's behaviour in isolation from the values and expectations prevalent in the society that shapes their thinking. These values and expectations apply to and are experienced by women as well as men. The widespread phenomenon in the Great Lakes region of raped women being stigmatized by their families and communities suggests that ideologies of gender operating at a fundamental social and cultural level provide fertile ground for sexual violence to flourish in the absence of serious attempts at censure.

The picture implied by the international response to sexual violence during conflict in the Great Lakes – man with gun, vulnerable woman – is rigid and one-dimensional, a 'one-size-fits-all masculinity' (Shepherd, 2008, p. 41). This picture obscures the possibility that brutal and violent rape might constitute one end of a continuum that might also include non-military rape, other forms of coercive sex and indeed other forms of oppressive behaviour (which might, incidentally, be perpetrated by either men or women, and the victims of which might likewise be either men or women). It similarly obscures the potential links between conflict and non-conflict situations (are things really so different during conflict, in essence?), between military personnel and the societies they belong to and between societies torn apart by civil war, on the one hand, and the geopolitical order that regulates responses to war, on the other.

It is difficult to explain the rigidity and lack of functionality of this response, other than by concluding that the international community is in the grip of collective domination by what R. Charli Carpenter (2006) describes as the 'gender essentialisms' current in the humanitarian profession. Moreover, this single-vision approach is supported by an equally one-dimensional mainstream gender paradigm that extends into international policy on gender, conflict and security more broadly and helps to perpetuate the very power imbalances it seeks to undermine.[12] The problem is not that sexual violence does not happen or that it should not be condemned – of course it does, and of course it should. But the question is: does our conceptualization of the problem provide us with the tools to understand the complexity of the power dynamics involved and to change them – and if not, why not?

Starting again

At the heart of this discussion is the concept of 'gender' – what does it mean in this context and what should we use it to achieve? These questions are deeply contentious since the word has been adopted by a wide variety of interest groups, each of which infuses it with their own interpretation. Indeed, confusion over its meaning appears to have become a barrier to effective progress at the policy level, and this confusion may well have consequences for the implementation of policy strategies.[13]

> Gender: refers to the social attributes and opportunities associated with being male and female and the relationships between women and men and girls and boys, as well as the relations between women and those between men. These attributes, opportunities and relationships are socially constructed and are learned through socialization processes. They are context/time-specific and changeable. Gender determines what is expected, allowed and valued in a women or a man in a given context. In most societies there are differences and inequalities between women and men in responsibilities assigned, activities undertaken, access to and control over resources, as well as decision-making opportunities. Gender is part of the broader socio-cultural context. Other important criteria for socio-cultural analysis include class, race, poverty level, ethnic group and age. (OSAGI, n.d.)

What is contentious is not so much the definition of the word (see above for an authoritative example) as the conceptual paradigm within which it is used and the discourse that reflects this paradigm. Much of the international policy discourse on gender stems from a wish to validate that which has largely gone unrecognized in the past – namely, women's lived experiences and in particular women's own accounts and perceptions of these experiences. Given the searing and brutal nature of much of this experience, attention inevitably turns to the main perpetrators of this brutality, that is, men. However, as an analytical process this lacks explanatory power: it detaches men and women from their historical social and cultural contexts while also failing to account for the contradictory phenomena of male vulnerability and female aggression. We have yet to identify a society that positively values the capacity for brutal, violent rape or in which rape is practised by more than a minority of the population. Any explanation of how and why sexual violence occurs in some contexts and not in others therefore needs to be more sophisticated than the 'one-size-fits-all' version of masculinity in conflict alluded to above if it is to contribute to finding a way of changing things that goes beyond containment and protection.

What if we understood a gender framework as operating at a different and more abstract level; if, as Spike Peterson (2008, p. 2) suggests, it were 'not merely an empirical category of male-female difference, but an analytical category of masculine-feminine difference and hierarchy that constitutes a governing code'? Such an approach would require us to consider gender relations within a socio-psychological framework, looking beyond actual behaviours to the social relations that shape them and looking beyond social relations to the underlying ideologies of gender and how these are politically constructed and maintained.

As generations of radical social analysts have maintained, the most effective form of power is that which does not need to be overtly imposed since it has entered the value systems of both the powerful and the powerless: people accept it 'either because they can see or imagine no alternative to it, or because they see it as natural and unchangeable, or because they value it as divinely ordained and beneficial' (Lukes, 1974, p. 24). This suggests that the affective dimension of social relations is key, despite being relatively overlooked in analyses of conflict. Like Spike Peterson (2008, p. 2), we should insist on linking 'what we do' and 'how we think' with 'who we are', looking at the 'processes of subject-formation, and the complex politics these entail'. Power relations cannot then be reduced to simple dualities, such as men and women, armed and unarmed, but require complex hierarchies to be teased out within each separate context. Which men are the powerful ones, and what enables some men to have power over others – and indeed some women to have power over other women and over some men? How do communities, governments and global institutions help to shape these hierarchies and the ideological and psychological frameworks that underpin them?

The prevalence of sexual violence in the Great Lakes region offers an opportunity, not only to dig deeper into an understanding of the factors that have given rise to and perpetuate the phenomenon, but also to examine whether an alternative and more nuanced discursive approach to gender, focusing on understanding the dynamics of identity and power, might have stronger transformational potential. An immediate implication of this is the need for research and reflection about the perpetrators of sexual violence. Though basic data do exist about the perpetrators in some contexts (military or civilian, known to the victim or not, etc.), little is known about what distinguishes perpetrators from non-perpetrators or military from non-military perpetrators, what conditions have led them to commit such acts, how these acts are viewed by those around them and what the consequences of their actions for their own mental and physical health, as well as that of others, might be. We need insight into the value systems or thought processes that underpin their behaviour and into how and by whom those value systems are maintained. We need to understand where perpetrators fit into their societies of origin or into their occupational

259

roles, what sanctions are or are not applied and what rewards or opportunities they gain or forego through their behaviour. Despite the difficulties of reconstructing the past from inadequate records, some attempts could be made to find out how prevalent the phenomenon of sexual violence was in the past or what form it took and what factors may have led to change. In short, we need to understand men's agency and how it is affected by violent conflict.

Secondly, the insights gained from such reflection need to be translated into practical action for change. For better research to lead to better outcomes, the knowledge gained has to be shared inside and outside of the academy and to be expressed in language that resonates globally while having an impact locally, a balance that policy declarations notoriously fail to achieve. Without prejudicing the conclusions of any such research, one might tentatively expect it to demonstrate ways of generating greater holism and stronger complementarity in policy, investment and action – a greater range of interventions, with better coordination and synergy between them and a stronger emphasis on mechanisms that involve local communities and intervention agencies acting together in a shared search for solutions.

Conclusions

The above exploration of some of the issues surrounding the international response to sexual violence in the Great Lakes region has led us to consider the limitations of policy. While policy is an important resource if it enables us to mobilize funding streams and intellectual resources for concerns that might otherwise drop off the international agenda, at the same time there is a need for constant vigilance against the 'dumbing down' and narrowing of focus that the achievement of policy consensus may entail. The language of policy work on HIV and AIDS and on sexual violence often seems to be overly technical, detached from the varied contexts to which policy has to adapt and forgetting that what we are really talking about is the nature and quality of sexual intimacy between individual human beings.

There is a fertile point of intersection between HIV and AIDS, sexual violence and a gendered approach to analysing violent conflict. We started with the proposition that HIV infection involves more than the physical process of transmission: the latter is crucially conditioned by the surrounding social and cultural contexts. At the same time, understanding the social and cultural dimensions of sexual relations is a key step in moving beyond approaches focusing on the containment of sexual violence in conflict settings and measures of protection, towards effective prevention. A gender analysis would provide us with a framework within which to describe the nature and the parameters of both sexual violence and HIV transmission and to understand more fully how to create the conditions that could lead to the elimination of both.

The link between HIV and sexual violence as policy issues is that both are essentially about relationships – specifically, relationships whose intimate nature brings to the fore people's deepest feelings about their identity and values. Community-based HIV prevention programmes (such as Stepping Stones,[14] for example) have demonstrated the importance for successful prevention of giving people the opportunity to build relationships based on mutual respect. The issue of sexual violence is important in HIV prevention, not only because violent sexual encounters enhance the risk of infection, but just as crucially, because the prevalence of sexual violence reflects a sort of existential crisis, one that narrows the possibility of interactions – between sexual partners, parents and children, leaders and community members – that are mutually fulfilling. Such a context creates ideal conditions for the spread of the virus.

What is the particular relevance of violent conflict in this interaction between HIV and sexual violence? The hypothesis suggested by the above analysis is that situations of violent conflict may have an impact that we pay insufficient attention to: namely, that they can inhibit the flourishing of relationships that are characterized by mutual respect in various ways. This may be because people are obliged by the exceptional circumstances of war to take on roles that would in normal times be seen as unacceptable, thereby alienating themselves from their peers and finding themselves in positions from which it is later difficult to be accepted back into the fold. It may be because the exigencies of war restrict communication between groups over a long period, so that afterwards trust becomes difficult to re-establish. Respect and trust do not figure prominently in the international policy agenda, but it may be critical to foster these in post-war contexts.

A gender lens can contribute powerfully to strategies for addressing HIV and AIDS, sexual violence and violent conflict. However, the approach taken to gender is critical. The above analysis indicates that three elements are essential to enhancing the transformational potential of gender frameworks. Firstly, gender frameworks need to enable the analysis of power relations and how these are sustained in a given setting, including by international policy-making and interventions. Secondly, and as part of this analysis, the frameworks need to operate at several levels at once, looking not only at the everyday behaviour of men and women but also at the structures within which power relations are manifested and at the underlying affective and ideological underpinnings of those structures. Thirdly, the frameworks need to seek the transformation of power relations by adopting a holistic view of society in which the abuse of rights is combated within an overall strategy of inclusiveness and affirmation for all social categories.

Acknowledgements

Thanks are due to International Alert for its support in the preparation of this chapter. An earlier version of this chapter was presented to the AIDS, Security and Conflict Initiative (ASCI) gender seminar held in London in May 2008. The aim of this chapter is to raise questions for discussion about the gender dimensions of the HIV and AIDS and security problematic and to suggest avenues for future research on sexual violence specifically. Thanks are due to participants at the ASCI meeting for their comments on the earlier draft and for the stimulating seminar discussion. The views presented here are the writer's alone.

Notes

1. Biological transference of the virus is rendered more likely when sex is accompanied by violence, and at the same time, sexual relations characterized by violence are statistically more likely to lead to infection (ELDIS, 2007; SVRI, 2007; WHO, 2004).

2. Paul Spiegel, medical epidemiologist, currently chief of public health for the UN High Commission on Refugees, led the 2007 study of HIV prevalence in seven conflict-affected countries, which concluded there was no evidence to substantiate frequently made assumptions that refugee populations fleeing from conflict act as vectors of HIV transmission into host populations (Spiegel et al., 2007).

3. Formal transition came to an end in 2004 in Rwanda, 2005 in Burundi and 2006 in the DRC. Civil war in Uganda ended in 1986. The agreement between the Government of Uganda and the northern Ugandan rebel movement, the Lord's Resistance Army, has been poised for signature since early 2008.

4. Moreover, there is substantial evidence of sexual violence being committed by international peacekeepers, notably in Somalia, Sierra Leone and Mozambique (see Graybill [2006] for a summary of the evidence).

5. CARE Burundi found that the psychosocial component of its sexual violence project needed improving in future (Zicherman, 2007). A UN/OCHA (Office for the Coordination of Humanitarian Affairs) evaluation of counselling projects undertaken in South Kivu, the DRC, in 2005 found that many were doing 'more harm than good' (Rodriguez, 2007, p. 46). More generally, doubts have been raised for some years about psychosocial interventions based on 'western approaches which presuppose the incidence of mental trauma and tend to take a simplistic view of the complex and evolving experiences of war-affected populations' (Summerfield, 1996).

6. For example, funding for microfinance projects may only be available in situations deemed to be in a 'development phase'.

7. The Cape Town Principles (UNICEF, 1997) define as a 'child soldier' any young person who has spent time with armed groups, whether or not they have borne arms. For more background on the 'invisibility' of girl ex-combatants generally, see Ayoo (2007); McKay and Mazurana (2004); and Save the Children (2005). The latter underscores the problem that the broad exclusion of girls from service provision is part and parcel of a general inability on the part of the international community to 'see' young adults and youth, in spite of a large body of policy directives on young people's rights.

8. Note that UN Security Council Resolution 1820 of June 2008 on sexual violence in conflict situations does not 'classify sexual violence as a war tactic' as some headlines have claimed but instead, somewhat cautiously, 'stresses that sexual violence, when used or commissioned as a tactic of war … can significantly exacerbate situations of armed conflict and may impede the restoration of international peace and security'.

9. See Dubravka Zarkov's (2001) path-breaking study of sexual violence against men in former Yugoslavia, and the way it was reported in the Serbian press, for conclusive evidence that women are not unique in suffering sexual violence in wartime.

10. Pankhurst (2007) includes a broad review of evidence and analytical approaches.

11. Donna Pankhurst (2007), reviewing the academic literature on gender in post-conflict situations, gives little credibility to current explanations of male violence in existing research, although she finds some value in evidence that men's behaviour may be influenced by any early experience of experiencing, witnessing or carrying out violence.

12. See Shepherd (2008) for a textual critique of UNSCR 1325 and El-Bushra (2007) and Vincent (2001) for similar commentaries on the discourse on women and peacebuilding.

13. Shahrashoub Razavi and Carol Miller's prescient 1995 review of the evolution of gender as a concept in international policy underlined a number of dilemmas in the conceptual shift from WID (women in development) to GAD (gender and development). They argued that GAD provided broader analytical scope, opening up new mechanisms for women's advancement by linking it to social and cultural frameworks. However, they also predicted that progress would be subject to, among other things, the danger that 'gender mainstreaming' would lead to radical policy agendas being sidestepped and that confusion about the 'real meaning' of gender would result in the continuing mystification of gender policy.

14. See the Stepping Stones website at http://www.steppingstonesfeedback.org/ (accessed 5 September 2008).

References

Aciro, K. 2007. Child mothers in the Northern Uganda conflict. S. H. Ayoo (ed.), *'Lost Generation'— Young People and Conflict in Africa*. Nairobi, ACORD/DCI, pp. 38–56.

Amnesty International. 2004. *Democratic Republic of Congo: Mass Rape – Time for Remedies*. London, Amnesty International Publications. http://www.amnesty.org/en/library/asset/AFR62/018/2004/en/dom-AFR620182004en.html (Accessed 17 August 2008.)

Anema, A., Joffres, M. R., Mills, E. and Spiegel, P. B. 2008. Widespread rape does not directly appear to increase the overall HIV prevalence in conflict-affected countries: So now what? *Emerging Themes in Epidemiology*, Vol. 5, No.11.

AVEGA (Association des Veuves du Genocide). 1999. *Survey on Violence Against Women in Rwanda*. Kigali, Mimeo.

Ayoo, S. J. (ed.). 2007. *'Lost Generation' – Young People and Conflict in Africa*. Nairobi, ACORD/DCI.

Bechler, R. 2008. Sexual violence: Not just a gender issue. *Open Democracy*. http://www.opendemocracy.net/blog/rosemary-bechler/2008/06/05/sexual-violence-not-just-a-gender-issue

Carpenter, R. C. 2006. *'Innocent Women and Children': Gender, Norms and the Protection of Civilians*. Aldershot, United Kingdom, Ashgate.

Cockburn, C. and Zarkov, D. (eds). 2000. *The Postwar Moment: Militaries, Masculinities and International Peacekeeping*. London, Lawrence and Wishart.

Congo Advocacy Coalition. 2008. *Update on Protection of Civilians in Eastern Congo's Peace Process*. http://hrw.org/english/docs/2008/07/28/congo19717.htm (Accessed 5 September 2008.)

Csete, J. and Kippenberg, J. 2002. *The War Within the War: Sexual Violence Against Women and Girls in Eastern Congo*. New York, Human Rights Watch.

Dolan, C. 2002. Collapsing masculinities and weak states – A case study of northern Uganda. F. Cleaver (ed.), *Masculinities Matter! Men, Gender and Development*. London, Zed Press, pp. 57–83.

El-Bushra, J. 2007. Feminism, Gender, and Women's Peace Activism. *Development and Change*, Vol. 38, No. 1. The Hague, Institute of Social Studies, pp. 131–47.

El-Bushra, J. and Sahl, I. 2005. *Cycles of Violence: Gender Relations and Armed Conflict*. Nairobi, ACORD.

ELDIS. 2007. HIV and AIDS infection as a consequence of violence against women. http://www.eldis.org/index.cfm?objectId=C4E459CA-F5A8-8227-76FB6E0A6DC473FA (Accessed 2 January 2009.)

Eriksson Baaz, M. and Stern, M. 2008. Why do soldiers rape? Gender, violence and sexuality in the DRC Armed Forces. Unpublished paper, Goteborg University, Sweden.

Graybill, L. S. 2006. Peacekeepers in Africa and gender violence. *SSRC Quarterly Newsletter.* http://programs.ssrc.org/gsc/gsc_quarterly/newsletter5/content/graybill (Accessed 12 September 2008.)

Halperin, D. T. and Epstein H. 2004. Concurrent sexual partnerships help to explain Africa's high HIV prevalence: Implications for prevention. *Lancet,* Vol. 364, No. 9428, pp. 4–6.

Human Rights Watch. 2003. *Stolen Children: Abduction and Recruitment in Northern Uganda.* New York, Human Rights Watch, p. 5. http://www.hrw.org/reports/2003/uganda0303/uganda0403.pdf

International Alert and EASSI (Eastern African Sub-regional Support Initiative for the Advancement of Women). 2007. Women's political participation in countries emerging from conflict in the Great Lakes region of Africa. Report of EASSI/IA workshop held in Kampala in 2007.

International Alert, RFDA (Réseau des Femmes pour un Développement Associantif) and RFDP (Réseau des Femmes pour la Défense des Droits et la Paix). 2005. *Women's Bodies as a Battleground: Sexual Violence Against Women and Girls During the War in the Democratic Republic of Congo – South Kivu (1996–2003).* Bujumbura, DRC/Bukavu, DRC/London, RFDA/RFDP/International Alert.

Jacobson, R., Jacobs, S. and Marchbank, J. 2000. Introduction. S. Jacobs, R. Jacobson and J. Marchbank (eds), *States of Conflict: Gender, Violence and Resistance.* London, Zed Books, pp. 1–23.

Jewkes, R. 2007. Comprehensive response to rape needed in conflict settings. *Lancet,* Vol. 369, No. 9580, pp. 2140–141.

Kandanga, M. J. 2007. Girls affected by violence and conflict in Burundi. S. J. Ayoo (ed.), *'Lost Generation' – Young People and Conflict in Africa.* Nairobi, ACORD/DCI, pp. 14–37.

Kelly, L. 2000. Wars against women: Sexual violence, sexual politics and the militarised state. S. Jacobs, R. Jacobson and J. Marchbank (eds), *States of Conflict: Gender, Violence and Resistance.* London, Zed Books, pp. 45–65.

Klot, J. and DeLargy, P. 2007. Sexual violence and HIV/AIDS transmission. *Forced Migration Review,* No. 27, pp. 23–24.

Lukes, S. 1974. *Power: A Radical View.* Basingstoke, United Kingdom, Palgrave.

McKay, S. and Mazurana, D. 2004. *Where Are the Girls? Girls in Fighting Forces in Northern Uganda, Sierra Leone, and Mozambique: Their Lives During and After War.* Montréal, Canada, International Centre for Human Rights and Democratic Development.

Minzoni-Deroche, A. 2005. *Rape as a Tactic of War: Advocacy Paper*. Vatican City, Caritas International Advocacy and Lobbying Unit.

Mock, N., Duale, S. Brown, L. Mathys, E. O'Maonaigh, H., Abul-Husn, N. and Elliott, S. 2004. Conflict and HIV: A framework for risk assessment to prevent HIV in conflict-affected settings in Africa. *Emerging Themes in Epidemiology*, Vol. 1, No. 6. http://www.ete-online.com/content/1/1/6 (Accessed 1 August 2008.)

Moore, H. 1994. The problem of explaining violence in the social sciences. P. Harvey and P. Gow (eds), *Sex and Violence: Issues in Representation and Experience* London/New York, Routledge, pp. 138–55.

Moser, C. and Clark, F. (eds). 2001. *Victims, Perpetrators or Actors? Gender, Armed Conflict and Political Violence*. London, Zed Books.

Mukhta, P. 2000. Gender, community, nation: The myth of innocence. S. Jacobs, R. Jacobson and J. Marchbank (eds), *States of Conflict: Gender, Violence and Resistance*. London, Zed Books, pp. 163–78.

Nduwimana, F. 2004. *The Right to Survive: Sexual Violence, Women and HIV/AIDS*. Montréal, Canada, Rights and Democracy.

OSAGI (UN Office of the Special Adviser on Gender Issues and Advancement of Women). n.d. *Concepts and Definitions*. http://www.un.org/womenwatch/osagi/conceptsandefinitions.htm (Accessed 26 August 2008.)

Pankhurst, D. 2007. *Gender Issues in Post-War Contexts: A Review of Analysis and Experience, and Implications for Policies*. Bradford, United Kingdom, University of Bradford/UNRISD. (Working Paper 9.)

Peterson, V. S. 2008. Gendering informal economies in Iraq. Unpublished paper, London, London School of Economics.

Razavi, S. and Miller, C. 1995. *From WID to GAD: Conceptual Shifts in the Women and Development Discourse*. Geneva, UNRISD.

Rodriguez, C. 2007. Sexual violence in South Kivu, Congo. *Forced Migration Review*, No. 27, pp. 45–46.

Russell, W. 2007. Sexual violence against men and boys. *Forced Migration Review*, No. 27, pp. 22–23.

Save the Children. 2005. *Forgotten Casualties of War*. Westport, Conn., Save the Children. http://www.savethechildren.org.uk/scuk_cache/scuk/cache/cmsattach/2800_Forgottencasualties33395.pdf (Accessed 1 January 2007.)

Shepherd, L. 2008. *Gender, Violence and Security: Discourse as Practice*. London, Zed Books.

Spiegel, P., Bennedsen, A. R., Claass, J., Bruns, L., Patterson, N., Yiweza, D. and Schilperoord, M. 2007. Prevalence of HIV infection in conflict-affected and displaced people in seven sub-Saharan African countries: A systematic review. *Lancet*, Vol. 369, No. 9580, pp. 2187–195.

Summerfield, D. 1996. Assisting survivors of war and atrocity: Notes on 'psycho-social' issues for NGO workers. *Development in States of War.* Oxford, United Kingdom, Oxfam, pp. 85–89.

SVRI (Sexual Violence Research Initiative). 2007. *Sexual Violence and HIV Factsheet.* Pretoria, SVRI. http://www.aidsportal.org/repos/factsheet1.pdf (Accessed 2 January 2009.)

Turshen, M. 1998. Women's war stories. M. Turshen and C. Twagiramariya (eds), *What Do Women Do in Wartime? Gender and Conflict in Africa.* London, Zed Books, pp. 1–26.

——. 2001. The political economy of rape: An analysis of systematic rape and sexual abuse of women during armed conflict in Africa. C. Moser and F. Clark (eds), *Victims, Perpetrators or Actors: Gender, Armed Conflict and Political Violence.* London, Zed Books, pp. 55–68.

UNICEF (United Nations Children's Fund). 1997. *Cape Town Principles and Best Practices Adopted at the Symposium on the Prevention of Recruitment of Children into the Armed Forces and on Demobilisation and Social Reintegration of Child Soldiers in Africa.* Cape Town, UNICEF.

United Nations Security Council. 2008. *Resolution 1820.* 19 June.

Vincent, L. 2001. Engendering peace in Africa: A critical inquiry into some current thinking on the role of African women in peace-building. *African Journal on Conflict Resolution,* Vol. 2, No. 1, pp. 13–30. http://www.accord.org.za/ajcr/2001-1/accordr_v2_n1_a4.html (Accessed 12 May 2005.)

WHO (World Health Organization). 2004. *Violence Against Women and HIV/AIDS: Critical Intersections – Intimate Partner Violence and HIV/AIDS.* Geneva, WHO. http://www.who.int/gender/violence/en/vawinformationbrief.pdf (Accessed 1 January 2009.) (Information Bulletin Series, Number 1.)

Zarkov, D. 2001. The body of the other man: Sexual violence and the construction of masculinity, sexuality and ethnicity in the Croatian media. C. Moser and F. Clark (eds), *Victims, Perpetrators or Actors: Gender, Armed Conflict and Political Violence.* London, Zed Books, pp. 69–82.

Zicherman, N. 2007. Addressing sexual violence in post-conflict Burundi. *Forced Migration Review,* No. 27, pp. 48–49.

Section III: Cultures of Response

Introductory Essay

Mary Crewe

AIDS is not just about the stark reality of people dying, it is also crucially about representation, about silences and denial, about discrimination and stigma and about desire, force and coercion. As has been seen throughout the world, AIDS has the potential for generating social disruption, for challenging the fabric of social life and for inspiring rash and oppressive measures (Bayer, 1989, p. 4).

The chapters in this section show the need for a far more complex and sophisticated understanding of how societies and individuals respond to HIV interventions. They show the need to use the lens of culture to sharpen analysis of how prevention and treatment strategies produce new social forms and local responses. And they show the need to focus more on unintended consequences of public health interventions. They contribute to a growing debate about how to define or bound the concept of 'culture' and what it means specifically in the context of HIV and AIDS. And they highlight the need for even more rigorous analysis about how culture(s) can both transform the trajectory of epidemics and be transformed by them. They also show how, in the context of HIV and AIDS, various meanings of culture have become convenient avenues through which to evade debate.

Using culture as an analytic lens requires more than focusing on the norms and traditions through which people live their lives. It also draws attention to cultures that have uniquely arisen around this epidemic, including international cultures of response, the dominant culture of response, cultures of resistance and status quo, gender culture, and cultures of silence, of public

The designations employed and the presentation of material throughout this publication do not imply the expression of any opinion whatsoever on the part of UNESCO concerning the legal status of any country, territory or area or of its authorities, or concerning the delimitation of its frontiers or boundaries.
The ideas and opinions expressed in this publication are those of the authors and do not necessarily reflect the views of UNESCO and its Member States.

health and of human rights. All of these cultures are interwoven and shape how people understand their own particular cultural identities. Individually and collectively, they have influenced HIV and AIDS prevention and care responses and how we understand the societies and communities in which we are working. They have sharpened, and sometimes even blocked, how we are able to create new understanding and explanations for the complex social and personal lives people live. These cultures of response, resistance and retribution have made our work of understanding the epidemic and its prevention and treatment much more complicated.

HIV prevention and response is perhaps more difficult now than earlier in the epidemic. This is because at so many levels we are faced with an orthodoxy and culture of control that shuts down debate and leaves the explanations to 'celebrities and experts'. This orthodoxy has led to increasing attempts to homogenize responses and to use culture as a form of exclusion or inclusion. It seldom uses a cultural framework as a critical analytical tool to assess global HIV interventions. In this context, it might be helpful to heed Foucault, who reminds us to pay attention to who talks, who frames the question and who legitimates the answers and the questions.[1]

The chapters in this section bring a range of issues and dilemmas to the fore, including, for example, the work to defend and protect gay rights and openness in Namibia and the gender dynamics characterizing relationships between men who have sex with men and women (Robert Lorway); the social construction of wife inheritance in Uganda (Stella Nyanzi, Margaret Emodu-Walakira and Wilberforce Serwaniko); the ways in which international donors shape responses to epidemics and interventions (Haken Seckinelgin); how doctors, academics and activists have been able to work with governments in developing AIDS interventions that are sensitive to cultural norms (Orkideh Behrouzan); the unintended consequences of treatment programmes as they spur patients to have children and establish new families (Joséphine Aho and Vinh-Kim Nguyen); and how, counterintuitively, women outnumber men in treatment programmes in South Africa, raising challenges of how to design health care programmes and outreach messages (Nicoli Nattrass).

These chapters show that wherever there is power, there is resistance – but that resistance can take many forms. As suggested by Laclau and Mouffe, there is nothing inevitable or natural in struggles against power, and it is necessary to explain in each case the reasons for their emergence and different modulations (Smith, 1998, p. 6). The struggle against subordination and its particular forms cannot be explained simply to be the result of the situation of subordination.

All of the chapters in this section examine interventions that were designed to address the AIDS epidemic but where dominant explanations and understandings failed the people they were supposed to help. By examining the cultures of response to the epidemic, these chapters also closely document the lives of those affected by it. They explore the specific and particular cultural and social settings in which public health interventions take place and how they produce cultural forms and local responses that sharpen our understanding of the life experiences of those affected by the epidemic. Writing early in the epidemic, Stuart Hall emphasized that AIDS raises politically important cultural questions. AIDS, he argued, is also

> a question of who gets represented and who does not. ... the site at which the advance of sexual politics is being rolled back. It's a site at which not only people will die, but desire and pleasure will also die if certain metaphors do not survive, or survive in the wrong way. Unless we operate in this tension, we don't know what cultural studies can do. (cited in Proctor, 2004, p. 3)

International cultures of response

The dominant culture of the West has set the scene for much of the response to HIV and AIDS, both in terms of how the West described its own epidemic and, more important, in how it describes other epidemics, particularly the so-called African epidemic. This dominant culture established abstinence, fidelity and the nuclear family as universal social norms and assumed an element of choice in how people determine their social, personal and sexual relations. The developing world was, in many respects, caught up in this globalized response and its social categories: it formed a part of a particular worldview, and yet it was both judged by and excluded from that view. This created uneasy tension between 're-specting and understanding them' and trying to 'change and mainstream them'.

Notions of tradition and modernity are central to this tension, which plays itself out in conflicting claims to respect and protect traditional cultures and to challenge the traditional cultures and harmful practices that contribute to the epidemic. Here, the ways in which male circumcision, wife inheritance and African sexuality are discussed are particularly telling, as seen in the chapter by Nyanzi, Emodu-Walakira and Serwaniko. There is limited recognition of how dominant, patriarchal cultures in post-colonial societies collude with and feed into the epidemic. And there is also little understanding of how measures to promote gender equality frequently create gender inequality, with women being blamed for the spread of the epidemic and rendered more vulnerable through increased care burdens and the effects of poverty. The dominant culture can mask the challenges people face confronting HIV and AIDS while also overshadowing their efforts to resist the dominant culture.

Within this dominant culture, United Nations agencies and many donors are caught in a bind – they want globalized responses to be effective but, at the same time, recognize that they may fail precisely because a globalized response oversimplifies causes, affected communities and their responses. Seckinelgin's chapter explores how the invisibility and marginalization of intellectual critiques about these globalized and homogenized responses to the epidemic further silence important local knowledge about the impact of interventions and responses to it. The tyranny of the dominant mainstream will be one of the most lasting legacies of the failure of HIV prevention and response.

Cultures of resistance

This is not to suggest that there should be only localized or parochial interventions and responses to HIV and AIDS. After all, the world is obviously linked in a multitude of ways, and people move between various nations, cultures and societies. While cultural difference is often used to strengthen the various rhetorics of blame, cultures are too intermingled, their contents and case histories too interdependent and hybridized, to be separated into large and mostly ideological oppositions (Said, 1996). Nonetheless, the force of the silences and disjunctures that occur when international perceptions meet local intimacies argues in favour of adopting a more reflective and sensitive response to the ways in which nations and peoples are categorized and described in the HIV and AIDS epidemic. It also raises the possibility that international perceptions may be wrong and that challenging the ways in which people are positioned is both legitimate and necessary.

As the compelling chapter by Lorway shows, cultures of intervention can result in the creation of subcultures of resistance. For instance, gay men have been affected directly by this epidemic and indirectly by political forces and social mores that also gave voice to their exclusion and marginalization. Through this voice, they have been able to push a prevention agenda and a culture of openness in many areas. They have also been able to strengthen the voices of people living with HIV and the voices of sex workers, bisexual people and women. Even if this resistance culture is in certain places muted and constrained, the fact remains that AIDS has forced dominant cultures to take heed of these oppositional cultures and differing worldviews – even if (and here is the dilemma) they do so through the lens of the dominant worldview. HIV and AIDS interventions have not served oppositional cultures well as members of those cultures have always been treated as outsiders; this has led to most interventions eventually siding with oppressive dominant cultures.

Status quo culture

Status quo cultures are very difficult cultures to address because they reflect the world as it is rather than as it might be. This tension is beautifully explored in Behrouzan's chapter on the Islamic Republic of Iran and is touched upon in all the other essays in this section. Status quo cultures are resistant to opposition. They allow for rash and oppressive measures in the interest of the 'public good'. It is these cultures that can define people working within them while also challenging them as 'opponents'. These status quo cultures are reflected in sayings, such as 'it is not in my culture,' or 'we do not do things this way' or 'we have always done this … this way'. These cultures often fail to confront radical change and are threatened by it. They can assume the moral high ground and assert a worldview that is often not reflective of reality unfolding in their populations.

Gender culture

In gender cultures, a particular view of men and women is presented – for example, men are often portrayed as the problem and women as the victim. Of course, there are examples of 'real men' and of 'strong women,' but on the whole, the rhetoric is about how difficult it is to work with men and how women have to fight for their rights. While this is often true, it is unhelpful as it sets up a gender tension, which often leads people to revert to status quo cultures for explanations and evasions. The chapter by Aho and Nguyen, in describing the unplanned side effects of prevention and treatment interventions in West Africa, shows the danger of not taking gender relations seriously. It illustrates how gender interventions may paradoxically increase vulnerability to HIV and other forms of structural violence in targeted groups or may inadvertently decrease vulnerability in ways that are highly gendered.

Although more attention is now being paid to masculinities and femininities and the construction of men and women is more widely debated, dominant gender cultures continue to prevail, and HIV prevention has not yet found its way through this swamp. The chapter by Nattrass looks at the factors in South Africa that influence the ways that men and women access treatment facilities and the extent to which the provision of treatments and counselling can challenge these particular gender identities. Is this a way to get men to access the services of public health facilities more readily, and if so, how might this influence the ways in which men understand the epidemic, as well as the position of women, or the issues of vulnerability and power? Or, will placing men and their experiences back in the clinics position them in particular ways in relation to HIV and AIDS and gender relations?

Cultures of silence

Cultures of silence are the cultures that accept things even when they are known to be are wrong. These silences are different from those described in the chapters by Lorway and Seckinelgin but are implicit in those by Behrouzan and Nyanzi, Emodu-Walakira and Serwaniko. These are the cultures that are silent when the loud, booming voices of donor and agency orthodoxy, or indeed governments and civil society, demand things that we may be uneasy or ambivalent about. No one can support child-headed households on ethical grounds, quite apart from any other considerations, but there is a culture of silence around this; no one can really believe that it would be better to place children into households where they will be hungry for food, love and education, and yet the reigning culture of silence hampers any debate on the question. What has made us so scared and antagonistic to debate? Why do those who question testing or circumcision, wife inheritances or AIDS work in prisons feel that they need to be apologetic in this questioning? Cultures of silence are cultures of dishonesty about our societies and how we live in them.

Public health culture

Public health culture has taken on all kinds of symbolic powers – powers that overlook the urgency of the HIV and AIDS situation and the need to save lives. In the words of Michael Clatts (1994, pp. 93-95), a researcher working with injecting drug users:

The process has gone terribly awry – the undaunted search for quick-fix models forces us to crawl into very narrow boxes, it jeopardizes our ability to see the world as it is, as well as our ability to offer constructive ideas about how to change it. Such models inevitably end up trying to fit the subject to the technology rather than the other way round.

Public health culture is often indifferent to social discourse, social theory and critical debates. Through public health, interventions are developed that are presented as context-independent – in other words, they will work in all settings and at all times. Testing and circumcision are two examples of this. The powerful voice of public health silences the voices of dissent, of caution, of culture and of those who feel uneasy in the orthodox mainstream.

Human rights culture

It is worth examining where the voice of human rights culture is the loudest and most effective and who the forces are that attempt to silence it. Human rights culture has had its powerful critics, such as Kevin de Kock, who suggested that human rights–based approaches to HIV prevention might have diminished the roles of public health and social justice, which offer more applied and practical frameworks for HIV and AIDS prevention and care in Africa's devastating epidemic (de Kock et al., 2002, p. 67). It was this questioning of the relevance of human rights – the fact that human rights hinder public health officials and medical personnel in operating as they see fit – that led to the wide acceptance of mandatory testing, circumcision and other technologies of prevention that wanted to sidestep or reduce the human rights of the people concerned. And because of powerful biomedical voices, human rights culture became muted and wary in the face of the juggernaut of 'evidence-based approaches'. All of the chapters in this section have implications for how we theorize and ensure protection of fundamental human rights and challenge abuses of these rights.

In conclusion, all of these chapters point to the need for a far more sophisticated understanding of people's identity, behaviour, sexuality, culture and religious and political practices. The strength of these chapters is that they highlight the complex ways in which people make sense of their worlds, understand competing identity constructions and social explanations and strive to create alternative meanings. These chapters also show that we have greater resilience and dignity than mainstream orthodoxies are prepared to acknowledge or respect.

Notes

1. Foucault's work is complex and difficult, and so for the purposes of this commentary it is oversimplified. But briefly, according to Foucault, discourses develop and gain their determinative power as a consequence of interaction between four elements: objects – the things they are about; modes of enunciation – the way these things are spoken of; concepts – the intellectual constructs we need to speak about them; and strategies – the ways in which these constructs are combined or thematized. See this discussion in Woodiwiss (2003, pp. 19ff.).

References

Bayer R. 1989. *Private Acts, Social Consequences: AIDS and the Politics of Public Health*. New York, Free Press Macmillan.

Clatts, M. C. 1994. All the king's horses and all the king's men: Some personal reflections on ten years of AIDS ethnography. *Human Organization*, Vol. 53, No. 1, pp. 93–95.

Crewe, M. and Reddy, V. 2007. There are 1000 ways to wear a veil. Paper presented at the IASSCS Conference, Lima, Peru, 27–29 June.

de Kock, K. M., Mbori-Ngacha, D. and Marum, E. 2002. Shadow on the continent: Public health and HIV/AIDS in Africa in the 21st century. *Lancet*, Vol. 360, pp. 67–72.

Proctor, J. 2004. *Stuart Hall*. London, Routledge Critical Thinkers.

Said, E. W. 1996. *Representations of the Intellectual – The 1993 Reith Lectures*. New York, Vintage Books.

Smith, A. M. 1998. *Laclau and Mouffe: The Radical Democratic Imaginary*. London/New York, Routledge.

Woodiwiss, A. 2003. *Making Human Rights Work Globally*. London, Routledge Cavendish.

CHAPTER 11

Colonial silences, gender and sexuality: Unpacking international HIV and AIDS policy culture

Hakan Seckinelgin

The international HIV and AIDS policy 'culture' is not external to the local contexts within which people experience the disease. This chapter problematizes the role and the impact of international actors within this culture from the perspective of the people who are targeted by and experience the policies.

International policies formulated by multilateral entities, such as the World Health Organization (WHO), the Joint United Nations Programme on HIV/AIDS (UNAIDS) and the World Bank, have constructed HIV and AIDS as an exceptional disease. This is done through setting policy and programme priorities (such as prevention, treatment and mother-to-child transmission); identifying target beneficiary populations (according to age, gender and sexuality, for example); and defining what can be considered appropriate interventions (these include abstinence, condom use, sensitization, the use of drama techniques and treatment). In so doing, international organizations prescribe how people should live their lives and who should benefit from the resources associated with international policy interventions. These policies are, in general, silent on key questions relating to the pandemic, particularly gendered power relations, sex and pleasure. This silence is not neutral: it is based on fundamental assumptions about what is considered 'normal' within the prevailing policy environment.

In this chapter I present three linked arguments. First, I argue that both the articulation of HIV and AIDS as a problem and the policy frameworks developed to deal with this 'problem' are silent on key aspects of gender relations

The designations employed and the presentation of material throughout this publication do not imply the expression of any opinion whatsoever on the part of UNESCO concerning the legal status of any country, territory or area or of its authorities, or concerning the delimitation of its frontiers or boundaries.
The ideas and opinions expressed in this publication are those of the authors and do not necessarily reflect the views of UNESCO and its Member States.

in the everyday experiences of people living with the epidemic. These include localized power dynamics that influence gender relations, sex and the relevance of pleasure as a motivation for particular behaviours.

Second, I argue that these silences are linked to a particular biomedical framing of the pandemic by international organizations, which serves to limit policy negotiations on the technical aspects of HIV transmission. This creates a power dynamic analogous to that in colonial forms of administration, in which people's daily lives were only considered from the perspective of their productive and reproductive functions. In a similar way, the international HIV and AIDS policy culture has constructed those infected with, and affected by, HIV and AIDS as passive target populations.

The silences inherent in international policy discussions and negotiations, and their implicit assumptions about gender relations and sexual behaviour, are rooted in the history of public health responses. Peter Baldwin (2005) has observed that policy processes respond to emerging medical problems on the basis of earlier experiences with diseases and their associated difficulties. In the same vein, I argue that historical approaches within the international HIV and AIDS policy arena inform how HIV and AIDS policy tools are operationalized in developing countries. The colonial analogy illuminates the ways in which international policy processes can lead to classifying, influencing and altering the social organization of people's everyday lives. Furthermore, it highlights the power imbalances between those making policy and those targeted by it. The colonial analogy offers some important insights:

1. It shows how people are constructed as passive target populations and how inter- and intra-gender differences in their daily lives are reduced to rigid policy priorities. It also suggests that the categories constructed are not politically or ideologically neutral.

2. It locates these social constructions within the institutional fabric of international organizations and their policy processes. It highlights the way in which policy processes produce particular kinds of gendered outcomes by prioritizing certain issues, such as reproductive health, and by remaining silent about other issues, such as sex and pleasure.

3. It demonstrates that the political basis that informs the policy outcomes of international negotiations – usually presented as technical solutions – has impact on both people's lives and the trajectory of the epidemic.

My third argument is that the inability to engage with gender, and the failure to address the gendered nature of the HIV and AIDS epidemic, is masked by the self-validating 'success stories' promoted by advocacy groups and by the existence of global declarations and statements on gender. By remaining silent on aspects of gender relations that frame people's lived experiences, international organizations create outcomes that are paradoxically self-limiting.

Silences

The international policy environment constitutes a form of global governance of the HIV and AIDS pandemic (Seckinelgin, 2005). This governance process is both a result of, and a motivation for, an institutionalization process and the creation of systemic norms and values, which serve to subsume actors – including people identified as target groups – into the global framework (Seckinelgin, 2008, pp. 44–53). It is through this process that the colonial form of social engagement and substantive assumptions about gender and sexuality are reproduced and maintained.

Most international policy documents and interventions on HIV and AIDS are silent on important aspects of how sex and sexuality shape the risk of HIV transmission. This silence can take many forms. The first silence is around sex. When these documents and interventions do talk about or address sex, it is either in relation to the mechanics of sexual activity, with a focus on prevention techniques in the context of designated 'high-risk groups', or in relation to reproductive health and the family. The second silence is around social and cultural attitudes towards sex and the patterns of sexual relations in different local contexts, such as polygamy or sexual initiation or traditional practices, such as 'wife inheritance' (see Chapter 12), circumcision and female genital cutting. These are rarely, if ever, discussed. When they are, the discussion is generic and disembodied from the social context in which they occur.

This brings us to the third silence: the question of pleasure. The silence is especially resounding in the area of women's pleasure, where HIV prevention is largely focused on women's reproductive capacities. The fact that people like to have sex because it is pleasurable, however that enjoyment is described or experienced, is ignored. This silence has particularly significant consequences for HIV prevention interventions directed at adolescents since it makes discussions with young people about sex and sexualities difficult to initiate.

The absence of discussion about pleasure hides a fourth silence: the failure to acknowledge sexualities and sexual relations that fall outside prevailing definitions of heterosexuality. The construction of 'men who have sex with men' (MSM) as a targeted 'at-risk' group is based on epidemiological estimates of the risk of HIV infection during anal sex compared to vaginal sex, without necessarily taking into consideration that MSM may also have sex with women. Similarly, policies are silent about same-sex relations between women, whose vulnerability to HIV and AIDS may be shaped by social norms that emphasize marriage, regardless of sexual preference.

The fifth silence – around violence against women – neglects the role of forced and coerced sex and the attendant risks of HIV infection, regardless of whether it takes place within the family, at school, on the streets or in the context of armed conflict.

International processes and actors also play an unacknowledged role in enforcing a sixth silence about those infected with, and affected by, HIV and AIDS by making access to HIV-related resources conditional on identification with an internationally predefined category of HIV-related risk – be it a particular faith, age or sexual identity.

These silences, or omissions, have serious implications for policy-making. Current debates on HIV and AIDS give the impression that if we are able to focus on the mechanics of sex and HIV transmission, along with reproductive health and fertility, then we will be able to change the behaviours that expose people to the risk of HIV infection. This is not the case. Instead, mechanistic/technical policy responses project implicit and explicit criteria for accessing international resources that are based on assumptions about gender and sexuality that may not be grounded in, or correspond to, local realities and thus cannot change behaviour.

The role of international organizations in deciding what matters

Public health approaches to HIV and AIDS within international organizations tend to medicalize the identification of 'key populations' and ignore the complex relationships between sexual behaviour, sexuality and the broader socio-cultural environment. In terms of medical interventions for the general public, such an approach constructs MSM, including the 'subcategory' of sex workers, as 'bridging populations' that could spread the disease to the HIV negative population.

It has been noted by many activists working with people whose sexualities have been marginalized that the MSM construction allows these people to access resources from international public health policy interventions as long as they 'agree' to be considered as 'bridging populations', or vectors of the disease. In this way, policy interventions either maintain or reproduce the patterns of socio-economic marginalization that increase people's vulnerability to HIV infection.

The language that mediates HIV discourse within multilateral organizations and other fora is based primarily on behavioural aspects of public health concerns and frameworks (Seckinelgin, 2006).[1] This discourse both defines and confines its target groups according to a particular set of assumptions about the kinds of behaviours that create vulnerability to HIV. In so doing, specific categories of 'risk' and 'at-risk groups' are created – such as MSM, widow, truck driver, sex worker – that then both explicitly and implicitly define the ways that resources are accessed and therefore how programmes are implemented and beneficiaries selected.

For example, the introduction of MSM as a target at-risk group in the early 1990s was intended to 'reflect the idea that behaviour, not the identity, places individuals at risk for HIV infection' (Young and Meyer, 2005, p. 1144). This approach aimed to overcome identity-based problems and prejudices. It was thought that the term 'MSM', with its behavioural rather than identity connotations, would allow public health policies to improve their focus on vulnerable groups, but as of 2006, this aim has not been realized. According to the 2006 UNAIDS report, 'only 9% of men who have sex with men received any type of HIV prevention service in 2005' and 'fewer than 20% of MSM have access to resources' (p. 3, 110).

Reproductive and sexual health have also been used as a framework within which to approach HIV prevention. The World Health Organization (WHO, 2006, p. 1), for example, states:

> Knowledge of the HIV status is essential for tailoring reproductive health care and counselling according to the HIV status of women and to assist women in making decisions on such issues as the number, spacing and timing of pregnancies, use of contraceptive methods and infant-feeding practices.

While this seems a sensible approach to women's health, reading the document further makes it clear that the sexual in the document title (*Sexual and Reproductive Health of Women Living with HIV/AIDS*) means only reproductive health and family planning. Although the guidelines caution that: 'confining HIV testing and counselling to antenatal care and childbirth settings reinforces the perception that [the] primary objective of identifying HIV infection in women is to prevent transmission to infants rather than to benefit women themselves' (WHO, 2006, p. 9), attention to women's sexuality and health seems to be confined to general family and reproductive health matters.

The reproductive health approach is further legitimized by the expert claims made by international organizations on HIV trends. In its December 2004 report on the state of the epidemic, UNAIDS announced that AIDS is the most globalized epidemic in history and we are witnessing its growing 'feminization' (p. 8). With reference to the feminization of the epidemic, the report states:

> In the early days of the epidemic, men vastly outnumbered women among people infected with HIV. Indeed, it initially took the medical establishment some time and a great deal of evidence before it accepted the very idea that HIV was a threat to women. (p. 14)

'Nowhere', states the report, 'is the epidemic's "feminization" more apparent than in Sub-Saharan-Africa, where 57% of adults infected are women and 75% of young people infected are women and girls' (p. 22). By feminizing the disease, not only have women become one of the main target groups, but also interventions for women's health have been allowed to be located within the reproductive health framework as it was established prior to the feminization debate.

The language of public health embodies gender assumptions that designate expected sexual behaviour. Reproductive health is used as an entry point to discuss sexual health, but questions about why women have sex – beyond considerations of child-bearing – remain unarticulated. This public health framework both locates the cause of HIV in 'mothers' and confines women's sexuality – and attendant HIV risks – to the family and in relation to reproductive health. This is particularly true with respect to 'mother-to-child transmission' (MTCT), sometimes referred to as 'vertical transmission'. The move is not coincidental but follows a trajectory that developed during colonialism (Kanogo, 2005, p. 165). The increasing focus on women – or, rather, on their reproductive health – in HIV and AIDS policy frameworks suggests the continued existence of colonial preoccupations with family and reproductive health as a focus for intervention. This framework provides a pathway in which sexuality is medicalized from a particular gender position (Hunt, 1999; McClintock,

1995; Stoler, 1995, 2006). In its many diverse forms these colonial positions define women's sexuality primarily in terms of child-bearing/reproductive issues. People's own understanding of themselves is discounted in favour of a clinical categorization of their bodies as they relate to reproductive health concerns.

In the reproductive health and sexual rights framework, assumptions about women's roles in society and within the family have clear gender implications. For instance, in Chapter 7 of the Cairo Consensus (the outcome of the 1994 International Conference on Population and Development), women's sexuality and health are primarily considered from the perspective of reproductive health, which is located in the context of couples and families (see ICPD, 1994, chap. 7.2, 7.3). Similar links between women's sexual rights and the family context are evident in both the Beijing Platform for Action and the agenda of the Global Coalition on Women and AIDS, which was established by UNAIDS in 2004 as a response to the feminization of the epidemic (UNAIDS, 2006). A document produced by the Global Coalition on Women and AIDS (UNAIDS, 2007b, p.17) further elaborates:

> Reproductive and sexual health services are generally considered to comprise four elements: family planning or safe regulation of fertility; maternal health and nutrition; protection from sexually transmitted infections and reproductive rights.

It is clear that women's sexuality – at least as related to services provided for women – is directly located within the family and in relation to their reproductive capacity rather than in terms of the sociocultural and economic environment that shapes their individual expressions of sexual identity, autonomy and rights. However, the justification for this framework is not explicitly discussed or articulated; it is simply assumed to be relevant. In most cases, HIV prevention tools – such as those relating to voluntary counselling and testing (VCT) – deliver uniform messages about the nature of the disease, its attendant risks and outreach strategies for reaching a generic female target audience. In this regard, the assumptions made about women's sexuality and their sexual behaviour and practices actually limit the potential impacts of prevention, care and treatment strategies by framing factors that increase the risk of HIV infection in a family and behavioural context rather than in broader terms that draw attention to socio-structural factors. While there is no doubt that the impact of the epidemic on women is severe and debilitating, it is not clear that the discussion on feminization will change the situation if it does not associate factors increasing HIV vulnerability with patriarchal assumptions about gender and sexuality. Public health policies on HIV and AIDS currently construct 'target groups' with assumed, generalized and largely inaccurate social and sexual identities that are more likely to be ideologically relevant for the HIV and AIDS debate within the international policy arena. For this purpose, they simply 'make people up' (Hacking, 2002, p. 99). By providing a model for interventions in which certain categories of people are targeted according to their expected behaviour, other aspects of women's lives and their relationships – which may be more relevant to the risk of HIV transmission – are ignored (Seckinelgin, 2008).

Negotiations in the international system and questions about 'success'

The inability to engage with certain issues of gender and sexuality within the formal structures of the international HIV and AIDS policy culture serves to perpetuate the silences discussed earlier and ultimately affects the impact of HIV and AIDS prevention, care and treatment policies and programmes. There is no doubt that the work of international organizations in developing HIV and AIDS policies and tools has influenced responses to the epidemic in developing countries in general, and in Africa in particular. In order to understand what policy discussions are 'prescribing' for people, it is important to understand where these policies are coming from and the assumptions they bring to bear on people's everyday lives once they are implemented. With regard to multilateral and bilateral funding, priorities and targets may be established to advance bilateral policies that are not related to health or HIV and AIDS, such as those relating to intellectual property (trade-related aspects of intellectual property rights, or TRIPS) and even international security (the United States PEPFAR programme is housed within the US State Department).

Various entities within the HIV international policy arena claim that their HIV prevention strategies have been successful and assert that 'we know what works' or 'we know what works and the problem is scaling up' (Piot, 2005; UNAIDS, 2006). These claims are not, however, often based on any evidence, yet they are made to justify international policy prescriptions (Seckinelgin, 2008). Here the pronoun 'we' stands for international actors – who then become legitimate authorities – who assume that their 'knowledge' is relevant across diverse sociocultural, political and historical contexts. This technical policy discourse does not merely serve to rationalize policy implementation in various country contexts (Seckinelgin, 2006). It also becomes central to mediating who can participate in this process – both as policy and programme implementers and as beneficiaries. It constructs what it means to be infected with and affected by HIV and therefore the way those affected present themselves to 'external' communities of medical experts, as well as to their kin and community, in order to claim their 'entitlement' to HIV-related resources and benefits.

As I pointed out earlier, the process of the international framing of HIV and AIDS is linked to the ways in which international organizations have previously engaged with contagious diseases. Such historical precedents inform the existing policy tools that are operationalized in response to emerging diseases (Barnett and Whiteside, 2002). In other words, policies are the product of past experience and thus frame the present discussion. The history of the negotiation of reproductive health and sexual rights in the United Nations (UN) system is an important example of this process.

Successive United Nations conferences, from the 1975 First World Conference on Women in Mexico in 1975 to the 1995 Beijing Fourth World Conference on Women, created the platform for developing internationally agreed-upon normative standards for ensuring women's sexual and reproductive health and rights. These agreements emphasize women's rights as a fundamental global concern for everyone across the globe and the importance of the inclusion of such concerns in all policy discussions about the future of humanity. Many people have argued that the inclusion of reproductive and sexual health rights within the Beijing Platform for Action has been the most important factor in working towards the fulfilment of the human rights of women (Dunlop et al., 1996, p. 153). The Beijing Platform for Action shifted perceptions of women's health needs as a general concern related to overall population health to a recognition that women's reproductive and sexual health are fundamental human rights.

While this is considered a significant international 'success story' within the context of international policy negotiations, the extent of the victory beyond the United Nations system is unclear, particularly in the long term. In order to understand the potential for successfully addressing women's right to reproductive and sexual health outside the UN system, three issues need to be considered: firstly, the relevance of debates about the language used in international declarations; secondly, the relationship between the domestic policy concerns of United Nations Member States and international debates; and thirdly, the extent to which the activists who enabled and encouraged discussions during the international negotiations are able to do the same within their own countries. I will consider these issues in turn.

First, negotiation and diplomacy at United Nations meetings is by and large the result of concerted efforts on the part of Member States. They can influence debates through bilateral consultations outside, or on the margins of, UN meetings by negotiating the language of the final statements issued. According to Joan Dunlop et al. (1996, p. 154), 'the [Beijing] conference opened with 35 per cent of its Platform in "square brackets" because governments could not agree to terms'.[2] While agreement was reached on some of the issues by the end of the negotiations, twenty-eight points were still classified by Member States as 'formal reservations' (Dunlop et al., 1996, p. 154). In this way, Member States are able to focus on their own concerns and priorities, thereby limiting the debate. The resulting negotiated or compromised language is seen as a sign of success within the political context of international conferences, but it also results in a limited discussion of the issues.

Second, the link between domestic political interests and international policy is very clear in international debates and negotiations. In both Cairo and Beijing, alliances between more conservative Member States across the religious divides sought to influence the debate on women's equality with regard to inheritance, participation and reproductive health and sexual rights. At the same time, groups of progressive Member States played a central, oppositional role in negotiating with these conservative blocs. This point is further demonstrated by Dunlop et al. (1996, p. 155), who point out that the US position in Beijing in 1995 was characterized by the Clinton administration's 'low-key' approach, an approach that was 'silent at critical points due to the fear of domestic lobbies of Christian right'. In follow-up meetings, such as Beijing +10, the Bush administration adopted a radically different approach that reflected its very different policies regarding reproductive health and sexual rights issues, as reflected in changes to US national legislation and international funding policies in relation to abortion, sex work, family planning and HIV and AIDS. According to many participants in the Beijing +10 process, most of the debate was focused on defending the language of the actual Beijing declaration in the face of US attempts to renege on its commitments to reproductive health and sexual rights. In particular, the revival of the abortion-related gagging rule (the Mexico City Policy) in March 2001 was a major setback for the Beijing Platform in its attempts to make progress in the reproductive health and sexual rights debate during Beijing +10 (Bush, 2001, p. 17303). In addition, funding considerations have meant that the Bush administration's perspectives on women, marriage and the family, as outlined in the United States Leadership Against HIV/AIDS, Tuberculosis, and Malaria Act (US Congress, 2003, Section 301, 117 Stat. 733), have greatly influenced international HIV and AIDS policies and resource allocations and criteria.

Third, activists have participated in these debates either through the UN accreditation procedures for non-governmental organizations or as members of government delegations. It is important to consider the ability of many of these activists, within both civil society groups and Member States, to act when they are outside the United Nations system and in their own political contexts. Given that women's political representation and participation remain low, the implementation of the Beijing Platform for Action will be an uphill struggle in many countries. In addition, the actual commitment of individual Member States to applying statements on women's reproductive and sexual health rights, and their motivation in signing such statements, needs to be analysed. There is a gap between 'successful' outcomes of international conference politics and questionable outcomes in the field that is a function of the international system. On the one hand, those who have participated in the conferences can claim success. On the other, this 'success' is compromised by the influence and positions adopted by conservative Member States on international policy outcomes. These, in turn, pose challenges for implementation at the national level.

Ultimately, the international 'success story' further reinforces and masks the assumptions and silences surrounding gender and sexuality that have formed the basis for achieving international consensus. While there is no doubt that the reproductive health and sexual rights discussion has moved the international policy debate beyond the arena of population control, it still locates women and their sexuality in the context of their reproductive capacity. It remains unclear how far the claimed success represents a progressive agenda for women's rights and how far it challenges the historical gender assumptions that have dominated these debates. Furthermore, because the outcome of the international process is seen as a success, even questioning the substantive content of the claimed success is contentious. The success story thus becomes part of the international process that hides the impact of above-mentioned colonial assumptions about gender.

Conclusion

This chapter argues that international HIV and AIDS policy frameworks and the international organizations that develop them are not neutral but limited by the concerns, assumptions and prejudices of individual experts, the policies of non-governmental organizations and the negotiations conducted by UN Member States on the margins of important meetings. What is considered to be a successful achievement in the arena of international policy negotiations may not translate into successful policy implementation or positive outcomes in the everyday lives of people affected by HIV and AIDS in different sociocultural contexts. By articulating a typology of silences, the chapter highlights various assumptions about gender that are perpetuated through policies and interventions that will necessarily be limited in their concepts about HIV-related risks, as well as their ultimate impacts on people's lives. The most influential of these assumptions is that individual sexual behaviour and identity are fixed and unchanging across cultures and societies.

In sum, this chapter highlights four serious concerns about the implications of the ways in which international policy discourse has developed:

1. It is possible to argue that some HIV-prevention and sensitization campaigns may inadvertently reinforce and perpetuate the gender inequalities that exist in various societies.

2. Implicit assumptions about gender and sexuality become registers for further knowledge production and for framing evaluations of the impact of policy and programme implementation (Myerson et al., 2007).

3. People's actual experiences of gender relations and policies prescribed by the international policy regime remain opaque to policy analysts because the family and reproductive heath approach ignores the ways in which women engage with, and negotiate their, gender and sexuality in their everyday lives.

4. By using internationally agreed-upon policy language and tools, many actors – including activists – unintentionally reproduce and perpetuate the silences highlighted above.

Underlying each of these concerns is the tendency for the international HIV and AIDS policy culture to consider sex as a technical issue – the mechanics of which are located in a particular framework of sexuality and gender relations – that needs to be 'fixed' in order to deal with HIV and AIDS. However, HIV prevention campaigns must acknowledge that HIV-related risks and consequences are not only linked to reproductive health but also to sex and pleasure and other socio-structural determinants. We need to explicitly recognize these relationships in order to overcome the obstacles encountered by many of the interventions that seek to change sexual behaviour. Behavioural change only becomes possible if policy discourses provide meaningful descriptions that fit and engage with people's lived experiences.

Notes

1. As compared to the human rights discourse that dominates civil society activism in combating HIV-related stigma and discrimination.
2. In other words 35 per cent of the text under discussion was enclosed in square brackets to indicate lack of agreement by Member States. When agreements on the text are reached, the brackets are removed and the text is considered to be approved by all the parties involved.

References

Baldwin, P. 2005. *Disease and Democracy: The Industrialized World Faces AIDS.* Berkeley, Calif., University of California Press.

Barnett, T. and Whiteside, A. 2002. *AIDS in the Twenty-First Century: Disease and Globalization.* Basingstoke, United Kingdom, Palgrave MacMillan.

Bush, G. W. 2001. Restoration of the Mexico City policy: White House memorandum for the acting administrator of the US Agency for International Development. *Federal Register*, 29 March, Vol. 66, No. 61.

Dunlop, J., Kyte, R. and MacDonald, M. 1996. Women redrawing the map: The world after the Beijing and Cairo conferences. *SAIS Review*, Vol. 16, No. 1, pp. 153–65.

Hacking, I. 2002. Making up people. I. Hacking (ed.), *Historical Ontology.* Cambridge, Mass., Harvard University Press.

Hunt, N. R. 1999. *A Colonial Lexicon of Birth Ritual, Medicalization and Mobility in the Congo.* Berkeley, Calif., University of California Press.

ICPD (International Conference on Population and Development). 1994. *International Conference on Population and Development Programme of Action.* Cairo, UNFPA. http://www.unfpa.org/icpd (Accessed 25 January 2008.)

Kanogo, T. 2005. *African Womanhood in Colonial Kenya 1900–50.* Oxford, United Kingdom, James Currey.

McClintock, A. 1995. *Imperial Leather: Race, Gender and Sexuality in the Colonial Contest.* London, Routledge.

Myerson, M., Crawley, S. L., Anstey, E. H., Kessler, J. and Okopny, C. 2007. Who's zoomin' who? A feminist, queer content analysis of 'interdisciplinary' human sexuality textbooks. *Hypatia*, Vol. 22, No. 1, pp. 92–113.

Piot, P. 2005. Why AIDS is exceptional? Speech at London School of Economics, 8 February. http://www.lse.ac.uk/collections/LSEAIDS/pdfs/peter_piot_talk_020805.pdf (Accessed December 2007.)

Platform for Action. 1995. *4th World Women's Conference in Beijing.* New York, UNFPA. http//www.un.org/womenwatch/daw/beijing/platform/health.htm (Accessed 26 January 2008.)

Seckinelgin, H. 2005. A global disease and its governance: HIV/AIDS in sub-Saharan Africa and the agency of NGOs. *Global Governance*, Vol. 11, No. 3, pp. 351–68.

——. 2006. 'Civil society' and HIV/AIDS in Africa: The use of language as a transformative mechanism. *Journal of International Relations and Development*, Vol. 9, No. 1, pp. 1–26.

——. 2008. *International Politics of HIV/AIDS: Global Disease–Local Pain.* London, Routledge.

Stoler, A. M. 1995. *Race and The Education of Desire: Foucault's History of Sexuality and The Colonial Order of Desire.* Durham, NC, Duke University Press.

——. 2006. Intimidations of empire: Predicaments of the tactile and unseen. A. M. Stoler (ed.), *Haunted by Empire: Geographies of Intimacy in North American History.* Durham, NC, Duke University Press.

UNAIDS (Joint United Nations Programme on HIV/AIDS). 2004. *Report on the Global AIDS Epidemic.* Geneva, UNAIDS.

——. 2006. *Report on the Gobal AIDS Epidemic: A UNAIDS 10th Anniversary Special Edition.* Geneva, UNAIDS.

——. 2007a. *UNAIDS at Country Level: Supporting Countries as They Move Towards Universal Access.* Geneva, UNAIDS.

——. 2007b. *Keeping the Promise: An Agenda for Action on Women and AIDS.* Geneva, UNAIDS/Global Coalition on Women and AIDS.

USAID (US Agency for International Development). 2004. *Implementation of the United States Leadership Against HIV/AIDS, Tuberculosis and Malaria Act of 2003–Eligibility for Assistance, Limitation on the Use of Funds and Opposition to Prostitution and Sex Trafficking.* (Acquisition and Assistance Policy Directive 04-04.) http://www.usaid.gov/business/business_opportunities/cib/pdf/aapd04_04_original.pdf (Accessed 19 January 2008.)

US Congress. 2003. United States Leadership Against HIV/AIDS, Tuberculosis, and Malaria Act of 2003. Public Law 108-25. 108th Congress, 23 May. http://www.govtrack.us/congress/billtext.xpd?bill=h108-1298 (Accessed 17 January 2008.)

WHO (World Health Organization). 2006. *Sexual and Reproductive Health of Women Living with HIV/AIDS.* Geneva, WHO.

Young, R. M. and Meyer, I. 2005. The trouble with 'MSM' and 'WSW': Erasure of the sexual minority person in public health discourse. *American Journal of Public Health,* Vol. 195, No. 7, pp. 1144–149.

CHAPTER 12

'Sleeping with my dead husband's brother!' The impact of HIV and AIDS on widowhood and widow inheritance in Kampala, Uganda

Stella Nyanzi, Margaret Emodu-Walakira and
Wilberforce Serwaniko

Introduction

As death rates escalate due to the HIV and AIDS epidemic in sub-Saharan Africa, so do the numbers of widows and widowers (Barnett and Whiteside, 2002; De Cock et al., 2002; Hunter, 2003; Kalipeni et al., 2004). According to the Joint United Nations Programme on HIV/AIDS and the World Health Organization (UNAIDS/WHO, 2006), an estimated 24.5 million adults and children were living with HIV in sub-Saharan Africa at the end of 2005. In the same year, an estimated 2 million people died from AIDS-related illnesses. While there are statistics of those orphaned due to HIV and AIDS (an estimate of 12 million African children), no recent data exist about widowhood. However, earlier studies (Ntozi, 1997; Potash, 1986) reported widowhood rates in some contexts to be as high as 1 in 4 adult women.

There is also a lack of knowledge about the experience of widowhood in sub-Saharan Africa since the advent of HIV and AIDS. According to Potash (1986, p. 1), even 'the limited treatment given to widowhood has focussed on the wrong questions'. In scholarly discourse, advocacy and public policy, widows are variously referred to as invisible, excluded, marginalized, secluded, neglected, dependent, vulnerable, peripheral, outcasts, disempowered and reclusive.[1] Even where scholarly attention has been paid to this subject, Obbo (1986, p. 91, 86) contends that 'the women's point of view is muted' and that 'much of the literature focuses on norms, and little mention is made of actual practice'.

The designations employed and the presentation of material throughout this publication do not imply the expression of any opinion whatsoever on the part of UNESCO concerning the legal status of any country, territory or area or of its authorities, or concerning the delimitation of its frontiers or boundaries.
The ideas and opinions expressed in this publication are those of the authors and do not necessarily reflect the views of UNESCO and its Member States.

This chapter focuses on contemporary practices and values attached to widowhood and widow inheritance in Uganda. It explores the gendered nature of the widowhood experience in the context of the HIV and AIDS pandemic and examines the gender dimensions of contemporary widow inheritance among Baganda.[2, 3] The chapter draws its findings from forty-four qualitative individual interviews and seven focus group discussions carried out among the Baganda who were predominantly urban slum-dwellers across ten zones near the Kasubi market in Rubaga-North Division of Kampala.[4]

Unpacking the stigma of widowhood

According to the United Nations Division for the Advancement of Women (UNDAW/DESA, 2001, p. 2), 'in many developing countries the exact numbers of widows, their ages and other social and economic aspects of their lives are unknown.' There were no pre-existing records for death in the study area, unlike in developed countries where there are systematic official records of deaths, or general practice lists of deaths, that provide sampling frames for identifying and selecting widowed individuals.

The study found that residents in the study area sought health care for terminal illnesses from a range of sources, including public and private hospitals, clinics, pharmacies, traditional healers, churches, medical research centres and lay health workers. As they approached death, many patients had emigrated out of the city to their rural homes of origin to prepare for death because they believed they could take advantage of stronger networks of support and care within their family or clan or because the costs (financial, material and in terms of time) of care are reportedly lower in the villages than in the city.[5] Deaths were therefore more often reported and recorded in the village of origin rather than in the urban areas from which people returned.[6] Most of those who died in the city were transported back to their place of origin for burial, largely because of both severe restrictions on land ownership and land-use in the city and conformity with traditional cultural practices. Customary observances for the dead require that the deceased's kin – his or her lineage and clan – fulfil the funeral rites of burial and disposal, thereby obliging them to mobilize resources to transport the corpse. The notion of an abandoned corpse is decried as a-cultural: 'as though one lacks a clan'.

With the increasing number of deaths due to AIDS-related illnesses in Uganda, particularly prior to the public roll-out of antiretroviral therapy provision in 2004, the label of 'widowhood' became heavily imbued with stigma.[7] Widows and widowers are locally referred to as *Namwandu* and *Semwandu* respectively. Until recently, the use of these Luganda terms for individuals entitled them to receive sympathy, assistance and appropriate support. However, many widows interviewed for this research stated their aversion to being addressed by the title *Namwandu* because of the connotations more recently associated with the term:

> FIINA: For me, I do not want to be called *Namwandu* at all. If you use that label I feel a chill in my body. It takes me back to that place where my husband was just lying still before me. I do not want it at all. (23-year-old widow)

> VIOLA: People here do not know that I am a widow, even though my husband died of AIDS. Everybody calls me by my first name. In fact even the man I am now with does not believe I am a widow because he says that nobody calls me *Namwandu*. Maybe it is better that way. (32-year-old widow)

> NALUSWA: If you call these younger girls *Namwandu*, you will make enemies because they do not want people to know.
> PHOEBE: That is true. They fear because most people die today because of AIDS. They fear to be known.

> INTERVIEWER: But what is the problem of knowing?
> [Many participants talk at once.]
> NABANKEMA: Heh. They say that it will kill their deal of getting another man to marry them.
> NABBONA: That you are spoiling for them their market.
> NABOSA: Eh eh, who will go to her when they know that she may have the virus?
> NALUSWA: Leave it, leave it. If you want peace, you pretend not to know anything about it because it can become a serious problem for you. (Widows' group – mean age 38 years)

> FLAVIA: When I was first addressed as *Namwandu*, I cried a lot.
> INTERVIEWER: Where was this?
> FLAVIA: It was during the last funeral rites ceremony for my husband.

The clan leader said, 'Let *Namwandu* come and sit here in the middle.' I stayed in my place on the mat where I was sitting because it had
not yet sunk in my head that I was actually the one he was referring
to. Then my mother-in-law patted my shoulder, saying, '*Namwandu,
Namwandu*, he is telling you.' My friend, I cried a lot. I was pained. I
kept thinking, 'Now I am called *Namwandu*.' But later when I joined
the Mothers' Union,[8] they comforted me and said it is okay to be called
that way.

INTERVIEWER: Does it still affect you?

FLAVIA: No, not really. But I prefer to be called Mrs Mutebi, which is my
marital name. (52-year-old widow)

Generational differences in perceptions and attitudes towards the use of
this label were evident. While most younger widows did not appreciate being
given the title *Namwandu,* many older widows emphasized its historical merit,
notably its use in justifying requests for financial help or understanding when
bills, rent or school fees for orphans[9] were either late or not forthcoming.

There was general agreement among both the men and the women interviewed that being a widow or widower in contemporary Uganda tends to
raise suspicions that widowed individuals might be infected with HIV, which
is assumed to have caused the death of the deceased spouse. Three participants
whose husbands died of causes other than AIDS-related illnesses reported incidents during which they were mistakenly assumed to belong to associations
of people living with HIV (PLHIV) simply because they were widowed. One of
them, aged 32 years, reported that she continually felt compelled to correct this
impression by explaining that her husband was murdered and to the best of her
knowledge he was not HIV-positive at the time of his death.

The study revealed a dramatic transformation in the interpretation of widowhood among the Baganda. Twenty years ago, Obbo (1986, p. 105) wrote that

widowhood (*obwanamwandu*) is prestigious for women who have land
in their own right or who wish to emphasize their Christian leanings.
The title *Namwandu* (widow) so-and-so is rivalled only by *Mukyala*
(Mrs.) so-and-so. It seems to emphasize, 'I was once a respected married woman and although my husband is no longer alive, I wish to remain so'.

With the spread of the HIV and AIDS epidemic, the stigma associated with any
AIDS-related person began to affect widows and widowers, leaving surviving

spouses open to suspicions of HIV infection. This often serves as justification for both men and women to distance themselves from being identified as widowed. Contrary to Obbo's observations mentioned above, in our research, there was no prestige associated with widowhood, irrespective of property ownership and across religious affiliations.

Our research findings highlighted differences between AIDS- and non-AIDS-associated widowhood. The former connoted pollution, danger and 'bad sex' (that is, sex leading to infection and eventual death). By contrast, widowhood not associated with AIDS invoked sympathy and notions of loss and 'no sex' (an unspecified period of mourning for the dead spouse during which sex is abstained from). It was evident that many widows and widowers made efforts to be placed into the latter category. In the study, only three out of forty-four people talked openly about their HIV-positive status; this is probably because they were well known to the research team and were receiving HIV treatment. Others refused to participate in the study because they did not want to be identified as widowed or even denied a previous marriage or having lost a spouse (despite local gossip to the contrary).

Interpretations of widowhood were further complicated among individuals who had lost a marital partner but were remarried at the time of the study: 'I am remarried. I am no longer a widower. Do I still qualify for your study?' Younger widows in particular expressed multiple and conflicting perceptions about widowhood as a transitional phase that could culminate in the 'achievement' of remarriage and the subsequent loss of the label 'widow'. While some HIV-infected widows were quick to remarry in order to avoid the suspicion of infection, others used their status to discourage new sexual advances. Among older participants, a widow was understood to be anyone who experienced the death of a spouse, regardless of any subsequent change in marital status.[10] Where women had limited resources, remarriage was considered a practical strategy for supporting oneself and one's dependants. The local language developed new terms to reflect the growing incidence of remarriage following widowhood, such as *Naakafiisa ba biri* – twice widowed, *Naakafiisa basattu* – three-times widowed, and so on.[11] Indeed, men in polygynous unions pointed to the limitations of the English language to characterize their experience and marital status:

SWAIBU: I have got three wives now. But then my first wife died. In Luganda you could call me *kafiisa,* which means he who has lost someone to death. But it is a great insult to my other wives to call me widower in their hearing because they are still alive. They are still here with me. So how do you call me? Me, I am not a widower. (62-year-old widower)

The gendered dimensions of widowhood[12]

Men and women experience widowhood differently (Kalmijn, 2007; Lubben, 1989; Umberson et al., 1992). This is largely due to the politics of gender identity. African women are identified as wards of their male kin throughout their lives – first as the daughter of a father, then as the wife of a husband, the mother of a son, the widow of a deceased man – rather than being identified as women in their own right (Zulu, 1996). Our research confirmed the findings of early ethnographers (Kaggwa, 1905; Roscoe, 1911), which showed that women's status in Buganda (a patriarchal monarchical hierarchy) is derived from the significant male in their life, so that they are defined as the 'wife of a chief' or the 'daughter of a landowner'.[13] Landownership in Buganda has typically been a male domain, although more recent changes in the national constitution governing landownership have sought to redress violations of women's entitlement to land (Khadiagala, 2002). According to customary gender roles, men are considered to be providers, protectors and propagators of the lineage and clan and actors in the public domain. Women are seen as nurturers, homemakers, food preparers and (docile) actors in the private domain.

Customary approaches to marriage decree that men be proactive and women be passive recipients (Tamale, 2005) to the extent that men and/or their representatives (usually in the form of mediators, such as a paternal aunt, called *ssenga*) have the social authority to initiate sex education and awareness, propose a sexual relationship, determine whether or not marriages should proceed and establish the terms and format of the marriage ceremony (Nyanzi et al., 2001).[14]

In a customary marriage, the man, his kinsmen and his clan members pay a bride price to the woman's family. This typically takes the form of *omwenge omuganda* – local brew, clothes for the parents, food, money, animals, such as cattle or goats, and more recently, electrical goods, such as fridges, cookers and washing machines. In exchange, the woman moves from her parents' or her own home to her husband's household. She loses her name and adopts his. Decisions about child-bearing, sexual exchanges and child-rearing are all made by the husband. The wife bears children for him and his clan.[15] Unless the wife dies or is divorced, she is considered one of her husband's exclusive assets or possessions. The practice of polygyny allows men to marry additional wives[16] while restricting women to only one husband at a time (Musisi, 1991). Polyandry, the practice of women marrying several men, is taboo in Kiganda culture. However, having serial multiple marital partners is socially acceptable for women, especially after divorce or widowhood.

The implications of spousal death inevitably play out differently for widows and widowers. In this male-dominated society, whereas a widowed husband has the upper hand in determining the fate of his deceased wife's body, a widowed wife is almost always 'left' as one of the deceased man's many possessions in a list of commodities to be inherited by other members of his clan and lineage.[17] The widow cannot independently decide on the burial and funeral arrangements for her deceased husband. She submits to the choices and directives of his lineage and clan elders. She carries out his will, whether it was spoken or written. If the will was spoken, adults close to the deceased (but excluding his children and wives) confirm having witnessed him state his desires and articulate what these were.

Key informant interviews clarified that it is widely believed among the Baganda that a husband has the power to make decisions about his wife's fate after he dies, whereas the same authority does not extend to the wife. The influence of a husband over his wife or wives extends further than his lifetime because he is duty-bound to leave a will that specifies her future caretaker, residence, entitlements from his property and the possessions she must relinquish. All of the widows interviewed described the influence of their deceased husbands over the successive course of their lives, albeit to varying degrees (Nyanzi, 2004). None of the widowers interviewed attested to any such posthumous influence exerted by their wives.

As outlined above, patrilineal clan structures mean that women typically move from their own household to that of their husband on marriage. According to custom, a wife never gains membership in her husband's clan, although she can bear progeny who will be part of the clan. Marriage is potentially isolating and alienating for a bride; much depends on how her in-laws receive and respond to her. Her marital experience is shaped largely by the relationship(s) that she negotiates, cultivates and establishes with significant and influential members of her husband's family. While some widows spoke of cooperation, love, support and mutual respect from their in-laws, others reported varying levels of neutrality, indifference, neglect, rejection, hostility and enmity and even the need for legal recourse. For some, the relationship mixed civility, support and hostility depending on the issue at hand or the individuals involved. For others, the tone of relationships changed with time. Even where relationships had been characterized by mutual trust and respect, many reported that the death of their spouse had uncovered the malicious side of their in-laws.

Although no widowers in the study recounted experiences of suffering at the hands of their in-laws, many widows recalled name-calling and insults, as well as blame for causing their husband's death through witchcraft[18] or neglect or by infecting him with HIV. Some widows reported that their in-laws repossessed their property – including land, assets, motor vehicles, business enterprises, domestic wares and so on – through treachery, tricks and theft. Other widows were threatened with the loss of their children, a few actually forfeiting them either temporally or permanently to their in-laws.

> NABACHWA: It is when he died that I realized how greedy my in-laws were for his property. I was crying from the pain of losing him, and his older brother was busy organizing people to come see the land in case they wanted to buy it. He did not even ask me if that is what I was planning to do. I only got to know when the bank asked me for my signature just after the burial. (40-year-old widow)

> SYLVIA: I have heard stories of people whose in-laws are good to them when they become widows. For me, it was very difficult because my husband's family members are shameless. Imagine, his body was still lying in the coffin in the small house we were renting, and they were busy quarrelling about his shirts and shoes as they tried them on. They took the keys of the bedroom from me, went into his suitcase and bags and audibly distributed his few possessions – clothing, bed linen, the wall clock, his Sanyo FM radio, the paraffin lantern that was a wedding gift, our mattresses. They even shared the old crockery, wooden stools and charcoal stove that I had brought when I came into his house. Imagine, they never waited for the burial or the last funeral rites. They did not even think of our two little children.[19] They are shameless. After the burial, it was too much for me because my sister-in-law returned with a pickup truck and even took the *etogero* – the big clay pot outside on the veranda, in which we stored water. Since it was a rented house, I left and went back to my father. (37-year-old widow)

Nagawa: You see, he was sick for a long time, and I was treating him. At first his family used to come visiting when we were in hospital. They would bring some money or things to help us. Sometimes his mother would even ask me to take a break and go home while she stayed over and took my place by his side. But then as time passed and he got so sick and thin, always in and out of hospital, they frankly told me that they were tired of me and my witchcraft. My mother-in-law and her daughter said I was bewitching him so that I could take off with his wealth. Another time I overheard my mother-in-law telling the nurses that they were wasting time treating him with *edaggala ezungu* (European medicine) because she knew that I had bewitched him and only *edagala eganda* (traditional Kiganda medicine) would work. Imagine your in-laws saying such things about you. (42-year-old widow)

Eseza: They were belittling me and wanted to take my children away from me. So I took them to the attorney general. It was there that my brother-in-law said, 'That woman is sick. She has HIV because she gave it to my brother. We saw his medical notes. Now she wants to take our children. How does she think she will look after them when she is sick or when she dies? Unless of course she knows that she also infected them. Ah ah, if our children are fine, she must hand them over to us now, otherwise she must know that if she ever gets stuck, she cannot turn back to us for support. This thing ends here today.' He shamed me. (43-year-old widow)

One of the biggest challenges facing widows is the loss of their husband's wages and non-wage household contributions. All of the participants in the study articulated concerns about the increased financial and caregiving responsibilities relating to their children[20] after the death of their spouse. For widowers, the main challenge lies in meeting childcare needs; for widows, the principal concerns are financial: paying school fees and hospital bills and for food, clothing and shelter. It is therefore not surprising that a primary motivation for seeking a new partner and/or remarriage is to help to meet the demands of parenthood.

Henry: When she died the children were still too young to be left without the care and guidance of a mother.
Interviewer: How old were they?
Henry: Kigongo was 7, the twins were 6, and Kizza was 4. I could not

look after them well. Cooking food was very difficult. But also washing clothes, bathing them, making beds, eh-eh it was difficult for me to manage alone, even though I later got a housemaid. Afterwards my sisters and aunt introduced me to some women. I chose one of them. We are together. (39-year-old widower)

NALUGWA: Many women remarry out of concern for their orphaned children.
VIOLA: She looks at the unpaid school fees, their torn clothes and bare feet without fitting shoes, house rent ... yet a man can help her.
BUKIRWA: Sometimes she may even lack basics like salt, cooking oil, soap, charcoal or fuel for the lamp. Electricity is cut off. And yet there is a man who is interested in her who will provide for the children as well.
NALUMANSI: It is especially difficult if you are jobless yet there are many children depending on you. Either you accept marriage, otherwise some women sell themselves.
[Laughter from other participants.] (Widows' group – mean age 54 years)

Two of the widowers, aged 56 and 57, reported that they had chosen not to remarry even though they had both completed the socially accepted period of mourning and had carried out all of the last funeral rites for their dead wives.

JJUUKO: Can I remarry at this age with my grey hairs and return to buying nappies or baby bottles? My sons are of marriageable age. Shall we both be chasing after girls – father and sons? I prefer to remain single. (57-year-old widower)

SEJJABBI: For me, I abstain completely. Since my wife died, I stopped those things of women. I am focusing on getting my children through school. During the holidays I take them to their grandparents in our village home, where they help with the farm work. (56-year-old widower)

Other arrangements among widowers ranged from having 'informal' sexual partners who were kept secret from their children to cohabitation with partners or remarriage.

SEEZI: For me, I do not believe in bringing the new woman I am seeing into the home I made and shared with my late wife. I got a maid for the children. And I rented a two-room house for my woman, way from here. I go to her for I have needs as a man. It is better to have one person who helps me with my manly needs than to go here and there because I might catch some terrible illness there. My children do not know about her. It is not their business. (40-year-old widower)

Widowers' subsequent marital relationships follow customary traditions that involve the widower meeting the woman's family, expressing the intention of settling down with her, agreeing on and paying the bride price and arranging the public festivities that seal her position in his household as new wife and stepmother.

A central difference in the experiences of widows and widowers pertains to sexuality: their individual sexual autonomy, their right to choose sexual partner(s) or to be sexually active and their access to sexual and reproductive health services and care. Men have the autonomy to decide and act in the sexual realm as they choose. Even in the face of pressure from relatives – hinting, scheming or matchmaking – they are ultimately able to maintain decision-making control. Furthermore, as revealed by the two examples above, it is possible for individual men to go against the trend and choose to remain abstinent, unmarried or single. Paying sex workers is another alternative open to men, although none of our male interviewees admitted doing so. This autonomy, however, was not available to the widows in the study, particularly in the context of the sociocultural institution of widow inheritance, an integral component of customary Buganda society.

The customary 'script' of widow inheritance in Buganda

As highlighted in Nyanzi (2004), widow inheritance is a context-specific practice that is enacted differently depending on the historical moment, location, social strata, ethnicity, religion, age, class, country and so on. Here, the focus is on the social script of widow inheritance as narrated by the Baganda[21] study participants. Widow inheritance is founded upon the principle of levirate marriage and is a practice whereby the brothers of a deceased man are required to choose one from among themselves to marry the grieving widow in order to ensure further propagation of the clan. In Buganda, this practice extends beyond the natural biological brothers of the deceased to include all of his male relatives and descendants within his clan.[22] Because clan members are assumed to have contributed either in cash, kind or services towards the marriage ceremony of their kin, each is entitled to lay claim to the widow. In Luganda, the wife of a fellow clan member is referred to as *mukyala wange* (my wife) or *mukyala waffe* (our wife) by all clan members, male or female, elderly or young. Widow inheritance takes place after the husband's burial, when the widow undergoes a number of rites. According to custom, the new levirate guardian – locally known as the *mukuza* (levir) – is required to take on responsibility for the widow, her dependants and the deceased's business(es) or property if any exist.

> INTERVIEWER: When you say he takes over the widow, what do you actually mean? What responsibilities or activities does this involve? [Giggles.]
> NAKANDI: To take care of her like her husband was doing.
> NABITEEKO: To help her with any problem she may have. Also to counsel her about what to do with the orphans or how to support them.
> INTERVIEWER: Does it involve sex?
> BABIRYE: Hmm, it is difficult because different people do it differently. How can a man do for you so much, bringing food, money for electricity and water bills, paying school fees for the children, and you refuse him sex when he asks?
> ROZA: But that is weakness of character. If we all slept with everyone who does some kindness to us, where would the world be today?
> BABIRYE: But some people do it. They even have children with the *Bakuza*. Don't you see them, my friends?
> [Many voices in agreement.] Yes we hear about them.
> NAKANDI: But me I think it depends on someone's heart. We all have different hearts. Some are easily tempted and others can withstand.
> (Widows' group – mean age 38 years)

Negotiating widow inheritance

For twenty-five of the thirty-five widows interviewed, levirate guardians (*mukuza*) had been appointed during the ceremony of last funeral rites for the deceased.[23] At the same time, the *omusika w'omusaayi* (the blood heir of the deceased) was instated, along with the *lubuga*[24] (the female caretaker of the heir and other orphans). During the ceremony, the deceased's property was distributed among different relatives and friends, either in line with his written or spoken will or as the clan leaders deemed fit and fair. Where debts existed, plans for repayment – through liquidating assets, withdrawing monies from available bank balances or refinancing payments against future income from the deceased's financial assets, such as rental property or trade – were drawn up.[25]

None of the widows had any direct role in choosing their levirate guardian. In most cases, the decision is made in a meeting involving older clan members, lineage members and leaders of the deceased's clan. Widows are excluded from decision-making because they are outsiders to the clan. Potential candidates are nominated firstly by the deceased's immediate family and secondly by the wider kin-group at clan level. The levirate guardian is then selected through a system of self-elimination or by decree of the clan leaders. In rare cases, the levirate guardian is named in the deceased's will.

Many widows reported that they had accepted their *mukuza* but had not had any meaningful relationship with him subsequent to the last funeral rites ceremony. They reported highly infrequent encounters and little, if any, support. Some widows experienced verbal, physical or other abuse, sexual violence, loss of property, threats of dispossession, actual eviction from land or houses and being forced to give up their children.

Different explanations were given for power and authority exerted by the *mukuza* and their violation of the personhood, property, progeny and position of the widows. Some believed that these spring from cultural mandates, whereas others rejected this logic as a-cultural to the Baganda, or otherwise by appropriating human rights discourses. Many suggested that the levirs' personal greed, society's poverty, male privilege and the weakness that shook a widow's resolve to refuse sexual advances, leading to some widows themselves giving in to the abuse perpetrated by some in-laws, create the context for the power of the levirs. Some differences in explanation can be attributed to linguistic ambiguities.[26]

The experience of widowers

Those widowers interviewed who had completed their deceased wife's last funeral rites ceremonies revealed that their in-laws had selected an 'heiress' charged with the responsibility of looking after the children from among the dead woman's sisters or other female paternal relatives (usually a niece – a daughter of her brother, in keeping with clan membership). Because a mother's heir must be from her clan, it is not possible according to Kiganda custom for her children to be her heirs – they belong to their paternal clan only. All the widowers clarified that their relationships with the 'heiresses' were platonic and that they hardly ever saw them after the last funeral rites ceremony. According to the widowers, none of them had pursued the female heiresses for sex, and they considered the idea to be obscene and impossible. The reasons given for not becoming sexually involved with these women included: 'the girl was too young for me'; 'she was already married and was happy in her home with her husband and children'; 'I am HIV-positive and abstaining from sex to protect myself and other women'; 'there was no sexual attraction'; 'I didn't interpret the relationship that way'; and 'how could I possibly think about her like that when she grew up in my home, under the care of her big sister?' For these men, the act of installing an heiress in the place of their late wife is part of the ritual preservation of custom and purely symbolic, undertaken because 'the children need someone to step into the shoes of their mother'. None of the widowers felt pressured by culture, clan elders or other influential media to engage in any sexual activity with the heiresses. In most cases, the heiresses did not move into the home.

> JJUUKO: I do not know that the heiress to my wife was installed to do anything with me. If so, then she is not getting it from me because as far as I am concerned she is there for the sake of the children. In death, any parent must get an heir, otherwise she cannot rest in peace when there is no one to fulfil her responsibilities for her charges. If you do not give her an heiress, she will persistently haunt the family and even other members of the clan until you settle the issue. People will fall mad, heh! (57-year-old widower)

> SEKAMAANYA: The children were shown the heiress to their mother. I gave her my wife's clothes because the children were too young to wear them. But then I have never seen her again. She has never come to visit the children or even done anything for them. It is *akalombolombo k'ebyobuwangwa* (a cultural custom that doesn't mean much). (39-year-old widower)

In effect, the 'heiresses' do not impose any sexual relationship on the widowers in the name of customary practice, unlike claims about levirs and widows.

Available public provisions and social support

In Uganda, there is no social policy dealing specifically with widowed people. When asked about government policies or programmes that attempt to redress some aspects of the multiple layers of marginalization, abuse and violation faced by the widowed, study participants reported that they were not aware of any within the physical, social or political spaces they had access to. Widows in Masaka District agreed (Nyanzi, 2004). A common response across all of the interviews was that 'there are many projects targeting orphans left by the deceased but none for the spouse left behind'. This echoes a UN Division for the Advancement of Women report (UNDAW/DESA, 2001, p. 3), which concludes that:

> neglected by social policy researchers, international human rights activists and the women's movement, and consequently by Governments and the international community, the legal, social, cultural and economic status of the world's widows now requires urgent attention at all levels of society, given the extent and severity of the discrimination they experience.

We probed further, asking what the plethora of non-governmental organizations (NGOs) were doing for widows and widowers. Study participants stated that these institutions targeted groups of defined beneficiaries, such as PLHIV or war-affected and displaced people.

> JULIET: The biggest problem is that the one [NGO] that I know is TASO, which aims at people with AIDS. Me here, I am a widow with very similar problems to the ones faced by those other people who go to TASO. But then I cannot qualify to go for TASO because I am not infected with HIV. My husband died in a car accident. So the organization is not for all of us widows. They must test your blood for you to qualify. Otherwise you bring proof from your doctor that shows that you have it before you can become a benefiting member of the support they give. (36-year-old widow)

At the same time, however, participants whose deceased spouse was buried in one of the *ekiggya* (lineage graveyards) in the rural compounds often mentioned that they received social, emotional, financial and material support called *amataaba* from burial society members during the period immediately after the death. Known locally as *Munno Mukabi* (literally translated as 'your friend in times of trouble'), these burial societies are an integral part of village life in Buganda. They consist of a group of men and women from the village who come together to provide labour for tasks related to the processes leading up to the burial ceremony. These include cooking, cleaning, fetching water and fuelwood, constructing temporary shelters, such as tarpaulin tents or makeshift huts made from tree branches, twigs, hay or other fodder grasses and banana leaves, and so on, to cater for the relatives and friends who travel to attend the burial rituals in their neighbourhood. Operated on the principles of goodwill and reciprocity, *Munno Mukabi* burial societies suffered major setbacks in the crisis periods when deaths of AIDS-related illnesses increased dramatically, draining their resources and depriving beneficiaries of their support and assistance. However, some participants reported that the *Munno Mukabi* members in their village did provide assistance and coordinated the immediate response to the obituary and that they participated in relaying the public announcement of the spouse's death either by word of mouth or via public media, including radio, newspapers or television.

NAKUYA: The people of *Munno Mukabi* came in big numbers. They brought knives for peeling, brooms, large saucepans and even jerry cans to help with fetching water. They asked me what the plans were. I did not have a plan because I had never gone through this. I did not know what to do. I was waiting for my father-in-law to come and make the arrangements. But then the people of *Munno Mukabi* helped me to prepare things, like passing the word round the village, composing the death announcement to send to the radio station, writing a list of jobs to do. The elderly women told me to be brave because the death was just the beginning of a big test. 'How will you look after the children you have, if you do not strengthen yourself now? Be brave, be brave!' they said to me. (36-year-old widow)

SIKOLA: It was good that we had *Munno Mukabi* because they knew where I could get bark cloth to wrap his body in. They knew who could dig the grave quickly and cheaply. They even chose the priest who led the mass. You see I had not been living in the village. We only went there for Christmas holidays. So I did not know the system well when we took him back for burial. (25-year-old widow)

NAKKU: I feared the nights mostly. We spent two days with his body in the house because we were waiting for his oldest daughter who lives abroad. But at night, the members of *Munno Mukabi* came and slept in our compound, even before the relatives from far arrived. They were singing hymns throughout the night, around the big fire. They helped me go through those nights. (42-year-old widow)

All of the participants who held the burial in the city reported that they did not receive any assistance from a *Munno Mukabi* but instead mobilized the support of close family members, friends and colleagues and members of the associations to which they belonged.

NALONGO: During the death of your family members is when you see who your friends are. That is when you know who your people are: those who care about you and what you are going through. They will come and be by your side. They will comfort you and spend some time with you. (43-year-old widow)

NAMULI: People come to the burial. Your relatives. His relatives. The neighbours from the village … yes. But after the burial everybody departs, and you are left all alone looking at the house and the orphans. (45-year-old widow)

Most widowed people participating in the study had received some level of support from kin, society, churches, clubs or employers immediately after their spouse died. After the burial, however, they were often plunged into loneliness, isolation and seclusion. Many claimed to have suffered from neglect by family, society and the government, especially in cases where the last funeral rites were conducted at the same time as the burial ceremony.

Possible interventions

In the absence of public provisioning for the widowed, the cultural institution of widow inheritance – which has traditionally served to provide support to widows – could be a viable resource for adapting interventions. For instance clan elders, male kin, heirs and levirs are educated through community awareness programmes about alternative modes of caring for widows (and orphans) in ways that enhance their well-being and protect their multiple rights. However, this would require that the traditional Buganda leadership – including the Kabaka (King) and his cabinet, as well as clan leaders and elders – address the inherent patriarchal structures and mechanisms that perpetrate the multiple violations enacted through this institution. They could, for example, establish an educational programme to explicitly reject any such abuses carried out in the name of Kiganda culture.

As the Ugandan economy grows, the state could also increase its provision of public goods in the form of social protection for marginalized social groups, including poor widows and widowers. Potential interventions could include: the provision of low-cost housing, pensions and food grants; income-generation schemes; and the abolition of school fees for children with at least one dead parent. Subsidies could be provided to increase access to these services for poorer individuals. Harnessing community-based programmes, such as widow/widower support groups, and formally recognizing burial societies could also mobilize resources for widow empowerment.

Existing interventions that harness networks of grassroots human rights and legal advocacy organizations to focus attention on the plight of widows and widowers need to be strengthened. Community education about property rights, inheritance laws, will-making, marital rights in the event of spousal death and so on must be channelled through media outlets that reach marginalized social groups. Widows could also benefit from self-help associations and from sharing success stories and strategies for contesting abuse and subjugation through recourse to the law or personal resource mobilization. These associations would also make the widowed more visible as a disadvantaged and growing – though heterogeneous – group affected by HIV and AIDS.

Acknowledgements

Our study was funded by the Social Science Research Council's fellowship on HIV/AIDS and public health policy research in Africa (2006–2007). Dr Joseph Nyanzi, director of Mengo Hospital, offered invaluable administrative support and critical comments about the study design. Olive Sendagala, Charles Lutaaya, Mariam Sewanyana, Ivan Makumbi, Kasirye Ronald and Robert Bwire participated in phases of data collection. Jennifer Klot's critical engagement with an earlier draft enriched the chapter. We are grateful to the participants in the study for sharing their experiences with us.

Notes

1. Activism carried out by non-governmental organizations on behalf of widows in conflict situations has positioned war widows as a target group with respect to humanitarian aid, programmes and policies. This approach has been criticized by feminists, who argue that women's relationship status – that is, their status in relation to men – has become the main criteria for beneficiaries, to the exclusion of those widowed for other reasons or divorced, or single women. Thus there are classes of widows; some have interventions because they were for example married to army officials, and others lack specific targeting.

2. We have discussed elsewhere the contestation of sexual stereotypes associated with widowhood, lay-meaning-making systems of wills, survival strategies and how generational differentiation impacts on the everyday performances and processes of widowhood in urban Uganda (Nyanzi, 2004).

3. Luganda is the language, Buganda is the kingdom, the people are Baganda (singular Muganda), and the derivative adjective is Kiganda.

4. Fieldwork was conducted in 2006 and 2007 by the Community-Based Healthcare Programme of Mengo Hospital, Kampala. In the data collection, we triangulated ethnographic participant observation, qualitative individual interviews, focus group discussions and a policy review. Purposive, snowball and theoretical sampling techniques were combined. Informed consent was both verbal and written. Participation was voluntary. Transport fees and refreshments were provided for group sessions. Pseudonyms have been used in this chapter to ensure respondent anonymity.

5. Mukiza-Gapere and Ntozi (1995) and Ntozi (1997) discuss migration patterns during widowhood in Uganda.

6. Since Kasubi-Kawaala offers relatively cheap residence in the fringes of Kampala, the majority of its residents are migrant city workers who originate from various rural districts inside and outside Uganda. During key informant interviews, councillors from LCI and LCII levels confirmed that most residents in their jurisdiction died and were buried outside Kasubi-Kawaala.

7. See the section entitled "The gender dimensions of widowhood" for a description and discussion of the contested usage of this label for men as being a-cultural (defined as not belonging to local claims of culture) and foreign to everyday language, perhaps introduced by those unaware of proper Kiganda custom.

8. Based within the Anglican church, the Mothers' Union is a fellowship of all women who have been married by a minister, with international, regional, national and local chapters right down to the smallest parish. In the country, it is exclusive to Church of Uganda members.

9. See later in this chapter for an explanation of the use of the word 'orphan' in this context.

10. Potash (1986, p. 15) distinguishes between conceptualizations of widowhood as a phase between marriages or as an ongoing status.

11. These phrases are common in 'positive-living testimonies', where PLHIV publicly disclose and discuss the meaning of living with HIV. However, in other contexts, the experience of multiple spousal losses is culturally suspicious, with individuals shunned as potential marital partners lest they also 'kill' the new spouse. Rituals of cleansing are sometimes carried out in order to restore balance.

12. Given the accessibility and public visibility of widows compared to widowers, the final study sample comprised a ratio of 35 widows to 9 widowers.

13. Only men become chiefs. The only exceptions are women belonging to the royal class – princesses, queens and wives of royalty. Princesses are addressed as *Ssebo* (Sir). Despite an abundance of princesses, only princes ever ascend to the throne as kings.

14. These gender roles are reflected in Luganda language. The man is the active 'doer' of marriage: *awasa* – he marries. The woman is the passive party to whom marriage is 'done': *afumbirwa* – she gets married, *awasibwa* – she gets married.

15. Because Buganda is patrilineal, all children are born into their father's clan. Their identity, name, totem, kin, role and social position in the kingdom's hierarchy and inter-clan functions are predetermined by their father's clan. With the exception of royal wives, women can never 'own' their children within this system.

16. As long as the man can afford the bride price and performs the customary marriage ceremony, no other criteria – economic status, age, access to land, space, and so forth – can prevent him from marrying more wives.

17. Residence in customary social organization among the Baganda is both patrilocal and virilocal; thus children live in the father's household, and wives shift into their husband's household. Thus at the death of a husband, a widow has to justify why she should remain in the deceased's shelter, otherwise she risks dispossession or repossession by her in-laws.

18. Witchcraft is an ambivalent label in this context. Here it refers to appeals to spiritual evil forces to produce negative impacts on another person's life, business, well-being, health, and so forth.

19. Sylvia retained guardianship of all her children, although her in-laws took the property.

20. Local conceptualizations of orphanhood are highly ambivalent. According to custom, there are no orphans in Buganda because children belong to their patrilineal extended family and their father's clan. All paternal uncles are called *Taata*

omutto, meaning 'young father'. Paternal aunts are called *Ssenga,* alluding to the expression 'if you were a man you would be my father'. The term *abaana enfuuzi,* meaning 'children who have experienced parental death', is commonly applied to those who have lost either one or both biological parents. *Mulekwa,* meaning 'a child left behind by a deceased', is widely used by organizations. However, many Baganda elders reject this use of the term as a westernization, explaining that even when both parents die, children are left in the care of their extended family network and are thus not really '*bamulekwa*'.

21. Because ethnicity is one of the main frames through which the social construction and scripting of widow inheritance is mediated, our research was designed to include exclusively Baganda individuals. Indeed, there are many examples of study participants highlighting that 'that is what the Basoga, Banyankole or [some other ethnicity] do. It is not for us Baganda.'

22. Since clan members all claim descent from the same forefather, the clan is in effect a large extended family, with these kin ties valued and thereby respected through, for example, incest taboos. Therefore individuals of the same clan but from separate biological lineages cannot marry; although there is no bloodline connecting them, incest taboo observances apply to them because they are of the same clan. In Luganda, the nouns used for male members of one's clan are the same as for biological brothers – namely, *mwanyinaze* and *muganda wange,* as used by a sister and brother respectively.

23. Of the ten widows without a *mukuza,* nine had either not yet conducted the last funeral rites for their deceased husband – for reasons including lack of finances, failure of the in-laws to organize the rites, a falling out with the in-laws, the loss of the will, the deceased's debts, difficulties in scheduling or conflicting scheduling by the clan leaders – or the burial had only taken place recently.

24. Based on patrilineality, only members of the deceased man's clan are appointed as *lubuga.* She is therefore always one of the widow's in-laws.

25. See Nyanzi (2004) for a discussion of the multidimensional consequences of will-making in contemporary Uganda.

26. See Potash (1986) for an examination of the contradictions, overlaps and confusion surrounding the definition of the actual roles and responsibilities of the levir.

References

Barnett, T. and Whiteside, A. 2002. *AIDS in the Twenty-First Century: Disease and Globalization*. New York, Palgrave Macmillan.

Colson, E. 1951. The Plateau Tonga of Northern Rhodesia. E. Colson and M. Gluckman (eds), *Seven Tribes of British Central Africa*. Oxford, United Kingdom, Oxford University Press, pp. 94–162.

De Cock, K. M., Mbori-Ngacha, D. and Marum, E. 2002. Shadow on the continent: Public health and HIV/AIDS in Africa in the 21st century. *Lancet,* Vol. 360, No. 9326, pp. 67–72.

Edel, M. M. 1934. *The Customs of the Baganda by Sir Apollo Kagwa*. New York, Columbia University Press.

Evans-Pritchard, E. E. 1951. *Kinship and Marriage Among the Nuer*. Oxford, United Kingdom, Clarendon Press.

Fallers, L. A. 1969. *Law Without Precedent: Legal Ideas in Action in the Courts of Colonial Busoga*. Chicago/London, University of Chicago Press.

Goldschmidt, W. 1967. *Sebei Law*. Berkeley, Calif., University of California Press.

Goody, E. 1973. *Contexts of Kinship*. Cambridge, United Kingdom, Cambridge University Press.

Haydon, E. S. 1960. *Law and Justice in Buganda*. London, Butterworths.

Hunter, S. 2003. *Black Death: AIDS in Africa*. New York, Palgrave Macmillan.

Kagwa, A. 1905. *Ekitabo kye Mpisa za Baganda*. Kampala, Uganda Printing and Publishing Company.

Kalipeni, E., Craddock, S., Oppong, J. R. and Ghosh, J. (eds). 2004. *HIV and AIDS in Africa: Beyond Epidemiology*. Oxford, United Kingdom, Blackwell Publishing.

Kalmijn, M. 2007. Gender differences in the effects of divorce, widowhood and remarriage on intergenerational support: Does marriage protect fathers? *Social Forces,* Vol. 85, No. 3, pp. 1079–103.

Khadiagala, L. S. 2002. Justice and power in the adjudication of women's property rights in Uganda. *Africa Today,* Vol. 49, No. 2, pp. 101–21.

Kirwen, M. C. 1979. *African Widows*. Maryknoll, NY, Orbis.

Lubben, J. E. 1989. Gender differences in the relationship of widowhood and psychological well-being among low income elderly. *Women and Health,* Vol. 14, No. 3/4, pp. 161–89.

Mair, L. P. 1934. *An African People in the Twentieth Century*. London, Routledge.

Mukiza-Gapere, J. and Ntozi, J. P. M. 1995. Impact of AIDS on marriage patterns, customs and practices in Uganda. I. O. Orubuloye, J. C. Caldwell, P. Caldwell and Shail Jainin (eds), *The Third World AIDS Epidemic, Health Transition Review 5*

(Supplement), Canberra, Australia, Australian National University, pp. 201-08.

Musisi, N. B. 1991. Women, elite polygyny, and Buganda state formation. *Signs,* Vol. 16, No. 4, pp. 758–86.

Ntozi, J. P. M. 1997. Widowhood, remarriage and migration during the HIV/AIDS epidemic in Uganda. *Health Transition Review,* Suppl. 7, pp. 125–44.

Nyanzi, S. 2004. Widowhood, land wrangles and social stigma in the face of HIV/AIDS in south-western Uganda. *OSSREA Newsletter,* Vol. 1, No. 1, pp. 18–25.

Nyanzi, S., Pool, R. and Kinsman, J. 2001. The negotiation of sexual relationships among school pupils in south-western Uganda. *AIDS Care,* Vol. 13, No. 1, pp. 83–98.

Obbo, C. 1986. Some East African widows. B. Potash (ed.), W*idows in African Societies: Choices and Constraints.* Stanford, Calif., Stanford University Press, pp. 84–106.

Potash, B. 1986. An introduction: Widows in Africa. B. Potash (ed.), *Widows in African Societies: Choices and Constraints.* Stanford, Calif., Stanford University Press, pp. 1–43.

Richards, A. 1951. The Bemba of north-eastern Rhodesia. E. Colson and M. Gluckman (eds), *Seven Tribes of British Central Africa.* Oxford, United Kingdom, Oxford University Press, pp. 164–93.

Roscoe, J. 1911. *The Baganda.* London, Macmillan.

Stenning, D. J. 1959. *Savannah Nomads.* Oxford, United Kingdom, Oxford University Press.

Tamale, S. 2005. Eroticism, sensuality and 'women's secrets' among the Baganda: A critical analysis. *Feminist Africa,* Vol. 5, pp. 9–36.

Umberson, D., Wortman, C. B. and Kessler, R. C. 1992. Widowhood and depression: Explaining long-term gender differences in vulnerability. *Journal of Health and Social Behaviour,* Vol. 33, No. 1, pp. 10–24.

UNAIDS/WHO (Joint United Nations Programme on HIV/AIDS/World Health Organization). 2006. *Report on the Global AIDS Epidemic 2006.* Geneva, UNAIDS/WHO.

UNDAW/DESA (United Nations Division for the Advancement of Women, Department of Economic and Social Affairs). 2001. *Widowhood: The Invisible Women, Secluded or Excluded.* New York/Geneva, UNDAW. http://www.un.org/womenwatch/daw/public/wom_Dec%2001%20single%20pg.pdf

Zulu, E. M. 1996. Social and cultural factors affecting reproductive behaviour in Malawi. Ph.D. dissertation, Graduate Group in Demography, University of Pennsylvania, USA.

CHAPTER 13

An epidemic of meanings: HIV and AIDS in Iran and the significance of history, language and gender

Orkideh Behrouzan

As if it was just a disease – a very serious one, but just a disease. Not a curse, not a punishment, not an embarrassment. Without 'meaning', and not necessarily a death sentence.

Susan Sontag (1989, p. 102)

[AIDS is] a nexus where multiple meanings, stories and discourses intersect and overlap, reinforce and subvert each other.

Paula Treichler (1987)

In 2004, the World Health Organization (WHO) awarded 'best practice certification' to the HIV and AIDS programmes of the Islamic Republic of Iran. How this certification was obtained, and indeed the recognition it reflected, is a story of considerable interest. While it is a truism that any global set of policy goals is localized in very different ways, this case is both a dramatic illustration and a model for Iranian health care practitioners and international policy-makers about negotiating meaning and discourse across social strata and in a highly complex and sensitive political setting. Given the Islamic legal codes that have been in effect since 1979, some of the health policies of the Islamic Republic of Iran, such as providing heroin addicts with syringes and methadone treatment or making available free HIV testing, counselling and treatment in government clinics, have been considered radical and progressive by the international community. But how these policies were negotiated demonstrates yet another truism: one size does not fit all – neither across societies, nor within complex national societies.

The designations employed and the presentation of material throughout this publication do not imply the expression of any opinion whatsoever on the part of UNESCO concerning the legal status of any country, territory or area or of its authorities, or concerning the delimitation of its frontiers or boundaries.
The ideas and opinions expressed in this publication are those of the authors and do not necessarily reflect the views of UNESCO and its Member States.

The identification of HIV and AIDS in Iranian prisons in the 1990s slowly led to visibility and public acknowledgement of the existence of an epidemic that was sexually transmitted and drug-related, and catalysed a paradigm shift that led to new policy approaches and public perceptions of the problem. This shift took place more than a decade after the first registered case of HIV and AIDS was diagnosed in 1987 – a haemophiliac child who had received contaminated blood. In the early 1990s, AIDS was perceived by policy-makers and the general public as a Western disease, and imported blood products were blamed for the infections that had occurred in Iran.

The paradigm shift in AIDS policy was facilitated by the efforts of numerous physicians. Some physicians worked with the middle-class medical networks and radio and television programmes in Tehran. Some worked with drug users and the socially abandoned. And some designed a carefully targeted advocacy movement in Kermanshah in western Iran, which eventually led to the creation of the National Strategic Plan for Fighting HIV and AIDS. The shift in policy approaches and public perceptions involved delicate and careful work around the stigma associated with HIV and AIDS and depended on the initiative of individual health policy leaders. A national programme grew out of a provincial initiative, and it highlights a key sensitivity to stigma, an element that is particularly intense in small provincial settings.

More generally, the response to HIV and AIDS in the Islamic Republic of Iran continues to be negotiated and modulated through specific historical and sociocultural discourses revolving around gender, sexuality, addiction and criminality. In listening to official accounts, one needs to read between the lines to find out how this nexus was negotiated and continues to be renegotiated. The linguistics of these negotiations required, and continue to require, strategic avoidance of contentious political issues that could easily have disrupted, and could still disrupt, efforts to mount effective HIV and AIDS and harm reduction programmes, particularly surrounding the cultural categories of homosexuality (not just men having sex with men, or the WHO's category of MSM [men who have sex with men]) and sex outside of marriage.

Focusing on the epidemiology of HIV transmission in prisons played a key role in the formulation of effective policies. The initial ambivalent reaction to the epidemiological discovery of an AIDS epidemic in prisons, however, exemplifies the self-defeating pitfalls of *not* negotiating the problem in culturally situated ways. Even so, the linguistic and semiotic negotiations that eventually allowed the launch of successful policies also obscured and delayed public recognition of other important vectors of the spread of HIV and AIDS, such as the infection of women in heterosexual relationships.

This chapter provides an example of the troubled relationship between an approach that adopts a universalistic language and one that focuses on local particularities. The policy lessons from Iran indicate that education programmes in medical schools and for health practitioners need to apply critical cultural analyses and promote different language tools for leaders in various social or professional strata, for example, clerics, bureaucrats, social workers and media professionals.

In analyzing the epidemic in the Islamic Republic of Iran, I draw on insights from the work of Paula Treichler in the United States. Treichler was among the first to draw attention to a largely invisible epidemic among women and African Americans; her findings were made at a time when the media and public health authorities were focusing on the disease among men who have sex with men. Treichler exposed the ways in which population-based epidemiological indicators of HIV masked impacts on other 'risk groups', thereby creating a hidden epidemic. João Biehl (2007), too, pointed to a similar hidden epidemic among uncounted men who have sex with men in Brazil and concluded that the manner in which statistics were compiled led Brazilian authorities to claim more success for their model of dealing with HIV and AIDS than was in fact warranted. In her work, Treichler also stressed something further, namely that the epidemic was a semiotic machine that generated an overabundance of meanings for and possible interpretations of epidemiological data that shape, and shift, the course of the epidemic through responses to it. In this context, the crisis and the response to it are continually redefined (Treichler, 1987). In a similar fashion, this chapter considers the AIDS epidemic in Iran to be both biomedical and cultural in its inception and evolution.

This chapter provides an account of the linguistic, historical and gender semiotics that have had a hand in shaping the discourse on HIV and AIDS in Iran since the 1990s. Attention is then drawn to the interplay between the biomedical and epidemiological approaches adopted by the WHO towards HIV and AIDS and the local social and cultural realities that shape HIV risk and response. Without such attention to social and cultural realities, effective modes of intervention will keep escaping us.

Semiotic machines and epidemics: Language, gender and medicine

In Iran, two distinct stratifications of language remain central to the epidemic and associated policy-making processes, namely: (a) formal-informal intra-linguistic code-switching; (b) cross-linguistic switching between Persian (Farsi) and the English used by the WHO and other transnational agencies; and (c) cross-linguistic switching between Persian and other local dialects and languages inside Iran. In formal-informal code-switching, even the tone of voice, gesture, facial expression and expectations about how to structure the responses of the other person contribute to meanings and interpretations that construct new concepts. Like all vernaculars, Persian (along with local dialects and other languages spoken in Iran, including Kurdish, Azeri, Baluchi and Arabic) carries discourses of sexuality and stigma that are negotiated in discourses on HIV and AIDS, whether consciously or not, in the clinic or in intimate daily talk, in policy discourses or in popular explanations of those discourses.

As a first approximation, one might point to prostitution, paedophilia and prisons as three heavily charged semantic fields that do not translate directly into their English equivalents. The Persian word *fahsha* (loosely translated as prostitution) is a broad term of moral disapprobation for a variety of sexual behaviours, including extramarital sexual relations for women. This term is highly pejorative, as are most of the terms used to discuss the sex industry, although significations and usages vary, from the terms *roospi,* for prostitute, and *roospigari,* for prostitution, to more recently introduced terms, *zanan e khiabani* (street walkers) and *dokhtaran e farari* (runaway girls), that have been used to refer to the now widespread and visible population of young women leaving their – often traditional or poor – families in search of a better future in the streets of major cities.

Similar complexities and stigma surround terms for imprisonment and prisoner (*khalafkar, 'obash, arazel* – all pejorative terms for criminals). The Persian expression for prisons (*zendan*) conveys more than a mere physical place of confinement and is sometimes understood as a place where a number of activities take place, such as needle sharing, that, in turn, intensify the risk of HIV infection. Understanding the role of prisons in the spread of HIV and AIDS was critical to the policy paradigm shift that occurred in the 1990s; however, the emphasis on prisons as sites for HIV transmission had a paradoxical effect. On the one hand, it highlighted the risks associated with infection through injecting drugs and needle sharing in prisons, and this facilitated programs under the name of dealing with drug addiction. But on the other hand, it obscured other modes of transmission. Moreover, it overlooked the fact that the first prisons to become associated with HIV and AIDS were those in the provinces that suffered the brunt of the war between Iran and Iraq and its aftermath of psychosocial effects.

Paedophilia is another term that carries culturally specific significations. It is roughly translated as *bacheh-bazi* (*bacheh* meaning child and *bazi* meaning playing with, and specifically to have sexual tendencies towards a child). The term in the Persian language is rich in meaning as it alludes to a wide range of homosocial relations and forms part of venerable poetic traditions, daily sexual anecdotes and joking (particularly in male circles), discourses on local male bonding and the national and transnational discourses on homosexuality that are shaped by media (often the internet). It is not uncommon for lay people to understand and use the concepts of homosexuality, transsexuality and paedophilia interchangeably. Many still confuse homosexuals with transvestites or sexually abused young boys. More important, homosexuality is often understood as an exclusively male phenomenon; even then, particularly in the light of definitions associated with sharia law, it is often technically reduced to *lavat* (sodomy, pederasty, the act of anal penetration involving two men or a man and a boy). Currently, women are almost absent from the religious and legal discourse of homosexuality.

As the above examples illustrate, meaning cannot just be 'translated' literally or 'mapped' from one language to another without consideration of how the cultural geography reworks connotations and layers of signification. The range and changes in usages and new coinages of words provide indices of historical changes and of past strata of more liberated or more puritanical sexual language. Sexual vocabulary in Persian conveys a range of sentiments, emotions, judgments and insults that create a sharp division between informal and formal languages and that differ sharply from their equivalents in Western colloquial, academic, scientific and policy discourse. They are often mixed in with borrowed terms from Western medical and non-Persian lexicons, which also include transliterations aimed at creating words in Persian that have no, or relatively little, stigma attached to them. For instance, in the new Iranian blogosphere and in the Iranian discourse of sexuality, the Western term homosexual is also translated as *ham-jens-gara* (homosexual, literally: one who likes the same sex); similarly, the coinage of the term *degar-bash* for queer (emphasizing the otherness of one's sexuality and orientation; *degar* meaning other, different) generated lively debates – in the Iranian blogosphere in particular – that explored the possibilities within the Persian language for new words to convey the inclusive concept of queer. In conversations, on the other hand, particularly in male-only circles, jokes and slurs use a wide range of terms that are still considered pejorative, from *khahar* (sister, sissy) to references to body parts. Interestingly, in the diaspora, young émigrés usually code-switch to the English word *gay*, but some have recently begun using the term *khosh-hal* (happy, gay) when among English-speaking people in an attempt to work around the stigma still associated with the term gay, not necessarily only among Iranians, but also in the West.

Despite the absence of grammatical gender identifiers for nouns in Persian, these examples show how Persian can still deploy gender, hierarchy and moral charge. The Iranian culture of reference and signification needs to be acknowledged and understood and is at risk of being lost in translation. Such gendered language expands and shapes social categories, affecting the ways in which sex and gender are communicated. The discourse on HIV and AIDS in Iran is restrained by a large burden of taboos, sexual disciplining, contrasts of public versus private spheres and historical constructions of meaning. Gender is not just about the female body but also about larger social categories and moral distinctions. With respect to policy-making, therefore, one cannot assume the gender aspect of the AIDS epidemic is addressed by simply including women in our analysis. Attention must also be given to gender roles and power relations that are rooted in language and negotiated in multiple sites of power.

Overlapping and converging strategies toward a national policy

Prominent medical professionals in Iran, such as Dr Minoo Mohraz, were among the first to raise awareness on HIV and AIDS in the country. By the early 1990s, a National AIDS Committee was established that included representatives from several government ministries. By making appeals on television and in other public discussions, medical professionals began to promote safer sex and protection from other pathways of infection, particularly in prisons.

As a result of the growing number of new case reports of HIV (especially among needle-sharing injecting drug users), the Ministry of Health and Medical Education set out to screen key populations. Drug-user prisoners were among the first key populations to be screened. In 1997, an epidemiological study in three prisons in the cities of Kerman, Shiraz and Kermanshah reported a high – almost 100 per cent – prevalence of HIV infection among inmate populations (Alaei, 2006). Initially, official reactions to the shocking results were ambiguous. Efforts were made to suppress the results and to segregate the HIV-positive inmates in a separate ward in Kermanshah's case and redistribute prisoners from the other two cities, which would have potentially created additional risks. Somewhat inevitably, Kermanshah was recognized as one of the cities with an HIV and AIDS crisis. Although other cities and their prisons may have been suffering from similarly high rates of HIV infection among injecting drug users at the time, data was not available to substantiate that case.

Medical professionals, such as Dr Minoo Mohraz, reached for government policy attention and emphasized education and awareness programmes while at the same time providing clinical care for HIV-positive patients in their own practices, which were mainly in Tehran. Eventually one of the first referral centres for HIV-positive patients was established in the infectious disease ward of Tehran University's Imam Khomeini hospital. In addition, within the body of the National AIDS Committee, a subcommittee, the National Harm Reduction Committee, was founded in 2002. This committee included representatives from the Ministry of Health and Medical Education, Drug Control Headquarters, the police, the judiciary, the Prison Organization, the Welfare Organization, academic centres and Islamic Republic of Iran Broadcasting (Mokri and Schottenfeld, 2008).

While Tehran and other major cities hosted an array of well-known clinicians with some experience with HIV and AIDS, the situation in smaller cities and provincial settings was somewhat different. Around the same time as Kermanshah was understood to have 400 HIV-positive patients, two physicians from Kermanshah, Arash Alaei and Kamiar Alaei, returned to their hometown after graduating from medical school to serve their post-graduation service and join other medical experts involved in tackling the HIV crisis. When they began their work, Dr Kamiar Alaei recalls, they requested an unmarked office in the city's main university clinic, Kermanshah's University of Medical Sciences, deliberately avoiding any public association with HIV and AIDS (Alaei, 2006). The physicians started with the prison reports to follow up on HIV-positive prisoners; 176 of the prisoners had already died, according to Dr Kamiar Alaei. The physicians' first evaluations indicated that the leading cause of death among former prison inmates living with HIV and AIDS was not from AIDS-related diseases but, instead, from suicide. They concluded that stigma was the first obstacle to providing medical support; the majority of these patients had been disowned by their families and communities. The physicians' team grew as they started to reach out to families, wives and relatives in order to educate them about the disease, its aetiology and its modes of transmission. With the help of local clerics and other professionals, including prison officials, they engaged in a low-key, person-to-person community outreach using peer referrals and gradually convinced people to accept voluntary testing and counselling. After this confidence-building phase within the community and among national health care administrators, the Kermanshah team was also able to get supplies to provide treatment for HIV-positive patients. Eventually, and with the formation of provincial AIDS committees, health professionals managed to involve organizations such as the Red Crescent and the Imam Khomeini Emdad Committee in order to extend outreach to other key populations, and to women in particular.

This approach was successful because it acknowledged the gendered configuration of the community and motivated people to voluntarily seek testing and care rather than further marginalizing affected persons. 'You should never forget to base your program on your own society, your own demographics, your own religion and culture', advises Dr Kamiar Alaei in an interview. At issue in this moral economy was not just the well-being of those living with HIV but also the implications for family members in relation to social and economic status and even their ability to negotiate proper marriages for their daughters. In light of anxieties around arranging marriages and in an attempt to break the psychosocial dangers of social isolation, the doctors even engaged in some successful matchmaking programmes in their efforts to promote safer sex and a safer lifestyle for HIV-positive individuals.

Meanwhile, it gradually emerged that HIV and AIDS policies would need to respond to two converging epidemics: HIV and AIDS, and drug use (Ohiri et al., 2006). According to United Nations statistics, Iran has the highest rate of drug addiction in the world: 2.8 per cent of the population over the age of fifteen, or some 4 million users (Vick, 2005). Iran has a long history of battling various kinds of addiction. Even before the Islamic revolution, opium addiction was rife, and a 'Fighting Opium and Alcohol Use' committee had been formed in the aftermath of the foreign occupation and socio-economic crisis of the Second World War (Chehrazi, 2005). Over the years that followed, laws had subsequently been introduced that authorized various approaches, such as supply-reduction, criminalization and treatment. Even though drug trafficking was a capital crime, supplies of opium were made available by the government to registered addicts, programmes for addiction treatment were initiated and limited supplies of opium poppies were grown to meet these demands. After the 1979 revolution, a criminal approach to drug abuse prevailed in policy-making (for a historical account of Iran's shifts among repressive, restitutive and rehabilitative penal policies, see Fischer, 1989).

From 1979 to 1994, the government did not allow medical treatment of drug users, and it was the judiciary system that took primary charge of dealing with them (Mokri and Schottenfeld, 2008). In the 1990s, in the aftermath of the

Iran-Iraq War and with the huge increase in heroin production in Afghanistan, the nature of drug addiction in Iran shifted dramatically from smoking opium to swallowing opium balls, injecting heroin and taking 'crack' (not crack cocaine)[1] and 'glass' (methamphetamines). In response, the Islamic Republic of Iran eventually adopted 'harm reduction' policies consisting of treatment and counselling and thus medicalized and decriminalized addiction (Ohiri et al., 2006).

The official approval of harm reduction policies by the highest ranks of governmental officials was in part a reflection of expert communication with the Ministry of Health and Medical Education. Among expert initiatives, the Persepolis NGO (non-governmental organization) was one of the prominent models of contextualized and integral approaches within the framework of harm reduction. Dr Nassirimanesh, the founder and director of Persepolis, promotes a pragmatic mix of approaches to drug addiction by providing needle exchange and free-of-charge methadone programmes under the same umbrella; upon arrival at the drop-in centres, clients are provided with kits consisting of syringes, alcohol pads, foil for smoking opium and a large metal spoon to cook heroin.

In 2006, at the IHRA (International Harm Reduction Association) conference at the British Columbia Centre for Excellence in HIV/AIDS, Dr Nassirimanesh presented his centre's four-pillar approach to drug use as one that aims at changing behaviour and focuses on reintegration of the patient through realistic attention to the social and familial demands on the drug user. The centre's approach additionally relies on the collaboration of different strata of professionals, from nurses and social workers to doctors, counsellors and policy-makers. He passionately condemns strict abstinence-centred approaches for their unrealistic message and expectations. He also points to the failure of criminal approaches over time: 'When you arrest or kill an addict, you damage their family and you automatically create a machinery of drug use through their children who are hurt' (Nassirimanesh, 2006). In fact, as criminal approaches to drug use were replaced with milder policies, such as 'vocational camps' that still focused on supply reduction and abstinence, nothing really changed, except prisons became more crowded. Instead, Nassirimanesh advocates a peer-driven model, even hiring recovering drug users as staff, to provide social support, promote self-esteem and encourage reintegration into productive lifestyles. The philosophy, as he often reports, is that the street is often the best university; the model regards the drug user not as the problem but as the source for its solutions.

The materialization of methadone maintenance treatment (MMT) and needle exchange programs was initiated by the convergence of such expert voices. Ali Hashemi, head of the cabinet-level Drug Control Headquarters, notes that the country had paid a heavy price for the zero-tolerance drug policy imposed by successive governments following the Islamic Revolution in 1979 (Vick, 2005). And Dr Azarakhsh Mokri, director of the Iranian National Centre for Addiction Studies, has even suggested that the state should cultivate opium poppies again to control the drug trade (Harrison, 2004). Experts believe that the current set of progressive policies is due to, among other things, the role of NGOs and civil society in advocacy and community outreach efforts, cooperation with the Ministry of Health and Medical Education and informed advocacy by some senior policy-makers (Ohiri et al., 2006). As a result, a National Harm Reduction Committee was established that incorporated members from various ministries, medical schools, academic centres and NGOs.

Meanwhile, in 2000, Kermanshah's medical team established triangular clinics to serve three groups: injecting drug users, patients with sexually transmitted infections (STIs) and people living with HIV (PLHIV). These clinics are run by the Ministry of Health and Medical Education and host general practitioners, clinical psychologists, nurses and social workers. The clinics now offer needle exchange, methadone maintenance treatment (after MMT was allowed and reintroduced in 2002), condoms, treatment for STIs, general medical care, referral for voluntary counselling and testing, and even help in contracting marriages to counter the severe isolation, depression and suicide attempts of those who are living with HIV and AIDS. In some cases, they also provide highly active antiretroviral therapy (HAART) for persons with HIV (Mokri and Schottenfeld, 2008). The aim of the 'triangular' idea was to diffuse and reduce stigma associated with each of these overlapping populations by avoiding direct reference to HIV and AIDS and to increase the effectiveness of interventions by bringing these three groups together.

The triangular clinic idea seemed to work, and with the involvement of governmental and non-governmental organizations, it eventually formed the basis for a National Strategic Plan for Fighting HIV and AIDS and was awarded best practice certification by the WHO in 2004 for prevention and care activities on behalf of injecting drug abusers (WHO, 2004). The contrast with previous failed attempts by a physician and parliamentarian to establish a national AIDS hospital in Kermanshah is striking and is explained by the fact that those attempts were top-down initiatives, with no preparatory grass-roots-level work carried out. Moreover, they were insensitive to stigma-related issues by insisting on in-patient care in a regular hospital setting, where interactions be-tween people living with HIV and AIDS and the general public could occur (Aman and Maher, 2006).

By October 2006, sixty-seven cities and fifty-seven prisons in Iran had triangular clinics. The clinics are under the supervision of the medical uni-versities in each province and have been supported by several Iranian NGOs. The National Research Institute of Tuberculosis and Lung Disease at Shahid Beheshti Medical University and the Pars Institute (run by Drs Kamiar and Arash Alaei)[2] are among these collaborators. Other similar clinics include the three Persepolis harm reduction centres in low-income districts of south Tehran run by Dr Nassirimanesh, the House of Sun drug treatment centre for women in Tehran (Fathi, 2008), the Congress60 drug treatment centre, and the Aftab Society detox clinic in north Tehran, which caters to higher-income groups.

The Kermanshah case is an example of the mobilizing function of lan-guage and highlights the significance of multiple layers of meaning in local narratives (Alaei and Alaei, 2005). When the Kermanshah medical team that began AIDS advocacy in Kermanshah in 1997 ultimately succeeded in imple-menting policies such as the needle exchange programmes in prisons, it was because they had personally engaged with the clergy of the city and established a dialogue with prominent officials, both within and outside the penitentiary system; through such negotiations the gendered configuration of the commu-nity's moral economy came to be acknowledged and strategically redirected. A combination of medical and cultural analyses resulted in the successful strategy of condom distribution in prisons – a significant achievement considering that condom distribution had been far from acceptable to prison authorities.

Given that the act of sexual intercourse between men is explicitly des-ignated as a sin in the country's Islamic law framework, health professionals faced a dilemma in framing and legitimizing the use of condoms in a men's prison. According to Dr Kamiar Alaei (2006), this was achieved by exploiting a loophole in prison regulations that allowed prisoners to enjoy occasional day-long *Morakhasi-e Shar'i* visits (breaks and family visits allowed by religion), and as sexual encounter between spouses during these visits was accepted, con-doms could be distributed, in much larger quantities though than one would normally expect for a family visit. This new policy was approved by the clergy charged with overseeing conditions in prisons and later became implemented in official regulations.

The local doctors were familiar with the local moral landscape; their per-sonal connections to relevant officials and institutions, as well as their gender, gave them mobility within prisons, organizations and ministries. For instance, as natives of Kermanshah and being able to speak Kurdish, it was possible for the Alaeis and their colleagues to gain access to the community and make a significant contribution to normalizing the HIV and AIDS discourse.

The intentional focus on the decriminalization and medicalization of drug addiction contributed to the realization of the National Strategic Plan for Fighting HIV and AIDS, which subsequently led to policies for free HIV testing, counselling and AIDS treatment, as well as a successful proposal for a grant from the Global Fund to Fight AIDS, Tuberculosis and Malaria. Consequently, Iranian doctors began to organize workshops for health professionals from central Asia and member countries of the Organisation of the Islamic Conference.

As already indicated, AIDS advocacy and activism were not limited to Kermanshah. Many medical professionals, activist groups and NGOs contributed to the emergence of Iranian AIDS discourses. Dr Minoo Mohraz, for instance, was among the first physicians to bring the issue of HIV and AIDS to the attention of policy-makers. As a secular, female university professor and physician at the University of Tehran, Professor Mohraz had a very different position from that held by the young doctors in Kermanshah. It was Minoo Mohraz who for the first time, in 2001, used the word 'condom' on national TV. 'I said if they won't let me talk about condoms and sexual behaviour, I wouldn't come on the programme. So they said I could talk,' she recalls (MacFarquhar, 2002). Professor Mohraz's pragmatic approach and advocacy of safer sex, safer injection and HIV and AIDS education over almost two decades have turned her into one of the most visible faces of HIV and AIDS campaigns among the educated middle class and the medical community. Today, such attempts at speaking about AIDS are supported by clerics, who have come to agree with the importance and significance of fighting AIDS. Most important, a mandate from the supreme leader, Ayatollah Ali Khamenei, facilitated a clerical and official response to the crisis. Similarly, Ayatollah Shahroudi, the head of the justice system in Iran, called for the cooperation of the justice system with the National Harm Reduction Committee.

These parallel sites of contestation – one around prisons, the other around sex education – are each associated with radically different approaches to HIV prevention and response and with distinct moral codes and linguistic pragmatics. While western medical language was used to raise public awareness about AIDS, in the case of the policy shifts around prisons, stigma was contested and reconfigured through community outreach and grass-roots-level advocacy.

While, like elsewhere, the AIDS epidemic remains a gendered one in Iran, these contrasting and converging strategies demonstrate that simply focusing on *risk groups* and *behaviours* (defined and treated universally) will be less effective than focusing on finer-grained understandings of local moral economies, an individual's position in social and sexual networks, and stratified networks and languages. It is crucial to explore the genealogies of how risk behaviours are shaped in their historical, linguistic and cultural relations.

Multiple faces of epidemics: Across and within societies

Medical training and practice in Iran have adopted western models of knowledge production, professional language and ethics. In so doing, they have at times overlooked the diversity of local forms of life and the dynamics of how epidemics spread and mutate socially. While HIV and AIDS narratives in the United States first evolved around homosexuality (and the need to break widespread homophobia), the epidemic in Iran became publicly visible in discourses on injecting drug use in prisons. If, in Iran, the AIDS epidemic had been linked primarily to homosexuality, the ensuing public dialogue and public health interventions would have most likely been more inhibited. According to Ministry of Health and Medical Education reports, there are 4 million drug users currently living in the country, 400,000 of whom use heroin intravenously. Since the early days of the epidemic and given the marginalization of sexual discourses, articulations of addiction were not considered as controversial as those related to sexual transmission. However, by focusing on HIV transmission through drug use in prisons, other transmission dynamics and realities were underemphasized in the 'official' discourses, with implications for both data collection and the role of social and gender relations in the design of interventions.

Although HIV can be spread by shared-needle injection of drugs, official discourse claiming that people were becoming infected by HIV mainly through the use of drugs in prisons effectively masked multiple realities and varying social patterns of transmission within Iran. Addiction-centred interventions have played a role in shaping and changing the dynamics of the epidemic through the ways statistics are collected, social relations are treated and power relations are gendered. Social patterns of transmission vary within Iran. For instance, in the south-western province of Baluchistan, the main mode of transmission is sexual, and HIV and AIDS are more prevalent among females and children than among males (BBC Persian Service, 2007). A case study of the village of

Saravan, where polygamy is common, shows that many women were infected by husbands returning home from long business trips to the Gulf countries. According to the Ministry of Health and Medical Education, more than 76 per cent of these patients living with HIV contracted the virus through sexual transmission (*Etemaad-e-Melli*, 2007). However, in the western provinces of Iran that were devastated by the war with Iraq, intravenous drug use remains the dominant mode of transmission. These variations in the epidemic and how it is spreading were obscured by the almost exclusive attention of official discourse on prisons.

With its battery of quantitative datasets, biomedicine tends to rely on epidemiology to monitor the dynamics of epidemics, thereby reducing the variety of practices and understandings to a static variable called 'culture'. This understanding is increasingly at odds with that of anthropologists, who consider the concept of culture to be highly situational, dynamic and continually under negotiation (Fischer, 2007). An epidemiological account of disease tends to be reductive and attribute fixed roles to individuals, episodes and gender. It is thus oblivious to the overlapping and shifting cultural dynamics of simultaneous epidemic forms of the same disease. Epidemiology tends also to downplay the power relations that occur among various professional groups, such as epidemiologists, pathologists, general physicians, virologists, clergy, bureaucrats, politicians, journalists and others (Hammonds, 1999; Latour, 1988; Rosenberg, 1992). AIDS policy in Iran, with its emphasis on biomedicine, relied heavily on statistics and the medicalization of drug addiction as an HIV risk factor. Although this had the positive effect of increasing local awareness and understanding of transmission risk and international recognition of HIV prevention efforts, it also may have shifted attention away from the sociocultural context and gender relations contributing to increased risk of HIV infection.

Given the centrality of the masculine public image of injecting drug use, the vulnerability of women often becomes invisible. As women make up only about 6 per cent of the total cases of HIV and AIDS in the country (official statistics of the Ministry of Health and Medical Education as of December 2008, http://www.behdasht.gov.ir), women and children living with HIV and AIDS are marginalized, particularly in places like Saravan. Health policies have often failed to address the fact that the wives of people with a drug addiction become infected with HIV through sexual relations with their husbands; however, today peer-referral systems are beginning to address the issue. Meanwhile, health professionals foresee a change in the dominant mode of transmission from injecting drug use to unsafe sex (*Etemaad-e-Melli*, 2007). This will make the gender dimension of power relations even more significant, including the still-taboo subject of homosexuality.

The language of *risk* in epidemiology also provides a meta-narrative that assumes its own legitimacy and often gives false assurance of having dealt with the social aspects of illness. Moral imperatives in this technical risk language focus on the individual rather than on societal realities. Biologizing, medicalizing and individualizing – and thus depoliticizing the categories of risk – can mask important parts of the course of an epidemic. For instance, when rituals, traditional wisdom and embodied cultural identities are perceived by western biomedicine as risk factors, they tend to undermine the compelling reasons that drive individuals to resort to such practices, even as recognized and calculated risks, so that groups, power and identities can be maintained (Frankenberg, 1993). For example, many injecting drug users in prisons choose to share needles, even when clean needles are available, as a gesture of solidarity and collective ritual. Therefore, the subjectivity of interveners, doctors and patients, illness narratives, life stories of people living with HIV and AIDS, emotions, desires and local and temporal junctions of intervention should be taken into account in the equation of HIV and AIDS discourse. This is why an anthropologically informed understanding of *risk* and *behaviour* is necessary for proper intervention to become possible. In expanding the focus of attention from a pathology-disease-patient perspective to broader social contexts that account for multiple causalities, there is a need for a reflexive and critical approach that analyses what medical professionals foreground or marginalize.

Post-rupture contexts: The social face of the epidemic

'Drug use', 'prostitution', 'unsafe sex' and 'MSM' are professionalized, even sanitized, terms of art in the response to HIV and AIDS. HIV and AIDS evolved not only as a viral-biological issue but also as a merging point for social forces that were crucial in the construction of the epidemic's risk factors. Yet by the time HIV and AIDS became visible as a medical and social problem in Iran, policy transformations were being formulated for an epidemic of drug use that, by the 1990s, had already developed its own distinct modes and features. It was through the coupling of these two epidemics and the work of advocacy groups that massive policy shifts came to be formulated.

One cannot deal with the issues of drugs and the evolution of the AIDS epidemic in Iran without taking into consideration the devastating eight-year war (1980–1988) between Iran and Iraq. The war caused psychological problems, poverty and displacement, uprooting families, distorting gender relations and creating financial difficulties for countless people. As in many post-conflict societies, self-destructive behaviours, including substance abuse, addiction and sexual deviance became widespread. Studies have shown that high rates of suicide over the past decade have occurred in the western provinces of Iran, the former front line in the war with Iraq. Psychiatrists have speculated about a similarly high prevalence of dysphoric and anxiety disorders, although statistics are hard to come by. The relationship between the war and psychological problems has become a part of everyday discourse and anecdotal knowledge of family struggles, and a sizable number of Iranian films have explored these issues (Fischer, 2004).

The Iraqi invasion of the oil-rich Iranian city of Khoramshahr in 1980 began a war in which an estimated one million people died, changing the male-to-female ratio of the population and creating large numbers of injured and traumatized survivors, including those injured by Saddam Hussein's brutal chemical attacks on the city of Sardasht (known now to Iranians as *shahr-e-shimiayi,* the chemical city). In Sardasht, even those who at the time of the attack were not visibly affected are now developing serious physical and psychological problems after more than two decades (Ghazanfari et al., 2009; Saadat 2006).[3] The war trauma extended though a long process of prisoner-of-war exchanges, which went on until 2003.

While the war led to a series of lifestyle and behavioural changes, a fertility boom – encouraged in the early years of the war – has resulted in today's overwhelmingly young population. During the war, the Islamic Republic of Iran pursued a pro-natalist policy, which rapidly doubled the country's population, from 30 million at the time of the revolution to 65 million by the end of the 1980s. After the war, the country successfully reversed course, bringing the fertility rate to a nearly stable replacement level through educational campaigns and a family-control plan that reached both urban and rural communities. As a result, today's overwhelmingly young population has had to deal with a changing social landscape. That half of injecting drug users are reported to have started injecting after 1993 (Nassirimanesh et al., 2005) raises questions about the demobilization of war veterans, rising rates of unemployment and inflation and a widespread sense of lack of opportunity among the young.

While many post-conflict societies experience disruptions and dysfunctions, including drug abuse, the characteristics and particular circumstances of each case vary dramatically. In the case of Iran, many of these particular circumstances can be obscured by a characterization in professionalized and universalized terms, such as drugs, prostitution and unsafe sex.

The Iran-Iraq War had a devastating impact on the country's western provinces, but the displacement of individuals and families and the negative socio-economic conditions resulting from the war affected many other parts of the country as well. Twenty-seven years of sanctions imposed on Iran by the United States and other Western governments have also contributed to poverty, depression, isolation, social and psychological disaffection and uncertainty about the future. Concurrently, medical professionals are concerned about how the growth of the HIV/AIDS epidemic in the newly independent countries to the north might affect the dynamics of the epidemic in Iran (Nassirimanesh et al., 2005). In addition, official statistics show significant increases in crime rates in the post-war era, as reflected in the rising number of prisoners – in prisons that have become primary sites for heroin addiction and the unsafe sharing of needles (Mokri, 2002). Internal migration, urbanization, unemployment, social conflicts and crime all provide fertile ground for the spread of drug use.

The rise, fall and resurgence of the Taliban in neighbouring Afghanistan and the huge increase in the production of opium and heroin that flows in from Afghanistan have also had a profound effect (Beyrer, 2001). The opium ban in Afghanistan in 2000 resulted in a temporary scarcity of opium in Iran. This triggered a massive shift in drug use to heroin injection. It is estimated that more than half of the drugs trafficked from Afghanistan to the European market pass through Iran (Nassirimanesh et al, 2005).

Yet, the situation in Afghanistan is only one of the factors playing a role in the dramatic shift in the pattern of addiction from smoking opium to heroin injection. Opium consumption – by way of smoking, dissolving in tea, sniffing and inhaling opium (*tariak*) or its residue (*shireh*) – has long been a common practice and at times even a semi-public social activity among the elderly and men. However, today heroin is injected by men and women who are much younger than the opium users of past generations. Heroin and crack are cheaper than opium and more elating – and all too readily available. Injection is also a more feasible choice given the way public and private spaces have been transformed in post-revolutionary Iran. In contrast to the public nature of smoking opium, the private nature of injection requires no more than a corner on a construction site and a few moments of spare time. The public image of the old *taryaki* man is now replaced with that of countless young men and women using drugs in active decades of their lives. Needle sharing occasionally moves from a necessity to a social form of life, but primarily in already segregated and stigmatized spaces, such as prisons. This privatization of drug use is, among other factors, linked to transforming configurations of public and private spaces.

The complex effects of social change are not limited to the poor and displaced. Globalization and media have introduced new, and often conflicting, behavioural codes that keep shaping complex identity categories in all sections of society. The middle classes are also experiencing the stress of shifting social patterns, beginning with the sharp increase in the numbers of well-educated young women, the rising age of marriage and changing gender roles and relations; this is enhanced by recent globalized communication technologies but also an extension of century-long processes. The diversity of moral codes, including strong homophobic narratives, confirms various contesting sentiments in the society, at once both liberalizing and traditionalizing.

Gender complexities

Among the formative features of the AIDS epidemic in Iran, both as medical disorder and as sociocultural (dis)order, are the stigmatization of sex, the suppression of women's sexual activity and competing conceptualizations about homosexuality. Leslie Butt (2002), a medical anthropologist, uses the term 'suffering stranger' to draw attention to subjectivities that are represented in ways that must fit bureaucratic criteria for international and national funding. In the same manner as Treichler, she warns that such bureaucratized categories can mask the absence of other sufferers' voices. People with a drug addiction in Iran can be considered an example of such bureaucratized categorization. Ministry of Health and Medical Education statistics from December 2008 indicate that there are 18,881 patients living with HIV and AIDS in Iran, of which only 6.5 per cent are women (http://www.behdasht.gov.ir). However, medical professionals estimate that there are as many as 70,000–100,000 people living with HIV and AIDS in the country and warn that the dominant mode of infection is shifting from shared needles to sex (*Etemad-e-Melli,* 2007). According to official statistics, more than 90 per cent of women living with HIV were infected by their husbands and could in the future transmit the virus to others through divorce and remarriage, adultery, mother-to-child transmission of HIV, exposure to blood or blood products, and so forth. While polygamy and reluctance to use condoms are common, modes of transmission often overlap: drug use is common among commercial sex workers, whereas the wives of drug dealers and addicts who at times confess to having committed a crime so that their husbands can continue to financially support the family face risk of exposure in prison through contaminated needles.

According to official reports, the number of commercial sex workers has grown very rapidly (Ghabrayi, 2004). However, since the revolution in 1979 they have been subjected to violence, both by men and by government policing and politicized attention, and are now designated as criminalized individuals. Although *sigheh,* or *mut'a,* marriage in Shi'ite law – a legal contract for legitimized limited-time marriages – is sometimes used as a means to avoid allegations of illegal sex work, in the absence of a more open public sexual discourse at the level of the family and society, intense and unsafe underground sexual activities have been reported in recent years (Kakaei, 2006). Not only is it extremely complicated to examine modes of transmission in such cases, but because women are more stigmatized by HIV than men, they are more reluctant to take part in screening programmes. Unofficial reports show that about 5 per cent of outpatient admissions in drug clinics are women who came to the clinic voluntarily and not through systematic screening. Access to women is in any case more difficult due to familial, social and civil constraints. This is reinforced by the secondary stigma that is attached to family and friends of women who are identified as living with HIV.

Emerging discourses and approaches

In these contexts, the emergence of a discourse on HIV and AIDS has paradoxically served to intensify an historical and ongoing panic generated by the topic of sex while at the same time it opens up space for a sexual discourse. The official discourse on HIV and AIDS, for the most part, falls under the rubric of injecting drug use, and in the shadow of this official discourse, health professionals have been able to partially deal with other key populations that are at risk of contracting HIV through unsafe sex practices. This official-unofficial separation of discourses will not be sustainable in the long term. The National Strategic Plan for Fighting HIV and AIDS, however, provides a golden opportunity for the decriminalization of so called illegitimate sexual activities, if only to better position the country to tackle the AIDS epidemic in its totality.

Over time, the more effective harm reduction policies have become, the more frequently AIDS and drugs have become interchangeable terms, not unlike the way HIV and AIDS became signifiers for controversies surrounding homosexuality in the early days of the epidemic in the United States. For Iran, the harm reduction policies, based upon the statistics of drug harm reduction, became the basis for the WHO's recognition of Iran as a best practice site. HIV and AIDS has become a signifier primarily for drug use and only occasionally for sex and a cluster of behavioural 'anomalies' unspoken and feared by doctors and lay people alike. Despite these distorting effects, on the bright side, the receptivity of Iranian policy-makers towards the significance of language and communication, in so far as medicalization, decriminalization and de-stigmatization of addiction are concerned, is a great example of pragmatism.

The Islamic Republic of Iran is unique when compared to most other Muslim countries as it has been able to face certain realities and discuss HIV and AIDS. The Ministry of Education instituted a pilot preventive education programme on HIV and AIDS in a few schools in Tehran in 2004. The programme trained volunteer students called Messengers of Health to educate not only their peers but also their families. A wider school-based initiative called by its English acronym FRESH (Focusing Resources on Effective School Health) was to be implemented in schools in 2006. An AIDS booklet for school students was published in 2005 by the UNAIDS office in Tehran and the Ministry of Education, to be distributed in schools as part of the school curriculum in 2006. Regardless of policy changes that followed, these initiatives opened up a space that paved the way for normalization of the HIV and AIDS discourse. On 23 April 2006, Osama Tawil, the head of the UNAIDS office in Tehran, elaborated on the issues at hand in a press interview with the daily newspaper *Shargh*:

> We need to extend dialogues between different sectors. An HIV-positive drug addict who leaves prison should not be left without support, as he puts his family and society at risk. *Fortunately, over the past few years, many unspoken issues are being dealt with, including safer sex, education and implementation of harm reduction initiatives* (emphasis added).

By exploiting the many possibilities that exist in the Shi'ite law and by avoiding a Western politically correct language, the state has so far made radical changes in the law, aiming medical outreach and access at injecting drug users rather than pursuing them as criminals. Similarly, a discourse of safer sex has opened up. The government has also provided patients that have developed AIDS with free medication, implanted multiple testing and counselling clinics around the country and collaborated with the United Nations Development

Programme and other international organizations, as well as with other countries. The National Strategic Plan for Fighting HIV and AIDS has managed to accommodate as many HIV and AIDS patients, including non–drug users, as possible under the umbrella of triangular clinics. By engaging the media and printing brochures and posters, the programme used peer education in institutions, such as the army and universities, in a number of cities as part of a pilot study and advocated peer referral to reach more people through prisoners, drug users and other patients (Alaei and Alaei, 2005). However, relying on peer referral to reach out to men and women engaged in unsafe practices does not grant these individuals legal security.

Regardless of the morally and religiously controversial nature of certain sexual activities as compared to injecting drugs, it still seems that similar potential spaces of negotiation can be used for other key populations. One example is the progressive reading of Shi'ite clerics on transsexuality as a physiological variation – transsexual operations are allowed and subsidized by the government – acknowledged and accommodated by both clerical rule and the medical profession. However, since homosexuality is categorically disallowed by current clerical interpretations, homosexuals have to choose between a sex-change operation, thereby 'returning' themselves to a heterosexual condition, or punishment if they choose to retain their homosexual identity. Nonetheless, conceptual spaces like this, including that of temporary marriage, can serve as entry points for negotiating and even articulating the reality of sexuality in its different forms and thus for mobilizing a broader discourse on HIV and AIDS (for more on *sigheh* marriage, see Haeri, 1989).

Conclusion: An epidemic of meanings

HIV and AIDS, like any other epidemic, need to be understood in both medical and sociocultural terms. Discursive terms and framings (drugs, harm reduction and so forth) recognize meanings and interpretations generated by an epidemic; but, in the absence of historical and socio-political context, may also become reifications that marginalize other potentially critical interpretations. Sanitized terminology – however useful and important in political struggles to decriminalize, to humanize suffering and to provide short-term acute therapy and more extended social support – is insufficient in the long term. Equally important to understanding the course of the evolution of an epidemic is an examination of the psychology of ruptures in time and space, such as those created by wars, political upheavals, disasters and economic catastrophes. The personal uncertainties, fears and desires of patients cannot be separated from social ones. Such ruptures afford opportunities for intervention and renewal amidst uncertainties about the future. But upheavals also contribute to disaffection and self-destructive behaviours that contribute to the spread of HIV and AIDS.

Gender is a pivotal pole around which meanings and power relations evolve and revolve. Gender, beyond inclusion of women, requires attention to gender roles, gendered (and gendering) languages, sexual histories of both men and women and the status of an individual in social and sexual networks. The common sense of society thus needs critical examination, including various chains of metaphors and significations, such as discourse surrounding pollution, promiscuity, shame, guilt, asymmetric power relations, homophobia, paedophilia, prostitution, injecting drug use, needles, invasions (military and viral), prison, masculinity, crime, poverty, economic and political challenges, westernization and 'westoxification', or cultural corruption by the West. All these issues are semantic relays in Iranian discourses surrounding, explaining and attempting to intervene in the AIDS epidemic. Multiple meanings of each of these concepts are gendered, putting the female or male body alternately at the centre of investigations.

Social medicine and medical anthropology scholarship on the suffering of individuals and societies (Kleinman et al., 1997) indicates that the solutions to major public health challenges, such as epidemics, must involve integrated development programmes (Farmer, 1992, 1999, 2003; Farmer et al., 1996). When it works well, competition among professionalized groups for the lead in dealing with epidemics can generate new knowledge and new modes of collaboration (Epstein, 1996; Hammonds, 1999; Latour, 1988; Rosenberg, 1992). The current hierarchy of disciplines, with medicine's revered status in Iran, maintains a distance between professions, particularly at the professional training levels. These walls need to be brought down; dialogue is needed among and between professionals. More emphasis needs to be placed on qualitative research extending beyond statistics and biology. In Iran, with the exception of a few programmes, history and anthropology do not form part of the curricula of science departments and medical schools. Art and literature, with their significant potential for dialogue and mass education, are sharply disconnected from medical sciences. Political science and religious studies could throw light on the roots of different interpretations of religious guidelines, but neither have found their way into faculties such as medical schools. Social medicine programmes exist in medical schools, and public health and hygiene faculties offer Master of Public Health programmes, but these programmes tend to be epidemiologically focused, with little investment in qualitative research methodologies or in conversation with medical anthropology programmes. In this context, not only does the medical profession's treatment of beliefs (culture) and 'non-science' reinforce existing stigmatizations surrounding illnesses, it is also counterproductive, as so-called misconceptions and beliefs of patients are, in fact, building blocks of meanings that construct the very social reality of such highly charged epidemics as the HIV and AIDS epidemic.

Medical schools need to provide a space for integrated and collaborative learning and could serve as a starting point for introducing the idea of cultural analysis and dynamic cultural processes to link clinical practices with historical and local contexts. Medical and professional communities themselves are not immune to prevailing sentiments and prejudices, including gendered ones. These methodologies and comparative perspectives could help practitioners to become better aware of the fact that some of the perspectives they take for granted may not always be right. Not only do the tools of social medicine and qualitative research need to be strengthened in public health and medical faculties, but medical anthropology faculties also need to be drawn into the conversation for mutual learning and strengthening of complementary professionals. A new track in the anthropology of biosciences and biotechnologies could contribute to such a process of innovative strengthening. The fact that medical universities are part of the Ministry of Health and Medical Education means that other allied services (social work and so forth) could use such courses. The clergy also has a role to play as they can provide bureaucrats, policy-makers and leaders with spaces to introduce policy changes. Meanwhile, the media have also participated in these medical and non-medical discourses. The argument and illustrations throughout this chapter have highlighted the need to enroll different segments of the population by using different tactics and providing them with the proper targeted language and cultural tools.

The AIDS epidemic in Iran has distinctive features, and customized approaches have already been adopted to address these features. While very interesting, pragmatic and internationally recognized paradigm shifts have been implemented to fight the epidemic, these should now prepare the way for further innovative strides.

Acknowledgements

I am most grateful to Professor Vinh-Kim Nguyen for his unconditional support in every step of this project. I also extend my thanks to Jennifer Klot and the organizers of and participants in the UNESCO/SSRC Expert Group Meeting in Paris for their constructive comments and insights. I wish to also thank Dr Kamiar Alaei for agreeing to be interviewed in 2006 when he was a Master of Public Health student at Harvard and for his comments on the chronology of HIV and AIDS responses. As a former student, I am in debt to Professor Minoo Mohraz's efforts, dedication and inspiration for following the topic of AIDS in Iran. My fondest gratitude goes to Professor Michael Fischer for his utterly useful comments and generous revisions of various drafts of this chapter.

In early stages of writing this chapter, the passing away of my grandmother flooded my own life with intimate and personal accounts of illness and suffering. At the end, it was her undying presence and her will to learning and caring for the ill that helped me resume writing again. It is to her that I dedicate this chapter.

Notes

1. What is called 'crack' in Iran is a compound of concentrated heroin. It is relatively cheap, available, odour-less and extremely addictive, which has made it a convenient choice of drugs for young people over recent years.

2. During the time that this piece was being written, Dr Arash Alaei and Dr Kamiar Alaei were arrested in Tehran in June 2008. In January 2009, they were tried and sentenced to six and three years, respectively, on the charges of participation in international conferences and exchanges, which according to the Iranian government, threatened the country's national security and allegedly contributed to the efforts led by Western governments to foster a soft revolution in Iran. The AIDS-related work of the two medical researchers in Iran was not included among the formal charges against them.

    Various professional groups and human rights organizations including Physicians for Human Rights, Amnesty International, international medical associations, the WHO, as well as the deans of the schools of public health at Harvard and at the State University of New York at Buffalo, where Kamiar Alaei had been a graduate student, have expressed their grave concern over the arrest of these physicians and called for their immediate release. As a testimony to their medical contributions, this piece goes into print, while they remain imprisoned.

3. Ghazanfari et al. (2009) include a bibliography of medical studies of Sardaht victims. See also victim testimony video, such as that provided by IranNegah (2008).

References

Alaei, K. 2006. Interviews with the author, Boston, Mass.

Alaei, K. and Alaei, A. 2005. Multi sectoral approach for HIV/STI prevention, care and support. *Culture, Health and Sexuality,* Vol. 7, Supp. 1, p. 54.

Aman, F. and Maher, H. 2006. Iran: Brothers change face of HIV, drug-addiction treatment. Interview with Arash Alaei and Kamiar Alaei, Radio Free Europe/ Radio Liberty, 3 October. http://www.rferl.org/content/Article/1071768.html

BBC (British Broadcasting Corporation). 2007. Further increase in the number of HIV-positive in Iran. *Persian Service,* 9 June. (In Persian.) http://www.bbc.co.uk/ persian/iran/story/2007/07/070709_shr-aids.shtml

Beyrer, C. 2001. Accelerating and disseminating across Asia. *Washington Quarterly,* Vol. 24, No. 1, pp. 211–25.

Biehl, J. 2007. *Will to Live: AIDS Therapies and the Politics of Survival.* Princeton, NJ, Princeton University Press.

Butt, L. 2002. The suffering stranger: Medical anthropology and international morality. *Medical Anthropology,* Vol. 21, pp. 1–24.

Chehrazi, E. 2005. *Memoir and Autobiography of Dr Ebrahim Chehrazi.* Tehran, Ashyanehketab Publishing. (In Persian.)

Epstein, S. 1996. *Impure Science: AIDS, Activism, and the Politics of Knowledge.* Berkeley, Calif., University of California Press.

Etemaad-e-Melli. 2007. 9 July. (In Persian.)

Farmer, P. 1992. *AIDS and Accusation: Haiti and the Geography of Blame.* Berkeley, Calif., University of California Press.

——. 1999. *Infections and Inequalities: The Modern Plagues.* Berkeley, Calif., University of California Press.

——. 2003. *Pathologies of Power: Health, Human Rights, and the New War on the Poor.* Berkeley, Calif., University of California Press.

Farmer, P., Connors, M. and Simmons, J. (eds). 1996. *Women, Poverty and AIDS: Sex, Drugs and Structural Violence.* Monroe, Maine, Common Courage Press.

Fathi, N. 2008. Iran fights scourge of addiction in plain view, stressing treatment. *New York Times* and *International Herald Tribune,* 27 June. http://www.iht.com/ articles/2008/06/27/africa/27addiction.php?page=1

Fischer, M. M. J. 1989. Legal postulates in flux: Justice, wit and hierarchy in Iran. D. H. Dwyer (ed.), *Law and Islam in the Middle East.* New York, Bergin and Garvey.

——. 2004. *Mute Dreams, Blind Owls, and Dispersed Knowledges: Persian Poesis in the Translational Circuitry.* Durham, NC, Duke University Press.

——. 2007. Culture and cultural analysis as experimental systems. *Cultural Anthropology,* Vol. 22, No. 1, pp. 1–65.

Frankenberg R. J. 1993. Risk: Anthropological and epidemiological narratives of prevention. S. Lindenbaum and M. Lock (eds), *Knowledge, Power and Practice: The Anthropology of Medicine and Everyday Life.* Berkeley, Calif., University of California Press.

Ghabrayi, N. 2004. Street women trade AIDS. *SharifNews.ir,* 23 November. (In Persian.) http://www.sharifnews.com/?1331

Ghazanfari, T. et al. 2009. Sardasht-Iran cohort study of chemical warfare victims: Design and methods. *Archives of Iranian Medicine,* Vol. 12, No. 1, pp. 51–54.

Haeri, S. 1989. *Law of Desire: Temporary Marriage in Shi'i Iran.* Syracuse, NY, Syracuse University Press.

Hammonds, E. 1999. *Childhood's Deadly Scourge: The Campaign to Control Diphtheria in New York City, 1880–1930.* Baltimore, Md., Johns Hopkins University Press.

Harrison, F. 2004. Tackling Iran's growing drugs problem. *BBC News,* 30 November. http://news.bbc.co.uk/2/hi/middle_east/4054703.stm

IranNegah. 2008. *Kurdish Chemical Weapon Victim of Sardasht.* Video recording. http://revver.com/video/820441/kurdish-chemical-weapon-victim-of-sardasht/

Kakaei, P. 2006. Yesterday's girls, today's streetwalkers. *Nameh Magazine,* No. 47, March. (In Persian.)

Kleinman, A., Das, V. and Lock, M. (eds). 1997. *Social Suffering.* Berkeley, Calif., University of California Press.

Latour, B. 1988. *The Pasteurization of France.* A. Sheridan and J. Law. (trans). Cambridge, Mass., Harvard University Press.

MacFarquhar, N. 2002. Condom as a problem word: Iran grapples with a surge in AIDS. *New York Times,* 4 April.

Mokri, A. 2002. Brief overview of the status of drug abuse in Iran. *Archive of Iranian Medicine,* Vol. 5, No. 3, pp. 184–90.

Mokri, A. and Schottenfeld, R. 2008. Drug abuse and HIV transmission in Iran – Responding to the public health challenges. D. D. Celentano and C. Beyrer (eds), *Public Health Aspects of HIV/AIDS in Low and Middle Income Countries.* New York, Springer Science and Business Media.

Nassirimanesh, B. 2006. Presentation, 17th International Conference on the Reduction of Drug Related Harm, Vancouver, Canada, May.

Nassirimanesh, B., Trace, M. and Roberts, M. 2005. *The Rise of Harm Reduction in the Islamic Republic of Iran.* Oxford, United Kingdom, Beckley Foundation Drug Policy Programme. (Briefing Paper Eight.)

Ohiri, K. et al. 2006. HIV/AIDS prevention among injecting drug users: Learning from harm reduction in Iran. Report, HIV Prevention Consultation, Tehran, 17–20 April.

Rosenberg, C. 1992. *Explaining Epidemics: And Other Studies in the History of Medicine.* New York, Cambridge University Press.

——. 1962. *The Cholera Years: The United States in 1832, 1849 and 1866.* Chicago, Ill., University of Chicago Press.

Saadat, M. 2006. Change in sex ratio at birth in Sardasht (north west of Iran) after chemical bombardment. *Journal of Epidemiology and Community Health,* Vol. 60, No. 2, p. 183.

Sontag, S. 2001. *Illness as Metaphor and AIDS and Its Metaphors.* New York, Picador.

Treichler, P. 1987. AIDS, homophobia and biomedical discourse: An epidemic of signification. *Cultural Studies,* Vol. 1, No. 3, pp. 263–305.

Vick, K. 2005. Opiates of the Iranian people: Despair drives world's highest addiction rate. *Washington Post,* 23 September. http://www.washingtonpost.com/wp-dyn/content/article/2005/09/22/AR2005092202287.html

WHO (World Health Organization). 2004. *Best Practice in HIV/AIDS Prevention and Care for Injecting Drug Abusers: The Triangular Clinic in Kermanshah, Islamic Republic of Iran.* Cairo, WHO Regional Office for the Eastern Mediterranean. (WHO-EM/STD/052/E.)

CHAPTER 14

Beyond the new geography of dissident gender-sexual identity categories: Masculinities, homosexualities and intimate partner violence in Namibia

Robert Lorway

Introduction

Great concern for the HIV vulnerability of African 'men who have sex with men' (MSM) resounded within the halls of international health research, policy and development following the 2006 International AIDS Conference in Toronto.[1] UNAIDS (Joint United Nations Programme on HIV/AIDS) and USAID (United States Agency for International Development) have earmarked significant amounts of financial resources for HIV prevention initiatives among MSM in southern Africa; HIV needs assessments in different sites and sero-prevalence and behavioural studies with MSM communities in South Africa, Malawi, Botswana, Zambia, Zimbabwe and Namibia are now well underway.[2]

Tied to local sexual minority rights NGOs (non-governmental organiza-tions), these new projects reinvigorate political debates surrounding 'African homosexuality' in southern Africa for they link discourses on social justice and sexual freedom with visions for healthier nation-states. Amid the resul-tant identity politics, internal struggles and uncertainties, health scientists pose a typological view of sexuality in an attempt to pinpoint the object of their intervention. In Namibia, on which this chapter focuses, one of the current health development techniques used to 'target' MSM for HIV prevention is the 'identification' of local forms of homosexuality. This approach operates under the assumption that MSM form discrete, definable (and therefore governable) subpopulations of 'sexual minorities'.[3] Ironically, such strategies to secure the

The designations employed and the presentation of material throughout this publication do not imply the expression of any opinion whatsoever on the part of UNESCO concerning the legal status of any country, territory or area or of its authorities, or concerning the delimitation of its frontiers or boundaries.
The ideas and opinions expressed in this publication are those of the authors and do not necessarily reflect the views of UNESCO and its Member States.

health and well-being of MSM through typologization serve to intensify ambivalences as individuals and communities become embroiled in debates about the nature of sexual freedom in Namibia.

In this chapter, I discuss the social construction of homosexuality during the height of human rights protests in Namibia, viewing this history as the basis of recent typological schemes for HIV prevention. In particular, I stress how initiatives of The Rainbow Project (TRP), an NGO active in sexual minority rights, employ 'culture' and local ideologies in the creation of 'indigenous' homosexualities. From this discussion, I argue that the emphasis placed upon sexual-gender 'types' overshadows how emerging identity politics refract through local forms of gender-class inequality to shape patterns in the sexual transmission of HIV between males. To stage my argument, I first illustrate the typological schemes that unfold through 'sexuality training' in Namibia. I then weigh these categories in view of observations made during ethnographic fieldwork to account for the emerging masculinities that accompany the proliferation of dissident gender-sexual identities. Based on anthropological findings, I assert that policy-makers concerned with the gendered dimensions of the HIV epidemic must also attend to the social arenas in which competing masculinities violently construe male homosexualities as relations that reflect wider gender inequalities between men and women.[4]

Eruption of identity politics

In 1997 Namibia's ruling party, the South West African People's Organization (SWAPO), publicly declared homosexuality to be a cultural practice imported from Europe that threatened the authenticity of traditional Namibian life, which was assumed to be heterosexual and oriented to reproduction (IGLHRC, 2003). The Rainbow Project, funded by Western European and North American development companies, mobilized local protest in response to the government-sanctioned, anti-homosexual rhetoric. International human rights networks rushed to support TRP en masse as the lively public controversy made local and international news headlines. Scholars also began to investigate 'African homosexualities', which Namibian gay rights activists then cited as evidence of the existence of African same-sex sexuality.[5] Initially, the most visible activists were teachers, academics, former anti-apartheid leaders, NGO directors and foreign embassy representatives, most of whom were white or coloured, well travelled and economically privileged when compared to most Namibians. Yet, it was mostly unemployed, black youth practising gender-sexual nonconformity who experienced the virulent fallout from the 'government hate speeches' in the form of intense discrimination (Lorway, 2006). In 2001, following President Sam Nujoma's call for the arrest, imprisonment and deportation of all gays and lesbians in Namibia, these youth, most of whom lived in the Township of Katutura, dominated the public demonstrations in Windhoek with open displays of defiance (Lorway, 2008c). Many of the youth who attended public forums stated, 'Where will I be deported? I'm a Namibian!'[6]

It is noteworthy, however, that most of the youth claimed that prior to their involvement in the human rights movement they had never heard the words 'gay' or 'lesbian' – though they did recollect local words used by elders to refer to gender-sexual difference. At the request of youth, TRP began to deliver 'sexuality training', during which staff defined the identity labels 'gay', 'lesbian', 'bisexual' and 'transgender'. In the next section, I recreate a scene from one of the many sexuality workshops I was permitted to attend and record in 2003. This description is intended to provide the reader with a sense of the cultural identity politics that pervade sexual minority rights development work in Namibia.

Learning sexuality

About thirty of us took our seats around a half circle that opened towards the front of the conference room where a confident 18-year-old called Travis[7] stood and welcomed us in English, Afrikaans and Damara. Despite his young age, Travis had already demonstrated his political commitment when he gave his 'coming out' story to the national newspaper, the *Namibian,* and later recited it during a public poetry-reading night organized by TRP, the feminist NGO Sister Namibia and the National Human Rights Society of Namibia (NHRS).

This was a special meeting for it was the first time that family members of lesbian, gay, bisexual and transgender youth had been invited to attend a TRP workshop. Lionel, the facilitator, who during an earlier interview identified himself as a 'coloured' born into a wealthy South African family, rose to assure everyone in Afrikaans, 'It's *not* a workshop, it's a talk shop. We talk openly about the issues here'.

Then a respected elder, the grandmother of a well-known local drag queen, stood and spoke in Damara:

I was supposed to go to a funeral, but because of this workshop I came here instead. I came here because of questions and answers – it is difficult for me. In 1940 I was born in the old location [of Katutura Township]. These days I see things – girls who look like boys, boys who look like girls, and now they are calling them homosexuals. In the old days, it might have been true that homosexuality existed there, but we didn't see it. And when I see it here now in my surroundings, I am asking myself, why? It's so hard to accept that women like to be men and men like to be women when in the beginning it was Eve and Adam. How do they become like what they are?

The director then said in Afrikaans: 'To look at that question, we must explain gender and sexual identity'. The grandmother again interrupted the facilitator: 'What we have done wrong is to begin without a prayer'. She then proceeded to lead our group in a prayer, saying in Damara:

Holy Father, I thank you. We don't know about [homosexuality] so God, I am involving you in this: You created Adam and Eve but there is a different lust among us, God. Let us understand this, God. I am asking this in Jesus Christ the Saviour's name, who has no beginning and no end. I thank you for being part of this. Amen.

The facilitator thanked the grandmother with a mildly uncomfortable smile and then opened the floor up for questions.

The first question came from a 23-year-old male participant who directed his query to the grandmother: 'I want to know if homosexuality started now or is it an age-old thing?' The grandmother responded by saying: 'I didn't know things like this. Me personally, I don't like it. It was me taking care of my grandson when he was a child. I saw him. He is a man, not a woman, and only now do I see these things … He's dressing up like a lady'.

Daphne, a 17-year-old who describes herself as a 'butch lesbian', pressed the question further in English, then switched to Afrikaans when she realised the elder was not following: 'But what about the traditional words !gamas in Damara and the Ovambo word eshenge? Doesn't that prove that homosexuality exists in Namibia?' The grandmother conceded and said she remembered hearing the word !gamas used when she was a child. She said it referred to a goat that had both male and female organs.

Another elder made a correction: 'No. It's a sheep'. Then another parent argued that !gamas referred to any animal that has both genitalia, and one of the youth insisted that !gamas is the traditional name for a homosexual. An intense debate broke out over the correct meaning of the word *!gamas,* and it continued until the facilitator tried to settle the argument by referring to the research of Kurt Falk, an anthropologist who conducted studies in ethno-sexology throughout southern Africa during the late nineteenth and early twentieth centuries. The facilitator explained that Falk recorded traditional names for 'homosexuality' in all of Namibia's ethnic groups.

Daphne then stated, in a stern tone, that parents know when their child is 'homosexual' because one girl may be good with cooking and cleaning in the home and another will be 'good outside', doing yard work and fixing cars (which is considered to be men's work). The parents and relatives silently nodded and seemed convinced by her explanation.

Next the facilitator began the education portion of the 'talk shop'. First, he distinguished between animals that are sexual and those that are 'asexual' by explaining how fish do not have 'sexual intercourse' during their reproductive cycle. Then, referring to humans, he drew a horizontal line across the flip-chart with three points, one at each end and one in the centre. He referred to it as the spectrum (or scale) of sexual identity, labelling each point with sexual identity categories: heterosexuality first on the left, bisexuality second in the middle and homosexuality on the right. He explained the differences in sexual identities by referring to the corresponding object of desire. 'Heterosexuals are attracted to the opposite gender. A homosexual is someone who is attracted to the same gender', he said (and so on). After asking the participants to think about where they felt they fit within the spectrum, the facilitator stated that homosexual prevalence is '10 per cent of all people' – a number once advanced by US sexologist Alfred Kinsey in the 1940s and 1950s. Amid a few giggles, the youth asked numerous questions, such as how to distinguish between a person who is a transgender and a butch lesbian. Then the facilitator continued his delineations by defining different forms of transgenderism: transsexuality, cross-dressing, transvestitism and 'gender bending'. The talk shop continued for more than two hours and ended with a round of applause for the facilitator and the translators. The elders seemed grateful, politely thanking TRP for imparting this information to them, and then closed with another prayer.

In the years following this event, TRP's 'sexuality lessons', lesbian and gay film showings, and workshops on safer sex and human rights awareness began to flourish as TRP expanded into the far corners of Namibia. Suddenly, small groups of provocative young black men and women, dressed in various degrees of drag, became extremely visible throughout the country. In the next section, I present three ethnographic sketches drawn from my field notes to demonstrate three interrelated issues. First, how TRP's sexuality-empowerment training fosters confidence in open displays of gender dissidence. Second, how enactments of gender nonconformity heighten erotic tensions and gender inequalities between young feminine males and local 'straight men'. Third, the unexpected economic transactions between feminine and masculine males that take place outside the discourse on sexual minority rights

Although my analysis is guided by interviews and focus groups conducted with more than 180 individuals between 2001 and 2008, I have chosen to concentrate on a series of discussions and interactions that transpired outside 'the formal data collection process', as cultural anthropologists often do in ethnographic research.

Telling secrets in Keetmanshoop

After a dizzying ride on a *kombi* (passenger van), I finally arrived at the centre of the small, southern Namibian town of Keetmanshoop, where I was welcomed by the Karas regional AIDS director for the Ministry of Health and Social Services (MOHSS). The fiery Liverpool native then whisked me away in the ministry van to her office so that I could finish preparing a workshop for a group of young males who had previously attended TRP's sexuality and safer sex training. The group had expressed to the AIDS director that they wanted to organize an HIV awareness group after several friends had fallen sick and died from AIDS. I was invited to meet with them to provide basic information around STIs (sexually transmitted infections) and conduct a focus group to learn more about their HIV-related concerns.

Once I finished preparing the workshop at the ministry office, the director and I headed to an empty, rundown sports stadium to meet with 'the guys', eight of whom warmly greeted us upon our arrival. Dressed in partial drag, they excitedly introduced themselves using women's names. A few wore lipstick, foundation and mascara; one teetered in women's heels, while another was wearing a short-cropped shirt that hovered above tightly hugging women's jeans.

After the introductions, Evert, who seemed very confident and outspoken, explained that their group frequently went about town dressed up like women. Residents were always excited to see them, he insisted. 'They think we are celebrities!' He continued by saying that when the mood hits him he likes to wear a glamorous white sundress out in public. 'People just adore us', he said gleefully. Changing the tone dramatically, the somewhat older group leader,

Sal, cut off Evert's enthusiasm by stating that the group travels around town together for protection; following the anti-homosexual government speeches in 2001, many young effeminate males had been beaten and sexually assaulted by local police officers and other men and relatives in their community.

As we got into the workshop discussion and came to the question of sexual partners, Evert stated that he sometimes has sex for money with truck drivers and miners who pass through Keetmanshoop.[8] Next, Sal smiled and said, 'In Keetmans there are so many gay men!' The group laughed in agreement, but I was left confused because there was only a small group before me. After enjoying my confusion for a moment, Sal finally explained that they regularly slept with 'straight men. Most of them are married or have girlfriends'.

A few months later I returned to Keetmans to conduct more formal ethnographic research. I learned that the young feminine males do in fact share close social and sexual networks with 'straight men'. At discos and more traditional 'long-arm' dances, married men and those with girlfriends dance freely with the feminine males, even in the presence of their female partners, who seem to pay little attention. At the opening of a new nightclub in Keetmans, I spoke with several of the young 'straight men' about their sexual relationships with feminine males. They were quite candid and repeatedly told me that they like to have sex with 'the moffies' because, as one man puts it, 'we can't get them pregnant or catch STIs from them'. Referring to HIV infection, another man told me in a later interview that 'it is safer to have sex with a moffie than a woman'.[9] Others provided explanations along the following lines for their same-sex sexual practices: 'It's expensive to get married, have a wife and a family. With moffies you don't have to worry about these things'.

When I interviewed several feminine males about their sexual relationships with 'straight men', I noted several patterns in their responses. Consistently they complained that straight men demand anal sex from them without condoms. They explained that refusal is difficult because it usually happens while they are intoxicated, late at night after they have been at the club. Furthermore, if they were to try to refuse the advances of straight men, they would get beaten. Several of them confided in me that they regularly experience physical violence at the hands of these men. Although they had acquired HIV transmission knowledge from TRP's safer sex workshops, they felt powerless to negotiate safer sex in their relationships. Sadly, most believed that they have already contracted HIV but were too terrified to get tested.[10]

Knowing that many residents in Keetmanshoop struggle with poverty, I asked the young feminine males if they ever receive any economic support in exchange for sex from men in their community. I reasoned that transactional sexual practices would create a certain dependency that influenced their 'willingness' to be with men who would coerce them into unprotected anal sex.[11] On the contrary, they told me that local 'straight men' often demand small sums of money or a beer from them in exchange for sex. I was puzzled, for it seemed counterintuitive: although 'moffies' were the feminine objects of straight men's desires, they were still expected to pay.[12] Sal explained that because 'moffies' have 'lots of friends at TRP' in Windhoek and get to travel to the capital city for TRP's special events, where they brush elbows with foreigners, national entertainers, embassy directors and even members of parliament, they are perceived as having greater access to economic resources. But why does this (perceived) financial and social capital not give feminine males bargaining power in their sexual relationships? Evert responded to a version of this question, stating in a matter-of-fact tone, 'Well, they're men. *They* decide what happens during sex'.

During interviews with other young feminine males living in Keetmanshoop, I asked why they desired sexual relationships with violent men who endanger their lives. Examples of responses I received to this question are:

1. 'I don't know why I like those rough guys; I just can't help it'.

2. 'We [moffies] can't have sex with each other because we're like sisters. I don't know why I want straight men; but [violence] is just what they do, 'cause they're real men'.

3. 'I prefer to go with the rough ones. I know I shouldn't, but I can't help it'.

These iterations of uncontrollable and unexplainable desires contrasted markedly with the confident discussion and enactments of sexual-gender nonconformity I witnessed during interviews, focus groups and workshops. Young feminine males articulated sophisticated understandings of their sexual selves, and they appeared self-possessed in their open expression of gender defiance. In many instances, through their association with TRP, young feminine males did in fact acquire greater access to socio-economic resources compared to other local men (Lorway, 2008c). It would seem that the road to sexual freedom opening up through TRP offered new possibilities for self-expression and social and economic mobility. Yet in intimate, sexual relationships with 'real men', 'moffies' remained oppressed. This led me to wonder if the emphasis in sexual minority rights discourse placed upon 'reclaiming' one's sexual selfhood inadvertently serves to normalize desires to be with violent men. Was their desire to be with rough men somehow conditioned by the very discourses on sexual freedom that celebrated same-sex sexual desire and gender nonconformity? Did sexuality training and empowerment unintentionally depoliticize the landscape of gender inequality in which homosexual identity was being interpreted? These questions recurred as I became more familiar with the daily lives of TRP youth in other parts of Namibia.

'Real Ovambo men'

Northern Namibia holds the largest proportion of the country's population. In the late 1960s, South African colonial officials designated the northern region of Ovamboland as the Bantustan ('homeland') for Oshivambo-speaking people, granting them a limited form of traditional self-rule. As the largest ethnic group, the Ovambo tribe came to comprise the strongest contingency in the liberation movement and today remains the most highly represented ethnic group among ruling SWAPO politicians. This tribal dominance informed use of traditionalist language in SWAPO's anti-homosexual rhetoric in the 1990s. SWAPO government officials asserted that whereas homosexuality may be found among Damara and Nama tribes in central and southern Namibia, it did not exist within the 'traditional cultures' of the north.[13] For this reason, TRP recognized the strategic political significance of heightening gay and lesbian visibility in this region.

In 2005 I was invited to the northern Namibian town of Oshakati to assist in the delivery of an HIV awareness workshop led by a Danish-funded NGO that worked in close partnership with TRP. As in Keetmans, all of the attendees were feminine males who had already taken part in TRP's sexuality training workshops. To my surprise, only one of the workshop participants, Tuhafeni, identified with the Ovambo ethnic group. He wore men's clothes, seemed rather shy and nervous and rarely spoke during the workshop. When I spoke with him during a tea break, he told me that he came from a very small village to live in Oshakati and that he would be severely punished if his community ever found out about his sexuality: 'In our culture it is forbidden to be a gay. Have you heard what will happen if they find out you are an *eshenge?* They will take a burning stick and put it in there [your anus] so you won't ever be able to have sex again'. I asked him if he knew of other Ovambo men who have sexual relationships with men. His mouth then widened into a large smile as he said, 'Oh, they are everywhere. But they will never come to an open meeting like this!'

Another workshop participant, Tuli, who is Nama-Damara-speaking, was far more expressive than Tuhafeni. He was quite spunky, wearing a 'belly shirt' and a small, bright-green purse over his shoulder, pressed daintily against his body with his elbow. In bold lettering across his shirt read the phrase 'Ignore him!', which seemed to match his agitated mood. He explained during the workshop that his 'Ovambo boyfriend' gave him a lot of trouble: he regularly cheated on him with other women, and when Tuli finally complained about it, his boyfriend smacked him across the face. 'He never wears a condom with me, even though I ask him!' Tuli exclaimed.

After the meeting, our group left the office to head to a small *cuca* shop (pub) for something to eat. A few of the feminine males lagged behind, and when we looked back, we watched as car after car with smiling, flirtatious men stopped beside them. When the men rolled down their windows to chat with them, Tuli and two of the other workshop participants took out their cellphones and began busily entering the phone numbers of their admirers. When Tuli and the others rejoined our group, one of them stated, 'Some of those Ovambo men aren't "real men". They are *eshenges* … in the closet. You wouldn't believe it when you get them alone in a room; they sometimes want *you* to [penetrate] *them*'. Tuli interjected with a discerning facial expression, 'I only like to go with real men … the ones who are bisexuals'. I admitted that I found Tuli's statement curious given his previous complaint about his boyfriend's sexual relationships with women and his unwillingness to wear condoms. I further examine this kind of irony in sexual desire in the next section through the lens of socio-economic status.

'Gay for pay'

For the gay community in the Windhoek Urban Area, 2005 was an exciting year: it saw the establishment of the first official gay club, known as Ekuta, in the heart of the commercial district.[14] An 'out', white, South African gay man owns and operates Ekuta, yet only a few local gay whites ever frequent the club. The club does, however, attract a diverse crowd of black men and women from the surrounding Townships of Katutura and Khomasdhal. TRP sponsors several parties and special events at Ekuta, making it a celebrated space for 'queer' Namibians. Although the club only stays open for a few months, I witnessed several interesting events there. Groups of masculine men began frequenting Ekuta, looking to pick up local gays.

One evening, at a private party organized by TRP, a group of feminine males sitting around a table at Ekuta began to cheer as their grinning friend, Maurice, arrived with a beautiful, muscular 'straight' boyfriend on his arm. Commenting on Maurice's trophy-like display of the local athlete, one of the feminine males at our table blurted out: 'Maurice is so lucky that he can afford him'. And indeed, Maurice was economically independent. By working for a tourism company, Maurice managed to escape the high rate of unemployment and low-paying jobs that plague the majority of people living in Katutura.

In the capital city of Windhoek, a new community of socially and economically mobile black gay men is beginning to establish its public presence.[15] They frequently date expatriates, with whom they have travelled to South Africa to sample a more cosmopolitan gay life. Some have had their educations paid for by wealthier white men. Many work in banking, hospitality and tourism and in NGOs, and their incomes make them the breadwinners in their families. Together with their wealthier boyfriends, they frequently throw lively parties in the affluent suburbs of Windhoek and invite poorer 'straight' black men who become boyfriends of both the white elite and local blacks who can 'afford' their company.

The new group of upwardly mobile, black gay men seems to be empowered and independent in every way. They are 'out', having attended many TRP workshops on sexuality and self-esteem. They are 'fabulously dressed' in the latest fashions and are able to attract their pick of beautiful men. Yet during private conversations and interviews many described their struggles with beatings, coerced anal sex and other forms of abuse at the hands of the straight men they date. Several of the feminine men discussed the damage they experience to their anus through forceful penetration, which in their descriptions sounds unambiguously like rape. Others received black eyes and other bodily bruises. During one interview, when the subject of sexual violence arose the respondent stated, 'I don't why. Maybe I'm crazy or something, but I really love those "homo-thugs" [rough guys]'. Economically disadvantaged, feminine males living in Katutura echoed this kind of narrative.

Herman left his small village up north to come to Windhoek 'to be himself', which, he claimed, TRP had helped him to achieve. When I first met him, he worked in an NGO as a cleaner, making barely enough to support himself. His low wages did allow him, however, to buy enough materials to build a small, one-room, makeshift home in Katutura, consisting of wiring, wooden beams, panelling and steel-sheet roofing. One day Herman came home to find his boyfriend having sex with a woman at his place. Feeling devastated, he told his boyfriend to leave because their relationship had to end. His boyfriend then destroyed his home by setting it on fire. Herman knew, of course, that he had little recourse: the police would never open a case file involving a same-sex relationship.[16]

A few days later, a group of us helped Herman to rebuild his home. In the course of our reconstruction, he began to talk about how he gave his boyfriend money, fed him and bought him alcohol even though he could hardly afford to support himself. Herman then admitted that his boyfriend regularly abused him physically and sexually and explained that he stayed with him for so long because he desired 'a man who is physically strong and powerful. I don't want to be with someone who is weak … like a woman'. In 2007, I returned to Herman's place only to find that his home had been damaged again, this time by his new boyfriend, a local boxer, who had broken in to steal some of Herman's possessions.

Conclusion

The aim of the foregoing account was not to imply that TRP's interventions have been the determining cause of the sexual violence that regularly occurs between masculine and feminine males in Namibia. After all, effeminate males may encounter sexual violence with rough men, regardless of whether or not they attend sexuality training workshops. And many of the feminine males I spoke with experienced sexual violence long before TRP ever formed. Instead, what I have tried to illuminate is the ironic way in which an ethic of sexual freedom has combined with oppressive gender power relations to configure homosexual identities.

Highlighting idioms of uncontrollable and unexplainable desire, I drew attention to the ways in which feminine males seem to subject themselves to sexual violence and considered their ironic desires as the unexpected (side) effects of techniques for developing sexual minority rights.[17] Indeed, these empowerment discourses direct the disenfranchised individual to recognize selfhood as a crucial site for sexual liberation. And as individuals and communities reflect upon the naturalness of their sexual being, the awareness of gender inequities becomes submerged in a universalistic project of sexual freedom, only to resurface as unexplainable and uncontrollable desires for 'real men' – their 'natural' sexual counterpart. Thus, my primary concern here lies with issues of political consciousness; prevailing gender power relations came into view only on the periphery of ethical projects aimed at liberating sexual minorities.

Many of my informants in Namibia diligently followed the road to a 'healthier' sexual life by getting to know and articulating their sexual desires, reinterpreting sexuality through local histories, participating in public protests, displaying gender nonconformity and pursuing their sexual objects of choice. Yet, like Herman's home, their practices of and aspirations to 'sexual freedom' have continually collapsed due to the everyday realities of sexual violence, discrimination, poverty and high HIV prevalence. Such ambivalent events, I argue, point to a form of violence that is inadvertently enacted through interventions that cast sexual-gender difference as decontexualized 'risk groups' or 'vulnerable populations of sexual minorities'. Without an understanding of the cultural politics and economies that govern everyday sexual life, sexual minority rights interventions may actually intensify the very processes that place same-sex-loving males at risk for HIV infection, as this chapter demonstrates.

The interventions I described are particularly effective at ushering in confident, feminine homosexualities, but they also inadvertently contribute to the naturalization of intimate-partner violence as male participants come to regard themselves as feminine subjects. Therefore, policy perspectives on 'gender inequality and HIV' need to enlarge their focus to include an understanding of the cultural embodiment of male femininities that emerge in contexts where gender inequality is already deeply socially entrenched.

Acknowledgements

I am extremely grateful for the support offered by staff and members of The Rainbow Project of Namibia, including Ian, Whoopi, Friedel, Carol, Linda, Madelene, Gina and the many other men and women who took time to share their personal experiences with me over the past eight years. Different phases of this research were generously supported by the Wenner-Gren Foundation for Anthropological Research, the Social Sciences and Humanities Research Council of Canada (SSHRC), the International Centre for Infectious Diseases (University of Manitoba) and the University of Toronto, Department of Anthropology.

Notes

1.   Unlike previous international AIDS conferences, researchers delivered numerous scientific presentations and posters devoted to the subject of MSM in Africa at the 2006 International AIDS Conference in Toronto (see, for example Eki and George, 2006; Lane et al., 2006; Porter et al., 2006).

2.   Here I am referring to a series of HIV-related needs assessments pertaining to sexual minorities in southern Africa managed by the Dutch humanitarian foundation Schorer. Their initiative, referred to as PRISM (Prevention Initiative for Sexual Minorities), explicitly directs local sexual minority rights organizations to view 'the community' as made up of various distinct 'target groups'. A team of health scientists based at Johns Hopkins University and the University of Toronto are currently conducting HIV seroprevalence and behavioural studies with MSM across southern Africa.

3.   The notion of 'sexual minorities' is cast in a similar mould as earlier epidemiological constructions of 'risk groups', which promotes the idea that same-sex-loving people form measurable subunits of the population.

4.   The route that gender inequality provides for HIV infection between men and women in Namibia is well documented in the public health and development literature (see Hunter, 2004; Iipinge and LeBeau, 2004; Iipinge et al., 2004). However, the definition of 'gender' employed in this body of research ignores the specific ways that 'gender inequalities' manifest themselves across diverse sexual relationships. National policy and research in Namibia ties the problem of 'gender inequality' to (putatively) heterosexual women. Lorway (2008a) discusses the constellation of gender inequalities that surround Namibian women who identify themselves as lesbian. Despite their pursuit of same-sex sexual relationships, these women become vulnerable to HIV infection through coerced and transactional sex with men, which is buttressed by the reassertion of ideal (heterosexual) female citizenship (Lorway, 2008b).

5.   Examples of scholarly literature cited during the public debates are Epprecht (1998), Gevisser and Cameron (1995) and Murray and Roscoe (1998).

6.   Author's field notes (14 August 2001).

7.   All names used in this chapter are pseudonyms.

8.   Keetmanshoop is a vibrant hub for South African truck drivers and other foreign-national migrant labourers.

9.   These myths pertaining to the homosexual transmission of HIV are consistent with responses in Katutura (Lorway, 2006).

10. This reluctance to get tested is by no means peculiar to feminine males in Namibia.

11. This is the explanation provided in much of the literature on transactional sex in Africa (Hallman, 2004; Jewkes et al., 2006; Leclerc-Madlala, 2003; Swidler and Walkins, 2007; Wojcicki, 2002*a*).

12. This practice complicates the picture of gender power dynamics drawn by Wojcicki (2002*b*) in her discussion of women's susceptibility to violence and powerlessness to negotiate safer sex when accepting a drink from a man, having 'drank his money'.

13. Khaxas and Wieringa (2005) offer a compelling counter-interpretation, arguing that the openness around same-sexuality in Damara communities can be traced to pre-colonial subsistence, ownership and inheritance practices that were egalitarian.

14. There were, of course, many smaller *shebeens* (informal, often unlicensed, drinking establishments) and clubs known to welcome gays and lesbians (such as Casablanca, Club Thriller, Sparks and Club Remix) at different points in time. Donna Bella's is currently regarded as Windhoek's main gay club; however, most of my informants consider it to be a 'club for whites' and tend not to frequent it, except during special TRP events.

15. The emergence of sexual life I describe in this section somewhat parallels Nguyen's (2005, p. 248) description of 'sexual modernity' in Abidjan. However, 'homosocial' culture in Katutura Township during the 1970s and 1980s took shape around the social networks that connected bachelor compounds.

16. Current domestic violence legislation explicitly accords protection to individuals in 'different sex' relationships and therefore discriminates against Namibians in same-sex relationships.

17. I therefore avoid the suggestion of 'masochism' and 'learned helplessness' often associated with 'battered wife syndrome' (Walker, 1979).

References

Eki, G. O. and George, E. 2006. Rectal microbicides and the fight against HIV/AIDS among men who have sex with men (MSM) in Nigeria. AIDS 2006 – XVI International AIDS Conference, 13–18 August, Toronto, Canada. *Abstract CDC02092.* Geneva, International AIDS Society (IAS). http://www.iasociety.org/ Default.aspx?pageId=11&abstractId=2190670 (Accessed 6 September 2008.)

Epprecht, M. 1998. The 'unsaying' of indigenous homosexualities in Zimbabwe: Mapping a blind spot in an African sexuality. *Journal of Southern African Studies,* Vol. 24, No. 4, pp. 631–51. http://www.scphis.org/pdf/epprecht.pdf (Accessed 6 September 2008.)

Gevisser, M. and Cameron, E. (eds). 1995. *Defiant Desire: Gay and Lesbian Lives in South Africa.* New York, Routledge.

Hallman, K. 2004. *Socioeconomic Disadvantage and Unsafe Sexual Behaviors Among Young Women and Men in South Africa.* New York, Population Council. (Policy Research Division Working Paper No. 190.) http://www.popcouncil.org/pdfs/ wp/190.pdf (Accessed 6 September 2008.)

Hunter, J. (ed.). 2004. *Beijing +10: The Way Forward – An Introduction to Gender Issues in Namibia.* Windhoek, Namibian Institute of Democracy. http://www.nid.org. na/pub_docs/nid_gender.pdf (Accessed 6 September 2008.)

IGLHRC (International Gay and Lesbian Human Rights Commission). 2003. *International: Criminalization and Decriminalization of Homosexual Acts.* New York, IGLHRC. http://www.iglhrc.org/cgi-bin/iowa/article/takeaction/ resourcecenter/817.html

Iipinge, E. and LeBeau, D. 2004. *Beyond Inequalities: Women in Namibia.* Windhoek/ Harare, University of Namibia Press/Southern African Resource and Documentation Centre.

Iipinge, S., Hofnie, K. and Friedman, S. 2004. *The Relationship between Gender Roles and HIV Infection in Namibia.* Windhoek, University of Namibia Press.

Jewkes, R., Dunkleb, K., Koss, M. P., Levin, J. B., Nduna, M. et al. 2006. Rape perpetration by young, rural South African men: Prevalence, patterns and risk factors. *Social Science and Medicine,* Vol. 63, No. 11, pp. 2949–961.

Khaxas, E. and Wieringa, S. 2005. 'I am a pet goat, I will not be slaughtered': Female masculinity and femme strength amongst the Damara in Namibia. R. Morgan and S. Wieringa (eds), *Tommy Boys, Lesbian Men and Ancestral Wives.* Johannesburg, Jacana Media, pp. 123–96.

Lane, T., McIntyre, J. and Morin, S. 2006. High-risk sex among black MSM in South Africa: Results from the Gauteng MSM survey. AIDS 2006 – XVI International

AIDS Conference, 13–18 August, Toronto, Canada. *Abstract WEPE0717*. Geneva, International AIDS Society (IAS). http://www.iasociety.org/Default.aspx?pageId= 11&abstractId=2194562 (Accessed 6 September 2008.)

Leclerc-Madlala, S. 2003. Transactional sex and the pursuit of modernity. *Social Dynamics*, Vol. 29, No. 2, pp. 213–33. http://www.healthdev.org/eforums/ Editor/assets/accelerating-prevention/Transactional_sex_and_the_pursuit_of_ modernity.pdf (Accessed 6 September 2008.)

Lorway, R. 2006. Dispelling 'heterosexual African AIDS' in Namibia: Same-sex sexuality in the township of Katutura. *Culture, Health and Sexuality*, Vol. 8, No. 5, pp. 435–49.

——. 2008*a*. Defiant desire in Namibia: Female sexual-gender transgression and the making of political being. *American Ethnologist*, Vol. 35, No. 1, pp. 20–33.

——. 2008*b*. Pursuing sexual freedom in a time of AIDS: Exploring the HIV-vulnerability of lesbian women in a Namibian township. *EthnoScripts*, Vol. 10, No. 1, pp. 65–82.

——. 2008*c*. 'Where can I be deported?' Thinking through the 'foreigner fetish' in Namibia. *Medical Anthropology*, Vol. 27, No. 1, pp. 70–97.

Murray, S. O. and Roscoe, W. (eds). 1998. *Boy-Wives and Female-Husbands: Studies in African Homosexualities*. New York, Palgrave.

Nguyen, V. K. 2005. Uses and pleasures: Sexual modernity, HIV/AIDS and confessional technologies in a West African metropolis. V. Adams and S. Pigg (eds), *The Moral Object of Sex: Science, Development, and Sexuality in Global Perspective*. Durham, NC, Duke University Press, pp. 1–20.

Porter, R., Cobbina, M. D., Hanson, K., Dupree, J. D., Akanlu, G., Kaplan M. et al. 2006. An exploratory study of MSM social networks in Ghana. AIDS 2006 – XVI International AIDS Conference, 13–18 August, Toronto, Canada. *Abstract THPE0458*. Geneva, International AIDS Society (IAS). http://www.iasociety.org/ Default.aspx?pageId=11&abstractId=2199652 (Accessed 6 September 2008.)

Swidler, A. and Walkins, S. C. 2007. Ties of dependence: AIDS and transactional sex in Malawi. *Studies in Family Planning*, Vol. 38, No. 3, pp. 147–62.

Walker, L. E. 1979. *The Battered Woman*. New York, Harper and Row.

Wojcicki, J. M. 2002*a*. Commercial sex work or *Ukuphanda*? Sex for money exchange in Soweto and Hammanskraal Area, South Africa. *Culture, Medicine, and Psychiatry*, Vol. 26, pp. 339–70.

——. 2002*b*. 'She drank his money': Survival sex and the problem of violence in taverns in Gauteng Province, South Africa. *Medical Anthropology Quarterly*, Vol. 16, No. 3, pp. 267–93.

CHAPTER 15

Neglecting gender in HIV prevention and treatment programmes: Notes from experiences in West Africa

Joséphine Aho and Vinh-Kim Nguyen

The concept of gender is often only used as shorthand for acknowledging so-cial differences between women and men, or for the disaggregation by sex of beneficiaries or personnel. As the introduction to this volume makes clear, the concept of gender refers to the translation of biological sex into social differ-ence, including differences in power. Many of the mainstream interventions that aim to address HIV – including those that specifically target women – and that are the staple elements of our response to the epidemic regularly fail to engage with the realities of power within gendered relationships between in-dividuals (including those of the same sex) in everyday life. In this chapter, we show how this lack of attention to gendered power relations in life 'outside' an intervention leads to unintended and perhaps even dangerous consequences. We show how interventions may paradoxically increase vulnerability to HIV and other forms of structural violence in the groups they target. Likewise, in-terventions may unintentionally decrease vulnerability in ways that are highly gendered. These perverse, or unexpected, consequences are often not captured because of a reliance on standardized interventions and socially 'thin' measures of intervention impact that do not capture the 'thickness' of men and women's social and political relationships. We have chosen two examples from our work in various West African settings to illustrate unintended consequences of HIV prevention and treatment programmes, one in the Republic of Guinea and the other in Côte d'Ivoire. In terms of prevention, we examine both the impact of an intervention targeting a core group of 'high-risk' sex workers, and attempts

The designations employed and the presentation of material throughout this publication do not imply the expression of any opinion whatsoever on the part of UNESCO concerning the legal status of any country, territory or area or of its authorities, or concerning the delimitation of its frontiers or boundaries.
The ideas and opinions expressed in this publication are those of the authors and do not necessarily reflect the views of UNESCO and its Member States.

to address HIV risk in men who have sex with men (MSM) in Africa. In terms of treatment, we examine the impact of antiretroviral treatment programmes on the women who are their principal beneficiaries in Africa.

Targeting core groups

The HIV epidemic is particularly overwhelming in southern and eastern Africa. Most countries in these regions suffer HIV prevalence of more than 10 per cent. The situation is different in West Africa, where most countries have low overall prevalence and where most transmission occurs within subpopulations at higher risk of infection called 'core groups'. These groups often consist of vulnerable individuals, such as migrants or sex workers. Where the epidemic is concentrated in core groups, it has been demonstrated that targeting these groups may be a cost-effective strategy in terms of the reduction of overall population seroprevalence. However, the consequences of these interventions for members of the core groups themselves have been under-explored.

In public health terms, an intervention is defined as a set of organized actions taken in order to correct a problematic situation in a given area, at a given time; a strategy is defined as the logic behind an intervention or series of interventions. Most of the international HIV and AIDS guidelines recommend choosing a strategy or intervention based on the context in which it will be applied. A good understanding of that context is therefore indispensable. However, the portrait of a context can often be biased or incomplete because of the types of indicators used to describe it. Indeed, both the dynamic of the epidemic and portraits of it require more than the use of indicators, such as changes in seroprevalence and seroincidence, or the quality of knowledge, attitudes and practices in certain populations, as we will see in the following examples.

Our first case study examines an intervention aimed at female sex workers in Conakry, Republic of Guinea, a West African country of about 9 million people. The overall HIV seroprevalence in Guinea was 1.5 per cent in 2005, whereas among female sex workers it was as high as 42 per cent in 2001. Female sex workers are a biologically and socially vulnerable population as they tend to have lower educational attainment, limited access to resources and low socio-economic status and often experience increased stigma due to cultural and social norms. In a low-prevalence setting, they are also seen as a core group. Isolating this group epidemiologically by reducing transmission has been shown to be an effective strategy for preventing the generalization of the epidemic. Many interventions have therefore focused on this population; condom distribution, communication for behavioural change, and screening for and treatment of sexually transmitted infections (STIs) are regularly offered. In Guinea, these interventions are carried out through 'adapted health care' clinics (*services adaptés*), with international support at the beginning. The project we examined focuses on the syndromic control of STIs: diagnosis and treatment are based on symptoms rather than on more expensive lab tests, and populations at increased risk of HIV infection, such as sex workers, are targeted through the provision of preventive and curative services to them and their clients. There are currently five clinics of this kind in Conakry that offer stigma-free care for sex workers by increasing access to care as well as providing screening for and treatment of STIs.

Voluntary counselling and testing (VCT) was also considered for the sex workers seen at the clinics. VCT may be important for achieving a comprehensive and effective HIV prevention strategy. Some studies have shown that VCT can reduce HIV incidence through primary prevention (the avoidance of new infections) (VCT Efficacy Study Group, 2000). VCT may also contribute to secondary prevention by facilitating early access to health care for HIV-positive people and has been proven to be a cost-effective intervention, particularly for groups at higher risk of infection where HIV prevalence is low among the local population. To assess the acceptability of VCT among sex workers in Conakry, we conducted a longitudinal quantitative study on 421 female sex workers in 2005 and 2006. Qualitative data were also collected through interviews and focus groups. We examined perceived barriers to and benefits of testing sex workers and offered them VCT conducted by trained counsellors in the adapted health care clinics to increase confidentiality. The study was conducted in cooperation with different actors working towards HIV prevention for sex workers, including non-governmental organizations (NGOs), health facilities with adapted health care clinics and the Guinean National Institute of Public Health.

We found that almost 100 per cent of the sex workers agreed to HIV testing (elsewhere, rates are only around 80 per cent) and that 92 per cent of them returned for their results. One explanation given by the sex workers for these high rates was their perception of being at high risk of infection and their desire to be able to plan for the future. Most of the sex workers (84 per cent) accepted VCT solely in order to establish their sero-status, whereas only 13 per cent did so because they were anxious about their sexual behaviour and the behaviour of their sexual partners.

Some sex workers wanted to know their sero-status because they felt responsible for their own health and that of their relatives, which they said could be compromised by their 'dirty work'. Other sex workers, however, reported less altruistic explanations for the high acceptability rates of VCT. Some pub managers and bar owners asked women to be tested so that they could reassure their clients of the 'safety' of their bar. They also required that women present their (negative) test results in order to work in their establishment. This suggests that being found to be HIV-positive may have exposed some women to ostracism and greater economic insecurity. It also throws doubt on the voluntary component of VCT. Meanwhile, even where bar owners did not ask for test results, some sex workers felt that they had to tell others of their HIV test results, particularly when co-workers were doing so at the adapted health care clinic or the prostitution site. Peer pressure was an important explanatory factor behind the high rate of notification found among sex workers in Conakry (more than 80 per cent). In fact, other sex workers and bar owners or managers were the main people to whom sero-status was revealed (more than 50 per cent), outranking steady partners (around 30 per cent) and health workers (only 8 per cent).

Relations between sex workers and health care workers are often ambivalent, and it can at times be unclear whether the health care workers are working in the interests of the sex workers. It was reported that before the VCT acceptability study in Conakry, a brothel owner sent women to be tested by his personal physician when he noticed that they were getting malaria too often. As a consequence of similar actions, sex workers often mistrust health workers as it is difficult to know where their allegiances lie. Qualitative data from the VCT study showed that sex workers who did not undergo VCT feared not only a positive result and therefore stigma but also breaches of confidentiality. Indeed, there was concern that the VCT study was conducted to identify seropositive sex workers in order to 'publish' their names and render them vulnerable to ostracism.

Women who engage in sex work are among the most vulnerable in society. In this case, the sex workers targeted by the programme had turned to sex work because they could not find other gainful employment. We do not currently know how the fear of stigma will influence prevention efforts by dissuading some members of the most vulnerable populations from engaging with them. In the case of transactional sex, it may be important to assess power relations between pimps and sex workers and collaboration or competition among sex workers as these can have an influence both on the risk of HIV infection and on responses to interventions aimed at this group. These variables should be established before implementing any new intervention and used to adjust existing prevention strategies. Other factors, such as the reasons why women become sex workers, as well as the causes and effects of high mobility within this population, may also be important objects of study.

The adverse effects that intensive prevention efforts may have on some groups must also be taken into account when implementing HIV prevention strategies. Prevention is often seen as a business, with everybody wanting a 'piece of the pie'. That 'pie' includes the resources allocated by prevention programmes, which often justify funding on the basis of prevention targets, such as the number of sex workers or associated actors, such as pimps, who have been engaged in interventions. In the case of the VCT study, some bar owners may have forced sex workers to participate in the study in order to obtain benefits, such as free condoms, from the many NGOs involved in prevention efforts. At the opposite extreme, our study revealed that some pimps refused all prevention interventions: 'We have to die from something anyway; AIDS or something else, it doesn't matter. I don't want to see you around my girls.' In a situation where many research projects are being undertaken, there may be an escalation of compensation: 'How much will you give me for my participation? Organization X gave us more.' In addition, myths and rumours were rife: 'We know that you want to take our blood to sell it.'

Prevention programmes may unwittingly be taking advantage of, or even increasing, women's social vulnerability – or may be perceived to be, even when this is not the case. Short-term gains in terms of a reduced risk of HIV infection may be offset by longer-term increases in social vulnerability: for instance, coercing women into VCT programmes may decrease HIV transmission, but coerced women are particularly socially vulnerable and will become even more so if they are ostracized because they are HIV-positive. Moreover, if VCT programmes are seen to be exacerbating vulnerability, women will increasingly avoid them.

Interventions do not exist in a vacuum, a fact we tend to forget. They interact with the context, changing it and changing in response to it. Previous or contemporary interventions form part of this context. There are always unexpected and unintended positive and negative effects as well as expected and desired effects of an intervention. Understanding the epidemic therefore requires an understanding of the dynamics and impacts of the interventions and research undertaken in a given context as these may shape future behaviour or responses to future interventions.

Similar phenomena were reported in the context of prevention interventions aimed at men who have sex with men in four West African countries that we cannot identify because of the sensitive nature of the issue. There has been growing attention paid to MSM in Africa, after a long period during which talk of men having sex with men was largely avoided. Initial studies have suggested that MSM have higher rates of sexually transmitted infections, including HIV, as well as many female partners (Wade et al., 2005). This has sparked concern that MSM may be a new (or newly discovered) 'core group' and therefore qualify for the same kinds of targeted interventions as sex workers.

Efforts have therefore increasingly been devoted to surveying MSM and supporting efforts to organize them into groups, as well as provide access to STI treatment and HIV prevention through specialized clinics modelled on the clinics for sex workers described above. Often located within these existing clinics, new clinics for MSM offer the same package of services that has been developed for sex workers, including STI screening and treatment, VCT and, in some cases, expedited access to antiretroviral therapy (ART). This approach is 'gendered' to the extent that it applies an approach developed for vulnerable women to a group of men identified on the basis of their sexual behaviour. When we conducted interviews with beneficiaries of these interventions, a paradox emerged. The clients of these services appreciated the access to medical care that they would not otherwise have had and, most of all, the sympathetic attention from some of the clinic workers. However, the clinics had some difficulties in responding to this new clientele. Some health care workers were clearly still uncomfortable working with MSM, seeking, for example, to categorize clients by their preferred sexual position. While condoms were freely available, lubricant was more difficult to come by. In addition, prevention materials were still largely aimed at a heterosexual population. More generally, the MSM group was narrowly identified by a sexual behaviour that was used without differentiation to define very different people – rich and poor, powerful and vulnerable, and so forth. As a result, it was difficult to adequately tailor prevention strategies to men from wildly different circumstances whose only common denominator was having sex with other men. The paradox in this situation lies in the fact that these interventions for MSM may have had the effect of increasing the vulnerability of some men who were identified as homosexual because of their participation in prevention activities. In two countries, men attending prevention activities were beaten, some severely, by local thugs. In a third country, a workshop arranged by a western NGO for organizations interested in working with MSM from throughout Africa went well, despite the country's refusal to allow research involving MSM. However, one participant, upon his return to his home country, denounced his compatriots who had attended the meeting, leading to their arrest and beating.

The implications of these stories echo Robert Lorway's concern elsewhere in this volume: they demonstrate how gender dynamics – the ways in which ideas about gender roles structure power relations – can affect men as well as women and how the effects of HIV-prevention interventions are refracted through these dynamics and may actually magnify power imbalances. Prevention interventions for sex workers have to take into account the power relations that structure their lives and which mean that the consequences of peer pressure can have major economic consequences. Indeed, while peer pressure is often viewed in prevention programmes as a positive force for moulding behaviour, our example reveals its darker, coercive side. Can programmes that rely on peer pressure square with a human rights and gender-based approach? The corollary of this situation is those programmes targeting MSM using a standardized intervention that, although initially developed for sex workers, remained blind to how gender structures power relations. In this case, too, prevention programmes enhance vulnerability by exposing MSM to coercive, and even violent, forms of peer pressure to conform to masculine gender norms.

ARV families

Until very recently, one of the largely unnoticed side effects of the expanded use of antiretroviral therapy in Africa has been an unexpected baby boom. This baby boom – and the reasons why it has escaped attention – reveals the implications of a more thorough approach for taking gender into account in treatment roll-out.

The issue first came to our attention in 2003, during conversations with a collaborator, Abou. Abou told us that he was worried about something that he suspected was happening in the self-help group for people living with HIV that he had founded. While his administrative responsibilities meant that he could no longer participate in the discussion groups that had helped him 'come out' about being HIV-positive himself, he kept close tabs on what was a growing – and increasingly unmanageable – community of people living with HIV. Abou had been able to secure a reliable supply of medication for almost 200 people from different international sources. As he was himself undertaking ART, Abou knew only too well the importance of taking the medication properly – that is, with quasi-military discipline – in order to ensure that the treatment worked. Over the past year, however, a number of women had dropped out of the treatment programme – even though they were doing well on the medicines. Now some had returned to the programme, each with a new-born slung behind her back. Abou suspected that they were dropping out of the programme to get pregnant, their newfound health having translated into a newfound desire for a child.

We organized a meeting with a group of about fifty women who were receiving ART to address the issue. The meeting was part of a therapeutic out-ing organized to discuss the importance of adherence to the medication and was facilitated by one of the nurses involved in the treatment programme. The question of pregnancy was soon raised, and the nurse responded by saying that pregnancy was 'not indicated' for HIV-positive women, particularly those receiving treatment. He was quickly shouted down by the women, who made it clear that they viewed this response as unacceptable paternalism. Discussions we subsequently had with many of the women and health care workers revealed a fundamental difference in perspective between the two groups. For the wom-en, ART offered health and, with health, the opportunity to found or enlarge a family. The powerful effects of the treatment – the dramatic weight gain, the gradual disappearance of ailments – confirmed for these women that the life-giving properties of ART could translate into the precious gift of children.

For the health care workers, however, the success of the medication cre-ated a confusing situation. Drilled in the imperatives of HIV prevention, with careers that until the advent of ART had largely involved encouraging safer sex, particularly for HIV-positive people, they felt that the desire for pregnancy resulting from the success of the treatment was to be condemned. ART is a bio-medical technology that was brought to Africa as part of the HIV prevention industry and is therefore embedded with a mission to promote sexual restraint. Once on African soil, this mission to prevent HIV dovetailed with a conserva-tive moral culture. In addition, ART came linked to the requirement for adher-ence, a behavioural demand that seamlessly integrated with HIV prevention messages to take the shape of a moral agenda: if unprotected sex was discour-aged for people undergoing treatment, pregnancy was equally 'not indicated'.

This example shows how an apparently gender-neutral biomedical tech-nology is in fact encoded with unexamined and gendered assumptions. In this case, it was assumed that women receiving ART treatment should not get preg-nant. The effective use of ART requires patients to comply with strict time-tables; where access to this medication has been a struggle, its use is freighted with expectations of compliance, not only with medication schedules, but also with a host of biomedical imperatives, such as safer sex. These unexamined expectations are revealed when ART is used by women who do not necessarily value biomedical compliance above the competing claims of their own and their partner's desire for love and a family. For health care workers, delivering the ART and making sure that patients take the medication properly is about restoring individual health, not reinforcing social ties or reproducing the future. The lack of communication on this issue potentially compromised some women's treatment as they felt compelled to drop out of the ART programme once they got pregnant, with the risk that they might acquire resistance to some of the antiretroviral medications they were taking.[1]

The stakes are high. Millions of women are now taking ART or will soon be included in ART programmes, and most of them are of child-bearing age. Gender plays an important role in the social expectations of women as mothers and indeed in forming a woman's desire to raise a family. Researchers have confirmed Abou's suspicion that a significant proportion of women in ART programmes will become pregnant: according to two recent studies, between 15 per cent and 20 per cent of women become pregnant during the first three years of ART treatment (Andia et al., 2008; Ekouvi et al., 2008). These studies also show that pregnancy correlates with the previous death of a child and that women may not always notify their partners that they are HIV-positive, probably because of the risk of violence and exclusion. Other studies suggest that people 'serosort', choosing to use protection if only one partner is HIV-positive and to forego it when both are positive, to increase pleasure and/or with pregnancy in mind (Berry et al., 2008; Williamson et al., 2008). Our work with women undertaking ART treatment makes it clear that having children – founding or enlarging a family – is of enormous concern to HIV-positive women. In many Western societies, tremendous social and economic changes have created a context in which having children is not as great a priority as it was in the past. However, for many other women and men around the world – whatever their economic situation, social background or cultural and religious beliefs – bringing children into the world is of paramount importance. Being confronted with such a devastating diagnosis as HIV infection, we have found, adds particular urgency to this goal, to the extent that for many women life-saving ART is ultimately only meaningful if it can translate into a healthy and growing family. It has also emerged from our discussions with women in ART programmes that having children is a means to re-establish ties with family in order to compensate for the alienation they have experienced subsequent to a diagnosis of HIV infection. Significantly, practically nothing is known about the desire for children of men in treatment programmes.

The desire for children is, of course, tied to a sense of family obligations and status and is profoundly shaped by prevailing ideas and norms about the role of women. Until recently, addressing the issue of gender in ART scale-up has largely been confined to concerns about access to treatment and the social impacts of VCT, suggesting that there has been a selective form of gender-blindness in the treatment-focused response to the epidemic. As noted above, the desire for children may have a meaningful impact on decisions to undertake and adhere to ART, for instance. Yet this has not been addressed in the initial scale-up of treatment. Until recently, there have not been any guidelines for counselling women who might want to have children while undertaking ART, nor has there been any acknowledgement that this should be systematically discussed with women patients.

While it may seem obvious that many of these women desire children and will get pregnant, it is remarkable that this highly gendered issue has been utterly absent from the extensive political, policy, implementation and research discussions that have surrounded ART roll-out. Attention is increasingly being paid to this issue, which exemplifies how failing to think about gender can lead to significant unintended consequences. The ART baby boom can be seen as a positive outcome of treatment programmes; paying more attention to gender and the gendered implications of these programmes may help to keep it so. Moreover, the desire for pregnancy offers an important opportunity for HIV prevention, particularly in the case of serodiscordant partners (that is, when one partner is HIV-positive and the other is not). Discussing desire for children with couples offers a valuable opportunity to discuss prevention and explore options for having children safely.

Conclusion

This chapter has discussed some examples of how a lack of attention to gender in the response to the epidemic has generated unexpected consequences. Because gender plays such an important role in everyday life and gender relations have enormous economic and social implications for men and women, a lack of attention to gender has the potential to compromise or undermine the response to the epidemic. Prevention programmes may actually enhance vulnerability and increase the risk of HIV infection. Alternatively, these unexpected consequences may represent missed opportunities to respond to the epidemic. Treatment programmes could serve to strengthen prevention efforts by encouraging the open discussion of safe child-bearing.

While gender is a significant force that shapes and refracts the response to the epidemic, it does not follow that gendered effects are the same everywhere. Power relations and economic circumstances are not only strongly gendered but also highly localized. Gendering the response to the epidemic therefore requires serious and careful attention to local realities and taking into account the perspectives of both men and women. This can be a challenge when programmes are developed and implemented by people who may be socially, culturally and geographically far removed from programme beneficiaries. Meeting these challenges will require that gender issues in prevention and treatment programmes be identified through ongoing and meaningful dialogue with the men and women these programmes seek to benefit.

Notes

1. Stopping ART treatment – which consists of a cocktail of three antiretroviral medications – can favour the mutation of the virus, which becomes resistant to those drugs in the cocktail that linger longer in the blood. It is therefore recommended that patients never stop taking their medications without consulting a physician, who can adjust treatment in such a way as to minimize the likelihood of resistance.

References

Andia, I. et al. 2008. Highly active antiretroviral therapy and increased use of contraceptives among HIV-positive women during expanding access to antiretrovrial therapy in Mbarara, Uganda. *American Journal of Public Health,* Vol. 99, No. 2, pp. 34–347.

Berry, M. et al. 2008. The internet, HIV sero-sorting and transmission risk among men who have sex with men, San Francisco. *AIDS,* Vol. 22, No. 6, pp. 787–89.

Ekouvi, D. K. et al. 2008. Antiretroviral therapy in pregnant women with advanced HIV disease and pregnancy outcomes in Abidjan, Côte-d'Ivoire. *AIDS,* Vol. 22, No. 14, pp. 1815–820.

VCT Efficacy Study Group. 2000. Efficacy of voluntary HIV-1 counselling and testing in individuals and couples in Kenya, Tanzania and Trinidad. *Lancet,* Vol. 356, No. 9224, pp. 103–12.

Wade, S. W., Kane, C. T., Diallo, P. A. N. et al. 2005. HIV infection and sexually transmitted infections among men who have sex with men in Senegal. *AIDS,* Vol. 19, pp. 2133–140.

Williamson, L. M. et al. 2008. Sexual risk behaviour and knowledge of HIV status among community samples of gay men in the UK. *AIDS,* Vol. 22, No. 9, pp. 1063–070.

CHAPTER 16

AIDS, gender and access to antiretroviral treatment in South Africa

Nicoli Nattrass

Sex and gender are at the heart of the African AIDS epidemic. Most HIV infections occur through sexual intercourse and most occur among women. This is widely attributed to the inferior socio-economic status of women, yet the gendered nature of the AIDS epidemic is more complex than this. Not only do the very social norms that reinforce dominant masculine identities also expose men to the risk of HIV infection, but they also undermine their access to treatment.

This chapter explores the role of gender in shaping the AIDS epidemic and structuring access to highly active antiretroviral therapy (HAART) in South Africa. South Africa is an important case study because it has the greatest number of HIV-positive people living within its borders and the largest HAART programme in the world. The chapter shows that women are at greater risk of HIV infection than men but are more likely to access HAART once they become sick with AIDS. Drawing from, and building on, earlier work (Nattrass, 2008a), it argues that the main reason for the under-representation of men in HAART programmes is that constructions of masculinity militate against accessing care for all illnesses.

Gender and HIV infection

The HIV epidemic is becoming increasingly 'feminized' as it spreads into the general heterosexual population. Women now account for 50 per cent of

The designations employed and the presentation of material throughout this publication do not imply the expression of any opinion whatsoever on the part of UNESCO concerning the legal status of any country, territory or area or of its authorities, or concerning the delimitation of its frontiers or boundaries. The ideas and opinions expressed in this publication are those of the authors and do not necessarily reflect the views of UNESCO and its Member States.

global HIV infections and 61 per cent of HIV infections in sub-Saharan Africa (UNAIDS, 2007). The situation facing young South African women is especially worrying: according to the most recent national HIV prevalence survey, 24 per cent of women aged 20–24 were HIV-positive – a rate four times higher than that for men the same age (Shisana et al., 2005).

Data on the South African AIDS epidemic come from three sources: the antenatal clinic survey (i.e. data on pregnant women); occasional national sample surveys of HIV prevalence; and the ASSA2003 demographic model (developed and updated by the Actuarial Society of South Africa). Figure 1 shows selected output from the ASSA model as well as 'raw' data from the antenatal clinic survey and the most recent national survey. The picture shows consistently higher HIV prevalence among women than men.

The ASSA model utilizes mortality data by age, gender and race to 'calibrate' the model – that is, to make sure that its HIV prevalence projections

Figure 1. HIV prevalence in South Africa

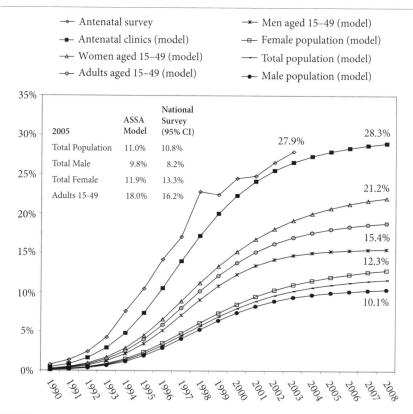

are not only consistent with antenatal survey data but are also able to predict known patterns of deaths over time. Figure 2 shows that the number of reported deaths in young age groups has risen over threefold since 1996 and that the increase has been especially dramatic for young women. (As the ASSA model projections follow these actual trends very closely, the model can be used as a reliable basis for interrogating trends in the South African AIDS epidemic – including the expected number of people needing HAART, as discussed below.)

The particular vulnerability of women to HIV has biological roots in that women are more vulnerable to contracting HIV from a single act of unprotected sex than men.[1] However, it is commonly accepted that this is exacerbated by socio-economic factors that reinforce the inferior status of women, thereby rendering them less able to negotiate, or afford, safer sexual practices (UNAIDS, 2005). Accordingly, empowering women is now a widely accepted dimension of HIV prevention. The UNAIDS-led Global Coalition on Women and AIDS (2005) has identified seven action areas to address women's vulnerability to HIV: improved reproductive care; reducing violence against women; protecting property and inheritance rights of women; ensuring equal access for females to treatment and care; supporting efforts to provide universal education for girls; supporting improved community care with a special focus on women; and promoting safer sex technologies that are controlled by women, such as the female condom and microbicides.

Empowering women is an admirable developmental objective in its own right. However, to be effective, interventions need to concentrate on gender – that is, on how constructions of the feminine role and masculine identity are synergistic and intertwined – rather than on women per se. In the case of HIV, the flip side of the norms and practices that oppress women are those that define masculinity in ways that put both men and women at risk – such as the linkage of male identity with an unwillingness to negotiate sexual behaviour with women, 'skin-on-skin' penetrative sex and multiple sexual partnering (e.g. Brown et al., 2005; Campbell, 1995; Simpson, 2005). These notions of masculinity have shown remarkable resilience in the face of the AIDS epidemic. There is a saying in rural Namibia that 'if you do not die of AIDS you are not a man'. As Brown et al. (2005) note, this suggests that AIDS is extending 'what it means to be a man into the grave' rather than bringing about the major behaviour changes necessary to save the lives of both men and women.

Empowering women thus also requires reaching out to men (UNAIDS, 2000) and challenging entrenched sexual cultures. This, however, is especially

Figure 2. ASSA2003: Actual and projected female (top) and male (bottom) deaths (entire country)

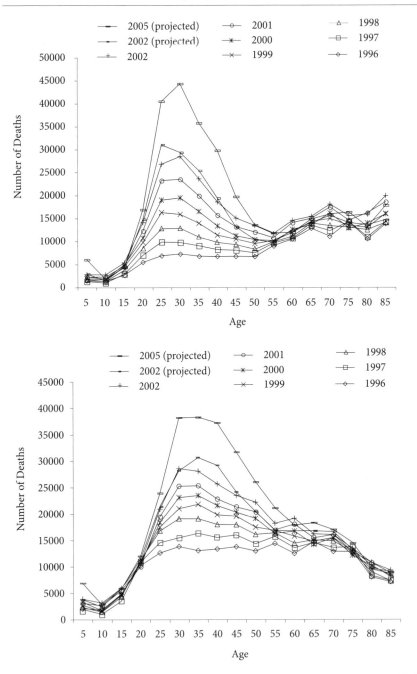

difficult when risky sexual behaviours are reinforced by socio-economic factors. For example, dangerous working environments, such as mining in South Africa and fishing in the Great Lakes region in East Africa, encourage a fatalistic approach to life that undermines HIV prevention efforts (Campbell, 1997, 2003; Seeley and Allison, 2005). The rise in unemployment and socio-economic insecurity has also been linked to the practice of multiple sexual partnering and transactional sex. According to Hunter (2002, 2005, 2007), mass unemployment in South Africa has made it increasingly difficult for men to become heads of independent households, and marriage rates have fallen precipitously. Men have responded by constructing their masculine identities around the number of sexual partners they have, and women by forging stronger bonds within their kinship networks and establishing relationships with more than one sexual partner. According to Swidler and Watkins (2007), this development is consistent with the broader pattern of patron-client ties that are fundamental to African social life. Interventions that do not take into account this broader context are thus unlikely to succeed.

There is some evidence that sexual behaviour is changing in parts of sub-Saharan Africa (notably increased condom use with casual partners). However, the picture is contradictory with some countries recording an increase in the number of people recording multiple sexual partners and others a decrease. The situation remains dire in South Africa, with no sign of decreasing HIV infection levels among young people (UNAIDS, 2007). There are some indications that AIDS is beginning to influence sexual behaviour among young South African men, but identities of manhood remain tied to dominance in sexual relationships (Harrison et al., 2006). The prospects are not good for a significant decline in HIV infections anytime soon.

Gender and access to HAART

In contrast to the burgeoning literature on gender and HIV infection in Africa, relatively little is known about the way gender shapes access to HAART for those sick with AIDS.[2] Since the launch of the Global Fund to Fight AIDS, Tuberculosis and Malaria in January 2002 and subsequent mobilization of resources by the World Health Organization (WHO) and the United States President's Emergency Plan for AIDS Relief (PEPFAR), the numbers of people in developing countries accessing HAART have grown substantially (Nattrass, 2006; WHO, 2006), reaching about 2 million people by 2007 (WHO/UNAIDS/

UNICEF, 2007). As this drive to expand access to treatment took off, the Global Coalition on Women and AIDS expressed concern that AIDS-related gender biases would continue and that men would dominate access to HAART. This was understandable in the light of evidence from Algeria, Togo and the Democratic Republic of the Congo showing that households were less likely to seek medical attention for girls than boys (Tursz and Crost, 1999). Concerns about men dominating access to HAART were fuelled also by early reports from Kenya showing that men with AIDS were twice as likely as their female counterparts to be admitted to hospitals (UNAIDS Inter-agency Task Team on Young People, 2006, p. 167) and from Zambia indicating that men were accessing HAART in disproportionately high numbers. International agencies working in the AIDS arena thus started calling for measures to be taken to ensure that women had equitable access to HAART (UNAIDS/UNFPA/UNIFEM, 2004).

However, as the roll-out of HAART progressed it appeared that men were not benefiting disproportionately (UNAIDS Inter-agency Task Team on Young People, 2006). As of December 2005, only in Ethiopia and Ghana were fewer women accessing HAART than would be expected given the gender composition of the epidemic – whereas in South Africa, Burundi, Cambodia, China and Panama, more women were accessing HAART than expected (WHO, 2006). The following section describes how the ASSA2003 model can be used to show that men in South Africa are accessing HAART in disproportionately lower numbers than expected.

What is the expected gender balance of people needing HAART in South Africa?

The South African AIDS epidemic is located overwhelmingly in the majority black African population, which comprises four-fifths of the total population (see Figure 3). As of 2005, over half of white South Africans estimated to be eligible for HAART were receiving it, whereas less than a fifth of other population groups who needed to be on HAART were actually receiving it. This points to continuing racial inequalities in post-apartheid South Africa and to the importance of the roll-out of HAART in the public sector for reaching Africans living with AIDS.

In May 2001, the international non-governmental organization Médecins Sans Frontières (MSF), in collaboration with the Provincial Administration of

Figure 3. South Africa's AIDS epidemic by population group

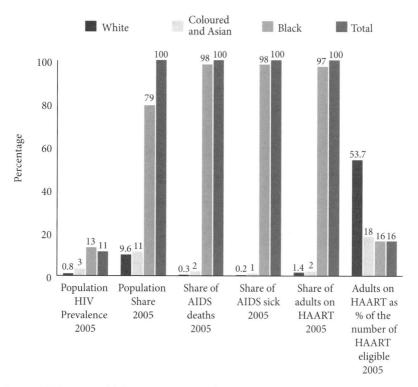

Source: ASSA2003 model (http://www.actuarialsociety.org.za/Resource-Centre/Aids-Model/ Models-274.aspx).

the Western Cape, launched South Africa's first public sector HAART project in Khayelitsha (an African township outside of Cape Town).[3] The World Health Organization subsequently flagged the project as a successful example of how HAART could be provided to people with AIDS in resource-constrained settings (MSF et al., 2003). Since 2004, HAART has become more generally available in the public sector. Data from the Khayelitsha cohort of HAART patients shows that about 70 per cent of HAART patients are female and that this has not changed over time (Coetzee et al., 2004; Western Cape Department of Health, 2006). This gender pattern is replicated in HAART programmes throughout South and southern Africa (Nachega et al., 2006; UNAIDS Inter-agency Task Team on Young People, 2006; Western Cape Department of Health, 2006).

One would, of course, expect more women than men to be on HAART given that HIV infection rates are higher among women. However, the ASSA model shows that the proportion of women on HAART is significantly higher than would be expected given demographic trends. The model predicts that of the total number of black people with AIDS-related sicknesses (and hence eligible for HAART) in the Western Cape, 57 per cent are likely to be women – a significantly lower figure than the 70 per cent experienced by the Khayelitsha programme. Conversely, 43 per cent of AIDS-sick people are predicted to be men, yet men only comprise 30 per cent of those on HAART programmes.

Why might men be less able to access HAART than women?

A WHO (2006) report on global access to HIV antiretroviral therapy speculated that the relative overrepresentation of women in HAART programmes in most developing countries could be because women are better integrated into community networks and thus have better health care information and are better able to access public health facilities than men – especially where these women access programmes to prevent mother-to-child transmission (PMTCT). However, a study from Côte d'Ivoire found that even among patients at HIV referral centres, men were less likely than women to become HAART patients (Msellati et al., 2003), thus suggesting that the problem of male access to HAART was broader than that of accessing health care facilities in the first place. A national survey in South Africa found no gender-based differences regarding knowledge of HIV testing services or the existence of HAART: roughly four out of five men and women were aware of both (Shisana et al., 2005). And, although many women said they had tested for HIV because they were pregnant (a very gender specific reason), the same survey found no significant gender differences in HIV testing patterns (Shisana et al., 2005). Thus, in South Africa's case, gender differences in access to HAART cannot be attributed to PMTCT programmes or different levels of knowledge of relevant health facilities.

How, then, are we to understand a situation where the inferior socio-economic status of women contributes to their greater risk of becoming infected with HIV, yet once infected, they seem better able than men to access life-prolonging HAART? A possible explanation is that men are less likely to seek treatment for all ailments (AIDS-related or otherwise) than women because health-seeking behaviour in general is socially constructed and constitutive of gender identity. As Courtenay (2000) observes (with reference to the United States), by eschewing treatment, men reinforce strongly held cultural beliefs that men are more powerful and less vulnerable than women; that men's bodies are structurally more efficient and superior to women's bodies; [and] that asking for help and caring for one's health are feminine; and that the most powerful men among men are those for whom health and safety are irrelevant.

Similar notions of 'tough' masculine ideals and identity have been described recently for Zambia (Simpson, 2005), Namibia (Brown et al., 2005) and South Africa (Beck, 2004; Harrison et al., 2006; Hunter, 2005). In a 2004 survey of Khayelitsha, two-thirds of respondents agreed with the statement that 'men think of ill-health as a sign of weakness which is why they go to a doctor less often than women'.[4]

One could thus reasonably hypothesize that South African men with AIDS-related illnesses are less likely to access HAART than their female counterparts because masculine norms encourage them not to admit weakness and to avoid seeking treatment for all ailments for as long as possible. The fact that male South African HAART patients, whether in the public or private sector, have lower CD4 counts than women when starting HAART, that is, are sicker than women when starting treatment (Boulle et al., 2004; Coetzee et al., 2004; Nachega et al., 2006) is consistent with this hypothesis. And, as women are increasingly attending HAART clinics, this may undermine male access even further as clinics become constructed in the public mind as part of the feminine world.[5]

Do South African men access clinics less often than women?

Data from the most recent (1998) South African Demographic and Health Survey (DHS) show that significant differences do indeed exist between men and women with regard to health-seeking behaviour (see Table 1). This is true both within the total population and for (black) Africans only.[6] It was only with respect to the (generally low)[7] demand for alternative healers (traditional healers, herbalists and faith healers) that gender differences were insignificant.

Table 2 explores, using probit regression analysis, the determinants of whether an African is likely to have visited a government hospital or clinic in the past month. The analysis controls for gender, age, pregnancy and child-bearing age (to capture any possible other reason besides pregnancy, such as birth control injections, that would give women reasons specific to their biology to go to clinics more often than men). It also controls for ill-health (see explanatory variables 5 through 9), for socio-economic status (variables 10 through 13) and for whether respondents have sought health care from private doctors and alternative healers in the past month (variables 14 and 15). The analysis indicates that those of higher socio-economic status (who are also more likely to have visited a private doctor) are less likely to have visited government health facilities, whereas those of lower socio-economic status are more likely to have visited government health care facilities. Note also that the demand for alternative therapies and related interventions (from herbalists, traditional healers and faith healers) is complementary to, rather than competitive with, visiting government health care clinics – as indicated by the positive sign and statistical significance of variable 14 in Table 2.

The regression analysis demonstrates that even after controlling for age, socio-economic status and ill-health, men are significantly less likely to have visited a government health facility in the past month than women. According to the marginal effects analysis, the conditional predicted percentage of men visiting government health care facilities is 4.5 percentage points lower than that for women. In other words, we would expect the proportion of men attending government clinics to be 25 per cent lower (4.5/18.1 = 25 per cent) than that of women, purely because men are less likely to seek medical help than women.

Using this predicted 'masculinity effect' we should expect the proportion of male HAART patients to be 25 per cent lower than that of women. In other words, even though 43 per cent of people with AIDS-related illnesses (i.e. HAART-eligible patients) are men, the proportion of male HAART patients is likely to be 25 per cent lower (i.e. 36 per cent),[8] principally as a result of the general reluctance of men to seek medical attention for any disease. Given that the actual percentage of men accessing HAART is 30 per cent, as opposed to our predicted 36 per cent, there remains a small additional difference (6 per cent) still to be accounted for in explaining gender differences in access to HAART.

One possible explanation for this HAART-specific difference in health-seeking behaviour is that men may prefer to seek out traditional healers rather than go to HAART clinics when they contract an AIDS-related illness. However, a quantitative analysis of survey data from Khayelitsha shows no significant differences between men and women in this regard (Nattrass, 2008a). Explanations for this additional reluctance on the part of men to seek treatment for AIDS thus need to be sought elsewhere.

Table 1. DHS question 'During the last month have you been to any of the following health services for medical care for yourself?'

TOTAL POPULATION (N=13,348)	MEN	WOMEN	TOTAL
Any kind of health care (government or private hospital, district surgeon clinic, chemist shop, private doctor, traditional healer, herbalist or faith healer)	28.3%	39.2%	34.7%
	Pearson chi2(1) = 175.0791 Pr = 0.000		
Government hospital or clinic	10.4%	17.4%	14.5%
	Pearson chi2(1) = 130.9413 Pr = 0.000		
Private doctor in the past month for yourself	8.7%	11.6%	10.4%
	Pearson chi2(1) = 30.2681 Pr = 0.000		
Traditional healer, herbalist or faith healer	3.2%	3.7%	3.5%
	Pearson chi2(1) = 2.9634 Pr = 0.085		
AFRICAN POPULATION	MEN	WOMEN	TOTAL
Any kind of health care (government or private hospital, district surgeon clinic, chemist shop, private doctor, traditional healer, herbalist or faith healer)	25.5%	36.1%	31.8%
	Pearson chi2(1) = 132.0014 Pr = 0.000		
Government hospital or clinic	10.9%	18.1%	15.2%
	Pearson chi2(1) = 103.2091 Pr = 0.000		
Private doctor in the past month for yourself	6.2%	8.9%	7.8%
	Pearson chi2(1) = 24.9089 Pr = 0.000		
Traditional healer, herbalist or faith healer	4.0%	4.6%	4.3%
	Pearson chi2(1) = 2.3074 Pr = 0.129		

Source: South African Demographic and Health Survey, 1998.

Table 2. Probit regression analysis of whether African respondents visited a government hospital or clinic in the past month for medical care for themselves

EXPLANATORY VARIABLES	DF/DX	STD ERROR	Z	P>|z|	X-BAR
1. Male	-.04488	.006024	-7.26	0.000	.417291
2. Age	.0009177	.000299	3.07	0.002	38.4196
3. People of child-bearing age (proxied as 15–40 years old)	.023209	.010773	2.14	0.033	.564579
4. Pregnant women	.128742	.038732	4.05	0.000	.009814
5. Record of ill-health (proxied as people who have been told by a medical professional that they have, or have had, cancer, TB, asthma, high blood pressure, diabetes, a stroke, heart attack or angina, high blood pressure, high blood cholesterol or emphysema.)	.059924	.008773	7.35	0.000	.245805
6. Underweight (body mass index of less than 18.5)	.018429	.010676	1.80	0.073	.098816
7. Obese	-.00941	.007140	-1.30	0.195	.202877
8. On medication (proxied as those who report taking any prescribed medication regularly)	.220328	.013862	19.41	0.000	.140321
9. Self-assessed breathing problems (those who report that they feel they have less breath when exerting themselves than other people their age)	.059437	.008425	7.69	0.000	.185721
10. Live in informal, unserviced housing (proxied as those living without any toilet facilities)	.018937	009610	2.05	0.041	.117621

EXPLANATORY VARIABLES	DF/DX	STD ERROR	Z	P>|z|	X-BAR
11. Live in informal housing with basic services (proxied as those using a 'bucket' toilet system)	.049636	.012510	4.37	0.000	.075966
12. Live in formal housing with internal plumbing	-.04971	.006126	-7.77	0.000	.366497
13. Worked for pay in the past twelve months	-.02568	006210	-4.03	0.000	.339077
14. Has visited an alternative healer in the past month	.072954	.018701	4.47	0.000	.036301
15. Has visited a private doctor in the past month	-.05406	.007252	-6.32	0.000	.101663
Observed P	.143168				
Predicted P (at x-bar)	.120817				
Pseudo R-squared	.1137				
Number of observations	13348				

Note: dF/dx is for discrete change of dummy variable from 0 to 1, z and P>|z| are the test of the underlying coefficient being 0.

Conclusion

One of the most important, but not sole, reasons why men are accessing HAART in disproportionate numbers to women is that men, in general, seek treatment for poor health less readily than women. Gendered norms that make it difficult for men to admit any health-related weakness and seek medical attention are probably at the heart of the problem. In the context of the AIDS epidemic, this means that although men are biologically less vulnerable to HIV infection than women, their chances of surviving AIDS are lower because they are less able than women to access HAART. This is a tragedy for the men concerned and for their dependants.

An obvious policy prescription is that interventions need to recognize that health-seeking behaviour comprises a set of social acts and practices that simultaneously demonstrate and construct gender. So, for example, policy-makers should attempt to attract men to clinics that are construed by them as forming part of a 'feminine' world. Special attempts should therefore be made to reach out to men in places understood to be masculine spaces. Depending on the context these could be, for example, STI (sexually transmitted infection) clinics predominantly frequented by men, sporting events, and so forth. There is a clear need for new and innovative interventions that take social constructions of gender seriously and that tailor interventions to the lived experiences of men. Research on the effectiveness of interventions to improve uptake of health services stresses the importance of community-level interventions, but the evidence is limited and success appears to be context-bound (UNAIDS Inter-agency Task Team on Young People, 2006). There are no one-size-fits-all easy solutions.

Given that male identity itself is tied up with risky behaviour and an unwillingness to seek medical attention of any kind, it is difficult to know what policy prescriptions to follow. Culture is constantly being contested and shaped through everyday interactions, thereby creating windows of opportunity for shaping social norms and practices in ways that might encourage men to seek medical treatment for AIDS-related illnesses. But what kinds of interventions are appropriate in this regard? One option is to provide opportunities for men to engage with each other in peer-led discussion groups in the hope that these interactions will generate new understandings and conceptions of masculinities that are more conducive to health management. However, approaches that seek to challenge norms and behaviours through group-based discursive strategies are to a large extent contingent upon the general context and have a chequered history – indeed, one such community-level intervention of this kind among South African sex workers and mine workers was ineffective, if not counterproductive (Campbell, 2003). A recent overview of HIV prevention interventions, while acknowledging that peer-driven interventions could potentially work, reported that the evidence was limited and contradictory and that more research and testing was needed (UNAIDS Inter-agency Task Team on Young People, 2006).

Another way of potentially reshaping gender norms is to recognize that multiple sexual partnerships are part of what Swidler and Watkins (2007) refer to as 'broader patterns of patron-client relationships': 'Just as women need patrons to provide them with material benefits, men need clients who provide them with an outward display of power, prestige and social dominance and an inward sense of behaving morally'. Their research in Malawi demonstrated that men feel obliged to support multiple partners as they view this as part of their social duty to redistribute wealth to the needy. However, social norms are increasingly turning against men who 'selfishly' spread HIV as a consequence.

Swidler and Watkins suggest that there is growing space for innovative measures to reproduce patron-client ties in a non-sexual context, for example by encouraging men to give money to the poor through churches and mosques and recognizing them publicly for their generosity. However, they note that until the pervasive insecurity that characterizes African life (whether from drought, pests or structural adjustment) is overcome, patron-client relations (including at a sexual level) are likely to continue as a form of social insurance.

Another option is to explore new and innovative mass media campaigns, including educational messages challenging prevailing norms during televised sports programmes and radio and television soap operas. Mass media campaigns have been successful in increasing condom use and encouraging greater discussions on negotiating sexual encounters (UNAIDS Inter-agency Task Team on Young People, 2006), so there is room here for extending the effort into challenging gender constructions. However, this would require appropriate and relevant programming.

If public personalities from politics, entertainment and sports were to disclose their HIV-positive status and speak openly about the benefits of going on antiretroviral therapy, it would probably also help challenge masculine stereotypes about AIDS-related health-seeking behaviour. However, so far in South Africa, the only high-profile man to speak out in this way is a white, gay judge (Cameron, 2005). His stance, although brave and important, is not likely to resonate with African heterosexual men. Unfortunately the only high-profile black man who has disclosed his HIV status publicly – a radio personality known as 'Khabzela' – decided to reject HAART in favour of seeking a cure from alternative therapists and traditional healers. According to his biographer (McGregor, 2005), this was closely tied up with his sense of self and need to be in control: 'Acknowledging how ill he was and submitting to the treatment required to make him well would have required a temporary surrender of his independence, a reversion to an infantile state'. His decision to reject chronic medication and seek a cure from traditional healers put him back in the driver's seat: 'Once again, there were people fawning over him. He had power. He could make a healer famous by trying out his or her cure'. A great opportunity to challenge the prevailing perceptions about masculine behaviour was thus missed, and Khabzela died a painful and unnecessary death – in large part because of them.

The fact that President Mbeki's health minister (1999–2008) cast doubts on the benefits of HAART and lent her support to the purveyors of untested alternative therapies, including sending Tina van der Maas (a retired Dutch nurse who claims to be able to treat HIV with a nutritional remedy and who is widely acknowledged to be a charlatan) to Khabzela's sickbed to treat him with a dubious concoction, certainly did not help the situation (Nattrass, 2007, 2008b). Worse still from the point of view of challenging South African masculinities was the widely publicized rape trial in 2006 of Jacob Zuma, the then deputy president of the African National Congress (and since December 2007, the president of the ANC). Although he was ultimately found not guilty of raping the HIV-positive complainant, Zuma made a series of gaffs that continue to haunt his political life – the most notorious being his statements about how he had had sex with her despite not having a condom because it was against Zulu culture to leave a woman in a state of arousal and about how he had dealt with her HIV status by having a shower immediately afterwards (Gordin, 2006). Statements such as these reinforce masculine identity and risky behaviours rather than challenge them. Until high-profile men, such as Jacob Zuma and others, start to question and confront the behaviours that link masculinity to unprotected sex and having multiple partners, there is probably very little that micro-level behavioural interventions can achieve.

Notes

1. Women are between two and four times more likely than men to contract HIV from a sexual encounter. The reasons for this include higher concentrations of HIV in semen than in vaginal fluid, the larger area of exposed female genital surface area, the longer period of exposure to semen in the vaginal tract and the greater permeability of the mucous membranes in the vagina compared to the penis (see summary of evidence in Baylies and Bujra, 2001, p. 5).

2. People living with HIV do not need antiretroviral treatment until they are diagnosed as having developed AIDS. This usually occurs within eight to ten years of infection after the body's immune system has been so weakened that the patient is vulnerable to increasing numbers of opportunistic infections.

3. See Coetzee et al. (2004) and Naimak (2006) for more details about this programme.

4. Data drawn from a survey conducted in Khayelitsha in 2004 by the AIDS and Society Research Unit of the University of Cape Town.

5. I once interviewed an HIV-positive man who was living in close proximity to one of the best HAART clinics in the Western Cape. He had tuberculosis, and I advised him to go to the clinic to investigate whether he needed to go onto HAART. He refused, saying that the clinic was for 'women and children'. Initially I thought he was demonstrating ignorance but subsequently came to understand that this perception was rooted in local understandings and that for him to go to the clinic was to threaten his identity as a man.

6. The term 'African' is used to refer to black South Africans.

7. Only 4.3 per cent of Africans (and 3.5 per cent of the total population) reported that they had visited such an alternative healer in the past month.

8. 36 per cent = $(0.75*0.43)/((0.75*0.43)+ 0.57)$.

References

Baylies, C. and Bujra, J. 2001. *AIDS, Sexuality and Gender in Africa: Collective Strategies and Struggles in Tanzania and Zambia.* London, Routledge.

Beck, D. 2004. Men and ARVs: How does being a man affect access to antiretroviral therapy in South Africa? An investigation among Xhosa-speaking men in Khayelitsha. Cape Town, Centre for Social Science Research, University of Cape Town. (CSSR Working Paper no. 80.) http://www.cssr.uct.ac.za

Boulle, A., Michaels, D. and Hildebrand, K. 2004. Gender aspects of access to ART and treatment outcomes in a South African township. Unpublished presentation, Infectious Disease Epidemiology Unit, School of Public Health, University of Cape Town.

Brown, J., Sorrell, J. and Raffaelli, M. 2005. An exploratory study of constructions of masculinity, sexuality and HIV/AIDS in Namibia, Southern Africa. *Culture, Health and Sexuality,* Vol. 7, No. 6, pp. 585–98.

Cameron, E. 2005. *Witness to AIDS.* Cape Town, David Philip.

Campbell, C. 1992. Learning to kill? Masculinity, the family and violence in Natal. *Journal of Southern African Studies,* Vol. 18, No. 3, pp. 614–28.

——. 1995. Male gender roles and sexuality: Implications for women's AIDS risk and prevention. *Social Science and Medicine,* Vol. 41, No. 2, pp. 197–210.

——. 1997. Migrancy, masculine identities and AIDS: The psychosocial context of HIV transmission on the South African gold mines. *Social Science and Medicine,* Vol. 45, No. 2, pp. 273–81.

——. 2003. *Letting them Die: Why HIV/AIDS Intervention Programs Fail.* Oxford, James Currey.

Coetzee, D., Hildebrand, K., Boulle, A., Maartens, G., Louis, F., Labatala, V., Reuter, H., Ntwana, N. and Goemare, E. 2004. Outcomes after two years of providing antiretroviral treatment in Khayelitsha, South Africa. *AIDS,* Vol. 18, pp. 887–95.

Courtenay, W. 2000. Constructions of masculinity and their influence on men's well-being: A theory of gender and health. *Social Science and Medicine,* Vol. 50, pp. 1385–401.

Global Coalition on Women and AIDS. 2005. *2005: Progress Report.* Geneva, UNAIDS. http://data.unaids.org/pub/Report/2006/20060530_RE_GCWA_ ProgReport_2005_en.pdf

Gordin, J. 2006. A country of living dangerously. *Sunday Independent,* 24 December.

Harrison, A., O'Sullivan, L., Hoffman, S., Dolezal, C. and Morrell, R. 2006. Gender role and relationship norms among young adults in South Africa: Measuring the context of masculinity and HIV risk. *Journal of Urban Health,* Vol. 83, No. 4, pp. 709–22.

Hunter, M. 2002. The materiality of everyday sex: Thinking beyond 'Prostitution'. *African Studies*, Vol. 61, No. 1, pp. 99–120.

——. Cultural politics and masculinities: Multiple-partners in historical perspective in KwaZulu-Natal. *Culture, Health and Sexuality*, Vol. 7, No. 4, pp. 389–403.

——. The changing political economy of sex in South Africa: The significance of unemployment and inequalities to the scale of the AIDS pandemic. *Social Science and Medicine*, Vol. 64, pp. 689–700.

Macheke, C. and Campbell, C. 1998. Perceptions of HIV/AIDS on a Johannesburg gold mine. *South African Journal of Psychology*, Vol. 28, No. 3, pp. 146–53.

McGregor, L. 2005. *Khabzela: The Life and Times of a South African*. Johannesburg, Jacana Media.

MSF/UCT/PAWC (Médicins sans Frontières South Africa/University of Capetown/ Provincial Administration of the Western Cape). 2003. *Antiretroviral Therapy in Primary Health Care: Experience of the Khayelisha Program in South Africa (Case Study)*. Geneva, WHO. http://www.who.int/hiv/pub/prev_care/en/South_ Africa_E.pdf#search=%22khayelitsha%20best%20practice%20antiretroviral%22

Msellati, P., Juillet-Amari, A., Prudhomme, J., Akribi, A., Coulibaly-Traore, D., Souville, M. and Moatti, J. for the Côte d'Ivoire HIV Drug Access Initiative Socio-Behavioural Evaluation Group. 2003. Socio-economic and health characteristics of HIV-infected patients seeking care in relation to access to the Drug Access Initiative and to antiretroviral treatment in Côte d'Ivoire. *AIDS*, Vol.17, Suppl. 3, pp. s63–s68.

Nachega, J., Hislop, M., Dowdy, D., Lo, M., Omer, S., Regensberg, L., Chaisson, R. and Maartens, G. 2006. Adherence to highly active antiretroviral therapy assessed by pharmacy claims predicts survival in HIV-infected South African adults. *Journal of Acquired Immune Deficiency Syndromes*, Vol. 43, No. 1, pp. 78–84.

Naimak, T. 2006. *Antiretroviral Treatment in the Western Cape: A Success Story Facilitated by the Global Fund*. Cape Town, Centre for Social Science Research, University of Cape Town. (Working Paper Number 161.) http://www.cssr.uct. ac.za/pubs_cssr.html

Nattrass, N. 2006. What determines cross-country access to antiretroviral treatment? *Development Policy Review*, Vol. 24, No. 3, pp. 321–37.

——. 2007. *Mortal Combat: AIDS Denialism and the Fight for Antiretroviral Treatment in South Africa*. Pietermaritzburg, South Africa, University of KwaZulu-Natal Press.

——. 2008*a*. Gender and access to antiretrovirals in South Africa. *Feminist Economics*, Vol. 14, No. 4, pp. 19–36.

——. 2008*b*. AIDS and the scientific governance of medicine in post-apartheid South Africa. *African Affairs*, Vol. 107, No. 427, pp. 157–76.

Seeley, J. and Allison, E. 2005. HIV/AIDS in fishing communities: Challenges to delivering antiretroviral therapy to vulnerable groups. *AIDS Care*, Vol. 17, No. 6, pp. 688–97.

Shisana, O., Rehle, T., Simbayi, L., Parker, W., Zuma, K., Bhana, A., Connolly, C., Jooste S. and Pillay, V. 2005. *South African National HIV Prevalence, HIV Incidence, Behaviour and Communication Survey, 2005.* Pretoria, Human Sciences Research Council.

Simpson, A. 2005. Sons and fathers/boys to men in the time of AIDS: Learning masculinity in Zambia. *Journal of Southern African Studies*, Vol. 31, No. 3, pp. 569–86.

Swidler, A. and Watkins, S. C. 2007. Ties of dependence: AIDS and transactional sex in rural Malawi. *Studies in Family Planning*, Vol. 38, No. 3, pp. 147–62.

Tursz, A. and Crost, M. 1999. An epidemiological study of gender issues in health care seeking behaviour and care of under five children in developing countries. *Revue d'Epidemiologie et de Sante Publique*, Vol. 47, Suppl. 2, pp. 133–56.

UNAIDS (Joint United Nations Programme on HIV/AIDS). 2000. *Men and AIDS: A Gendered Approach* (World AIDS Campaign). Geneva, UNAIDS.

——. (Joint United Nations Programme on HIV/AIDS). 2005. *Intensifying HIV Prevention: UNAIDS Policy Position Paper.* Geneva, UNAIDS.

——. (Joint United Nations Programme on HIV/AIDS). 2007. *2007 AIDS Epidemic Update.* Geneva, UNAIDS. Available on: http://data.unaids.org/pub/EPISlides/2007/2007_epiupdate_en.pdf

UNAIDS Inter-agency Task Team on Young People. 2006. *Preventing HIV/AIDS in Young People: A Systematic Review of the Evidence from Developing Countries.* Geneva, WHO.

UNAIDS/UNFPA/UNIFEM (Joint United Nations Programme on HIV/AIDS/United Nations Population Fund/United Nations Development Fund for Women). 2004. *Women and HIV/AIDS: Confronting the Crisis.* Geneva, UNAIDS. http://www.unfpa.org/upload/lib_pub_file/308_filename_women_aids1.pdf

Western Cape Department of Health. 2006. *The Western Cape Antiretroviral Programme: Monitoring Report.* Cape Town, Provincial Administration of the Western Cape.

WHO (World Health Organization). 2006. *Progress of Global Access to HIV Antiretroviral Therapy: A Report on '3 by 5 and Beyond.* Geneva, WHO. http://www.who.int/hiv/progreport2006_en.pdf

WHO/UNAIDS/UNICEF (World Health Organization/Joint United Nations Programme on HIV/AIDS/United Nations Childrens Fund). 2007. *Towards Universal Access: Scaling up Priority HIV/AIDS Interventions in the Health Sector, Progress Report, April 2007.* Geneva, WHO. http://www.who.int/hiv/mediacentre/univeral_access_progress_report_en.pdf

Section IV: Cultures of Measurement

Introductory Essay

Philip Setel

Introduction

The section title 'Cultures of measurement' calls us to critically examine quantitative research and evaluation on HIV and AIDS.[1] It calls us to expose and question some of the most taken-for-granted assumptions in the practice of measurement. The chapters in this section bring a few key questions to the fore, including:

- Why are we measuring in the first place?

- Are we really measuring what we think we are measuring?

- Ultimately, for whom and in whose interest is measurement being conducted?

These simple questions are rarely posed but deserve candid answers.

Measurement for learning and improvement

Among other reasons, we measure in order to learn and improve. In the context of HIV and AIDS, measurement in this vein is most often about uncovering the social, epidemiologic, demographic and economic aspects of the pandemic. Measurement needed to discover, develop and deliver new or emerging

The designations employed and the presentation of material throughout this publication do not imply the expression of any opinion whatsoever on the part of UNESCO concerning the legal status of any country, territory or area or of its authorities, or concerning the delimitation of its frontiers or boundaries.
The ideas and opinions expressed in this publication are those of the authors and do not necessarily reflect the views of UNESCO and its Member States.

interventions fits within this purpose as well. It also informs the design and implementation of interventions based on established tools to prevent HIV and AIDS and care for and support those affected by the disease. It establishes the efficacy and effectiveness of new programmes, describes the multiplicity of the disease's impacts and contexts and helps to quantify the various barriers, failures and successes in the struggle to slow and reverse the swathe of suffering that AIDS has cut through our world.

All the chapters in this section share this purpose. All address audiences who need measurement for strategic action and yet have tended to adopt a more utilitarian view of measurement as being mainly for the purpose of 'tracking progress' or for donor accountability. By speaking to the second question posed above (are we really measuring what we think we're measuring?), they challenge us to place conventional analytical categories in context in a way that more rigorously uncovers the experience of women and children in the third decade of the AIDS pandemic.

The chapters do this in two related ways. Those by Patrick Heuveline and Jeremy Seekings, for example, force a reconsideration of what survey researchers would call the 'construct validity' of taken-for-granted categories, such as 'orphan' and 'household' – both clearly central to the way in which poorer women experience and are affected by HIV. Chapters by Rania Antonopouolus and Taun Toay, Charlotte Watts, and Catherine Pirkle, on the other hand, ask us to broaden the scope of measurement. They extend our view to areas such as structural interventions and how violence contributes to the risk of HIV infection in women. In the case of the economic value of work that women perform in caring for the AIDS-ill and -affected, we quantify aspects of gender and the experience of AIDS that are so taken for granted they are literally invisible in conventional economic analysis.

Based on these insights, the chapters all contain policy recommendations, options or warnings that the authors intend as nudges in the ribs of policy-makers, who may have grown a little cozy on donor money and the stupefying drumbeat of progress indicator reporting that donors demand. Charlotte Watts in particular points to a 'measurement industry' of counting sex acts and asks point blank, 'Is this enough?' Her recommendations extend not only to what should be done in terms of program interventions but also to changing the status quo of measurement in AIDS.

Measurement for accountability

In reading the following chapters, it should be apparent that there is a purpose of being accountable with measurement that underlies the analysis, in addition to a desire to contribute new knowledge for improving our response to HIV and AIDS. Sadly, the phrase 'measurement for accountability' is too often inferred to mean 'accountability to donors.' This is not the primary mode of accountability to which these authors attribute their purpose, but it is important to consider for a moment how donor accountability has affected measurement in the AIDS epidemic, if not global health in general.

From the vantage point of the donors and multilateral organizations, there is a growing need to demonstrate that the vastly scaled-up resources available to address the epidemic are being spent on the intended interventions, are attaining the desired levels of coverage and, where possible, are contributing to blunting the trajectory and mitigating the impact of the epidemic. While this volume does not directly address the issue of measurement for donor accountability, it is important to understand this wider context of data and information production on AIDS.

For donor nations and the citizenries whose taxes are allocated to responding to HIV, the need for a rigourous and reasonable program of accountability is entirely rational and, in itself, uncontroversial. At the same time, any critical reflection on the social production of quantitative knowledge of AIDS would be remiss in failing to point out the degree to which the donor accountability tail has long wagged the measurement dog. The result is a host of largely unintended and, too often, unfortunate consequences. Regardless of how well the needs for accountability are met, there is rarely an explicit discussion among research and measurement funders about the trade-offs being made by privileging this purpose for data and information production. The funds allocated to measurement for accountability reduce those available for other purposes of measurement. While data products can be repurposed, repackaged and reanalysed to some extent for uses other than those for which they were originally produced, there are limits to how far this can be taken. Although large-scale program evaluations are carried out, the opportunity to learn lessons and improve practice generally takes a distant second place to the accountability function of the evaluation. In other words, there is a much greater emphasis on establishing whether targeted outcomes and impacts have been achieved than on learning about why they have or have not been accomplished and using that information to improve.

Donors have created multimillion-dollar indicator factories largely based on global programmes of household surveys repeated every two to five years. This 'industry,' as Charlotte Watts terms it, is more a cult than a culture, whose main adherents, aside from the donors who are purchasing the indicator packages, include researchers and statistical modellers. Modellers use large standardized data sets to construct and quantify counterfactual indicators of impact (e.g. 'AIDS cases averted' or 'AIDS deaths averted'). These estimates are frequently based more on assumption than actual evidence and are often projections rolled many years into the future. The agencies and analysts who implement population surveys and furnish indicators at the donors' behest represent a powerful bloc in the social production of scientific knowledge of AIDS. The measures of progress and estimates of global population health impact derived from these measures are lauded as being the highest 'quality' information available – hence the most valuable, reliable and of the highest priority for further investment. Even though there is clearly great and useful global knowledge to be unlocked from the production of these data sets, the reality is that it is often the leftovers from this well-laid table that feed those whose purposes in measuring are of a different appetite.

None of this should be taken to suggest that donor accountability is bad or in any way unnecessary. In fact a solid dose of accountability and 'results-based disbursement' policies, such as those of the Global Fund to Fight AIDS, Tuberculosis and Malaria, is no doubt a healthy corrective to inefficient public health systems where little accountability existed either to populations served or to those providing a large proportion of annual health budgets. There are also some enduring benefits to country information systems that have arisen alongside the increased accountability premiums that affected countries are paying. Improvements in routine facility-based health information systems, national health accounts and analytical capacity in statistical offices are examples of this.

It should also be noted that survey data and models built upon them are agnostic about the uses to which they are put. The best modelling in AIDS, much of it supported by the United States Agency for International Development (USAID) and the Joint United Nations Programme on HIV/AIDS (UNAIDS), is not primarily about donor accountability but instead is primarily used as a learning and priority-setting aid. This type of modelling permits stakeholders at the country and global level to create scenarios under which the costs and effects of different programme designs and combination interventions are predicted and forces choices, trade-offs and assumptions about what works out into the open air of debate.

Accountability reframed

The second type of measurement for accountability – the type that these chapters espouse – is to those infected and affected by HIV and AIDS. Measurement for this purpose requires us to be more concerned with accounting for the contexts and complex experiences of those people and populations than with deriving standard indicators for cross-country comparisons of levels and trends. This, in turn, leads to the kinds of measurement projects undertaken in this volume, including studies that force us to be as certain as we can be that we are indeed measuring what we intend to measure and ought to be measuring and that the primary needs and interests served are those of the AIDS affected.

Those who are skilled at producing such analyses possess a powerful gift. They can craft analysis and couch recommendations in a language understood well by those who have the ability to allocate human and financial resources to support what works in fighting AIDS, to investigate the most promising new approaches and to constantly learn and improve. Let us hope that they are listening.

Notes

1. The views expressed are those of the author and do not necessarily reflect those of the Bill and Melinda Gates Foundation.

CHAPTER 17

Epidemiological fallacies: Beyond methodological individualism

Catherine Pirkle

One of the themes running through this volume is that many of the factors contributing to how gender is expressed and interpreted, as well as formulated and reformulated, in the context of the HIV epidemic occur at multiple levels and are often far removed from the individual. These factors include, among others, globalization, migration, violence and international trade. They also include how interventions are implemented and interpreted in the field as well as how they can reproduce and aggravate the very factors that placed women (or men) at risk in the first place. The manner by which gender influences the epidemic is multifaceted and encompasses everything from the biological to the global; it is also dependent upon how gender is defined and understood. Many of those who work on the epidemic (e.g. clinicians, public health workers and policy-makers) are traditionally members of disciplines that require numerical estimates to describe the importance of such factors and are thus faced with the difficult task of determining how to measure and interpret these factors. While no single measure can capture every aspect of gender, certain measures may be better suited than others.

In public health research, efforts are made to provide scientific evidence that will guide strategies and policies aimed at improving the health of populations. However, this is a broad mandate requiring decisions as to the realm of inquiry. For example, in HIV research, there are important debates concerning which aspects of the epidemic warrant more attention, such as prevention, testing, treatment and/or care. These decisions are often value-laden and driven

The designations employed and the presentation of material throughout this publication do not imply the expression of any opinion whatsoever on the part of UNESCO concerning the legal status of any country, territory or area or of its authorities, or concerning the delimitation of its frontiers or boundaries.
The ideas and opinions expressed in this publication are those of the authors and do not necessarily reflect the views of UNESCO and its Member States.

by social, political and economic considerations; they are also constrained by the research methods themselves (Schwartz and Carpenter, 1999). Many of the methods developed for public health research (largely derived from epidemiology) are designed to respond to a very particular question: why do certain individuals become ill and not others? However, these methods do not fare as well when trying to respond to related questions, such as why certain populations are sicker than others (Rose, 2001; Schwartz and Carpenter, 1999). Consequently, researchers often use methods developed to answer the first question and attempt to extrapolate the second. As a result, we have a relatively clear idea of the reasons why particular individuals become infected with HIV (e.g. risky sex, injection drug use) but a less clear understanding of why certain populations, such as those in southern and eastern Africa, are experiencing high rates of HIV infection. Our ability to measure which individuals have more sexual partners, engage in unprotected sex and/or are involved in sex work does not necessarily help us understand the context in which these behaviours occur nor the public health significance of these behaviours at a population level.

This chapter is broadly divided into two sections. In the first, I begin by illustrating some of the limitations of commonly used public health research methods in regards to the HIV and AIDS epidemic. In doing so, I will describe the predominant paradigm in epidemiology[1] – the most influential field of study in determining public health research design and methodology. I will describe how this paradigm is ill-equipped to understand the largely social nature of the epidemic as the focus is almost exclusively on the individual. In the second section, I will describe why methods stemming from this paradigm may not be entirely adequate for studying gender and HIV as gender can be understood as a structural characteristic, or as a characteristic influenced by broad historical and social processes and relatively uniformly accepted within a given population. In this section, I provide an example from my own research to demonstrate the importance of looking across populations as the role of gender may be more easily gauged across populations than from within. Finally, I conclude by presenting some potential future directions for measuring and intervening on gender. In all, I hope to demonstrate that whereas it is broadly accepted that gender plays a determining role in many HIV epidemics across the world, it is not yet clear how this is best measured. Gender is not well-captured by predominant epidemiological methods, which have difficulties linking gender, as a structural characteristic, to individual outcomes.

The epidemiological paradigm of HIV

While epidemiology and public health are separate fields of inquiry, they are nevertheless tightly intertwined, particularly as far as the research is concerned. Epidemiology, loosely defined as the study of disease occurrence and other health-related conditions, works in conjunction with public health to improve population health. However, the present paradigm in epidemiology may have implicitly set aside the achievement of public health ends (Last, 2000; Susser and Susser, 1996a) as the focus is nearly exclusively on a cornucopia of factors, particularly behaviours, that relate to the health of individuals, specifically high-risk individuals, and not to that of entire populations. As the sections to follow will show, this focus on the individual, referred to as 'methodological individualism', does very little to help us understand and respond to what is happening at the level of a population. In the case of HIV, where entire populations are at stake, this methodological individualism greatly limits our ability to understand risk at a population level.

Current epidemiological practice has been described by some researchers as typified by a 'black box' paradigm (Susser and Susser, 1996a; 1996b). According to this paradigm, exposure to possible risk factors is related to health outcomes (morbidity or mortality) and does not incorporate the obligation to interpolate either intervening factors or even pathogenesis. Current research methods attempt to establish the probability that certain factors, such as multiple sexual partners, and a disease outcome, such as HIV infection, are linked. The basic idea is to test whether these factors lead to enhanced or reduced risk of disease – explaining why the black box paradigm of epidemiology has also been termed the risk factor paradigm (Schwartz and Diez-Roux, 2001). However, in determining the statistical probability that a risk factor is related to a particular disease outcome, the contextual determinants of this risk, as well as the causal mechanisms by which the risk translates to disease, are largely ignored.

The black box paradigm of epidemiology, with its emphasis on risk factors and its implied focus on individuals, has left us ill-equipped to deal with the HIV epidemic. Current epidemiologic methods have helped us to answer questions regarding the causative organism behind AIDS as well as the critical risk factors, and yet, most preventive efforts, particularly in sub-Saharan Africa, have met with little or no success. Knowledge of risk factors (unprotected sex, multiple or concurrent sexual partners, injection drug use, etc.) and resulting interventions that focus solely on modifying the behaviours of individuals have been shown to be insufficient (Aggleton, 2004; Dowsett, 2003; Parker, 2001, 2002; Susser and Susser, 1996*a*, 1996*b*). Researchers describing the HIV epidemic over ten years ago stated, 'No vaccine now in prospect seems likely to achieve the efficacy level that could also achieve epidemic control. Absent of such efficacy, the failure to control the disease resides in our lack of understanding of transmission and illness in the social context. We know which social behaviours need to change, but we know little about how to change them, even when entire societies are at stake' (Susser and Susser, 1996*a*, p. 671). Sadly, it seems that this statement is as applicable as ever.

Limitations of the black box

Within any field of inquiry, there are inherent limitations to the measurement tools available to the researcher; epidemiology is no exception. Some of the most commonly employed methods for elucidating possible disease risk factors include observational studies, such as case-control and cohort study designs. These observational studies have led to important discoveries of public health significance, such as the associations between smoking and lung cancer and between folate deficiency and neural tube defects (Susser and Susser, 1996a). However, these study designs predominantly focus attention on individuals and within-population comparisons, an important limitation, particularly in diseases of largely social origin (Rose, 2001).

In deciding which measurement tools to employ – such as which study design to favour – one must first determine the study question. For example, the question 'Why do some individuals have HIV?' is entirely different from 'Why do certain populations have a high prevalence of HIV while in others, it is rare?' Whereas in one case, certain individuals may have HIV because they engage in high-risk behaviours, certain populations may in other cases have high prevalence of HIV because of poverty, failing health systems, large migrating populations or unstable governments. Using traditional epidemiological methods, we may come to understand why variations of disease occur within a population but entirely miss the more important public health question of why disease is prevalent in that population and not in another (Rose, 2001). To demonstrate, take the example of a case-control study design. Employing such a study design, an attempt is made to determine which risk factors, or exposures, differ between those who have an illness (cases) and those who do not (controls). In so doing, the researcher will attempt, to the best of his or her ability, to ensure that cases and controls are as similar as possible in terms of their base population experience and thus weed out those exposures that differ between groups (ill and not ill). That is to say, the goal is to ensure that the two groups are similarly represented in terms of important population characteristics, particularly time and place, in order to avoid bias. By doing so, the researcher ensures that whatever factor is found to be related to the disease outcome of interest is not due to the fact that his or her cases and controls were not comparable at an individual level. However, in order for a case-control study to work properly, the assumption is that there is variability in the study individuals in terms of the sought-after exposure. In other words, some cases are exposed to some hypothesized risk factor and the controls are not.

This variability in exposure may not always be the case. In certain populations, everyone may be exposed, but certain individuals may be more susceptible than others. In a population where this is the case, the prevalence of disease may be much higher but unexplainable by solely looking at individuals from within. By looking at individuals within this population, we can only determine those individuals most predisposed to this ubiquitous force relative to one another and will be incapable of accounting for the high absolute number of individuals falling ill. For example, we could attempt to determine what characteristics differentiated HIV-positive women from HIV-negative women in a single population of a particular country (for instance, we could do this same study twice, once in a high prevalence African country and once in a low-prevalence African country). In both studies, we are likely to arrive at the same conclusion: high-risk or multiple sexual partners, sex work, migration, and so forth, differentiated these women. However, determining these risk factors tells us very little about why one population has a high prevalence of HIV, whereas the other does not. This is because we were comparing individuals relative to one another and not trying to elucidate what factor may be affecting the entire population in a manner that causes one to experience high levels of HIV, whereas the other does not. Put in another way, what is the reason for, or cause of, a large number of women engaging in risky behaviours in one population versus another (e.g. high rates of poverty, limited educational opportunities, sexual violence, etc)? It is this cause that interests us as it is the cause driving population risk and high overall levels of infection.

Is gender a risk factor?

HIV has affected more women worldwide than any other life-threatening infectious disease. Women account for nearly half of all people in the world living with HIV and account for 60 per cent of those living with the virus in sub-Saharan Africa. The disproportionate number of women infected with the disease has been referred to as the feminization of the epidemic and reflects women's greater social and biological vulnerability to infection (Quinn and Overbaugh, 2005; Turmen, 2003). While biological factors that increase women's chances of infection are important contributors to their disproportionate rates of infection, it is social factors that drive the epidemic in women. Social factors, such as poverty, economic exploitation, gender power, sexual oppression and racism, have interactive and synergistic effects in determining the social vulnerability of groups and individuals to HIV. Women's social vulnerability stems from gender norms shaping attitudes towards information on sex, sexuality, sexual risk-taking and fidelity (Quinn and Overbaugh, 2005). It is also shaped by women's unequal access to economic resources, education and health care. Many of these factors are far beyond a woman's control and unlikely to be amenable, on a large scale, to programmes directed at the individual.

In much HIV research, gender is often used as a demographic category or to describe a set of general behaviours associated with men or, more frequently, women. Often, the term gender is used simply as a synonym for 'women' (Dowsett, 2003), with little consideration of the larger social context that creates gendered social relations, power differentials and eventually HIV risk. In general, this division of male versus female is entered into statistical models in order to see whether there is increased risk of HIV infection associated with sex, and specifically with being female. This same division is likewise used to determine which sex engages more often in known or proposed risk behaviours. From these findings, researchers then extrapolate as to how gender (the 'socialized' component of sex) can explain these observed differences between the sexes. Unfortunately, this form of extrapolation implicitly assumes that gender is a behavioural characteristic played out and controlled at the level of the individual, and the inherent assumption is that these 'gendered' behaviours can be altered. It also tends to assume that these social gender effects are stable across class, geographical location and time. As the example in the next section will show, gender may not necessarily be stable, even within the same country, and before researchers make that assumption, it must first be validated. Overall, gender is distinct from a mere differentiation of the sexes and can be seen 'as something that underpins the very organization and systems of daily life' (Dowsett, 2003, p. 21). Instead of an individual attribute determined by biology and played out in behaviour, gender should be seen as something more powerful, something more akin to a social structure or organizational principle (Dowsett, 2003; Parker et al., 2000) and thus very difficult to alter at the level of the individual. Interventions based solely on the assumption that gender is a malleable behavioural characteristic will be innately flawed as they will fail to recognize that gender is constrained by social norms and expectations.

Are all women the same?

While gender, more than any other factor, dominates the HIV and AIDS epidemic (Dowsett, 2003), its influence is unlikely to be found at the level of the individual. Women are indeed becoming infected much faster than men; while biology may be in part responsible for this, women's greater vulnerability is likely to be found at a structural level. Factors such as women's almost universally unequal access to social and economic resources and the consequences (powerlessness and sexual violence, poverty and sex work, etc.) may be more critical determinants of HIV than any individual attributes found to differentiate men from women, particularly within a single population. That is, men and women within a population tend to be more alike than those across populations (Dowsett, 2003). In other words, women from different populations will be much more dissimilar than men and women from the same population.

For example, a study I have been participating in for the past two years in Mali has examined the determinants of adherence in a cohort of patients starting antiretroviral therapy (ART) for the first time. Treatment programs across Africa have demonstrated that patients are initiating treatment very late, often with median CD4 cell counts between 80 and 100 cells/μl, despite international recommendations of 200–350 cells/μl. This late treatment initiation, with advanced to very advanced HIV disease, is associated with a several-fold increased risk of dying within the first several months of treatment (Hill and Wood, 2007). Therefore, I explored socio-demographic factors that may or may not be associated with patients initiating treatment when they were very ill. My analysis showed important differences between patients from the capital of Bamako and those, mostly rural, patients living outside the capital. This finding was not surprising as it is generally understood that urban capital populations are composed of individuals quite different from those living outside the capital. However, surprisingly, for those living outside the capital, the differences between men and women were much less important than the differences between capital and non-capital residents (Table 1).

In fact, my analysis showed that women were not as sick with HIV when they came for treatment as men, who sought treatment when their HIV was more advanced. Fewer women from the capital were arriving with advanced HIV disease than men,[2] but once I looked outside the capital, this advantage for women was lost. In fact, more important than any difference between men and women from either group was the difference between women from the capital and women from outside the capital. What this example demonstrates is the importance of looking across population groups; it also supports the idea that men and women within a single population may be more alike than members of the same sex across populations. This is not unexpected because if gender is truly more of a social structure than an individual attribute, its effects would be exerted on both men and women within a single population and be very difficult to disentangle at an individual level but more discernable across populations. Returning to the example above, it is possible that the factors determining why people arrive for ART with advanced HIV disease may be similar for men and women outside the capital (or that other factors overtake sex differences in terms of importance) but different for those within the capital.[3] Exploring these factors would be informative as to both populations.

Overall, attempting solely to understand what distinguishes male and female HIV risk within a population will tell us very little as to how gender, as a structural characteristic, influences the epidemic. Instead, it may be more informative to look across populations to see how gender is constructed differently between high- and low-HIV-prevalence populations and then aim our

Table 1. Advanced HIV disease in those residing in Bamako versus outside of Bamako, stratified by sex

	LOCATION OF RESIDENCE	N	ADVANCED HIV DISEASE (N=115)	OR, CI 95%	P-VALUE
WOMEN	Bamako	142	50 (35.%)	2.278 (1.165–4.453)	0.012
	Outside Bamako	47	26 (55.3%)		
MEN	Bamako	54	27 (50.0%)	1.33 (0.483–3.681)	0.616
	Outside Bamako	21	12 (57.1%)		

414

prevention interventions at these structures. At the very least, looking across populations may help us to prioritize which 'risks' are most important to public health policy. Using the Malian example above, it is clear that there is a differential association between sex and late treatment initiation in patients from the capital of Mali. Whether or not this difference is due to gender warrants further investigation. At present, we hypothesize that this difference may be attributable to child-bearing, with women being tested earlier and having a more intense clinical follow-up than men as a result of antenatal care. However, for women from outside of the capital, their advantage over men is lost. Both men and women from outside the capital start treatment at a dangerously late stage of HIV disease. The important question is thus: why do approximately the same proportion of men start treatment late, irrespective of their location of residence, whereas for women, there is a dramatic increase in the proportion starting treatment late (from 35.2 per cent to 55.3 per cent)? Are women from outside the capital less educated, less empowered, less financially well-off than their counterparts in the capital? Is this not the case for men? Even with this simple example, it is evident that there is something structuring risk differently for men and women starting ART treatment in Mali and that if I had simply lumped all men and women together, I would have mistakenly assumed that women had an advantage over men when it comes to treatment initiation, whereas in fact, only women from the capital have this advantage. By better understanding these 'structures of risk', we can develop interventions that attempt to modify the risk environment and not simply individual behaviours. In the Malian example, this structure of risk may very well be the different social structures defining the expression of gender in urban versus rural populations.

Intervening on gender

The increasing feminization of the epidemic calls for a greater focus on gender at the forefront of the response to HIV and AIDS. In doing so, efforts should support long-term and gender-specific approaches in order to alter the gendered contexts in which risk occurs. If gender is viewed as central to HIV risk, then a new wave of more nuanced public health interventions can emerge (Dworkin and Ehrhardt, 2007). However, these interventions ought to be grounded in the limitations inherent to measuring gender. If one accepts that gender is more than a demographic category and rather a social structure shaped by time and place, then one's measures and resulting interventions need to reflect that conceptualization. At present, most policies and interventions are based on research that does not actually look at gender because, instead, this research is measuring sex.

With few exceptions,[4] most researchers recognize the influence of social structures on HIV transmission. However, these influences are not reflected in the measures chosen to represent them, most particularly because of the use of sex as synonym for gender. By measuring gender as an individual attribute, in the form of sex, one may commit the atomistic fallacy. That is, one wrongly assumes that the forces applying to individuals are the same as those applying to entire populations. A partial and simple resolution to this problem is to stratify analyses by sex. Underlying this approach is the philosophy that women are not the counterfactual of men, and thus, one downside of this method is that the results for women should not be compared directly with the results for men. However, by employing stratification by sex, one can continue to use individual-level attributes to gain insight into the structuring role of gender on HIV risk. This is because the researcher is performing separate analyses on each sex, implicitly controlling for sex, but looking for other risk factors in-and-above sex that affect HIV risk. For example, I could hypothetically find that in men, migration is an important risk factor for HIV transmission, whereas in women, food insecurity is an important risk factor. This type of finding helps to develop hypotheses about how gender structures risk differently for men and women, as in this case, one could propose that different gendered household responsibilities – being the breadwinner (men) versus the nurturer (women) – influence HIV risk. Nonetheless, while useful, this approach does not totally eliminate the problem that it is difficult to measure the role of gender at an individual level, and other conceptualizations also need to reflect the structural nature of gender on the HIV epidemic.

It is important to make distinctions between intermediate and macro-level risk factors. For example, measuring a macro-level factor, such as differing economic opportunities between men and women, may reflect gender inequities; however, the downside is that it may be difficult to relate in a causal manner to HIV. Nevertheless, improving women's economic opportunities may shift power relationships and offer opportunities outside the sex industry, thus greatly reducing HIV risk (Blankenship et al., 2006). At a population level, such changes could have dramatic impacts on HIV transmission. On the other hand, measuring a more intermediate factor, such as the levels of sexual violence in a population, may provide a more identifiable link between gender and HIV transmission as the route of exposure is more evident. However, measuring and intervening on sexual violence may not resolve the more systemic problem that led to the high levels of sexual violence in the first place and may thus be less effective at changing the risk environment and HIV transmission.

Recent interventions have begun to emerge that attempt to alter the underlying factors that place women at greater risk than men. These interventions are often referred to as structural interventions as they presume a certain degree of social causation behind public health problems and view individual agency as constrained or shaped by larger social, economic and political structures (Blankenship et al., 2006). For example, in South Africa, researchers have combined provision of microfinance with gender equity training in order to alter the risk environment in which women find themselves (Pronyk et al., 2006).[5] Interventions such as these are unique in that they recognize multiple layers of factors guiding gendered risk. First, the microfinance element of the intervention takes into consideration the impact of economic insecurity on the community and, in a disproportionate manner, on women. Second, the gender equity component works to empower women and provide them with the individual tools necessary to alter their own risk environment. As a result, this type of intervention aims at altering both proximal and distal risk factors. In moving beyond methodological individualism, this type of intervention takes into account the fact that risk attributable to gender is not simply owing to a person being born female but also a result of larger contextual factors, such as economic insecurity. Likewise, the indicators employed in this study incorporated these differences. Indicators varied from economic security to individual behaviours instead of focusing exclusively on the latter. Unfortunately, the aforementioned study was incapable of detecting any links between the intervention and actual HIV transmission, reflecting the enormous difficulty associated with linking structural factors and specific health outcomes in a causal manner and also pointing to the fact that there are only a small number of studies presenting conceptually rich causal models linking structural determinants and infection. A longer follow-up period in the study may have allowed for the detection of differences in HIV transmission between the intervention groups, which is an unfortunate consequence of a research paradigm in which most studies are only financed for a short period of time and are expected to produce significant results in such a time period. Nevertheless, it is a promising first step as certain intermediate factors shown to be associated with HIV transmission, such as sexual violence, were reduced. While this example demonstrates the difficulty of researching gender in a public health context, it does provide evidence that gender as a structural characteristic, and not only sex and sex-related behaviours, can be addressed by our epidemiological methods and that conceptual and methodological advances are possible.

Conclusion

In looking at the global distribution of HIV and AIDS, particularly those disproportionately affected by the epidemic, it has been stated (Parker, 2002, p. 343):

> It is impossible not to be impressed by the extent to which a range of structural inequalities intersect and combine to shape the character of the HIV/AIDS epidemic ... It is in the spaces of poverty, racism, gender inequality and sexual oppression that the HIV epidemic continues today.

The key word in this statement is structural, as opposed to individual. At this stage in the epidemic, we are keenly aware of the risk factors facing most individuals, namely, number of sexual partners, sexual mixing, safer sex strategies, and so forth. Measuring these factors at the level of the individual helps us to determine who will get infected but does little to explain the contextual factors behind why certain populations have much higher rates of infection than others. Only by looking past the individual to the structural characteristics of populations can we begin to answer the question of why certain populations are disproportionately affected. Engaging the question of gender in such a manner is an obvious first step as the increasing feminization of the epidemic presents a clear public health priority.

Notes

1. For a more in-depth discussion of this topic, see Susser and Susser (1996*a*, pp. 668–73) and Susser and Susser (1996*b*, pp. 674–77).

2. Women may be starting treatment earlier than men because of voluntary testing and counselling during antenatal care. The average age of women starting treatment in our cohort was 33 (41 in men), during their child-bearing years.

3. The advantage of women in the capital may reflect a greater access to HIV testing during antenatal care because, in Mali, a high percentage of women from the capital receive antenatal care (94.2 per cent), but this percentage drops dramatically in women living outside Bamako (32.0–74.8 per cent, depending on the region). If the entry point for ART for many women is antenatal care, then this would help to explain why fewer women in Bamako arrive with advanced HIV disease than those from outside of Bamako as these women have more limited access to antenatal care. This would, of course, greatly explain the advantage of women over men in the capital.

4. For an example of such an exception see Chin (2007).

5. Microfinance is not without controversy; in some cases, microfinance may have exacerbated gender inequities and contributed to sexual violence (Goetz and Gupta, 1996).

References

Aggleton, P. 2004. Sexuality, HIV prevention, vulnerability and risk. *Journal of Psychology and Human Sexuality,* Vol. 16, No. 1, pp. 1–11.

Blankenship, K. M., Friedman, S. R., Dworkin, S. and Mantell, J. E. 2006. Structural interventions: Concepts, challenges and opportunities for research. *Journal of Urban Health,* Vol. 83, No. 1, pp. 59–72.

Chin, J. 2007. *The AIDS Pandemic: The Collision of Epidemiology with Political Correctness.* Oxford, United Kingdom, Radcliffe Publishing.

Dowsett, G. W. 2003. Some considerations on sexuality and gender in the context of AIDS. *Reproductive Health Matters,* Vol. 11, No. 22, pp. 21–29.

Dworkin, S. L. and Ehrhardt, A. A. 2007. Going beyond 'ABC' to include 'GEM': Critical reflections on progress in the HIV/AIDS epidemic. *American Journal of Public Health,* Vol. 97, No. 1, pp. 13–18.

Goetz, A. M. and Gupta, R. S. 1996. Who takes the credit? Gender, power, and control over loan use in rural credit programmes in Bangladesh. *World Development,* Vol. 24, No. 1, pp. 45–63.

Hill, A. and Wood, E. 2007. Balancing effectiveness and access to HIV treatment in the developing world. *AIDS,* Vol. 21, No. 3, pp. 361–63.

Last, J. M. 2000. *A Dictionary of Epidemiology,* 4th edn. New York, Oxford University Press.

Parker, R. 2001. Sexuality, culture, and power in HIV/AIDS research. *Annual Review of Anthropology,* Vol. 30, pp. 163–79.

——. 2002. The global HIV/AIDS pandemic, structural inequalities, and the politics of international health. *American Journal of Public Health,* Vol. 92, No. 3, pp. 343–46.

Parker, R. G., Easton, D. and Klein, C. H. 2000. Structural barriers and facilitators in HIV prevention: A review of international research. *AIDS,* Vol. 14, pp. S22–S32.

Pronyk, P. M., Hargreaves, J. R., Kim, J. C., Morison, L. A., Phetla, G., Watts, C., Busza, J. and Porter, J. D. 2006. Effect of a structural intervention for the prevention of intimate-partner violence and HIV in rural South Africa: A cluster randomised trial. *Lancet,* Vol. 368, No. 9551, pp. 1973–983.

Quinn, T. C. and Overbaugh, J. 2005. HIV/AIDS in women: An expanding epidemic. *Science,* Vol. 308, No. 5728, pp. 1582–583.

Rose, G. 2001. Sick individuals and sick populations. *International Journal of Epidemiology,* Vol. 30, pp. 427–32.

Schwartz, S. and Carpenter, K. M. 1999. The right answer for the wrong question: Consequences of type III error for public health research. *American Journal of Public Health,* Vol. 89, No. 8, pp. 1175–180.

Schwartz, S. and Diez-Roux, A. V. 2001. Commentary: Causes of incidence and causes of cases—a Durkheimian perspective on Rose. *International Journal of Epidemiology,* Vol. 30, No. 3, pp. 435–39.

Susser, M. and Susser, E. 1996*a.* Choosing a future for epidemiology: I. Eras and paradigms. *American Journal of Public Health,* Vol. 86, No. 5, pp. 668–73.

——. 1996*b.* Choosing a future for epidemiology: II. From black box to Chinese boxes and eco-epidemiology. *American Journal of Public Health,* Vol. 86, No. 5, pp. 674–77.

Turmen, T. 2003. Gender and HIV/AIDS. *International Journal of Gynaecological Obstetrics,* Vol. 82, No. 3, pp. 411–18.

CHAPTER 18

Measuring the gendered consequences of AIDS: Household dynamics and poverty in South Africa

Jeremy Seekings

The direct effects of AIDS are particularly daunting in South Africa. It is estimated that one in five South Africans between the ages of 25 and 49 is HIV-positive and that between 2 and 3 million people have died of an AIDS-related illness. Life expectancy has declined, reversing the developmental gains of previous decades (Dorrington et al., 2006). AIDS also affects many people indirectly. When breadwinners or caregivers fall sick, not only do they themselves become dependent on someone else (economically and for their own health care), but their dependants do as well. The indirect effects may become even worse if a breadwinner or caregiver dies. Very often, changes in dependency entail physical movement as dependants and caregivers alike move between 'households', perhaps over long distances. The consequences of AIDS thus reverberate through processes of household dissolution or fragmentation, on the one hand, and formation or augmentation, on the other.

Yet, little is known about the indirect consequences of AIDS on other members of households, families, kinship groups or communities. In this chapter I examine some of the conceptual and methodological difficulties in examining the indirect consequences of AIDS. I focus in particular on the challenges of analysing 'household' dynamics – including how extended families or networks of kin respond to the illness or death of members by moving dependants and caregivers from household to household and the very real limits to the capacities of extended families or kin to mitigate AIDS-related impoverishment in these ways. Too little information is collected about households, and

The designations employed and the presentation of material throughout this publication do not imply the expression of any opinion whatsoever on the part of UNESCO concerning the legal status of any country, territory or area or of its authorities, or concerning the delimitation of its frontiers or boundaries.
The ideas and opinions expressed in this publication are those of the authors and do not necessarily reflect the views of UNESCO and its Member States.

the questions that are asked often reflect the very inaccurate assumption that households are neat, discrete and stable units.

The conclusions of this chapter are methodological, concerning the need to collect information in new ways if we are to understand the indirect (and gendered) effects of AIDS. Before arriving at these conclusions, however, the chapter first summarizes why this is important. In South Africa, women face AIDS with increased access to employment and public grants but diminished access to 'social' resources (for them or children in their care) through kin (especially husbands and kin through marriage, or paternal kin for children). The nature of kinship has changed dramatically, and this has profound implications for the indirect effects of AIDS. Research needs to pay far more attention to ways that households and kinship are constructed, and especially the claims that individuals can make on (and their responsibilities to) other people.

AIDS, individuals and households

People living with HIV or those suffering from an AIDS-related illness are generally considered – in policies and programmes – as individual patients. Even children orphaned by AIDS are typically viewed as individuals, disconnected from broader social relationships. One consequence of this is that, in South Africa, there does not seem to be any good data on the distribution within or between households of HIV infection, AIDS sickness or AIDS mortality. Nor is it known if people living with HIV or those suffering from an AIDS-related illness – and consequently mortality and orphanhood – are concentrated in a smaller number of households or spread thinly across a larger number of households. In neglecting the household, studies cannot examine easily changes in households over time.

Available data from general household surveys find very low self-reported levels of AIDS-related illnesses or death, whether among respondents or co-resident household members. Dedicated HIV-focused surveys – such as, in South Africa, surveys conducted by the Human Sciences Research Council (HSRC) in 2002 and 2005 – have more potential to show intra- and inter-household patterns and consequences of AIDS-affectedness. The 2005 HSRC survey interviewed and tested up to three members of sampled households, with a total of 23,275 individuals interviewed in 10,584 households (although one in three interviewed individuals refused to be tested). But the published report (Shisana et al., 2005) does not discuss HIV data by household, that is, it provides no indication of the extent to which HIV infection is clustered within households (and the HSRC does not make the data available for external analysis). Nor does the pioneering demographic model designed for the Actuarial Society of South Africa (ASSA) appear to have any household-level component and hence any estimate of the proportion of households including people living with HIV.

If HIV and AIDS were randomly distributed across the population, in a province such as the Eastern Cape, between one-third and one-half of all households would include an HIV-positive member, and perhaps one in 25 would include a family member who is currently suffering from an AIDS-related illness. Perhaps half of the adult population would have lost a relatively close family member – a child, sibling, nephew/niece or cousin – to AIDS. However, as HIV is unlikely to be distributed randomly, the actual proportions will be smaller than these. In other words, a smaller number of people will have been affected disproportionately.

The only readily available data on the indirect consequences of AIDS are data on parental mortality. The ASSA model estimated that in South Africa in 2006 there were 1.5 million maternal orphans, two-thirds of whom were orphaned as a result of AIDS (reasons for emphasizing maternal orphanhood are discussed further below). The ASSA model predicts that the number of maternal orphans under the age of 18 would rise to about 2.5 million in 2015 (Dorrington et al., 2006). Ardington's (2007) meticulous study of South African survey data indicates a clear rise in rates of orphanhood. Over the twelve-year period from 1993 to 2005, the proportion of children whose mother had died tripled, the proportion whose father had died doubled, and the proportion who were double orphans (i.e. with deceased mothers and fathers) had risen faster still (although from a much lower base). In 2005, by the age of 17, more than a quarter of children had a deceased father, more than one in ten had a deceased mother, and 6 per cent were double orphans. Conversely, in a province like the Eastern Cape, 5 per cent of households include a maternal orphan aged under 14, and 10 per cent of households include a maternal orphan aged under 18.[1]

Orphanhood is one of the causes of inter-household 'migration' and household recomposition. But in fact, orphanhood need not result in migration. Maternal orphans are not the only children who do not live with their mothers: for every maternal orphan in South Africa there are three other similar-aged non-orphans living apart from their mothers.[2] If the (already absent) mother of such a child dies, then orphanhood might not result in any change in either the child's living arrangements or financial provision for the child. Nonetheless, a rise in orphanhood will generally result in many children moving between households, from living with mothers to living with other members of the kinship group. Other reasons why AIDS is resulting in increased numbers of children moving between households include the impaired ability of sick caregivers to care for children, financial difficulties when breadwinners fall sick and the need for children themselves to care for ailing kin. These reasons might explain why many non-orphaned children live apart from their mothers. Adults also might move between households, for all of these reasons.

The indirect social, psychological and economic effects of AIDS on children and adults who are not themselves sick depend on the opportunities for – and decisions about – household recomposition, that is, decisions about who lives where and with whom. The indirect effects of AIDS will be mitigated if dependants can be accommodated by kin with the financial capacity and emotional willingness to care for them, or if kin can move into the household of a sick person to provide financial support and care for the person and that person's dependants, or even if kin can support financially people suffering from an AIDS-related illness and their dependants. In short, the indirect effects of AIDS depend in significant part on the capacity and willingness of the 'extended family' or kin group.

This crucial dimension to the consequences of AIDS remains largely unresearched. In the early 2000s, the AIDS pandemic prompted a flurry of apocalyptic assertions about the critical situation facing orphans and orphanhood in general. High mortality rates would produce large numbers of children orphaned by AIDS, who would grow up in deprived social environments (perhaps even on the street), become mal-socialized and end up as juvenile delinquents, precipitating a breakdown in the social fabric. Such assertions may have increased attention to the pandemic and its victims, but they were somewhat exaggerated and based on little or no evidence. African societies have long cared for large numbers of orphans, as well as the very much larger number of children living apart from their biological parents, through the extended family. As Bray (2003) has argued, the moral panic around children orphaned by AIDS underestimated the capacity of the extended family to raise children, including orphans, and misrepresented the real challenges facing orphans and other children.

In countering apocalyptic assertions, however, there is a danger that the capacity of the extended family to accommodate the indirect (as well as direct) victims of the pandemic underestimates the strains and changes occurring in kinship practices and householding. The claims that can be made on kin are shaped by norms inherited from the past, but these norms have been recast in the face of dramatic social and economic changes over the past century.

These changes are fundamentally gendered. At the beginning of the twenty-first century, many South African women have access to the economic resources to make their own independent decisions about householding and caring for others. At the same time, most women have fewer social resources than in the past, in terms of the claims that they can make on others.

Such subtle changes in the social and cultural landscape tend to be overlooked in debates about AIDS. The 2009 report of the Joint Learning Initiative on Children and HIV/AIDS (JLICA) emphasizes the 'home truths' that 'millions of children' – including especially orphans – and 'their families' have been neglected in the global response to AIDS. The report rightly points to the care given to AIDS-affected children in many parts of the world by kin and recommends that such familial ties be strengthened rather than replaced by state institutions. The report sensibly notes that many 'orphans' – if these are defined as children who have lost one parent – have a surviving parent, that even double or maternal orphans are generally cared for by kin and that even these orphans are often little or no worse off than non-orphans. But the report presents a largely uncritical, even romanticized view of the 'family' and pays little attention to the specific changes occurring in familial and kin relationships and the implications of these for the effects of AIDS.

Kinship: Ideal and reality

Forty years ago, Fortes (1969, p. 242) described the ideal of kinship (the 'axiom of amity') in stark terms in his classic *Kinship and the Social Order*: 'Kinship is binding; it creates inescapable moral claims and obligations'.

> What the rule posits is that 'kinsfolk' have irresistible claims on one another's support and consideration in contradistinction to 'non-kinsmen', simply by reason of the fact that they are kin. Kinsfolk must ideally share – hence the frequent invocation of brotherhood as the model of generalized kinship; and they must, ideally, do so without putting a price on what they give. Reciprocal giving between kinsfolk is supposed to be done freely and not in submission to coercive sanctions or in response to contractual obligations.

Fortes contrasted the responsibilities between kin with the very conditional relationships between non-kin, which entail 'a sort of book-keeping' and 'an element of deliberate calculation' of reciprocity (Fortes, 1969, p. 246; Radcliffe-

Brown and Forde, 1950). It is this unconditional provision of hospitality or assistance that constitutes one meaning of the 'extended family':

> The extended family has proved a marvelous security for those for whom, otherwise, there was no security at all. The extended family is a net wide enough to gather the child who falls from the feeble control of neglectful parents, it receives the widow, tolerates the batty, gives status to grannies. (Barker quoted in Murray, 1981, p. 101)

Monica Wilson wrote that 'South Africa has lived on the capital of a very strong African family system' (quoted in Murray, 1981, p. 171).

In South (and much of southern) Africa, the reality however often failed to match this ideal as the twentieth century progressed. In Monica Wilson's words, in 1975, the capital of a strong family system 'has been squandered' (quoted in Murray, 1981, p. 171). Wilson herself was very aware of how the practice of kinship was being transformed, having studied changing rural societies in the Eastern Cape since the early 1930s. In 1948–1949, she was one of the leading members of a team of researchers who studied the district of Keiskammahoek. Historically, she reported, a married woman would live with her husband in his parents' homestead for some time, only later forming a separate homestead, usually close by. By 1948–1949, however, married men were forming their own households as soon as possible, 'influenced by the sense of economic individualism acquired by the younger generation in the course of their labour migration experiences' (Wilson et al., 1952, p. 46). Wives, also, were more impatient to escape the control of their mothers-in-law. But readily available land on which to establish new homesteads became scarce. Unable to farm, more and more married men worked as migrant labourers. Indeed, there were so few able-bodied adults in the district for most of the year that remaining kin tended to form larger households in order to share domestic and agricultural work. At the same time, agnatic kin (that is, kin related through the father's side) accounted for less than half of the recorded instances of people helping each other with agricultural labour; affinal kin (that is, kin related by marriage) and non-kin together were more important. Among other reasons, the physical separation of husbands and wives led to marriages becoming unstable and to a significant proportion of women with children living with their own kin after being divorced or deserted by their husbands.

Marital and broader kin relationships were further strained by a shortage of available land[3] and stagnant rural production at a time of population growth, combined with expanding industrial and urban employment opportunities (primarily for men) and restrictions on migration by dependent women and children. A marker of apparently increasing conflict was the frequency of witchcraft accusations, most commonly between a man's mother and his wife (accusations occurring in both directions). Increasingly, women called on their own kin for help, not only when their husbands died (which was not uncommon among migrant mine workers) or deserted them, but also when husbands were away working. But a woman's own kin was not a reliable source of support. Unmarried or childless women were especially vulnerable to poverty, and elderly widows were left impoverished when their sons left to work and failed to remit any of their earnings. Even close kin could 'abscond'. Houghton and Walton (1952, p. 99), who conducted the economic component of the 1948–1949 Keiskammahoek study, describe a typical poor family, comprising an elderly widow, three co-resident children and two sons who had moved to the cities to work. The oldest son had stopped sending money home, and the second son did not send enough to support his kin. 'All last year is very hard through no food', the widow said; 'I can only say that if my Lord God had not opened the hearts of my neighbours we would have been in a very bad condition. They always gave us something to eat'.

The need to make claims on kin increased at the same time as the capacity of kin to meet these claims declined. The declining value of subsistence agriculture meant ever greater dependence on migrant remittances, but migrants' wages remained very low through the 1950s and into the 1960s. The situation deteriorated when many migrant workers were affected by rising unemployment in the 1970s and 1980s. By 1993, only one in four poor households in South Africa was engaged in any kind of subsistence agriculture. The unemployment rate stood at almost 30 per cent (and at more than 70 per cent in the poorest income decile) (Seekings and Nattrass, 2005). Elderly pensioners – disproportionately women[4] – who received a generous non-contributory, government old-age pension were now called on to support their unemployed children and dependent grandchildren (Møller and Sotshongaye, 1996; Sagner and Mtati, 1999). The poorest households in South Africa (i.e. in the poorest income quintile) were those in which no members were eligible for a pension: the mere fact of receiving a pension was enough to raise a household out of severe poverty. Very poor households therefore remained dependent on remittances, but overall, pensions were more valuable than private remittances to the poor (Seekings and Nattrass, 2005). Patterns of dependency and household composition changed over the course of the twentieth century as the material basis of householding shifted from land to migrant remittances and finally to old-age pensions. A situation in which men controlled land and dominated employment has given way to one in which women are almost equal players in the labour market and receive the lion's share of pensions and grants through the welfare state.

A variety of interrelated factors, including labour migration, apartheid-era 'influx control', deagrarianization, unemployment and old-age pensions, resulted in the creation of many multigenerational, extended family households in rural areas. In urban areas, extended-family households were also common, although many norms concerning kin had begun to change (Russell, 2003). The relaxation and then abolition of influx control allowed more rapid urbaniza-tion, especially among women and children, raising new choices about where to live, and with whom. A rapid expansion in urban housing achieved through government housing subsidies and massive rezoning of agricultural land for residential purposes resulted in household fragmentation and accelerated intra-urban mobility. Under apartheid, families were often 'divided' between town and countryside; now they are often dispersed across several urban resi-dences, as well as a rural 'home'.

The consequence of all of these factors in South Africa was what anthro-pologists termed 'domestic fluidity' (Ross, 1996; Spiegel, 1996; Spiegel et al.,1996). Household composition became fluid, in that adults and children moved frequently and readily from one household to another, whereas the boundaries of households became porous, in that diverse resources (includ-ing meals, shelter and care, as well as money) were shared across them. In the extreme case, as described by Ross (1996, p. 66) with respect to an informal settlement on the eastern perimeter of Cape Town:

> Children lodged with relatives and friends while their parents were mobile; adults moved between domestic units; people ate in different units to those in which they slept. … Residents created extensive but short-lived networks of support which stretched across and beyond the settlement, linking individuals into complex and extremely fluid so-cial interactions. So rapidly changing were these compounded knots of interacting individuals that they often appeared to have no boundaries save those imposed by situational immediacy.[5]

The result has been a great expansion of choice over who lives where and with whom, and hence of agency within the constraints of poverty and inherited norms of kinship. Neither households nor kinship are cast-iron structures within which individuals have clear responsibilities and claims.

Now, individuals can contest and negotiate the claims made on them, as well as the claims they make on others. The degree to which households and kinship retain their coherence and salience in the lives of individuals is proportional to the extent of their choice to invest in, or share, a common project. Household-formation and the practice of kinship thus entail 'social projects' among groups of individuals. Choice, however, does not mean the absence of constraint. Choices are likely to be made in a moral or normative framework that is grounded in past practices, and in the context of material constraints. This was the context into which AIDS arrived and which shapes the indirect effects of AIDS up to the present day.

Women's dependence and independence

South African women's experiences of HIV and AIDS will depend largely on their own agency, their material constraints and family relations. Compared to previous generations of women, South African women today have unprecedented direct access to the labour market, urban housing and financial assistance from the state. At the same time, the decline of both marriage and patrilinearity has led to the dismantling of kinship responsibilities among paternal kin and even diminished kinship obligations among maternal kin. In rural areas, this has meant reduced access to land for housing as well as farming. Improved access to the market ('commodification') and state ('decommodification') has coincided with diminished access to 'family' ('defamilialization') – to employ the conceptual framework of Esping-Andersen (1990, 1999).

One gendered dimension of the changing pattern of both child and adult dependants has been the decline of marriage, and especially of stable, enduring marriage, and the rising number of 'single parents' (almost all being 'single mothers') and children living apart from fathers. South Africa's marriage data are imprecise for a number of reasons (Budlender et al., 2004). Figure 1 presents data from the 2007 Community Survey, which distinguishes between different kinds of marriages (civil/religious, traditional/customary[6]), 'living together as married partners', and the unmarried (never married, widowed, separated and divorced). The figure presents data only for women classified as black (i.e. excluding 'coloured', 'Indian or Asian' and 'white' women with different cultural and class profiles and much lower HIV-prevalence). Among the older generation of women, marriage was the norm: four out of five older women are or have been married. Only about 60 per cent of women in their 40s are or have been married, and the figure is much lower still among people in their 30s. Currently married African women do not appear to be in a majority within any age category. These figures do not show conclusively that marriage rates are declining over time, but they do indicate that most women are living in non-marital arrangements of one kind or another.

The decline of marriage (and even steady cohabitation) means that few women have direct access to a husband's (or partner's) earnings or assets (such as land). Of African women aged 20–59, only one-third are currently co-resident with a husband (or living with a man as if married), with another 8 per cent married to an absent husband. Two-thirds of co-resident husbands are working, one-sixth are unemployed and one-sixth are not economically active (roughly divided between men who are too old and men who are disabled or sick). In total, therefore, at most 30 per cent of women in this age group have employed husbands, whether co-resident or absent.

Declining marital support is both the cause and the consequence of the steady increase in women's participation in the labour market. By 2006, 33 per cent of African women aged 20–59 were working, and another 41 per cent were unemployed (using the expanded definition of unemployment, i.e. including women who were not actively seeking work but wanted work and would take it if offered); only 26 per cent were not economically active. The unemployment rate was higher than among similarly aged men (56 per cent compared to 36 per cent), and the participation rate was lower (at 74 per cent compared to 85 per cent).[7] Women also predominate in a number of unskilled, less secure, low-earning sectors or occupations, including domestic work, so that the mean and median earnings of women are much lower than for men. Nonetheless, women account for 43 per cent of all formal employment and tend to predominate in the faster growing sectors and occupations, which means more jobs for women, even if they are not high-paying ones. In addition, the gender wage gap has been closing (Casale and Posel, 2002; Van der Westhuizen et al., 2007).

African women who are not working themselves are no more likely to be married to a working husband than women who are working. Women with unemployed husbands might have more reason to seek work, but their prospects of success are probably lower than women with employed husbands (because people tend to find employment through contacts who already have jobs). Indeed, non-working African women are much less likely to be supported by a husband (whether co-resident or absent) than they are by a co-resident non-spouse. This is true even among married women. It is co-residence, not marriage, that is important in patterns of support for poor women.

Figure 1. Marital status by age, African women, 2007

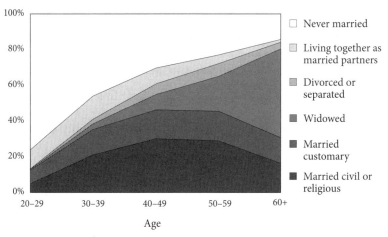

Source: Statistics South Africa (2007).

This point – that marriage has ceased to be the predominant vector of support for women – can perhaps be made more simply. Among African women aged 20–59, only one in six women is not working but living with a working husband. Just over one-third are not working but being supported by some member of the household other than a husband (for example, a mother with a pension, a working son or daughter, or a sibling). Only 10 per cent of African women in this age category are not working and being supported by someone outside of the household, and absent husbands comprise at most one-third of these external benefactors.

At the same time as labour force participation has been rising, there has been a dramatic increase in women's access to non-contributory pensions and grants. The age structure of the African population hardly changed in the 1950s and 1960s, but from 1970 the proportion of those at a pensionable age rose slowly, just as the real value of the old-age pension was being increased. By 2001, there were almost three times as many African women as African men of pensionable age (in part because women were then eligible for the pension at the age of 60, whereas men had to wait until 65, and also partly because women live longer). Women also account for a majority of all disability grants. Most child support grants, which are much more modest in value than the old-age pension or disability grant, are also paid to mothers. The consequence is that a clear majority of all African women aged 20–59 live in households that receive at least one grant, and more than one third live in households that receive two or more grants. Grants form the major source of support for the almost one-half of African women of working age who are neither employed themselves nor married to a working husband.[8]

More than one-third of all adult South African women (aged 18+) work, and slightly more receive one or other welfare grant. One-fifth to one-quarter of adult women remain entirely dependent on kin. In some cases it is because kin have jobs, in others because it is the kin who are eligible for state pensions or grants. But kinship ties no longer provide a secure safety net. It is not just that supportive husbands are uncommon, but more generally, the husband's kin are often hostile to claims made by wives (and especially ex-wives), even when there are children involved. Even a woman's own kin may be either unable or unwilling to support additional dependants.

In societies that are historically patrilineal (i.e. the paternal line of descent is privileged), virilocal (i.e. married women and their children generally live with the children's father's family, unless or until they form an independent household) and deeply patriarchal, the rising number of unmarried women poses all sorts of cultural, social and economic problems, especially for the women themselves. Claassens and Ngubane (2008) summarize some of the difficulties facing unmarried women in rural areas:

> Women are often evicted when their marriages break down or end. In particular, widows are often evicted from their married homes by their husbands' families. Divorced or widowed women who return to their natal home when their marriages end are often made unwelcome and are evicted by their brothers. Unmarried sisters are often evicted from their natal homes by their married brothers after their parents die. This occurs because sons assert that they alone inherit the land, even where the father may have chosen his daughter to be responsible for the family home. … Women, particularly single women, struggle to access residential land because traditional leaders generally refuse to allocate land to women.

Unsurprisingly, a rising number of rural women seem to prefer securing their own, independent access to land and, if necessary, avoiding marriage entirely in order to avoid the ensuing insecurity.

In case after case, men – and paternal kin more generally – decline responsibility for both male and female children, many of whom end up living with maternal kin. Although such children might be aware of their paternal descent and the paternal kin might observe some of the cultural rituals associated with patrilinearity, it seems likely that there will be – or perhaps already is – a collapse of patrilineal inheritance.

The radius of responsibility and the impact of AIDS: Two case studies

Joyce was 21 years old when she was diagnosed as HIV-positive in 2002.[9] She was living with her boyfriend and their 3-year-old son in a low-income neighbourhood in Cape Town. She apparently did not live with her boyfriend as much through choice as necessity because she had been renting a room but could not afford to do so after leaving a job as a domestic worker. When she told her boyfriend that she was HIV-positive, he urged her to keep her status secret. But Joyce told two of her siblings – a sister who lived nearby and a brother (and his wife) who lived elsewhere in Cape Town. When Joyce told her family that she was being hit by her boyfriend, her sister suggested that she move into her home, where the sister lived with her partner and two children. Joyce's mother, who lived in the Eastern Cape, heard a rumour about Joyce's status and reportedly became ill as a result, prompting Joyce to deny her status to her mother.

Joyce's case this far indicates many common aspects of kinship and residence. A set of siblings, originally from the Eastern Cape, are distributed across Cape Town (and even further afield) while the mother remains in the rural 'home'. The pattern of Joyce's disclosure is typical: she first informs one kinsman or kinswoman, and if that person does not react negatively, she will inform another. Women are often reluctant to disclose to their mothers, but this seems to be more a matter of concern for the effect on the mother (as in Joyce's case) or perhaps shame because very rarely do mothers react with hostility when a child discloses. In Joyce's case, the sister accommodates her, but not so much because she is HIV-positive as because she is the victim of physical abuse by her boyfriend. This is a clear case of domestic fluidity, as Joyce moved frequently between 'households' (as had her son, who had variously lived with Joyce in Cape Town and with Joyce's mother in the Eastern Cape).

A year later, Joyce's sister asked her to leave. It seems that the dispute had a material base in that resources were tight in the household. Joyce herself received a child support grant for her son. But Joyce's sister said that the cost of supporting Joyce and her son (as well as other visiting relatives) was 'too much for our household'. But the conflict went beyond this. Joyce's sister complained that Joyce did not help sufficiently in the household, and Joyce complained that her sister treated her like a domestic worker. Joyce's sister said that she felt she needed to 'teach Joyce how to be responsible'. Joyce's sister was an HIV peer educator so certainly knew about HIV.[10]

Joyce and her son lived hand-to-mouth for a while, sleeping as 'visitors' with an 'aunt' from the same village in the Eastern Cape but homeless during the day. Joyce soon found part-time employment and rented a room in her employer's backyard. In 2004, however, Joyce fell sick. Despite starting on HAART, she died while visiting her mother in the Eastern Cape at Christmas. Joyce's son was cared for by her mother, but her sister was to bring him back to Cape Town to live with her.

Joyce's story indicates the limits of even close kinship. Her sister's decision to evict her (and her son) reflected neither stigma nor, on its own, financial constraints. Rather, it reflected conflict over what Joyce should contribute – in terms of labour, not money – to the household and how her sister should treat her. This is frequently the case with HIV-positive people of working age who are in sufficiently good health to work. Joyce, for her part, was determined to remain as independent as possible. Evicted by her sister, she did not exercise a claim on her brother, who lived elsewhere in Cape Town, making instead a partial claim on her 'aunt' (by sleeping but not living in her home).

Noncebuzi was in her early 30s when her 'husband' – a carpenter – was shot and killed in a robbery.[11] They were living in Durban, with their two children, in a shack in the backyard of one of his aunts' houses. After the husband's death, the aunt evicted Noncebuzi (who was pregnant and sick) and her children, saying that 'because the person you were staying with died, we don't have room for you any more'. It turns out that Noncebuzi and her 'husband' had not been married, and he had not paid 'damages' for fathering her children. She rented a shack for a while, then moved in with cousins for a few weeks and then returned to her mother's home in a rural area. She was unable to stay in Durban because she could not afford to rent a backyard shack. It is unclear why she did not stay longer with her cousin – or other kin – in Durban, but it is likely that her kin were reluctant to support her and her children as dependants. In this case, as in many other cases, it is the mother who finally takes in the sick son or daughter, despite poverty. She joined not only her mother but also her grandmother. Between them they received three government grants, as well as irregular remittances from a cousin (who grew up in the family, like a brother), and received some support from neighbours.

These cases are not the most extreme. In some cases, people have no supportive kin to whom they can turn. In general, however, mothers will accommodate even adult children, perhaps more readily daughters than sons. A mother's death is therefore a major economic setback for unemployed adults. If someone has several siblings, it is unlikely that they will all decline to help. If a child is orphaned, then a wider range of kin will accept some responsibility, although orphaned teenagers sometimes struggle to find a new home with kin. Maternal kin generally care for orphans in much the same way as for the much larger number of non-orphaned children living apart from their mothers. In a society characterized by unemployment and poverty, many non-orphaned children are moved from kin to kin, and there is little evidence that they are disadvantaged relative to biological children in the same households. There is little evidence that boys are treated better or worse than girls.

Working-age adults in good health are in general the category of people least likely to be able to exercise claims on kin, that is, to be viewed as 'deserving'. Partners, husbands and in-laws are very unreliable. Overall, the 'radius of responsibility' among kin has shrunk dramatically on the paternal side and significantly but less dramatically on the maternal side as well. Responsibilities are also exercised more often through cohabitation rather than through remittances. The primary mechanism for private 'redistribution' to the poor and needy is probably no longer through remittances, that is, the movement of financial resources between households, but rather through movements of people – especially women and/or their children – between households.

Understanding kinship and households as resources

Given the apparent limits to the responsibility of kin, analysis of household dynamics needs to go beyond an assertion of 'domestic fluidity'. It is necessary to identify patterns in the behaviour and the norms of household composition and inter-kin responsibility. Unfortunately, most survey research in South Africa, both during and after apartheid, underestimates the complexity of the financial links, fluid composition and porous boundaries of households. Post-apartheid South Africa has seen an explosion of survey research, and data are collected on almost every aspect of citizens' lives (Seekings, 2001). However, these surveys typically collect data as if households were neat, discrete and stable units.

Most surveys collect data according to who is currently resident and more occasionally on household 'members' who are (temporarily) elsewhere. Data are often collected inconsistently even between surveys presented as a series.

Many surveys ask about remittances sent and received but typically do so at the household level without identifying precisely who in the household sends remittances or receives them, or who elsewhere was the source of remittances sent into the household, or who elsewhere was the recipient of remittances sent out of the household (Posel and Casale, 2006). Surveys such as the General Household Survey now ask how non-employed individuals support themselves, including whether they are 'supported by persons not in the household', but they do not ask who these benefactors are. A lack of clarity as to who should be counted as a member of the household gives rise to confusion and ambiguity with regard to who may be the head of the household (Budlender, 2003). Household members are typically identified by their relationship to the 'head of the household', which provides insufficient information about how members are related to each other. In addition, surveys generally fail to distinguish between paternal and maternal kin, and until recently, they also failed to explore the fluidity (over time) or porosity (over space) of households. Finally, surveys rarely enquire as to who (other than biological parents) is absent (or why), that is, which children of resident household members, or siblings of resident children, are living elsewhere, as well as how old they are and why they are elsewhere.

Some recent surveys have begun to probe these issues, but the difficulties of doing so through a highly structured survey instrument are immense. For example, the Cape Area Panel Study – a panel study of adolescents and young adults in Cape Town[12] – asks some questions about household porosity (e.g. how often do you eat meals in other households? Do you consider yourself a member of any other household?), asks about absent children and explores household dynamics over time by recording household composition in successive 'waves' of the panel study. Good data are still missing on a number of these questions, for example, how resources are distributed within the household. Precisely what financial assistance and assistance in kind flows informally or irregularly to each individual within the household, or out of the household? Which kin (and non-kin) provide such assistance, and which kin do not? Precisely why do individuals join or leave the household, what alternatives do they have, and what choices do they make? To answer such questions, data would need to be collected not only over time (through a panel study) but probably also separately from each and every individual in the household, using a more elastic conception of the household than has informed most 'household surveys', and structured questionnaires would need to be accompanied by more unstructured interviews. This might require abandoning altogether the concept of a household.

Acknowledgements

This chapter draws on a research project on AIDS, Household Dynamics and Poverty in South Africa, funded primarily by the Rockefeller Brothers Fund (http://www.rbf.org). I am grateful to the Fund as well as to the other researchers on this project – especially Rachel Bray and David Neves, who provided the two case studies presented here.

Notes

1. South Africa General Household Survey 2006, my calculations. A minority – about one-quarter to one-third – of these households include more than one maternal orphan.

2. This is demonstrated in any of the national household surveys in South Africa, including the General Household Surveys conducted annually since 2002.

3. Not so much because of an absolute scarcity, but because so much land was set aside for white ownership and/or use under apartheid.

4. Not only do women live longer, but until recently women became eligible for the non-contributory old-age pension at the age of 60, whereas men had to wait until 65. The age of eligibility for men is now being reduced to 60 also.

5. See also Ross (2003), Henderson (1999), and Ramphele (2002).

6. A small number of polygamous marriages are included.

7. Data from the 2006 General Household Survey.

8. Data from 2001 Population Census, 2006 and 2007 General Household Surveys and 2007 Community Survey.

9. The case study of Joyce is from Bray (2008).

10. It is unclear how or whether her work in HIV peer education affected her response to her sister.

11. This case is drawn from Neves (2008).

12. More information is available at http://www.caps.uct.ac.za.

References

Ardington, C. 2007. Orphanhood and schooling in South Africa: Trends in the vulnerability of orphans between 1993 and 2005. Unpublished paper, University of Cape Town, Southern African Labour and Development Research Unit.

Bray, R. 2003. *Predicting the Social Consequences of Orphanhood in South Africa.* Cape Town, Centre for Social Science Research, University of Cape Town. (CSSR Working Paper No. 29.)

——. 2008. *The Influences of AIDS-Related Morbidity and Mortality on Change in Urban Households: An Ethnographic Study.* Cape Town, Centre for Social Science Research, University of Cape Town. (CSSR Working Paper No. 235.)

Budlender, D. 2003. The debate about household headship. *Social Dynamics,* Vol. 29, No. 2, pp. 48–72.

Budlender, D., Chobokoane, N. and Simelane, S. 2004. Marriage patterns in South Africa: Methodological and substantive issues. *Southern African Journal of Demography,* Vol. 9, No. 1, pp. 1–25.

Casale, D. and Posel, D. 2002. The feminisation of the labour force in South Africa: An analysis of recent data and trends. *South African Journal of Economics,* Vol. 70, No. 1, pp. 56–84.

Claassens, A. and Ngubane, S. 2008. Women, land and power: The impact of the Community Land Rights Act. A. Claassens and B. Cousins (eds), *Land, Power and Custom: Controversies Generated by South Africa's Communal Land Rights Act,* Cape Town, University of Cape Town Press, pp. 154–83.

Dorrington, R. E., Johnson, L., Bradshaw, D. and Daniel, T. 2006. *The Demographic Impact of HIV/AIDS in South Africa: National and Provincial Indicators for 2006.* Cape Town, Centre for Actuarial Research, South African Medical Research Council and Actuarial Society of South Africa.

Esping-Andersen, G. 1990. *Three Worlds of Welfare Capitalism.* Oxford, United Kingdom, Oxford University Press.

——. 1999. *Social Foundations of Post-Industrial Economies.* Oxford, United Kingdom, Oxford University Press.

Fortes, M. 1969. *Kinship and the Social Order.* London, Routledge/Kegan Paul.

Henderson, P. 1999. Living with fragility: Children in new crossroads. Ph.D. thesis, University of Cape Town.

Houghton, D. H. and Walton, E. 1952. *The Economy of a Native Reserve,* Vol. II of *Keiskammahoek Rural Survey.* Pietermaritzburg, South Africa, Shuter and Shooter.

JLICA (Joint Learning Initiative on Children and HIV/AIDS). 2009. *Home Truths: Facing the Facts on Children, AIDS and Poverty.* JLICA.

Møller, V. and Sotshongaye, A. 1996. My family eat this money too: Pension sharing and self-respect among Zulu grandmothers. *South African Journal of Gerontology,* Vol. 5, No. 2, pp. 9–19.

Murray, C. 1981. *Families Divided: The Impact of Migrant Labour in Lesotho.* Cambridge, United Kingdom, Cambridge University Press.

Neves, D. 2008. *The Impact of Illness and Death on Migration Back to the Eastern Cape.* Cape Town, Centre for Social Science Research, University of Cape Town. (CSSR Working Paper No. 229.)

Posel, D. and Casale, D. 2006. Internal labour migration and household poverty in post-apartheid South Africa. H. Bhorat and R. Kanbur (eds), *Poverty and Policy in Post-Apartheid South Africa.* Pretoria, Human Sciences Research Council, pp. 351–65.

Radcliffe-Brown, A. R. and Forde, D. (eds). 1950. *African Systems of Kinship and Marriage.* Oxford, United Kingdom, Oxford University Press.

Ramphele, M. 2002. *Steering by the Stars: Being Young in South Africa.* Cape Town, Tafelberg.

Ross, F. 1996. Diffusing domesticity: Domestic fluidity in Die Bos. *Social Dynamics,* Vol. 22, No. 1, pp. 55–71.

——. 2003. Dependents and dependence: A case study of housing and heuristics in an informal settlement in the Western Cape. *Social Dynamics,* Vol. 29, No. 2, pp. 132–52.

Russell, M. 2003. Are urban black families nuclear? A comparative study of black and white South Africans family norms. *Social Dynamics,* Vol. 29, No. 2, pp. 153–76.

Sagner, A. and Mtati, R. 1999. Politics of pension sharing in urban South Africa. *Ageing and Society,* Vol. 19, pp. 393–416.

Seekings, J. 2001. The uneven development of quantitative social science in South Africa. *Social Dynamics,* Vol. 27, No. 1, pp. 1–36.

Seekings, J. and Nattrass, N. 2005. *Class, Race and Inequality in South Africa.* New Haven, Conn., Yale University Press.

Shisana, O., Rehle, T., Simbayi, L., Parker, W., Zuma, K. et al. 2005. *South African National HIV Prevalence, HIV Incidence, Behaviour and Communication Survey 2005.* Pretoria, Human Sciences Research Council.

Spiegel, A. 1996. Introduction: Domestic fluidity in South Africa. *Social Dynamics,* Vol. 22, No. 1, pp. 5–6.

Spiegel, A., Watson, V. and Wilkinson, P. 1996. Domestic diversity and fluidity among some African households in Greater Cape Town. *Social Dynamics,* Vol. 22, No. 1, pp. 7–30.

Van der Westhuizen, C., Goga, S. and Oosthuizen, M. 2007. *Women in the South African Labour Market, 1995–2005.* Cape Town, Development Policy Research Unit, University of Cape Town. (DPRU Working Paper No. 07/118.)

Wilson, M., Kaplan, S., Maki, T. and Walton, E. 1952. *Social Structure,* Vol. I of *Keiskammahoek Rural Survey.* Pietermaritzburg, South Africa, Shuter and Shooter.

CHAPTER 19

Measuring the impacts of the HIV epidemic on household structure and gender relations

Patrick Heuveline

For much of the twentieth century, the global health transition brought about reductions in adult mortality as well as in the proportions of deaths due to infectious diseases transmitted from person to person. This reduced the risk of losing a spouse, a parent and particularly both parents. Unfortunately, the AIDS epidemic is reversing these trends in some populations. According to household survey data, up to 19 per cent of children under the age of 15 in some sub-Saharan African countries are paternal or maternal orphans (Bicego et al., 2003; Case et al., 2004; Monasch and Boerma, 2004). Comparisons of these data with model simulations suggest that this figure underestimates the proportion of these orphans (Grassly et al., 2004).

The disproportionate loss of individuals in their most productive years to AIDS raises concerns over the welfare of both social institutions and the surviving members of affected families. It may also impact on gender relations in the affected countries because the responsibility to care for sick individuals typically differs according to gender and because the welfare of the survivors may also be affected by their gender. Assessing the downstream impact of the HIV epidemic on those who might not be infected but are clearly affected by the epidemic raises a number of measurement issues. This chapter will discuss these issues with a special emphasis on 'bilateral' (often referred to as double) orphans – that is, those who have lost both their parents. The low infectivity of HIV and the long period between HIV infection and the development of AIDS have meant that the proportion of bilateral orphans has remained low (in the

The designations employed and the presentation of material throughout this publication do not imply the expression of any opinion whatsoever on the part of UNESCO concerning the legal status of any country, territory or area or of its authorities, or concerning the delimitation of its frontiers or boundaries.
The ideas and opinions expressed in this publication are those of the authors and do not necessarily reflect the views of UNESCO and its Member States.

order of 2 per cent to 3 per cent in the worst-affected countries). As the epidemic matures, however, an increase in bilateral orphans appears inevitable, and non-governmental organizations, as well as national and international agencies, are preparing to address this challenging aspect of the 'AIDS-orphan crisis'.

Measuring the demographic impacts of the HIV epidemic: An overview

The first impact of the HIV epidemic to be recognized was the increase in mortality rates in countries where national HIV prevalence was expected to reach a few per cent. In those sub-Saharan countries where generalized epidemics were first recognized, typical adult mortality rates were in the order of ten to twenty deaths per thousand person-years. As an order of magnitude, it can be estimated that an adult HIV prevalence rate of 1 per cent to 2 per cent would, in a steady state and with ten years from infection to death, yield an additional one to two deaths per thousand person-years – that is, a 10 per cent increase in adult mortality. This simplistic calculation suggests that a 5 per cent prevalence could lead to a one-third increase in mortality – which is not a negligible change, for the purpose of population forecasting for example. However, since national epidemics are not typically in a steady state and competing causes of deaths must be adjusted for and vertical mother-to-child transmission at birth taken into account, the incorporation of the impact of the HIV epidemic on mortality rates into population forecasts is not as simple as the above calculation may suggest.

The incorporation into population forecasts of the deaths expected to result from HIV infection presents technical challenges and requires a number of assumptions about how other factors affecting demographic behaviours might also be changing as a result of a generalized HIV epidemic. In early demographic models of the epidemic, no impacts other than the premature deaths of HIV-positive individuals were assumed (Heuveline, 1997). Some models now factor in other non-behavioural impacts, such as the synergies between the prevalence of tuberculosis and of HIV, or the effect of HIV infection on conception and spontaneous abortion rates. However, a wide range of other potential 'downstream' effects of the epidemic are still ignored. Are the morbidity and mortality of HIV-negative individuals – particularly widows or widowers and orphans – unaffected by the HIV epidemic? Do the fertility choices made by the foster parents of these orphans remain unchanged when they have to care for additional children? Are the remarriage prospects of widows and widowers unchanged by the understanding of HIV transmission between spouses? Is age at marriage affected by the association of HIV status with certain age groups?

The implicit assumption that there are no impacts other than those explicitly modelled reflects the agnosticism of modellers with regard to many of these questions. The impressionistic accounts that do exist hardly amount to solid evidence that these other impacts are significant enough to warrant inclusion in reasonably sized models. There are several empirical obstacles to the constitution of a compelling body of evidence on the downstream impacts of the HIV epidemic. First, any impact assessment requires a benchmark. The HIV epidemic has attracted attention to, and large data collection projects about, populations that had been severely underserved in this respect. This has meant that demographers have had to rely on indirect estimates of mortality before the epidemic, rather than on hard data, to assess the mortality impact of the HIV epidemic. With regard to many of the other behaviours that affect reproduction or family construction, precious few ethnographic studies provide detailed accounts of specific, small populations. Anthropological studies over the years have revealed a great diversity in the kinship systems in sub-Saharan Africa (Radcliffe-Brown and Forde, 1950), and more recent survey data confirm the complexity of contemporary living arrangements (McDaniel and Zulu, 1996).

A second, related difficulty is that the benchmark needed to assess the impacts of the HIV epidemic is itself a moving target. The generalized HIV epidemic is about thirty years old in a number of countries, which have in the meantime witnessed a number of deep macrosocial transformations that are arguably inextricably linked to the epidemic: massive internal or international migration, the spread of formal education and, in some cases, prolonged warfare. Family systems and the institution of marriage were already changing at the onset of the epidemic (Parkin and Nyamwaya, 1987; Weisner et al., 1997). Even if we had a solid understanding of family systems and institutions at that point, we could not hold this past state to represent what the situation would be now if HIV did not exist.

In the absence of good benchmark data, evidence of the impacts of HIV has been sought primarily through analyses of cross-sectional survey data. The challenge of this analytical strategy is increasingly to define a comparison group for households directly affected by the epidemic. As households with HIV-positive members adapt to the morbidity and mortality burden, they may draw on kinship or other networks by borrowing cash or services and/or by receiving new members into the household or sending household members to other households. This adaptive reallocation of resources and individuals spreads the impacts of the epidemic across a larger number of households. For each household directly affected by the epidemic (in the sense of a member being infected with HIV), several other households are indirectly affected. A study in rural Uganda indicated that while nearly 20 per cent of adults were infected, 31.3 per cent of households had at least one HIV-positive adult resident (Nalugoda et al., 1997). With this prevalence level, the majority of households are likely to be affected by the epidemic, with impacts for the whole community. In any case, data from surveys that use households as units of analysis are problematic for the assessment of the downstream impacts of the epidemic because they collect data on the selected households in isolation from the network of households in which they operate. There is a risk that impact assessments that use this 'atomistic' approach will duplicate the failure of prevention-driven sex surveys that typically sampled individuals in isolation from their sexual networks. This approach classified the number of sexual partners as the key measure of risk, even though a simple probabilistic model suggests that the risk of infection is higher for a monogamous person with an infected partner than for a polygamous person with a combination of infected and uninfected partners (Smith, 1993) – as the growing prevalence among monogamous married woman painfully illustrates.

Longitudinal data collection is also required to establish the coping processes used by affected households to adapt to the impacts of the epidemic. Following the infection of one of its members with HIV, a household may experience a sequence of events that could include: the infection of an adult partner, the birth of an uninfected baby, the birth of an infected baby, the death of that HIV-positive baby as an infant or child, the death of the first infected adult, the death of his or her partner, and eventually dissolution of the household and fostering of the surviving children. This example only considers HIV status and household membership, but the sequence of relevant events might be even more complex. The use of household data surveys to identify households in which one member is HIV-positive at a given point in time as a single group fails to distinguish the different stages of responses to the epidemic. Depending on the stage a given household has reached in the complex sequence of responses, the different impacts of the epidemic might be weak or strong, transient or enduring, negative or even positive. Estimating the impacts of the epidemic on a cross-section of households directly affected by the epidemic but at different stages of their response to it may indicate only modest, average effects.

The above discussion suggests the need for longitudinal rather than cross-sectional data collection, preferably including results from before the appearance of HIV in a given population. A few relatively small-scale longitudinal data collection projects (such as demographic surveillance systems) may meet these criteria, but larger projects to study the epidemic have typically been initiated only after it has already begun to affect a population. As no particular data set is ideal, we must learn about the demographic impacts of the HIV epidemic by culling evidence from different projects with different strengths and weaknesses. This raises the question of how context-dependent these impacts may be – that is, how relevant what we can learn from one setting may be to another. This issue has generated substantial debate, which cannot be decisively settled here (if ever). I will simply argue that we have a better chance of generating relevant knowledge across settings by studying the processes or mechanisms through which households are affected by, and try to cope with, the epidemic than by focusing solely on 'outcomes' (by attempting to measure impacts in a given setting and at a given point in time). An understanding of the processes involved is also critical to designing successful interventions to protect the welfare of affected individuals, households and families.

The study of these processes requires a conceptualization of the pathways through which the epidemic operates. Developing such a conceptual framework for each of the potential downstream impacts of the epidemic is beyond the remit of this chapter. I will therefore illustrate the discussion by focusing on the impacts the epidemic may have on orphans. While numerous studies document the negative consequences of becoming an orphan at a young age, establishing the mechanisms that negatively and positively affect orphans is more scientifically challenging than it appears at first. This is due in part to the conceptual diversity of the mechanisms and in part to specific empirical challenges. I begin by developing an overall conceptual framework for articulating the mechanisms. I will then discuss the relevant empirical findings and limitations.

An illustrative conceptual framework

The well-being and successful development of children depend on physical and human resources and their ability to use these resources efficiently. Their access to many of those resources is indirect and mediated by a few privileged adult-child ties within a wider network of economic and cultural relationships. A child's well-being, development and, eventually, successful transition to adulthood therefore also depend both on the standing of these few adults in the wider network and on the strength of those ties, relative to other ties that may entail competing claims to the same resources. Within this general framework, we might expect orphans to be affected by the death of one or more parents both directly (such as through psychological impacts on their ability to use resources) and indirectly (through the reduction of their access to resources). The indirect effects may originate in two different types of changes. Firstly, the adults to whom orphans are still connected may face economic and psychological hardships affecting their own access to resources. Secondly, orphans might be less strongly connected to the adult(s) primarily responsible for their welfare after the death of a biological parent than they were to the deceased parent. Effects linked to the first type of change are household-level effects, whereas those linked to the second type might be termed 'relational' in that they depend on the orphan's relationship with the new responsible adult. Families can be resilient and able to cope in the long term with the hardships induced by a premature adult death, but even transitory effects may have a lasting impact on children who are involved in age-specific developmental tasks. Impacts therefore vary with the orphan's age when the parent dies. Moreover, these types of changes will affect paternal and maternal orphans differently – depending on the surviving adult's control over key resources and on kinship structures, which are highly gendered – but both will particularly impact on bilateral orphans.

With respect to household hardship, a seminal paper by Becker and Tomes (1979) illustrates the conditions under which investments in children's human capital may nonetheless remain optimal after a parental death. One of these conditions is that the household head faces no liquidity constraints. This may not be possible for adults in developing countries with no formal insurance markets. In a series of papers on India and Thailand, Townsend (1995) reports evidence of household consumption smoothing over time and across space, which indicates that some risk-sharing takes place between neighbours and within extended families. However, these informal mechanisms only provide partial 'insurance' and may be maintained partly by expectations of reciprocity. Households that include orphans and face chronic rather than temporary difficulties may appear less likely to reciprocate and therefore are less able to benefit from risk-sharing networks.

Another condition suggested by Becker and Tomes is intergenerational altruism, in particular that the adult decision-maker, caring equally about each child, bases his or her educational investments purely on the expected returns for each child (i.e. the effects of this education on their future productivity). Under this condition, investments in the education of orphans could still be affected by parental death, but only if lower returns relative to other children in the household are expected (for example due to the psychological impacts of the parent's death on their learning abilities). This condition should not be overlooked since placing orphans with relatives is one of the strategies that families may use to adapt to a premature adult death. According to the framework outlined above, this strategy can be seen as a trade-off between reducing household-level hardships by placing the orphan into a new household that is less directly affected by the death and increasing negative relational effects, that may arise from the orphan's weaker tie to the new household head. Sociobiological theory emphasizes one aspect of adult-child ties – genetic relatedness – which has evolved as a key determinant of adult investments in children since natural selection for inclusive fitness favours cooperative behaviour that benefits kin over indiscriminately altruistic behaviour. The corresponding prediction, known as Hamilton's rule (Hamilton, 1964), is that for a given activity with an energy cost for ego and a fitness benefit for ego's kin, the higher the coefficient of genetic relatedness between ego and a particular kin, the stronger the selection pressure. Accordingly, children are most likely to receive costly investments from their own biological parents. As for other relatives, cooperative rearing is expressed to the greatest extent between the closest genetic relatives, as amply confirmed by studies of bird species and mammals (Elmen, 1995). While the degree of genetic relatedness is the same between a child and her grandparents and the child and her aunts and uncles (the full siblings of either biological parent), grandparents invest equally in all their grandchildren, whereas aunts and uncles invest more in their own reproduction by caring for their own children first.

In addition to this genetic basis, social norms and institutions also affect cooperative child-rearing. The near-universal institutions of marriage and the family contribute to solidifying children's ties with their biological or social parents (Malinowski, 1930). However, the diffusion beyond or concentration on these parents of rights and responsibilities with regard to children has been found to vary greatly, both over time (Aries, 1962) and across societies (as illustrated by variations in the prevalence of fosterage). Sociologists have linked these local and temporal variations to macro-level changes ever since Durkheim (1897) argued that the economic and social transformations of his time were weakening the family. Similar concerns about the decline of social solidarity norms thought to have a protective influence on individual well-being have continued to emerge from studies of modernization and, more recently, of globalization. While it may still 'take a village to raise a child', it appears plausible that the development of the market weakens the authority of community elders as social and economic success can increasingly be achieved outside of the community. In high-income countries, the state has taken over some forms of assistance and can now to be considered as jointly responsible, with the family, for the health and well-being of its young people (Furstenberg, 1997). Even in these countries, however, parents continue to play an essential role in drawing the resources that children need from an increasingly complex institutional environment (McLanahan, 2000). In poorer countries, the state may lack the means to enforce universal programmes, such as compulsory schooling, and the continued reliance on the cooperation of parents or legal guardians is even greater. 'World-society' institutions (Meyer et al., 1997) – that is, international agencies and non-governmental organizations – may substitute for the state's lack of resources with various assistance programmes and at the same time become agents of further cultural change.

Empirical results and limitations

The theoretical perspectives outlined above suggest several ways in which young orphans may suffer compared to non-orphans, as well as several mechanisms that may alleviate these potential disadvantages. The existing research includes numerous studies of how several indicators of child well-being may differ between non-orphans and different orphan types, but there have been precious few attempts to tease out potential compensatory mechanisms. In a review of several case studies from sub-Saharan Africa, Heuveline (2004) reports that young fostered children present more problems of malnutrition and are under-represented in hospital admissions and that orphans present more mental-health problems than non-orphans but, at the same time, that orphanhood does not affect reported health and anthropometric measurements. In an analysis of eighteen national household surveys, Monasch and Boerma (2004) found that 1–4-year-old orphans are no more likely to be underweight than non-orphans of the same age. Neither did they find significant differences with respect to the working patterns of orphans and non-orphans, although they do acknowledge that caretakers may under-report children's workloads and that children undertaking the worst forms of child labour may not live in a household.

Educational outcomes are perhaps the most commonly studied indicators. Heuveline's (2004) review reveals conflicting evidence about school enrollment and school completion in sub-Saharan African case studies. The evidence varies by orphan type and gender, with recent studies providing more evidence of orphan disadvantages. Similar inconsistencies and trends emerge from analyses of national household surveys from the region. Lloyd and Blanc (1996) did not find differences between orphans and non-orphans in terms of enrolment status among 6–14-year-olds or grade attainment among 10–14-year-olds. However, differences between orphans – particularly bilateral orphans – and non-orphans were later reported for both enrolment status (Case et al., 2004; Monasch and Boerma, 2004) and grade attainment (Bicego et al., 2003). In cross-sectional studies, attributing such differences to parental death is complicated by the possibility that orphanhood might be 'endogenous'. This means that, with regard to some of the characteristics thought to be affected by becoming an orphan, families that lose an adult parent prematurely already differ from those that do not before the loss occurs. Perhaps the only longitudinal study to date that has allowed the authors to address this potential problem was undertaken by Evans and Miguel (2007). They confirm the endogenous nature of orphanhood and state that cross-sectional estimates of the differences between orphans and non-orphans are therefore likely to be biased. Other authors have derived statistical adjustments. Gertler et al. (2004), for instance, use propensity score matching to match orphans and non-orphans in their study of Indonesian orphans still living with one biological parent and find that parental death does have a strong net effect on a child's enrolment. Case and Ardington (2006) based their study in a South African demographic surveillance system in order to control for household characteristics before parental death; they also document significant effects of parental death on schooling outcomes. Interestingly, Evans and Miguel (2007) suggest gendered effects: (a) the impact of maternal death on schooling is greater than the effect of paternal death, and (b) the impact is greater for older girls.

In order to tease out disadvantages between and within households, Case et al. (2004) compare orphans and non-orphans in the same household using household-level fixed models. They find that orphans are disadvantaged at the individual level, regardless of gender. No real consensus has emerged, however, on wealth differentials between households with and without orphaned members. Using a simple count index of household durables as a proxy for household wealth, Case et al. (2004) report that, as a group, orphans live in poorer households, although this is primarily true for paternal orphans (there is no systematic difference for maternal or bilateral orphans). However, using an index of household durables based on principal component analysis, Bicego et al. (2003) report that orphans do not appear disadvantaged compared to non-orphans; this is borne out in further analysis carried out by the authors on

Zimbabwe, where the proportion of orphans is among the highest worldwide and the sample of orphans is therefore larger. This analysis suggests that in the time between the two most recent surveys, the proportion of bilateral orphans increased in the lowest wealth quintile and decreased in the second and third quintile, whereas no change occurred in the top two quintiles. The authors reason that these findings may be evidence that communities are finding it more difficult to deal with these orphans as their numbers increase and the ability to strategically place orphans becomes more constrained.

Most studies of child placement have focused on West Africa, where child fosterage is relatively common as it allows parents to take better-paid but remote jobs, children to study away from the parental home and families to cope with unforeseen crises (Isiugo-Abanihe, 1985; Madhavan, 2004). Studies in the region suggest that biological parents typically interact with foster parents and that the well-being of fostered children therefore continues to depend on the wider social relations between the biological and the foster parents (Bledsoe, 1990). The remedial effects of fosterage are thus more uncertain for bilateral orphans, whose parents can no longer play this role. Depending on the kinship structure in a particular society, fosterage consequences may also differ for maternal and paternal orphans. Case et al. (2004) find that individual-level disadvantages are lesser for orphans placed with their grandparents – a rather reassuring finding since grandparents are the most common foster parents in sub-Saharan Africa, followed by aunts and uncles (Bicego et al., 2003). A qualitative study in Thailand reveals that Thai parents also express a clear preference for grandparents as foster parents should they not be able to care for their children themselves (Safman, 2003). Like orphanhood itself, however, placement decisions may be endogenous, and the outcomes for children who are placed with a given social parent may differ from those who are not. Using another statistical correction (instrumental variables) to address the possibility of endogenous living arrangements, Bishai et al. (2003) report that, in rural Uganda, not only does the presence of both parents in the household increase the odds of child survival, but the degree of biological relatedness of a child to the head of household is also positively associated with child survival.

Discussion

It is anticipated that the HIV epidemic will result in increasing numbers of orphans. Various theoretical perspectives converge in suggesting that this trend may be one of the least ambiguous negative impacts of the epidemic. However, the empirical record of orphan disadvantages is perhaps not as compelling as one might expect given this theoretical basis. Some authors have been able to address some of the analytical problems of studying orphans, but many aspects of the conceptual framework remain poorly understood. These shortcomings are largely due to the empirical limitations of the household surveys to which analysts must often resort. I have extensively discussed these limitations but emphasize that a particularly important restriction with regard to the study of orphans is that these surveys are designed for other purposes and do not typically collect retrospective information on conditions at the time of parental death and the wider environment in which households operate.

In addition, although the epidemic is already thirty years old, it might be too early to observe its most serious effects on orphans. There is clear evidence that the number of female-headed households is increasing, as is the number of children who do not live with both of their biological parents. Such households have historically been relatively common in southern Africa, for instance, where men often migrate for work, leaving women in charge of the household for long periods of time. However, because many of these female heads of household are themselves HIV-positive, we can expect a growth in the number of bilateral orphans. The fate of these bilateral orphans – so far relatively rare – is difficult to anticipate precisely because their numbers might remain too small in population-based surveys to allow for investigations of the multiple sources of between-orphan heterogeneity.

A more sanguine view is that family systems in the most affected populations have evolved to deal with high adult mortality and that families have been relatively resilient and able to protect their members from some of the consequences of the epidemic (Caldwell, 1997). While it is possible that certain cultural features, such as flexibility regarding kinship and living arrangements, have played a positive role in mediating the impacts of the epidemic, others may have contributed to its spread. These include asymmetrical gender relationships, age differences between sexual partners and sexual violence against women. These cultural factors have sometimes meant that paternal and maternal orphans are affected differently – based on which parent has control over key resources. As I have discussed, some studies indicate that the loss of mothers has a greater impact on aspects such as schooling outcomes.

The dominant model in the response to the epidemic has been based on the external delivery of an elusive vaccine to affected populations rather than on working with these populations to moderate the cultural factors that contribute to the epidemic. Aside from this external delivery of medical expertise model, the burden of the disease has largely been left in the domestic and familial domains. As a result, responsibility for the care of people living with HIV has fallen predominantly to women, which has reinforced traditional and gendered divisions of responsibilities within households. At the same time, in the context of scarce resources for HIV interventions, decisions about which interventions to pursue are embedded in existing gender relationships. Male circumcision programmes, for instance, directly target men and may therefore appear to neglect women and young children as a vulnerable population (Hankins, 2007; Rennie et al., 2007). Although models of this intervention are reassuring with regard to the potential protection of adult women as well as men, they also show that it can have quite different impacts on different generations, depending on the age at which boys and men are targeted (Clark and Eaton, 2008). There is a legitimate concern that, until they heal completely, newly circumcised men may in fact be more likely to infect their female partners (Altman, 2008). Another, broader concern is that advocating the benefits of male circumcision may lead to confusion about and contribute to maintaining some forms of female sexual mutilation that are controversially referred to as female circumcision and may therefore appear to be the female equivalent of male circumcision (Hankins, 2007). The case of male circumcision demonstrates that while HIV intervention policies may be cast in terms of objective and detached cost-benefit considerations, their potential success and eventual impacts depend on the wider context of existing gender and intergenerational asymmetries.

Acknowledgements

This article was written while the author was a fellow at the Center for Advanced Study in the Behavioral Sciences and was supported in part by a William T. Grant Foundation Scholar Award. The author thanks these institutions for their support and the participants of the Expert Group Meeting held on 4 and 5 October 2007 in Paris for their comments on an earlier version of this article – Jennifer Klot, Vinh-Kim Nguyen and Philip Setel in particular. None of these institutions or persons is responsible for the views expressed or for the errors that might remain in this article.

References

Altman, L. K. 2008. Male circumcision no aid to women in study. *New York Times,* 4 February.

Aries, P. 1962. *Centuries of Childhood.* New York, Vintage Books.

Becker, G. and Tomes, N. 1979. An equilibrium theory of the distribution of income and intergenerational mobility. *Journal of Political Economy,* Vol. 87, No. 6, pp. 1153–1158.

Bicego, G., Rutstein S. and Johnson, K. 2003. Dimensions of the emerging orphan crisis in sub-Saharan Africa. *Social Science and Medicine,* Vol. 56, No. 6, pp. 1235–247.

Bishai, D., Suliman, E., Brahmbhatt, H., Wabwire-Mangen, F., Kigozi, G., Sewankambo, N., Serwadda, D., Wawer, M. and Gray, R. 2003. Does biological relatedness affect survival? *Demographic Research,* Vol. 8, pp. 261–78.

Bledsoe, C. 1990. The social management of fertility: Child fosterage among the Mende of Sierra Leone. W. P. Handwerker (ed.), *Births and Power: Social Change and the Politics of Reproduction.* Boulder, Colo., Westview Press, pp. 81–101.

Caldwell, J. C. 1997. The impact of the African AIDS epidemic. *Health Transition Review,* Vol. 7, Suppl. 2, pp. 169–88.

Case, A. and Ardington, C. 2006. The impact of parental death on school outcomes: Longitudinal evidence from South Africa. *Demography,* Vol. 43, No. 3, pp. 401–20.

Case, A., Paxson, C. and Ableidinger, J. 2004. Orphans in Africa: Parental death, poverty, and school enrollment. *Demography,* Vol. 41, No. 3, pp. 483–508.

Clark, S. J. and Eaton, J. W. 2008. Demographic consequences of the HIV epidemics and effects of different male circumcision intervention designs: Suggestive findings of microsimulation. Seattle, Wa., University of Washington Center for Statistics and the Social Sciences. (Working Paper No. 85.)

Durkheim, E. 1897. *Suicide: A Study in Sociology.* New York, Free Press.

Elmen, S. T. 1995. An evolutionary theory of the family. *Proceedings of the National Academy of Science of the United States of America,* Vol. 92, No. 18, pp. 8092–099.

Evans, D. K. and Miguel. E. 2007. Orphans and schooling in Africa: A longitudinal analysis. *Demography,* Vol. 44, No. 1, pp. 35–37.

Furstenberg, F. F. J. 1997. State-family alliances and children's welfare: A research agenda. *Childhood,* Vol. 4, No. 2, pp. 183–92.

Gertler, P., Levine, D. I. and Ames, M. 2004. Parental death and schooling. *Review of Economics and Statistics,* Vol. 86, No. 1, pp. 211–25.

Grassly, N. C., Lewis, J. J. C., Mahy, M., Walker, N. and Timaeus, I. M. 2004. Comparison of household-survey estimates with projection of mortality and orphan numbers in sub-Saharan Africa in the era of HIV/AIDS. *Population Studies,* Vol. 58, No. 2, pp. 207–17.

Hamilton, W. D. 1964. The genetical evolution of social behavior II. *Journal of Theoretical Biology,* Vol. 7, pp. 17–52.

Hankins, S. 2007. Male circumcision: Implications for women as sexual partners and parents. *Reproductive Health Matters,* Vol. 15, No. 29, pp. 62–67.

Heuveline, P. 1997. AIDS and population growth in sub-Saharan Africa: Assessing the sensitivity of projections. *Population Research and Policy Review,* Vol. 16, pp. 531–60.

_____. 2004. Impact of the HIV epidemic on population and household structure: The dynamics and evidence to-date. *AIDS,* Vol. 18, Suppl. 2, pp. S45–S53.

Isiugo-Abanihe, U. C. 1985. Child fosterage in West Africa. *Population and Development Review,* Vol. 11, No. 1, pp. 53–73.

Lloyd C. B. and Blanc, A. K. 1996. Children's schooling in sub-Saharan Africa: The role of fathers, mothers, and others. *Population and Development Review,* Vol. 22, No. 2, pp. 265–98.

Madhavan, S. 2004. Fosterage patterns in the age of AIDS: Continuity and change. *Social Science and Medicine,* Vol. 58, No. 7, pp. 1443–454.

Malinowski, B. 1930. Parenthood, the basis of social structure. R. L. Coser (ed.), *The Family: Its Structure and Functions.* New York, St Martin's Press, pp. 3–19.

McDaniel, A. and Zulu, E. 1996. Mothers, fathers and children: Regional patterns in child-parent residence in sub-Saharan Africa. *African Population Studies,* Vol. 11, pp. 1–28.

McLanahan, S. S. 2000. Family, state, and child wellbeing. *Annual Review of Sociology,* Vol. 26, pp. 703–06.

Meyer, J. W., Boli, J., Thomas, G. M. and Ramirez, F. O. 1997. World society and the nation-state. *American Journal of Sociology,* Vol. 103, No. 1, pp. 144–81.

Monasch, R. A. and Boerma, T. B. 2004. Orphanhood and childcare patterns in sub-Saharan Africa: An analysis of national surveys from 40 countries. *AIDS,* Vol. 18, Suppl. 2, pp. S55–S65.

Nalugoda, F., Wawer, M. J., Konde-Lule, J. K., Menon, R., Gray, R. H., Serwadda D. et al. 1997. HIV infection in rural households, Rakai district, Uganda. *Health Transition Review,* Vol. 7, Suppl. 2, pp. 127–40.

Parkin, D. J. and Nyamwaya, D. 1987. *Transformations of African Marriage.* Manchester, United Kingdom, Manchester University Press.

Radcliffe-Brown, A. R. and Forde, D. (eds). 1950. *African Systems of Kinship and Marriage*. London/New York, Oxford University Press.

Rennie S., Muula, A. S. and Westreich, D. 2007. Male circumcision and HIV prevention: Ethical, medical and public health tradeoffs in low-income countries. *Journal of Medical Ethics,* Vol. 33, No. 6, pp. 357–61.

Safman, R. M. 2003. Assessing the impact of orphanhood on Thai children affected by AIDS and their caregivers. *AIDS Care,* Vol. 16, No. 1, pp. 11–19.

Smith, H. L. 1993. On the limited utility of KAP-style survey data in the practical epidemiology of AIDS, with reference to the AIDS epidemic in Chile. *Health Transition Review,* Vol. 3, No. 1, pp. 1–15.

Statistics South Africa. 2007. *Community Survey 2007,* revised version. Statistical Release P0301, 24 October. http://www.statssa.gov.za/publications/P0301/P0301.pdf

Townsend, R. M. 1995. Consumption insurance: An evaluation of risk-bearing systems in low-income economies. *Journal of Economic Perspectives,* Vol. 9, No. 3, pp. 83–102.

Weisner, T. S., Bradley, C. and Kilbride, P. L. (eds). 1997. *African Families and the Crisis of Social Change.* Westport, Conn., Bergin and Garvey.

CHAPTER 20

Behind the scenes of sex and sexual debut: Unpacking measurement

Charlotte Watts

Introduction: A research industry in counting sex acts

The chapters in this volume illustrate the danger of oversimplifications and generalizations. They also illustrate the need to learn from qualitative research about the contexts in which unsafe sex occurs, including the situations in which power is given or taken away from people and which fundamentally undermine an individual's ability to protect himself or herself from HIV infection.

This chapter focuses on the issue of sexual behaviour measurement, its influence on the way that we have understood the HIV and AIDS epidemic and how to intervene effectively. To date, quantitative research on sexual behaviour has focused largely on trying to estimate the numbers of sexual partners and levels of condom use among different groups around the world. This focus builds on mathematical modelling and epidemiological research that illustrates how the rate of spread of the HIV epidemic is fundamentally influenced by the number of sexual partners that a person has, the number of sex acts and the probability of HIV transmission following sexual relations with one or more partners. This in turn is dependent upon levels of condom use and whether a partner may be more infectious (for example, if they are in the initial, high-viraemia phase of HIV infection or if either partner has another sexually transmitted infection) (Anderson and May, 1988).

A research industry to measure these dimensions of sexual behaviour has developed in recent years, and a large body of quantitative research now

The designations employed and the presentation of material throughout this publication do not imply the expression of any opinion whatsoever on the part of UNESCO concerning the legal status of any country, territory or area or of its authorities, or concerning the delimitation of its frontiers or boundaries.
The ideas and opinions expressed in this publication are those of the authors and do not necessarily reflect the views of UNESCO and its Member States.

focuses on collecting representative data on the numbers of sex acts that people have, the consistency of condom use in these sexual relations and the forms of partnership that people have – with broad categories being used to group partners into one-off partners, casual relationships, steady partnerships and sex for money or goods. These categories are being used to better understand the potential levels of risk associated with different forms of heterosexual and same-sex sexual relationships.

The data on the basis of these analytic categories have been used to map out patterns of behavioural risk and to inform and interpret the success of HIV and AIDS interventions. Researchers are continually refining their measurement tools, and findings are used to monitor trends in sexual behaviour and condom use, assess levels of success in HIV prevention strategies and project the epidemic's future trajectory. Yet, is this enough? Although these data on patterns of sexual behaviour help us to better understand patterns of risk and the potential for HIV transmission, the data do not help us to understand the motivations and driving forces behind these behaviours, which are central to understanding how to intervene effectively.

Violence against women as a neglected risk factor for HIV infection

Over the past decade there has been a growing body of research focusing on different forms of violence against women. Survey research is starting to illustrate the extent to which, globally, violence against women is a common reality in girls and women's lives, with violence potentially starting early in their lives and continuing for many years. Alongside this work, there is emerging evidence that suggests that different forms of violence may be associated with different levels of risk for infection with HIV and other STIs (sexually transmitted infections). For example, in South Africa, urban pregnant women attending antenatal services who had violent partners were 50 per cent more likely to be infected than other women (Dunkle et al., 2004). Similarly, in Tanzania, the odds of reporting violence have been found to be ten times higher for young, HIV-positive women compared to young, HIV-negative women (Maman et al., 2002). In Goa, India, the risk of incident STI among married women reporting violence was three times higher than among married women whose partners had not been violent (Weiss et al., 2008).

Research on violence against women is starting to illustrate the complex and multifaceted ways in which violence and the fear of violence impact on women's ability to protect themselves from HIV and other STIs. As discussed below, gender inequalities and violence impact on the age and circumstances of first sex as well the dynamics of sexual relationships and sexual negotiations over a woman's lifespan.

The reality of sexual debut

In sub-Saharan Africa, 59 per cent of the HIV-infected among 15–49-year-olds are women, and 75 per cent of the HIV-infected among young people are female (UNAIDS, 2006). Researchers have therefore begun to assess ways of reducing adolescents' risk of HIV infection, and particularly the high vulnerability of young girls to HIV infection. An important focus for prevention has been on how to delay the onset of sexual activity, including the promotion of 'abstinence' messages.

Yet, there has been far more limited attention paid to the circumstances under which the first sexual experience occurs and the extent to which this experience (and/or later sexual activity) may or may not be consensual. Violence research is starting to illustrate that for many women and some men the reality is that sexual debut is coerced. Studies from sub-Saharan Africa find that the prevalence ranges from 15 per cent to over 40 per cent of all women (see for example, Buga et al., 1996; Glover et al., 2003; Matasha et al., 1998; Moore et al., 2007; Rwenge, 2000; Somse et al., 1993).

The reality of forced sex both within and outside marriage is an issue of concern to the HIV and development community and illustrates the need to move beyond messages of abstinence to address the issue of sexual assault. Similarly, the issues of rape, conflict-related sexual violence and forced and early marriages require serious attention as part of a gendered HIV response.

A recognition of the extent of sexual assault on young girls requires that we move beyond using euphemisms, such as 'sugar-daddies', to more meaningful discussions about whether it is acceptable for older men to buy or coerce sex with young girls. HIV education for youth needs to not only provide them with the biological facts on HIV transmission and methods of HIV prevention but to also meaningfully discuss sexual relationships, power and control within relationships, consent and coercion, as well as respect and responsibility.

Violence within primary partnerships

In southern and East Africa in particular, where HIV prevalence may be as high as 30 per cent, it is increasingly recognized that women are often at high risk of HIV infection within their primary partnerships. Again, there is also growing evidence of the extent to which violence occurs within intimate partnerships. For example, the World Health Organization (WHO) recently worked with partners around the world to conduct large-scale surveys on women's experiences of physical and sexual violence. Research teams, consisting of both academic and women's organizations, worked together to collect representative data on women's experiences of different acts of violence around the world (Garcia-Moreno et al., 2005), with support being given to women requesting assistance.

As part of this study, surveys were conducted in three sub-Saharan African countries – Ethiopia, the United Republic of Tanzania and Namibia. In these settings, between 36 per cent and 71 per cent of ever partnered women reported having been physically or sexually assaulted by their partner (Garcia-Moreno et al., 2006). Between 20 per cent and 54 per cent of women also reported that they had been victims of violence in the previous year.

It is interesting to note that several studies are also starting to highlight a clustering of risk behaviours, with men who are violent also being more likely to have other behaviour that puts them, and their partners, at risk of being infected with HIV and STIs. In India, men who had extramarital sex were six times more likely to report sexual abuse of their wives than men who remained faithful. Moreover, men who reported an STI were 2.5 times more likely to report abusing their wives than men who did not report an STI. Similarly, in Cape Town, South Africa, men who reported sexual violence against intimate partners were nearly twice as likely to have multiple partners compared to those who did not report sexual violence (WHO/Global Coalition on Women and AIDS, 2003a). These findings highlight the central role of masculinity and that abusive men are more likely to engage in extramarital sex, acquire STIs and place their primary partners at higher risk for STIs, including through coerced sex.

Violence against sex workers and other marginalized groups

So far we have highlighted the high levels of violence against women and girls. Research also shows that sex workers (both men and women) may experience very high levels of physical and sexual violence by clients and men in positions of power, such as pimps or the police, as well as in their primary relationships. For example, in Bangladesh, between 52 per cent and 60 per cent of street-based sex workers report being raped by men in uniform in the previous twelve months, and between 41 per cent and 51 per cent reported being raped by local criminals; in Namibia, 72 per cent of 148 sex workers interviewed reported being abused; in India, 70 per cent of sex workers in a survey reported being beaten by the police, and more than 80 per cent had been arrested without evidence (WHO/Global Coalition on Women and AIDS, 2003b).

This violence is targeted at both male and female sex workers: a survey of street-based sex workers in Cambodia found that over 50 per cent of female sex workers and just under 50 per cent of male sex workers reported being gang raped, on average by five to six men at a time. When asked about the last gang rape, three-quarters reported being tied or held down; 70 per cent had weapons used against them, and 50 per cent reported bleeding (Jenkins et al., 2006).

Women who are trafficked or bonded into sex work are even more likely to be subjected to the control of their pimps or brothel owners, who can decide how many clients they see in a day, whether condoms are used and how long they will stay within a particular setting.

Moving beyond counting sex acts, partners and condom use

Often quantitative behavioural surveys focus on trying to understand risk by getting data that can be used to count sex acts, partnerships and condom use. However, the reality of violence that is missed by such an approach may mean that the data obtained have extremely limited value as a tool to inform programming.

The quote below comes from an interview with a street-based female sex worker in Cambodia (Jenkins et al., 2006), who describes being raped by three policemen:

> I came out and the policeman started his first sex. He sexed me with a condom. He took about twenty minutes the first time. He started a second time of sex and I saw the same two men coming in the room. They watched the policeman f***ing me on the bed under a bright light. I asked the policeman to tell them to get out of the room, but he refused and forced me to have sex with them when he finished. Both men raped me with condoms. One man used special condoms. It hurt me very

much. He did not stop although I pleaded with them to stop … these men raped me twice each until they were tired. I was freed about 3 a.m. (Street-based sex worker, Cambodia)

Contrasting this narrative with what would be documented if we had used a structured questionnaire to interview this woman illustrates the severe limitations of a quantitative approach that does not seek to understand the underlying contexts in which sex occurs. Simply counting the number of sex acts a woman has had would lead to a conclusion that this woman has had sex with three men. As condoms were used in each sex act, this would be seen as a 'success' in the response to HIV. But is it good enough that, in this circumstance, male rapists knew to use a condom? Clearly not.

This woman's testimony also illustrates how issues of power, control, coercion and violence can be hidden if we do not ask the right questions and how we may miss the underlying structural factors that determine who is in control; these are the questions that need to be addressed if change is to occur.

Getting to the core of gender relations

With the growth of research on violence against women, we are starting to gain a more informed understanding about the unequal power relations that may often underpin sexual relationships and exchange. Yet HIV funding, programmes and policies have been relatively slow to respond to this evidence. Despite almost two generations of quantitative surveys on sexual behaviour around the world, HIV survey research often does not ask women about their experiences of violence – be it physical, sexual or economic.

The lack of recognition of the context of gender inequality and gender-based violence in current national and international HIV programming in part results from an overreliance on simple, reductionist ways of measuring sexual behaviour to inform programming. A focus on sexual partners and sex acts leads to prevention messages that encourage people to abstain from sex, have fewer partners and use condoms. While each of these strategies is important, they fail to acknowledge the difficulties that many groups will have in acting on these messages due to violence and unequal power relations in which sex may occur.

With the growing awareness of the high prevalence of violence against women, it is important to broaden our existing concepts about sexual behaviour and prevention to respond to this reality. Documented levels of violence illustrate the absurdity of an overreliance on promoting abstinence, behavioural change and condom use as our primary model of HIV prevention. Centrally, the reality of violence against women highlights the need to move from the implicit assumption that sex is consensual and the need to explicitly address gender inequality and violence as part of our HIV response.

Unfortunately there are no quick and easy solutions. A number of recent initiatives are seeking to challenge gender-based violence and the unequal gender power relationships that underpin it. These include programmes that explicitly integrate issues of gender, coercion and consent into sexual health education for youth and explicitly discuss with girls how to recognize and avoid risk situations; support voluntary counselling; and provide testing and anti-retroviral therapy staff for support to women disclosing or fearing violence as well as the direct provision of counselling, support and post-exposure prophylaxis to girls and women who have been raped.

UNAIDS and the Global Coalition on Women and AIDS recommend that national programmes integrate strategies to reduce violence against women into national AIDS plans and strategies to increase access to essential AIDS services within violence prevention efforts – and ensure that these linkages are funded (Global Coalition on Women and AIDS, 2009). They highlight that such strategies should include:

- Supporting community-based training and information campaigns to change harmful norms and behaviours that perpetuate violence against women and reinforce its social acceptability, including working with men and communities to address violence as well as engaging women's, faith-based and other groups in preventing and coping with violence and its links to HIV.

- Promoting economic opportunities for women through microfinance and skills training to give women the tools and economic independence they need to avoid or escape violence and reduce their risk for HIV.

- Ensuring that HIV programs begin to address the realities of violence against women as a barrier to HIV services by providing training for HIV service providers to recognize the signs of violence and to offer basic counselling and social support and appropriate referrals for additional assistance, including legal services, where available.

- Providing training to law enforcement officials and others who may encounter victims of violence about the risk of HIV and proper referrals to prevention information, medical treatment and post-exposure prophylaxis, where appropriate, to reduce the immediate risk of HIV infection.

- Strengthening the legal and policy environment so that laws prohibiting violence against women are enacted and enforced, systems to report on the prevalence and acceptability of violence against women are established and maintained and monitoring mechanisms effectively feed into the design of national AIDS programs.

- Ensuring that organizations, particularly those with experience addressing violence against women, are represented on national AIDS councils and other relevant fora to help ensure that the link between violence against women and HIV is effectively addressed within the design and implementation of national AIDS programs.

Power and the HIV epidemic

Violence against women and marginalized groups is an expression of power inequalities between the perpetrator of violence and the person that they are assaulting. The levels of violence against women occurring globally illustrate the need to adopt a different approach to monitoring and understanding the HIV epidemics as well as to broaden our conceptualization of appropriate models of intervention. Current responses to HIV have failed to adequately understand and respond to the feminization of the HIV epidemic in sub-Saharan Africa and the high rates of infection among young girls and women, as compared to men and boys, in many African settings. In West Africa, Asia and Eastern Europe, where the HIV epidemic is more concentrated among marginalized populations, the power dynamics underlying sex work and the extent of violence against marginalized groups may also be large barriers to an effective response. Our responses to the HIV epidemic will only be meaningful if we include a more explicit focus on the disempowerment and marginalization of those affected most heavily by the HIV epidemic in different settings and on the contexts that support their disempowerment.

Quantitative research should not only seek to count partners, sex acts and condom use but also to document the circumstances in which sex occurs, including whether sex was coerced. The underlying dimensions of power and control that underpin some sexual behaviour also merit further research. There is a need to broaden our research perspective to ensure that we do not only focus on who is vulnerable within a particular setting but also seek to identify who is powerful and how this power shapes and affects HIV risk in that context. Although the use of quantitative research methods to explore these issues will always have its limitations, the inclusion of even a relatively simple set of carefully constructed questions would at least help make more explicit the extent of this issue and allow its relationship to HIV and the effectiveness of current HIV responses to be explored.

The challenge for research is how to incorporate such issues into research methods, and in particular, the data that are commonly collected across settings to inform programming, without falling into the same pitfalls of quantitative HIV behavioural research. Methodological research to identify how to move from simple categorizations of risk to gaining a more nuanced understanding of the factors underlying vulnerability, including the role of gender, economic, and power inequalities, is needed. This research has the potential to provide a more meaningful and gendered understanding of the HIV epidemic and its drivers and the important entry points for intervention.

References

Anderson, R. M. and May, R. M. 1988. Epidemiological parameters of HIV transmission. *Nature*, Vol. 333, No. 9, pp. 514–19.

Buga, G. A. et al. 1996. Sexual behaviour, contraceptive practice and reproductive health among school adolescents in rural Transkei. *South African Medical Journal*, Vol. 86, No. 5, pp. 523–27.

Diehr, P., Martin, D. C., Koepsell, T. and Cheadle, A. 1995. Breaking the matches in a paired t-test for community interventions when the number of pairs is small. *Statistics in Medicine*, Vol. 14, pp. 1491–504.

Dunkle, K. L., Jewkes, R. K., Brown, H. C., Gray, G. E., McIntryre, J. A. and Harlow, S. D. 2004. Gender-based violence, relationship power and risk of prevalent HIV infection among women attending antenatal clinics in Soweto, South Africa. *Lancet*, Vol. 363, pp. 1415–421.

Dworkin, S. L. and Ehrhardt, A. A. 2007. Going beyond ABC to include GEM (gender relations, economic contexts, and migration movements): Critical reflections on progress in the HIV/AIDS epidemic. *American Journal of Public Health*, Vol. 97, pp. 13–16.

Garcia-Moreno, C., Watts, C. H., Jansen, H., Ellsberg, M. and Heise, L. H. on behalf of the WHO Multi-country Study on Women's Health and Domestic Violence. 2006. The prevalence of violence against women: Findings from the WHO Multi-country Study on Women's Health and Domestic Violence. *Lancet*, Vol. 368, pp. 1260–269.

Global Coalition on Women and AIDS. 2009. *Stop Violence Against Women, Fight AIDS*, Issue 2. Geneva, UNAIDS. http://womenandaids.unaids.org/themes/docs/UNAIDS%20VAW%20Brief.pdf (Accessed 15 April 2009.)

Glover, E. K. et al. 2003. Sexual health experiences of adolescents in three Ghanaian towns. *International Family Planning Perspectives*, Vol. 29, No. 1, pp. 32–40.

Grinstead, O. et al. 1998. Sexual coercion, physical violence and HIV infection among women in steady relationships in Kigali, Rwanda. *AIDS and Behavior*, Vol. 2, No. 1, pp. 61–73.

Jenkins, C., Cambodian Prostitutes' Union, Women's Network for Unity and Sainsbury, C. 2006. *Violence and Exposure to HIV Among Sex Workers in Phnom Penh, Cambodia*. Washington DC, Policy Project. http://www.researchforsexwork.org/downloads/Jenkins-CambodiaFinal.pdf (Accessed 3 July 2008.)

Koenig, M. A., Lutalao, T., Zhao, F., Nalugoda, F., Wabwire-Mangen, F., Kiwanuka, N. et al. 2003. Domestic violence in rural Uganda: Evidence from a community-based study. *Bulletin of the World Health Organization*, Vol. 81, pp. 53–60.

Koenig, M. A., Zablotska, I., Lutalao, T., Nalugoda, F., Wagman, J. and Gray, R. 2004. Coerced first intercourse and reproductive health among adolescent women in Rakai, Uganda. *International Family Planning Perspectives,* Vol. 30, pp. 156 – 63.

Maman, S., Campbell, J., Sweat, M. D. and Gielen, A. 2000. The intersections of HIV and violence: Directions for future research and interventions. *Social Science and Medicine,* Vol. 50, pp. 459–78.

Maman, S., Mbwambo, J. K., Hogan, N. M. et al. 2002. HIV-positive women report more lifetime partner violence: Findings from a voluntary counseling and testing clinic in Dar es Salaam, Tanzania. *American Journal of Public Health,* Vol. 92, No. 8, pp. 1331–337.

Matasha, E. et al. 1998. Sexual and reproductive health among primary and secondary school pupils in Mwanza, Tanzania: Need for intervention. *AIDS Care,* Vol. 10, No. 5, pp. 571–82.

Moore, A. M., Awusabo-Asare, K., Madise, N., John-Langba, J. and Kumi-Kyereme, A. 2007. Coerced first sex among adolescent girls in sub-Saharan Africa: Prevalence and context. *African Journal of Reproductive Health,* Vol. 11, No. 3, pp. 62–82.

Rwenge, M. 2000. Sexual risk behaviors among young people in Bamenda, Cameroon. *International Family Planning Perspectives,* Vol. 26, No. 3, pp. 118–23, 130.

Somse, P. et al. 1993. Multiple sexual partners: Results of a national HIV/AIDS survey in the Central African Republic. *AIDS,* Vol. 7, No. 4, pp. 579–83.

UNAIDS (Joint United Nations Programme on HIV/AIDS). 2006. *HIV and AIDS Estimates and Data, 2005 and 2003.* Geneva, UNAIDS. http://data.unaids.org/pub/GlobalReport/2006/2006_GR_ANN2_en.pdf (Accessed 6 October 2008.)

Weiss, H. A., Patel, V., West, B., Peeling, R. W., Kirkwood, B. R. and Mabey, D. 2008. Spousal sexual violence and poverty are risk factors for sexually transmitted infections in women: A longitudinal study of women in Goa, India. *Sexually Transmitted Infections,* Vol. 84, pp. 133–139.

WHO (World Health Organization)/Global Coalition on Women and AIDS. 2003*a*. *Violence Against Women and HIV: Critical Intersections. Violence Against Women and HIV/AIDS.* Geneva, WHO. (Information Bulletin No 1.) http://www.who.int/gender/violence/en/vawinformationbrief.pdf (Accessed 1 April 2006.)

——. 2003*b*. *Violence Against Women and HIV: Critical Intersections. Violence against Sex Workers and HIV Prevention.* Geneva, WHO. (Information Bulletin No. 3.) http://www.who.int/gender/documents/sexworkers.pdf (Accessed 1 April 2006.)

CHAPTER 21

From unpaid to paid care work: The macroeconomic implications of HIV and AIDS on women's time-tax burdens

Rania Antonopoulos and Taun Toay

I. Introduction

Macroeconomics and macroeconomic modelling are very useful tools for policy-making purposes. They summarize complex links between the many production sectors of the economy; they provide insights into the interactions of multiple social actors, such as producers and consumers, workers and business owners, borrowers and lenders; and they neatly present us with information regarding income distribution, savings and investment, international trade and financial transactions. Above all, macroeconomic models serve as instruments that allow us to trace the impacts of both gradual and sudden changes on the economy. Such changes can take the form of food and gasoline price spikes, for example, or financial sector meltdowns, or natural or man-made disasters and so on, all of which induce economic adjustments. These 'shocks' can also take the form of public health disasters, such as the HIV epidemic.

Depending on the question under discussion and the level of disaggregation, these models can trace the economic impact of such events on distinct sectors of the economy and on different groups of people: wealthy versus poor, wage earners versus capital owners, rural versus urban households, men versus women. There is, however, a caveat. It must be kept in mind that, in describing an economy, traditional economics has concentrated on the marketized sections of the economy.

The designations employed and the presentation of material throughout this publication do not imply the expression of any opinion whatsoever on the part of UNESCO concerning the legal status of any country, territory or area or of its authorities, or concerning the delimitation of its frontiers or boundaries.
The ideas and opinions expressed in this publication are those of the authors and do not necessarily reflect the views of UNESCO and its Member States.

This market focus is problematic, especially for developing countries. The production of the necessities of life does take place within markets, but not exclusively. Much of what is needed is actually produced through unpaid work, an area outside the strict boundaries of marketized transactions.[1] These informal, or non-market, activities include: (family/household) subsistence-crop cultivation; the collection of basic necessities, like water and fuelwood; caring for children and the elderly; transforming raw ingredients into consumable meals; cleaning and maintaining a sanitary environment in the household; and performing volunteer community work. Excluding the economic activities and the social actors involved in unpaid work paints an incomplete picture of an economy.

The importance of unpaid work has been long recognized, and the 1993 United Nations System of National Accounts (SNA)[2] has provided detailed guidelines on including unpaid work in their estimates of annual production to all Member States. Yet economic models and macro-level analysis – with some notable exceptions – continue to use a lens that renders segments of the population invisible. The trouble is that where some people and their unpaid economic activities are missing from the models, we cannot decipher how unpaid activities and agents are affected by economic changes like the aforementioned 'shocks' – the benefits and costs incurred remain hidden, the difficulties faced in securing a livelihood undetectable. An 'out of sight, out of mind' attitude can lead to misguided policies and the partial or complete failure of interventions.

This is critical in the context of the HIV epidemic, where the intersection between unpaid care, gender and poverty has yet to receive adequate policy attention. It is well known that home-based and community-based care have emerged as key policy responses to the epidemic in many countries in sub-Saharan Africa, as well as South Africa. An underlying characteristic of this response is a reliance on family members and volunteers to provide care without remuneration and with little training or support. The response is due in part to the pressures that the illness has placed on existing health care capacities and fiscal budgets (Haacker, 2001; Oluwagbemiga, 2007).[3] Shortages of qualified nurses and other health care workers, reinforced by brain-drain migration patterns from developing to developed countries, have exacerbated the situation. At the same time, governments in the region that have been pursuing neoliberal policies have not responded adequately to the health care crisis. For people living with HIV (PLHIV) in poor households, family members and community volunteers have become the primary source of day-to-day care. It is estimated that between 70 per cent and 90 per cent of care in developing nations takes place in the home (Akintola, 2008; WHO, 2000).

Unpaid care work

Caring for the young, older people and the ill has traditionally been women's work around the world. This gendered division of labour is typically replicated in the context of HIV and AIDS. Women feed and bathe the ill and provide counselling and emotional support. In addition, they perform two other activities that provide unpaid care for members of households whose age and ability precludes them from performing these tasks on their own: household maintenance and reproduction tasks, such as cooking, cleaning up after meals, washing and ironing clothes and maintaining an overall sanitary and clean environment; and securing the necessary inputs into the aforementioned activities. The collection of water and fuel, for example, takes up to three full-time, unpaid work months per year (forty hours per week) in Benin and even longer in Bolivia (Charmes, 2006; Kes and Swaminathan, 2006). The amount of time dedicated to these tasks and activities is increased in the case of caring for chronically ill people – more water is needed for frequent bathing and cleaning and more hours are spent for physical and emotional support.

On the surface, the fact that women and children perform this work disproportionately is a 'private' matter. However, there now exists a vast literature that argues otherwise on a variety of levels. It is suggested that the increased burden of unpaid work affects women's ability to engage in paid work and subsistence production; limits their participation in community events and the political process; leaves them with less time to upgrade their skills and acquire new knowledge; and gives them less time for other necessary activities, including caring for themselves. As a consequence, patterns of unpaid work reinforce existing gender inequalities in labour-force participation, wage differentials and political representation and in meeting basic needs, such as food security. The danger that young girls – and boys, albeit to a lesser degree – will be removed from school or spend long hours on household chores and on supervising younger children is cause for concern (Akintola, 2004*b*, 2008; Anglewicz et al., 2005). Unfortunately, comprehensive data on shifts in time allocation within households that include people living with HIV are unavailable, and a coordinated international effort to gather such data is still lacking. Despite the overall dearth of information, fieldwork and small-scale studies provide adequate (if anecdotal) evidence of the effects of caring for PLHIV on women.[4]

Paradoxically, at the same time that communities with a high proportion of people living with HIV spend long hours performing unpaid care work, other households suffer from enforced 'idleness'. In the case of South Africa, labour force survey data (SSA, 2007) reveal that overall unemployment in late 2007 stood at 23 per cent; incorporating discouraged workers brings the rate to 36 per cent.[5] While the official rate appears to be an improvement over the previous year, the figure masks the fact that many people are dropping out of the labour force. In fact, statistical releases prior to 2003 provided enough detail to calculate that among black women and youth in former homelands unemployment reached a devastating 70 per cent to 80 per cent (SSA, 2002).[6] Many are ready, willing and able to engage in paid work but simply cannot find jobs. In some cases, both situations are experienced simultaneously within a household: too much unpaid care work, too few employment opportunities. In this context, the very meaning of 'volunteer' work has been contested. HIV and AIDS and poverty combine to reinforce one another in a vicious circle for all family members, including the patients themselves.

As joblessness and poverty are closely linked, public job creation has been used periodically by many countries as a policy intervention (Antonopoulos, 2007; Hirway and Terhal, 1994) to ameliorate the dire consequences and social ills that accompany them (Drèze and Sen, 1989). In such cases, the government assumes the role of the 'employer of last resort', creating minimum-wage jobs for the unemployed in projects that create and maintain physical infrastructure, such as roads and public sector assets. Such initiatives can be traced back as far as the fourth century in India (Drèze and Sen, 1989), where a scheme was introduced to avert famine. More recently, the New Deal was introduced by the United States Government to mitigate the effects of the Great Depression. In the era of structural adjustment, laissez-faire government and trickle-down economics, direct government job creation has for the most part fallen out of favour. However, there has been a recent revival of interest.[7] In 2005 India made a long-standing employment guarantee policy (EGP), which had been implemented in the State of Maharashtra since the 1970s, into a Constitutional Act. The National Rural Employment Guarantee Act entitles citizens residing in poor rural areas throughout the country to 100 days of employment per year at the minimum wage. In many ways, such an entitlement provides a lifeline for poor people and runs against neoliberal thinking that adheres to limited government and deficit reduction as a panacea for growth and income generation.

South Africa also introduced a national public job creation programme, the Expanded Public Works Programme (EPWP), in 2005, albeit on a much smaller scale. Despite the many challenges it faces, the programme[8] is unique in that projects are designed for the environmental and social sectors of the economy as well as for infrastructure. Two priority areas for job creation within the social sector have been identified: community and home-based care (CHBC) and early childhood development (ECD). Through these programmes, the EPWP has created a policy space to make a transition from unpaid to paid work in the care of the ill and of young children, including those orphaned due to the HIV epidemic.

The rest of this chapter explores the economy-wide implications of a scaled-up CHBC intervention in the EPWP for the social sector. Section II presents evidence of how unpaid work and unpaid care provisioning are distributed unequally across gender, employment status and income level in South Africa. Section III discusses the EPWP in the context of the opportunities and limitations it offers for community and home-based care. Section IV presents the economy-wide impacts of an enlarged social-sector intervention in CHBC. Section V concludes.

II. 'Invisible' workers

As described above, unpaid work activities include routine household maintenance work, such as cooking, cleaning, shopping, doing the laundry, caring for children and other daily tasks. The time spent on such activities can be thought of as a 'subsidy' to the economy, as a transfer or a 'gift' (Folbre, 1994) from one institution – the household/family – to the market and the state (Budlender, 2004; Folbre, 2006). It has been argued that without unpaid work and the services it provides, wages would need to be higher to allow the population to purchase these services in the market, or the public sector would have to provide them. It has also been suggested that it is women's unpaid work that increases to fill the gaps, particularly during times of crisis when income and public goods decrease (Elson, 2000; Picchio, 2003). In the context of HIV and AIDS, women's unpaid care work becomes both more essential and more taxing (Pradhan and Sundar, 2006).

The objective of this section is to describe how unpaid work is distributed according to factors relating to gender, unemployment and poverty in South Africa. Previous work with time use survey data (SSA, 2001) for South Africa has produced estimates of the time spent on various unpaid activities in twenty distinct types of households.[9] This investigation highlighted patterns of unpaid time allocation by poor versus non-poor households, the unskilled versus the skilled, men versus women and the unemployed versus the employed. The statistical analysis provided clear evidence that unpaid time contributions in general, and to care activities in particular, are higher and statistically significant for (a) women, (b) the unemployed and (c) those individuals living in poverty (Antonopoulos, 2008).

Figure 1 summarizes gender disparities in the daily time allocated to social care by income level and employment status.[10] The correlations are clear: across income level and employment status, women disproportionately carry unpaid work burdens.[11] Job opportunities, poverty and alleviating the social costs of HIV and AIDS in South Africa are inseparable issues and necessitate the inclusion of gender considerations in the formulation of policy responses. To summarize again, three issues are of key importance for this chapter: first, levels of unpaid care work are higher among those who cannot buy services and goods in the market due to lack of income; second, the unpaid work 'time tax' (a concept we will elaborate on shortly) is more pronounced among poor households and the unemployed; and third, when unpaid care work needs to increase, it is more than likely that women and girls will absorb the new demands placed on households (Opiyo et al., 2008).[12]

Adding unpaid HIV and AIDS care work to women's care burden

The added unpaid task of providing care in the home for the chronically ill or those in need of protracted treatment is largely the product of the shortened hospital stays dictated by the structural adjustment policies many developing nations undertook in the late 1980s (Loewenson, 1993). This informalization of treatment is not anecdotal. It is estimated that in the next seven years roughly 2 million more people of working age will become unable to work because of care duties, that is, the indirect impact of care can increase the direct impact of the illness when the burden of care falls on the household and the family (ILO, 2004). These indirect costs of care and the time spent on caring activities often go overlooked and undervalued as they are associated with less formal perceptions of work. Moreover, the burden of caring for people living with HIV is often borne in addition to traditional domestic duties, creating a further 'time tax' of unpaid work for caregivers. The increased time associated with care is referred to as a 'tax' because it provides a subsidy to the social sector. If one

Figure 1. Average time spent on social care by income and employment status

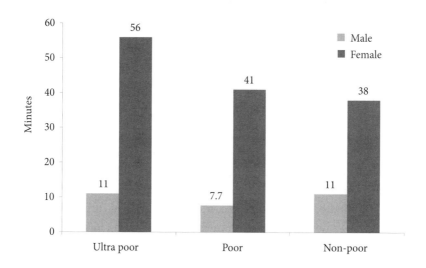

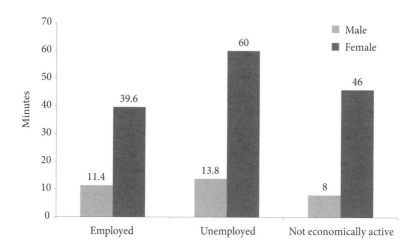

Source: Antonopoulos and Kim (2008).

views health care as a responsibility of the government, this cost is being shifted to the household in the context of HIV and AIDS, effectively taxing the time that individuals would devote to other efforts.

This shift in responsibility from formal to informal care is most clearly seen in the increasing reliance on community home-based care for the ill. An important distinction must be made here: 'care in the home' and 'home-based care' involve drastically different treatment programmes; yet, too often 'home-based care' is used as a catch-all term for both formal treatment programmes and the ad hoc care in the home largely provided by untrained women and girls. The distinction is visible in Africa, where home-based care access is limited, whereas care in the home by family members is widespread (Nsutebu et al., 2001; Ogden et al., 2006). Community home-based care, as we use the term, involves coordinated systems of care carried out by trained care providers and operated through non-governmental organizations (NGOs), formal health care outreach efforts and/or government programmes.

Within the home, care for people living with HIV is usually given by family members and/or by 'volunteer' caregivers recruited from the community (Akintola, 2004a, 2006). As discussed, this work creates an asymmetric 'time tax' borne largely by women – especially poor women – and children in developing countries, which limits other aspects of their social engagement (Taylor et al., 1996; WHO, 2002a). In some cases, it reduces the time spent on self-employment or market participation (Akintola, 2004a, 2004b). In others, it limits involvement in political processes, skills upgrading and the attending of school and medical appointments. It also reduces leisure and time available for self-care and sleep. This unpaid work can therefore lead to social exclusion, time poverty and the depletion of human capabilities.[13] In addition, caregivers often experience isolation, social stigma and psychological distress and lack basic education about both caregiving and HIV and AIDS (Lindsey et al., 2003; Nkosi et al., 2006; WHO, 2002b). This situation is exacerbated by poverty (Mehta and Gupta, 2005).

The need for informal home care for people living with HIV combines with other disadvantages to further destabilize households. Many households face the multiple burdens of high levels of unpaid work, unemployment and poverty. When HIV and AIDS and their associated care costs are added to the equation, the situation of already fragile households becomes even more precarious (Schatz and Ogunmefun, 2007; Steinberg et al., 2002). This multiplicity of disadvantages is particularly evident in South Africa.

III. South Africa and the EPWP

Although South Africa does not have the highest incidence of HIV globally – this unfortunate title is held by Swaziland – it does host the largest number of people living with HIV, estimated at 5.5 million (UNAIDS/WHO, 2006). Prevalence among those of prime working age are staggering (Figure 2). These high levels of infection sit largely atop the de facto system of home care. Thus, South Africa is shackled with the dual burden of rising national prevalence (Figure 3) and a state health care system under pressure, which increases home care needs. This trend forces households and communities to shoulder the brunt of time and other costs associated with care, a burden that, as we have seen, is strongly gendered (Akintola, 2008; Ogden et al., 2006; WHO, 2002a).

To make matters worse, South Africa's rampant unemployment and poverty rates still reflect the socio-economic and demographic divides that characterized the apartheid era. These deep social fissures provide the context for the high incidence of HIV infection, which correlates with factors contributing to the incidence of poverty (Figures 4 and 5). For example, shantytowns and isolated rural regions have the highest unemployment rates, the most poverty and the highest HIV prevalence in South Africa (CADRE, 2006; SSA, 2002).

To address these daunting inequities, the South Africa Government created the Expanded Public Works Programme (EPWP). It is within this framework that we argue for an expansion of the EPWP community and home-based care (CHBC) programme to help formalize the situation of the many unpaid workers performing care duties for people living with HIV.

In its current form, home care presents a host of problems, as primary carers and 'volunteers' are often untrained and unfunded and lack the necessary resources for adequate care provision. Apart from the individual strain this places on care providers and the opportunity costs of the time devoted to treatment, the lack of available resources and structured financial incentives encourages high turnover among 'volunteers'. It is our suggestion that the government can create more jobs in CHBC through the EPWP, offering the training and logistical support to address many of the problems in both home care and existing CHBC programmes.

The original EPWP/CHBC plan envisaged the full training of 19,616 practitioners, with a minimum of ten CHBC workers per clinic, using the Department of Health's norms and standards for care as a benchmark. This figure was to be increased based on geographic area and the socio-economic status of the beneficiaries. A later audit showed that there was a need to develop

Figure 2. PLHIV in South Africa (mid-2006)

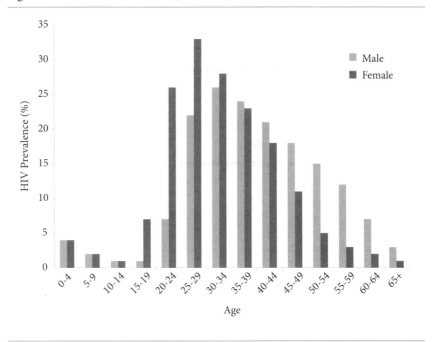

Figure 3. Rising Prevalence[14]

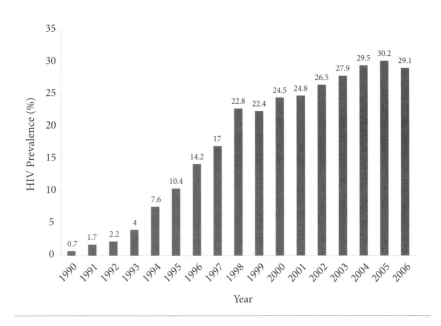

Figure 4. HIV Prevalance by employment status (2000)

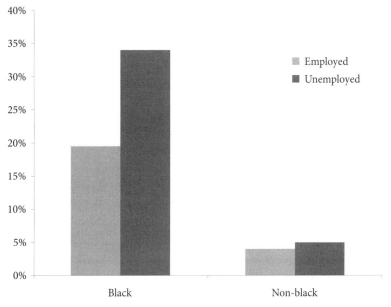

Source: Dorrington (2001).

Figure 5. Prevalence by job category (2000)

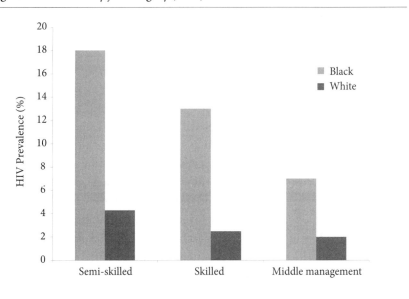

Source: Dorrington (2001).

a further 300 CHBC sites per year to cope with the increasing incidence of HIV and other terminal illnesses. This was equated to a further 3,000 care workers to be trained per year (Friedman et al., 2007).

The targeted beneficiaries of the original EPWP/CHBC programme were to be unpaid 'volunteers' who were unemployed and often the adult dependants of terminally ill people and people living with HIV who were not beneficiaries of a state grant. The EPWP was therefore seen as a critical component of the effort to deliver holistic HIV and AIDS- and tuberculosis-related services. It represented a strategic opportunity to address key areas in interventions at that time and aimed to put in place the foundations for the roll-out of a community health worker (CHW) programme by equipping thousands of unemployed people with the skills and experience to enter a CHW training programme. The steps taken to date, however, have been insufficient to address the challenges.

The EPWP provides work opportunities that generate a monthly stipend and are accompanied by enrolment in 'learnerships'[15] and other types of short courses that lead to accreditation. Skills development is therefore enhanced, as is the capacity to deliver quality services in areas with pressing need. The proposed EPWP/CHBC programme will also provide accredited training as well as an allowance and full-time work for existing volunteers. Beneficiaries of the CHBC programme will be both current 'volunteers' and the young men and women who will provide respite household-maintenance services (including fetching water and fuelwood) for the households of terminally ill people and people living with HIV.

Community and home-based care and the EPWP: An unfulfilled need

We propose that the EPWP/CHBC programme be revised and expanded to improve its impact on the care burdens of women and others. We suggest first a scaling-up in the order of an additional 110,000 jobs that would provide services to poor households in underserved areas by creating a cadre of community health workers, nutrition and food-security workers, directly observed therapy and voluntary counselling and testing practitioners, and tuberculosis (TB) and malaria officers. Those employed should not necessarily be the current care providers in the affected households; rather, they should be professionals who complete a graduated programme in home-based care and training in the provision of physical and emotional support for people living with HIV and their families.

Although the wage structure in our proposal is similar to that of the current EPWP for the social sector, we have expanded the list of job types. Most important, our proposal also extends the duration of enrolment for beneficiaries to two consecutive years per job, with employment for eleven months or 220–240 days per year. As mandated by the EPWP objectives, these proposed work opportunities should include dedicated time for workers/trainees to attend seminars and workshops that lead to certification or accreditation. It is proposed that 111,556 full-time EPWP jobs be created across the various job categories (including supervisory roles) at a projected annual cost of about 1.6 billion South African rand. This cost includes payments to EPWP workers as well as all other necessary input costs, allowances for workers' transport expenses and educational certification expenses. The job categories and number of jobs we propose, as well as the associated budgetary allocations we simulate, were developed through separate models for each job by a team of researchers under Dr Irwin Friedman's directorship at the Health Systems Trust in Durban (Friedman et al., 2007).

Detailed knowledge of South African institutions and constituents was needed in order to estimate the number of jobs required. This knowledge was complemented by demographic data, community survey data and health and educational data from a variety of South African survey documents. Several assumptions were extrapolated from this data, on the basis of which each model established the number of jobs required to extend service delivery and build local capacity. These results were then used as the raw data for the modelling simulations that will be discussed in the following section. Table 1 presents a summary of the estimates for all the job categories in the area of community and home-based care; these were derived from the individual models for each job.

Although we propose specific jobs as outlined above, it should be stressed that this is only a suggested framework for illustrative purposes and is not intended to constrain the programme. The flexibility of certain programmes to provide a variety of services has been key to successful community-based care elsewhere. While people in one area may greatly need counselling and bereavement support, others elsewhere may require help with gathering water or washing linens – or these needs may exist alongside one another. Only local knowledge can lead to informed decisions about the tasks to be performed by community health workers. Local staff must be given the freedom to change the roles and duties of caregivers. It should also be kept in mind that certain jobs are often gendered and/or stigmatized. While these are important issues to account for and discuss, they are beyond the scope of our proposal.

Table 1. Number and types of jobs for community and home-based care; estimated number of households served; and total cost of service delivery

Number of community health workers employed	15,797
Number of community caregivers employed	19,746
Number of TB /DOTS supporters employed	23,695
Number of community-based counselling and treatment workers	51,012
Number of malaria workers	1,305
Total number of community-based health workers (CHWs)	111,556
Number of supervisory jobs created	1,856
Total number of households served by CHWs (education, nutrition)	3,949,233
Total number of vulnerable households receiving home nursing care	197,462
Total number of TB patients receiving DOTS support	236,954
Total number of HIV-positive people receiving counselling/ART support	510,124
Total number of households involved in malaria control	652,648
% of population targeted (vulnerable households)	50%
Estimate of average household size	6
% of households in target population needing a dedicated community caregiver for CHBC	10%
Grand Total of All Costs (in rand)	**1,616,018,754**

The benefits of scaling-up

This proposed revised and expanded structure of training and job guarantees for CHBC workers addresses many of the shortcomings of the existing system. In a survey of community-based care, for example, Naidu (2005, p. 7) found that 'more than 50 per cent of CHBCs programmes in KwaZulu Natal [a South African province] did not have any full-time, paid staff members. Only 25 per cent of such programmes had 30 or more full-time, paid staff members'. Another important way to improve the quality of care in households is to provide better training and support for caregivers:

> Receiving preparatory information, continued training and support from the health workers might be important components influencing coping and provision of quality care among home-care providers. (Mohammad and Gikonyo, 2005, p. 4)

With guaranteed jobs in an expanded EPWP for CHBC, impoverished workers could gain access to useful training and provide a much-needed service in areas with inadequate health infrastructure. Paid workers who used to be unpaid volunteers have the added advantages of local knowledge and stake in the community and require little to no transport. Furthermore, promoting CHBC through an employment guarantee programme (EGP) would serve to remedy many of the problems facing existing volunteers by providing freedom from income constraints, reducing turnover and counteracting social stigmas. It would also relieve the increased burden of care activities within the household, freeing women and girls for other care activities while offering a formal income training that translates into employable skills. In remote areas, it would also help to reduce rural-to-urban migration, a trend that places migrants at greater risk of both HIV infection and poverty (CADRE, 2006).

Previous EGPs have demonstrated the benefits of top-down financial and technical support when paired with upward linkages and local input by NGOs and community-based organizations. Other authors have also argued in favour of linking CHBC with public employment guarantee programmes. Hunter (2005), in particular, also argues that the EPWP in South Africa can provide the resources and administrative logistics to extend CHBC to remote areas.

We should raise here the important caveat that we are not arguing that CHBC is the ideal method of addressing the HIV epidemic in South Africa. South Africa is faced with a pandemic that requires a multifaceted response. Addressing TB, orphan care, cultural practices, child care, social stigma and issues surrounding formal and informal health care are just a few of the many crucial aspects of a holistic response to the crisis. Furthermore, many people remain undiagnosed and outside the scope of prevention, treatment and support efforts (WHO, 2008). However, community home-based care is the most viable option available for many people living with HIV due to the inaccessibility and high cost of hospital care (Mohammad and Gikonyo, 2005). The shift towards home-based care has been so pronounced in some areas that it is most sensible to devote efforts to improving this type of care – even if it is not ideal.

Nor are we arguing that the EPWP in its current form is either a panacea or unproblematic. There has been criticism that the EPWP is an initiative that functions more to address cyclical poverty than the chronic indigence that plagues South Africa (McCord, 2005). Higher wages, prolonged periods of employment and additional institutional supports have been proposed as necessary amendments to the EPWP if a sustainable reduction in poverty among participating households is to be achieved (McCord and van Seventer, 2004). At the same time, however, the EPWP does have the potential to address even its own shortcomings through relatively minor adjustments. Moreover, the programme has already been politically sanctioned, creating the space to scale-up current efforts. In the next section we model a theoretical version of a gender-informed public employment programme, enlarged to meet the needs of South Africa. First, however, we highlight the gender implications of the proposed programme.

Gender dimensions of the EPWP for the social sector

As discussed earlier, time use data indicate that women shoulder the majority of the burden of taking care of the ill. Although we do not have sufficiently disaggregated time use information regarding HIV and AIDS, studies have shown that this pattern is repeated for TB, malaria and other chronic illnesses (WHO, 2002*a*). Women's care burdens are particularly disproportionate in ultra-poor and poor households in the former homelands and informal settlements in urban centers. For these women, CHBC is extremely important, especially in the context of the high HIV prevalence.

An expanded CHBC programme would therefore benefit women in a variety of ways. First, it would alleviate some of women's unpaid care work, as EPWP/CHBC workers would provide services (while in training) for their own communities. Second, it would benefit ultra-poor women with minimal educational attainment by providing them with jobs that do not require much immediate training as well as with adult education classes provided by those EPWP workers who are among the more educated members of the community. Increasing educational attainment has a strong impact on the wages of African women as staying in school until the GET (grade ten equivalent) doubles their monthly incomes and the female-male gap closes by 12 per cent (Antonopoulos, 2008). A well-designed EPWP can benefit low-skilled women of working age – but in order to achieve this outcome, the programme must be sustained for two years to allow enough time for advancement. Providing women with training, certification, work experience and income can be instrumental for their participation in the mainstream economy. Third, an expanded CHBC programme could mean that women will find formal jobs in the highly feminized sectors of health and education without facing too many barriers to entry once they have received certification. The feminized nature of these sectors may also mean that women are more likely than men to recognize and take advantage of the opportunity presented by EPWP employment. Previous experience in this area suggests that public employment programmes follow strongly gendered lines, depending on the tasks associated with the jobs. We provide an estimate below of the percentage of positions to be filled by women but intend neither to sanction nor challenge the gendered nature of care work. Social norms and gender roles are not discussed here due to space constraints and the policy focus of this chapter. Furthermore, while it is vital to address these issues, the EPWP is not an appropriate avenue through which to tackle issues embedded within cultural norms. Instead, the programme offers incentives and training that may help to narrow inequalities (related to income, race, gender and so on) in South African society.

IV. Macro modelling

Current modelling exercises offer insight into the macroeconomics impact of HIV and AIDS by measuring the loss of national output, taxes, investment and so on as a consequence of deaths caused by AIDS[16] (Bell et al., 2003; Bollinger et al., 1999; Ojha and Pradhan, 2006). As they focus on the marketized part of the economy they highlight three consequences in particular: (1) the fall in output and productivity caused by human capital loss and higher hiring and training costs due to AIDS deaths and/or the increased absenteeism of workers living with AIDS, (2) the lower efficiency of HIV-positive workers and (3) shifts in household and government spending towards health care. An additional virtue of some models is that they reveal details of the sectoral impacts of the epidemic (Ojha and Pradhan, 2006, p. xvi).

We divert from this general trend to provide insights into the potential macroeconomic impacts of turning unpaid, unrecognized and 'volunteer'[17] work into paid work. The lack of attention to unpaid caregivers in mainstream economic analysis and public discourse has also rendered them invisible in macroeconomic inquiry into and analysis of HIV and AIDS as measurements revolve around the formal sectors of the economy. By contrast, we aim to trace the changes that will result if the EPWP for the social sector is scaled-up in terms of CHBC. In other words, we investigate the impacts on the economy should the South Africa Government decide to hire workers exclusively from poor households to deliver care to households in need while in training.

When the government hires new workers under the EPWP, this spending represents an injection of capital into the economy in the form of wages and payments for other costs of the program (transportation, trainers, food production and so on). The expenditure of these wages will create increased demand for output from other economic sectors. Increased expenditure and income will be generated throughout the economy, in a process commonly referred to as the multiplier effect. This is the result of a new stimulus or increased demand in the economy, which will respond quite predictably by producing more output.

In other words, in addition to expanding much-needed services, such an intervention will bring about positive changes in employment, growth and poverty reduction for participating households. As we will see, it will also result in higher overall tax receipts, which will serve to partially offset the cost of the programme. Even more importantly, from our perspective, such an intervention will lead to: (a) the reduction of unpaid work burdens for those who currently perform such work; (b) an earned income for those who will be replacing them, accompanied by training and certification; (c) skill creation and accreditation for those who participate in the programme – who may or may not be the same people who currently provide unpaid care work; and (d) recognition within the world of paid work of hitherto undervalued care work.

To implement this policy, new government spending of 1.6 billion South African rand is required. The immediate impacts of this spending include the creation of jobs and income and increased delivery of CHBC services. Three more changes are expected to take place as a result of the intervention. First, in addition to the employment directly created by the programme, more workers will be hired elsewhere in the economy to fulfil the increased demand for output. Second, as general income levels increase it is possible that some forms of fiscal contributions will end up increasing government revenues, which will partially offset the initial budgetary impact of this new initiative. Finally, as most of the workers will come from poor households, there may be important consequences for poverty reduction, at least in those households whose members become EPWP/CHBC workers.

We summarize below the economy-wide implications of our suggested intervention, at a cost of 1.6 billion South African rand.

- **This capital injection will create new full-time, year-round EPWP jobs in the social sector.** Roughly 107,000 (96 per cent) of the 111,556 jobs will be allocated to unskilled members of poor households and the remaining to skilled supervisory workers.

- **In addition to direct job creation, about 37,000 more jobs will be created indirectly elsewhere in the economy.** We have estimated that for every three jobs the EPWP creates in CHBC, another job will be created somewhere else in the economy.

- **It is expected that almost 60 per cent of these jobs will be undertaken by women.** The intervention will generate 62,471 (55.99 per cent of the total jobs created directly by the programme) new positions for unskilled women at monthly wages of 500 South African rand for most workers and 1,000 South African rand for those in jobs with higher skill requirements. It is expected that women will undertake an additional 3,252 skilled jobs (2.9 per cent of the total jobs created directly by the programme).

- **The 1.6 billion South African rand corresponds to a meager 0.6 per cent of government expenditure at 2000 prices, or 0.2 per cent of GDP.** The budget we propose covers all labour payments as well as all other costs associated with service delivery and human capital development, supervisors' fees, training and certification expenses, and so forth.

- **The total impact on GDP growth is in the order of 1.8 per cent,** or 2.7 billion South African rand, and with an implied multiplier equal to 1.7 (2.7 billion ÷ 1.6 billion).

- **The resultant growth is pro-poor.** The overall incremental change of income will be 9.2 per cent for ultra-poor households, 5.6 per cent for poor households and 1.3 per cent for non-poor households.

- **All ultra-poor households participating in the EPWP will move above the ultra-poor poverty line,** and poverty will be reduced by 60 per cent to 80 per cent. **Poor households previously located above or around the ultra-poverty line will be lifted above the poverty line.** Our results indicate a need for the careful consideration of targeting. It may be the case that job rationing is required to favour the selection of ultra-poor households.

- **New direct and indirect taxes will be generated equal to about 500 million South African rand,** which will reduce the overall cost of the intervention by one-third (assuming there are no unanticipated leakages).

Beyond the multiplier analysis

We have considered the economy-wide impacts of the proposed intervention and examined its poverty dimensions. The types of jobs we have recommended are in social care, and they will therefore alleviate women's unpaid work burdens, especially for those poor and ultra-poor women who, as we have seen, contribute disproportionately to the provision of social and health care for their families and communities. Beyond the multiplier analysis, however, other aspects of the proposed programme are expected to yield benefits for all participants and women in particular.

- **Accreditation.** The work opportunities we have proposed include on-the-job training and dedicated time for attending seminars and workshops that lead to accreditation. Increased levels of certification and acquisition of human capital may lead to better job prospects in the formal markets and within the government sector at the provincial or municipal level.

- **Service delivery.** The most vulnerable households with members living with HIV will receive home-based care, counselling and better nutrition.

- **Generation of self-employment.** The potential asset accumulation resulting from EPWP employment, in combination with other government interventions that support and promote community-based development, may lead to the creation of new small businesses. It will be extremely important for community revitalization that earned income be spent on purchases from local shops and neighbours.

- **Participants will experience increased dignity within their communities, as well as a sense of fulfilment and self-worth.** Ours is a hypothetical policy scenario, which limits our ability to conduct a study of this aspect of the proposed intervention. However, other EPWP-related project evaluations, even those conducted by critics of this initiative, have shown that participants report a strong and positive association with the reduction of non-income poverty.

V. Conclusion

The proposed EPWP intervention will affect the labour market income of different types of households through an increase in wages from both direct and indirect employment. In terms of direct impact, our proposal will primarily result in income growth for poor and ultra-poor households.[18] In many ways, the efforts and resources currently devoted to this sector are not adequate to combat South Africa's unemployment and poverty. In addition, poverty is multifaceted and people living in poverty face a variety of deprivations. Income alone can bring individuals above the poverty line, but multiple deprivations require multiple interventions. Above all, it is our view that community revitalization and empowerment through local planning that promotes regional- and municipal-level development is what is truly needed. We have presented viable improvements to the existing de facto system of care for people living with HIV in South Africa, improvements that are achievable in the short term and have positive economic consequences – not to mention tolerable costs. Furthermore, under our proposed programme, skill mismatch will no longer serve as a political scapegoat – the skills are there if the political will is there to create a new public sector to facilitate them.

While one size never fits all in terms of policy proposals, our recommendations are specific to the historical context and current situation in South Africa. Similar efforts to link community needs with government employment guarantee programmes elsewhere should place local knowledge at the forefront of policy design. At the same time, our research relies on the widely applicable concept that unpaid work is often ignored and undervalued in economic analysis. If 'invisible' workers are not brought into the policy discussion, researchers and policy-makers alike run the risk of further marginalizing them through inattention and/or ignorance. In addition, without interventions designed with the gender asymmetries of unpaid work in mind, a huge part of the equation for addressing the social and economic toll of HIV and AIDS is missing.

While CHBC is not a solution to the South African HIV epidemic in and of itself, it does present one of the best opportunities for increasing the quality of care for people living with HIV. CHBC must become one part of a cohesive and far-reaching effort that brings together the government, international donors, NGOs, faith-based organizations and others that have an interest in addressing the pandemic that threatens to derail an entire continent. The problems arising out of the intersections between unemployment, HIV and AIDS and socio-economic inequalities in South Africa are already evident in the crime rates, racial tension and surges in violence against immigrants. We present a small but feasible part of the equation for South Africa in the hope of generating discussion and action on an issue of unprecedented urgency.

Notes

1. Official estimates of the share of market production of unpaid activities range from 30 per cent to 60 per cent of gross domestic product (GDP). See Australian Bureau of Statistics (2000), Statistics Finland (2006) and UNDP (1999).

2. The SNA guidelines provide the conceptual framework that sets the international statistical standard for the measurement and classification of economic activities. They consist of an integrated set of macroeconomic accounts, balance sheets and tables based on internationally agreed concepts, definitions, classifications and accounting rules that delineate the market economy. In addition, they provide a framework for constructing satellite accounts of unpaid work. For details see http://unstats.un.org/unsd/sna1993/introduction.asp (accessed 12 October 2008.)

3. Current bed occupancy in public hospitals in Kenya by AIDS patients is 50 per cent to 60 per cent. To ease both financial constraints and congestion in public health facilities, the Kenyan government (following suggestions from the World Bank and other donor agencies) has promoted cost-sharing in Kenyan public health facilities as well as home-based care for AIDS patients.

4. For a non-exhaustive list of such studies see: Anglewicz et al. (2005); Kes and Swaminathan (2006); Mehta and Gupta (2005); Nkosi et al. (2006); Steinberg et al. (2002); and Taylor et al. (1996).

5. Our calculations are based on the Labour Force Survey of September 2007, issued in March 2008, according to which there were 17,178,000 people in the labour force, of whom 13,234,000 were employed and 3,945,000 were unemployed (official definition). If the 3,425,000 discouraged work-seekers are incorporated in these figures, the labour force totals 20,603,000 people and the unemployment rate is 35.77 per cent (7.37 million divided by 20.603 million).

6. Statistics South Africa no longer reports figures for the ex-homelands, which are areas marred by rampant unemployment and indigence. Furthermore, discouraged-worker data are reported in such a way that it is no longer possible to recalculate the unemployment rate (using figures for those officially unemployed plus discouraged workers) by gender and race together, much less the paired data by age and region. The absence of such figures disguises some of the most telling socio-economic and demographic trends in post apartheid South Africa.

7. For case studies see http://www.economistsforfullemployment.org/ (accessed 12 October 2008) as well as Antonopoulos (2007).

8. Details of the programme can be found at the official website: http://www.epwp.gov.za/.

9. This analysis was part of a Levy project supported by the United Nations Development Programme (UNDP) titled Economy-wide Implications of Public Job Creation: Poverty and Gender Equality Implications. The 2001 Statistics South Africa time use survey we employed for this investigation covered all nine of South Africa's provinces; within each province, four different settlement types were visited: formal urban, informal urban, commercial farms and other rural settlements. In total, 8,564 households took part and data was collected for 14,553 respondents in three rounds (in February, June and October) so as to capture potential seasonal variations in time use. Combining the data with background schedule information, we reclassified unpaid work activities for twenty distinct household types, which allowed us to see beyond averages and to reveal the tremendous inequalities in unpaid work in different households.

10. Full documentation is provided in our Technical Social Accounting Matrix Report, which contains sections dedicated to the time use accounts and is available upon request from the authors.

11. We must stress here that correlation does not establish the direction of causality by any means (Folbre, 2006). Is it the case that women who must devote more time to unpaid work are therefore unable to work for pay? Or is it that, when women are unemployed, they do more unpaid work to compensate for the gaps that income poverty creates? We cannot answer this question, but what has emerged in other research is that being poor, unskilled and unemployed exacerbates the inequality of women in relation to other women and men. The time-tax from women in such households spending more of their time performing unpaid work reinforces these inequalities.

12. Opiyo et al. (2008) find that women assume the responsibility for care and that when adult women fall sick, it is their female children who care for the ill persons in the household, not their husbands or male children.

13. For documentation, see various reports at http://www.levy.org/undp-levy-conference (accessed 12 October 2008).

14. It is widely acknowledged that the Department of Health figures overestimate the HIV prevalence for the total population. This is largely the result of relying on prevalence among women attending antenatal clinics as a proxy for the overall infection rates. Given the demographics of the virus disproportionately impacting young women, the proxy estimate itself is inflated. Despite this methodological caveat, the prevalence rates by any measure are staggering, especially among segments of the population.

15. A 'learnership' combines work-based experience with structured learning and results in a qualification that is registered within the National Qualifications

Framework (NQF) by the South African Qualification Authority. A person who completes a 'learnership' will have a qualification that signals occupational competence and is recognized throughout the country. Each learnership consists of a specified number of credits and takes at least one year to complete. It may consist of a number of NQF-aligned short courses that make up the learnership curriculum. A learnership requires that a trainer, a coach, a mentor and an assessor assist the learner.

16. The underlying feature of many of these models is that they rely on formal household and expenditure data, often treating HIV and AIDS as a negative externality or 'shock' for worker productivity due to absenteeism and death. The absence of productive workers creates a drain on production that is often discussed in terms of the skill-intensity of certain sectors and/or overall GDP shortfalls against a 'no AIDS' baseline forecast (Barnett and Whiteside, 2006). The 'cost' of HIV and AIDS is presented by such models primarily as lost streams of future income and output resulting from the effects of HIV and AIDS in terms of illness and death.

17. To refer to many of these unpaid labourers as 'volunteers' is euphemistic in the sense that many of the workers would readily move to paid positions if the opportunity was present. Volunteering then is really just a forced alternative to idleness in areas with endemic poverty and high rates of unemployment.

18. Although what we propose is not a 'targeted' programme, the anticipated self-selection due to the low wages would replicate the effects of targeting. There is a strong assumption here that the reservation wage is pretty much the same across both poor and ultra-poor households, which implies the same supply of labour response to wage movements across the board. Future uses of our model and methodological approach for policy simulations may be able to further refine this assumption.

References

Akintola, O. 2004a. *Gendered Analysis of the Burden of Care on Family and Volunteer Caregivers in Uganda and South Africa*. Durban, South Africa, University of KwaZaulu-Natal, Health Economics and IIIV/AIDS Research Division.

——. 2004b. Home-based care: a gendered analysis of informal care giving for people with HIV/AIDS in a semi-rural South African setting. Ph.D. dissertation, University of KwaZulu-Natal.

——. 2006. Gendered home-based care in South Africa: More trouble for the troubled. *African Journal of AIDS Research*, Vol. 5, No. 3, pp. 237–47.

——. 2008. Costing unpaid AIDS care. Kigali, Mimeo.

Anglewicz, P., Bignami-Van Assche, S., Fleming, P., Van Assche, A. et. al. 2005. The impact of HIV/AIDS on intra-household time allocation in rural Malawi. Paper presented at the Southern Economic Association Meeting, 18–20 November, Washington DC.

Antonopoulos, R. 2007. *The Right to a Job, the Right Types of Projects*. New York, Levy Economics Institute. (Working Paper No. 516.)

——. 2008. The unpaid care work-paid work connection. Geneva, Policy Integration and Statistics Department, International Labour Office. (Working Paper No. 86.)

Antonopoulos, R. and Kim, K. 2008. Scaling up South Africa's expanded public works programme: A social sector intervention proposal. New York, Levy Economics Institute. http://www.levy.org/pubs/UNDP-Levy/EGS.html

Australian Bureau of Statistics. 2000. *Unpaid Work and the Australian Economy*. Canberra, Australia Bureau of Statistics.

Barnett, T. and Whiteside, A. 2006. *AIDS in the Twenty-First Century: Disease and Globalization*. New York, Palgrave Macmillan.

Bell, C., Devarajan, S. and Gersbach, H. 2003. The long-run economic costs of AIDS: Theory and an application to South Africa. Washington DC, World Bank. (World Bank Policy Research Working Paper No. 3152.)

Bollinger, L., Stover, J. and Seyoum, E. 1999. *The Economic Impact of AIDS in Ethiopia*. Washington DC, Futures Group International. http://www.policyproject.com/pubs/SEImpact/ethiopia.pdf (Accessed 10 September 2008.)

Budlender, D. 2004. *Why Should We Care About Unpaid Care Work?* Harare, Zimbabwe, United Nations Development Fund for Women, Regional Office for Southern Africa and the Indian Ocean States.

Budlender, D., Chobokoane, N. and Mpetsheni, Y. 2001. *A Survey of Time Use*. Pretoria, Statistics South Africa.

CADRE (Centre for AIDS Development, Research and Evaluation). 2006. *Live the Future – An Overview of Factors Underlying Future Trends: HIV and AIDS Scenarios for South Africa: 2005–2025*. Johannesburg, South Africa, CADRE on behalf of Metropolitan Holdings Limited.

Charmes, J. 2006. *A Review of Empirical Evidence on Time Use in Africa from UN Sponsored Surveys*. Washington DC, World Bank. (Working Paper No. 73.)

Dorrington, R. 2001. The demographic impact of HIV/AIDS in South Africa by province, race and class. Unpublished paper.

Dorrington, R., Johnson, L., Bradshaw, D. and Daniel, T. J. 2006. *The Demographic Impact of HIV/AIDS in South Africa: National and Provincial Indicators for 2006*. Cape Town, Centre for Actuarial Research, South African Medical Research Council and Actuarial Society of South Africa.

Drèze, J. and Sen, A. 1989. *Hunger and Public Action*. Oxford, United Kingdom, Oxford University Press.

Economic Commission for Europe. 2006. *Valuation of Unpaid Work by Women and Men in Estonia*. Geneva, Economic Commission for Europe.

Elson, D. 2000. *Progress of the World's Women 2000: UNIFEM Biennial Report*. New York, United Nations Development Fund for Women.

Folbre, N. 1994. *Who Pays for the Kids? Gender and the Structure of Constraint*. New York, Routledge.

——. 2006. Measuring care: Gender, empowerment, and the care economy. *Journal of Human Development,* Vol. 7, No. 2, pp. 183–99.

Friedman, I., Bhengu, L., Mothibe, N., Reynolds, N. et al. 2007. Volume one: Executive summary: Scaling up the EPWP social cluster. *Report for the DBSA Development Fund and the EPWP Social Sector*. Durban, Health Systems Trust. http://www.hst. org.za/uploads/files/EPWP_v1_exesum.pdf (Accessed 12 January 2009.)

Haacker, M. 2001. Providing health care to HIV patients in Southern Africa. New York, International Monetary Fund. (IMF Policy Discussion Paper.)

Hirway, I. and Terhal, P. 1994. *Towards Employment Guarantee in India: Indian and International Experiences in Rural Public Works Programmes*. New Delhi/ Thousand Oaks, Sage Publications.

Hunter, N. 2005. *An Assessment of How Government's Care Policy is Working in Practice: Findings from KwaZulu-Natal*. Durban, South Africa, University of KwaZulu-Natal, School of Development Studies. (Working Paper No. 42.)

ILO (International Labour Organization). 2004. Press release,12 July. (ILO/04/35.)

Kes, A. and Swaminathan, H. 2006. Gender, time-use and poverty in sub-Saharan Africa. Washington DC, World Bank. (Working Paper No. 73.)

Lindsey, E., Hirschfeld, M., Tlou, S. and Ncube, E. 2003. Home-based care in Botswana: Experiences of older women and young girls. *Health Care Women International,* Vol. 24, No. 6, pp. 486–501.

Loewenson, R. 1993. Structural adjustment and health policy in Africa. *International Journal of Health Service,* Vol. 23, No. 4., pp. 717–30.

McCord, A. 2005. Win-win or lose-lose? An examination of the use of public works as a social protection instrument in situations of chronic poverty. Paper presented at the Conference on Social Protection for Chronic Poverty, 23–24 February, University of Manchester, Institute for Development Policy and Management.

McCord, A. and van Seventer, D. E. 2004. The economy-wide impacts of the labour intensification of infrastructure expenditure in South Africa, African development and poverty reduction: The macro-micro linkage. Paper presented at the DPRU, TIPS and Cornell Conference on African Development and Poverty Reduction, the Macro-Micro Linkages, 13–15 October, Lord Charles Hotel, Somerset West, South Africa.

Mehta, A. K. and Gupta, S. 2005. *The Impact of HIV/AIDS on Women Care Givers in Situations of Poverty: Policy Issues.* New Delhi, UNIFEM.

Mohammad, N. and Gikonyo, J. 2005. *Operational Challenges: Community Home Based Care (CHBC) for PLWHA in Multi-country HIV/AIDS Programs (MAP) for Sub-Saharan Africa.* Washington DC, AIDS Campaign Team for Africa (ACTafrica). (Working Paper Series No. 88.)

Naidu, V. 2005. *The Evaluation of Costs and Process Indicators for Home Community Based Care (CHBC) Programmes – Phase 1 Report.* Johannesburg, South Africa, Health Economics Research Office (HERO), University of the Witwatersrand.

Nkosi, T. M., Kipp, W., Laing, L. and Mill, J. 2006. Family caregiving for AIDS patients in the Democratic Republic of Congo. *World Health and Population,* March.

Nsutebu, E. F., Walley, J., Mataka, E. and Simon, C. F. 2001. Scaling-up HIV/AIDS and TB home-based care: lessons from Zambia. *Health Policy and Planning,* Vol. 16, No. 3, pp. 240–47.

Ogden, J., Esim, S. and Grown, C. 2006. Expanding the care continuum for HIV/AIDS: Bringing carers into focus. *Health Policy and Planning,* No. 21, pp. 333–42.

Ojha, V. and Pradhan, B. 2006. *The Macroeconomic and Sectoral Impacts of HIV and AIDS in India: A CGE Study.* New York, United Nations Development Program.

Oluwagbemiga, A. E. 2007. HIV/AIDS and family support systems: A situation analysis of people living with HIV/AIDS in Lagos State. *Journal of Social Aspects of HIV/AIDS,* Vol. 4, No. 3, pp. 668–77.

Opiyo, P., Yamano, T. and Jayne, T. S. 2008. HIV/AIDS and home-based health care. *International Journal for Equity in Health,* Vol. 7, No. 8. http://www.equityhealthj.com/content/pdf/1475-9276-7-8.pdf (Accessed 12 January 2009.)

Picchio, A. 2003. *Unpaid Work and the Economy: A Gender Analysis of the Standards of Living.* London, Routledge.

Pradhan, B. and Sundar, R. 2006. *Gender Impact of HIV and AIDS in India.* New York, United Nations Development Program.

PROVIDE (Provincial Decision-making Enabling Project). 2003. *Social Accounting Matrices and Economic Modelling.* Elsenburg, South Africa, PROVIDE. (PROVIDE Background Paper 2003:4.)

——. 2004. *The Organising of Trade Data for Inclusion in a Social Accounting Matrix.* Elsenburg, South Africa, PROVIDE. (PROVIDE Technical Paper 2004:2.)

——. 2005*a. Creating a 2000 IES-LFS Database in STATA.* Elsenburg, South Africa, PROVIDE. (PROVIDE Technical Paper 2005:1.)

——. 2005*b. Forming Representative Household and Factor Groups for a South African SAM.* Elsenburg, South Africa, PROVIDE. (PROVIDE Technical Paper 2005:2.)

——. 2006*a. Compiling National, Multiregional and Regional Social Accounting Matrices for South Africa.* Elsenburg, South Africa, PROVIDE. (PROVIDE Technical Paper 2006:1.)

——. 2006*b. A Framework for SAM Estimation Using Cross Entropy and Sequential Disaggregation.* Elsenburg, South Africa, PROVIDE. (PROVIDE Technical Paper 2006:2.)

Schatz, E. and Ogunmefun, C. 2007. Caring and contributing: The role of older women in rural South African multi-generational households in the HIV/AIDS era. *World Development*, Vol. 35, No. 8, pp. 1390–1403.

South Africa Department of Health. 2007. *National HIV and Syphilis Prevalence Survey – South Africa 2006.* Pretoria, South Africa, Department of Health.

SSA (Statistics South Africa). 2001. *A Survey of Time Use: How South African Women and Men Spend Their Time.* Pretoria, Statistics South Africa.

——. 2002. *Labour Force Survey, September 2000.* Pretoria, Statistics South Africa.

——. 2007. *Labour Force Survey, September 2007.* Pretoria, Statistics South Africa.

Statistics Finland. 2006. *Household Production and Consumption in Finland 2001.* Helsinki, Statistics Finland.

Steinberg, M., Johnson, S. Schierhout, G. and Ndegwa, D. 2002. *HITTING HOME: How Households Cope With The Impact of the HIV/AIDS Epidemic. A Survey of Households Affected by HIV/AIDS in South Africa.* Washington DC, Henry J. Kaiser Family Foundation.

Taylor, L., Seeley, J. and Kajurac, E. 1996. Informal care for illness in rural southwest Uganda: The central role that women play. *Health Transition Review,* No. 6, pp. 49–56.

UNAIDS/WHO (Joint United Nations Programme on HIV/AIDS/World Health Organization). 2006. *Epidemiological Fact Sheets on HIV/AIDS and Sexually Transmitted Infections, 2006 Update (South Africa)*. Geneva, UNAIDS/WHO.

UNDP (United Nations Development Programme). 1999. Time-budget studies for measurement of human welfare. UNDP, *Integrating Paid and Unpaid Work into National Policies: Selected Papers*. New York, UNDP.

United Nations Statistical Division. 1993. *System of National Accounts*. New York, UN. http://unstats.un.org/unsd/sna1993/introduction.asp (Accessed 12 October 2008.)

WHO (World Health Organization). 2000. *Fact Sheets on HIV/AIDS for Nurses and Midwives*. Geneva, WHO.

——. 2002a. *Community Home-Based Care in Resource-Limited Settings: a Framework for Action*. Geneva, WHO.

——. 2002b. *Impact of AIDS on Older People in Africa*. Geneva, WHO.

——. 2008. *Toward Universal Access: Scaling Up Priority HIV/AIDS Interventions in the Health Sector – Progress Report*. Geneva, WHO.

Abstracts

Section I: The New Geography of HIV

Globalization and gendered vulnerabilities to HIV and AIDS in sub-Saharan Africa
Colleen O'Manique

Drawing on the insights of feminist political economy and the political economy of HIV and AIDS in sub-Saharan Africa, this chapter draws attention to the influence of global economic restructuring over the past three decades on the gendered dimensions of risk, vulnerability to HIV and AIDS and policy responses to it. The gendered dimensions of risk and resilience are about more than inequalities between men and women, boys and girls; rather, they are encoded in cultural practices at the household and community levels. The chapter argues that the global political economy is an important contributor to the feminization of the AIDS pandemic and that the pathways between deep structures and the feminization of HIV and AIDS include changes in gendered divisions of labour and power within households and communities, an increasing polarization in the distribution of income and resources, disruptions to local economies and the erosion of the exercise of citizenship.

Social exclusion: The gendering of adolescent HIV risk in South Africa
Kelly K. Hallman

This chapter investigates the links between community social cohesion, group membership and individual sexual behaviours that increase the risk of HIV among 14–18-year-olds in KwaZulu-Natal Province (South Africa). Social capital indices and then their components were used in successive multivariate regressions. The study showed that young men in more cohesive communities were less likely to have a non-consensual first sexual experience. Residing in a turbulent community was associated with an increased likelihood of multiple partners for both sexes. Greater perceived trust among neighbours mapped to higher ages for young women's sexual debut and a lower likelihood of non-consensual sex, as did membership in sports, study and religious groups. In particular, young women who were members of sports groups were less likely to experience non-consensual sex and were more than eleven times more likely to have used a condom during their last sexual encounter than young women who were not members. At the same time, membership in musical groups was associated with earlier sexual debut for young men. The study concludes that the design and targeting of HIV-prevention programmes for adolescents should incorporate such gendered social determinants of vulnerability.

HIV, male labour migration and female risk environments in the southern Caucasus
Cynthia J. Buckley

Who migrates? What are the effects of migration on the families of migrants? This chapter contributes to studies of HIV transmission and migration by focusing on migration as a household rather than an individual activity and by exploring how migration is linked, directly or indirectly, to behaviours related to increasing the risk of HIV infection among household members. It concentrates on migrant-sending families in the southern Caucasus, a region noted for wide-scale male labour migration and rapid increases in HIV incidence. Secondary statistics and insights from fieldwork in the region indicate that women in households from which a man has migrated are challenged in terms of relational and behavioural pathways to HIV exposure. The results point to the importance of considering all members of migrant households (including women and children) in establishing the effect of migration on the risk of HIV infection and the particular importance of viewing migrant wives as active social agents rather than passive partners exposed to risk only through the behaviour of their husbands.

HIV, sexual violence and exploitation during post-conflict transitions:
The case of Sierra Leone
Johannes John-Langba

The gendered dimensions of exposure to HIV during armed conflicts and in refugee and post-conflict situations in sub-Saharan Africa are still under-documented. In particular, very little is known about the varying patterns of female vulnerability to HIV in conflict zones, where women and girls are likely to be victims of sexual violence and exploitation. Using empirical re-search evidence from fieldwork conducted in sub-Saharan Africa, this chapter examines the patterns of women and girls' vulnerability to HIV during armed conflicts, refugee situations and post-conflict transitions. It presents evidence-based analysis of the impact of sexual and gender-based violence and exploita-tion on this vulnerability and in these contexts. These patterns suggest specific prevention approaches not only in terms of sexual and gender–based violence prevention and response but also of national HIV and AIDS policies and in-terventions in the region. Research evidence from the region suggests complex relationships between violence against women, gender norms – such as those associated with masculinity – and social problems, such as migration, poverty and crime, that require nuanced analyses for effective HIV and AIDS policy and practice interventions, particularly during armed conflicts and in refugee and post-conflict situations. In sub-Saharan Africa, conflict and displacement prepare the way for the spread of HIV by increasing individual and community risks of HIV infection through the increased vulnerability of women and girls to sexual violence and exploitation within an environment of decreased avail-ability and/or use of reproductive health and other health services as well as low levels of knowledge about HIV prevention and condom use.

The price of liberation: Economy, gender and HIV and AIDS in China
Shao Jing

In China, gender figures prominently in epidemiologically informed inter-ventions aimed at preventing the sexual transmission of HIV. However, as an anthropological investigation of the outbreak of HIV infection among com-mercial plasma donors in rural central China in the early 1990s suggests, a gendered understanding remains crucial in radically different epidemiologi-cal settings where sex may, or may not, be the primary route of transmission. The chapter presents three concurrent historical processes: agricultural sector reforms, health care reforms and the emergence of a plasma fractionation industry. It argues that the pathological confluence of these historical processes determined the scope and shape, that is, the geography and demography, of the HIV epidemic among plasma donors in rural central China. The chapter also uncovers the conditions for value to be extracted, not from labour, but from human plasma harvested from rural residents, and concludes that future efforts to curb the spread of HIV and to alleviate the suffering of those already infected should pay attention to these same conditions, especially as they are influenced by persistent gender inequalities that produce new forms of vulnerability.

Masculinity + HIV = risk: Exploring the relationship between masculinities, education and HIV in the Caribbean
David Plummer

Using qualitative data, this chapter analyses the impact on men of shifting gender roles in the Caribbean region. In recent decades, Caribbean women have made great strides in educational attainment. In contrast, gender taboos mean that opportunities for a boy to secure his gender identity have increasingly shifted away from educational achievements towards physical dominance, including through hard, physical, risk-taking, hyper-masculine activities, such as bullying, harassment, crime, violence and risky sexual behaviour. Boys who engage in intellectual pursuits are vulnerable to being considered 'suspect' by their peers. For example, boys who show a preference for reading regularly report homophobic criticism: homosexuality is perhaps the deepest masculine taboo of all. Likewise, through the twin mechanisms of masculine obligation and taboo, a wide range of risk-taking behaviours, including those related to vulnerability to HIV infection, have become resiliently embedded in the social fabric and are, as a result, extremely resistant to change. 'Social embedding' exerts its effect via gender roles, peer group dynamics, taboo and stigma, and socio-economic inequalities.

Section II: Cultures of Intervention

Representations of African women and AIDS in Bono's (PRODUCT) RED
Lisa Ann Richey

(PRODUCT) RED is a brand created to raise awareness and money for the Global Fund to Fight AIDS, Tuberculosis and Malaria by teaming up with iconic brands to produce RED-branded products. The advent of 'Brand Aid' explicitly linked to commerce, not philanthropy, reconfigures the modalities of funding international development assistance. RED is situated as a new kind of intervention in the international response to HIV and AIDS in Africa. The chapter considers (PRODUCT) RED as an example of cause-related marketing and consumer-driven philanthropy but also as a meaningful player in representing HIV and AIDS and Africa. The chapter draws on Treichler's work that argues that the representations of AIDS are critical to shaping the possibilities for understanding, responding to and living with the disease. (PRODUCT) RED's representation of HIV and AIDS distracts our attention from critical gender relations issues in the context of recipient societies in Africa and consumer societies in the North.

The life course of nevirapine and the culture of response to the global HIV & AIDS pandemic: Travelling in an emergency
Alton Phillips

Nevirapine has been lauded as a 'magic bullet' to prevent mother-to-child transmission (PMTCT) of HIV. Despite the availability of more effective regimens and concerns about the development of drug resistance, single-dose nevirapine has become one of the most widely used antiretroviral regimens for PMTCT in developing countries. To understand how this came about, the chapter traces the life course of nevirapine and its intersections with gender as it travels from clinical trials, becomes entangled in donor regulations on pharmaceutical procurement and ultimately enters the supply chains that distribute nevirapine and other ARVs to people living with HIV and AIDS. The story of nevirapine reveals the influential role of donors in shaping the culture of response to the pandemic and how this culture has been characterized by an 'emergency' mindset that focuses overwhelmingly on short-term goals, often to the detriment of more effective long-term strategies.

Horizontal approaches: Social protection and the response to HIV in Brazil
Inês Dourado, Vera Paiva and Francisco Inácio Bastos

This chapter discusses challenges faced by the Brazilian response to the HIV and AIDS pandemic, which has been marked by growing social inequalities, 'heterosexualization', 'pauperization' and 'interiorization' of the virus. It assesses the response in Brazil, coordinated by a government coalition, which included different stakeholders and civil society organizations and cooperated closely with international stakeholders. The chapter calls for innovative research to monitor hard-to-reach vulnerable populations and for initiatives to address persistent gender, regional, racial and age inequalities. The chapter concludes that Brazil's initiatives to curb the spread of HIV and AIDS have made great strides but, as one of the world's most unequal societies, much remains to be done.

How should we understand sexual violence and HIV and AIDS in conflict contexts?
Judy El-Bushra

Gaps in our understanding of the social context of HIV transmission hinder our capacity to provide an effective response in situations of violent conflict. To address this, the chapter explores the conflict-sexual violence-HIV and AIDS nexus from the perspective of gender relations. It summarizes evidence on sexual violence and international responses to it in the Democratic Republic of the Congo, Burundi, Rwanda and Uganda, suggesting that, despite strong policy advocacy and campaigning and increased project investment, the collective sum of policy, programme and political responses has failed to make a dent in overall levels of sexual violence in the Great Lakes region of Africa. The transformational potential of gender frameworks lies in their capacity to throw light on the nature and quality of human sexual relationships, but to achieve this they must incorporate an analysis of power relations, including the structures within which these are reproduced and their affective and ideological underpinnings.

Section III: Cultures of Response

Colonial silences, gender and sexuality: Unpacking international HIV and AIDS policy culture
Hakan Seckinelgin

This chapter analyses the international policy processes that have evolved over the past two decades in relation to HIV and AIDS interventions in developing countries. It identifies six dimensions of 'unexamined areas' in the ways that the policy processes are gendered. It argues that the gendered nature of international policies has impacted the way these policies have addressed questions of sexual behaviour and HIV and AIDS by constructing and reproducing silent gender prejudices within the policy implementation context. The chapter suggests that this is due to the gap that exists between policy perspectives and the way people think about their own sexual behaviour in their own sociocultural contexts. This gap is considered to be instrumental in considerations on why policies succeed or fail.

'Sleeping with my dead husband's brother!' The impact of HIV and AIDS on widowhood and widow inheritance in Kampala, Uganda
Stella Nyanzi, Margaret Emodu-Walakira and Wilberforce Serwaniko

This chapter explores interactions between HIV and AIDS, gendered experiences of widowhood and local enactments of widow inheritance in Kampala, Uganda. It is based on a study that triangulated policy review, participant observation, focus group discussions and individual interviews of thirty-five widows and nine widowers of Kiganda ethnicity. The study found that widows and widowers are increasingly stigmatized because they are suspected of being HIV-positive. Many of the participants reported ostracization, alienation or blame for HIV infection – particularly if their spouse died of an AIDS-related illness. During the funeral rites, a levir (typically the deceased husband's brother or kinsman) is appointed to take care of the widow. HIV and AIDS are reconfiguring the interactions between widows and levirs; in particular, sexual relationships between the two no longer occur because of the fear of (re-)infection. In addition, many levirs no longer offer the necessary support to widows and orphans. The chapter provides evidence that in order to compensate for this development and the lack of targeted public provision for widows and widowers, individuals are increasingly mobilizing informal support networks among their families and community, as well as in workplaces and religious organizations.

An epidemic of meanings: HIV and AIDS in Iran and the significance of history, language and gender
Orkideh Behrouzan

The AIDS epidemic needs to be understood in both medical and sociocultural terms. As the Islamic Republic of Iran's successful harm reduction policies have shown, the HIV and AIDS epidemic in the country has distinctive features and requires customized approaches. Gender is a pivotal pole around which meanings and power relations evolve and revolve. Addressing gendered aspects of the epidemic must go beyond the inclusion of women as a risk group: gender roles, gendered (and gendering) languages, the sexual histories of both men and women and the status of individuals in social and sexual networks also need to be examined. Historical and socio-political contexts provide important access to the dynamics of an epidemic. An understanding of the semantic relays in the Iranian HIV and AIDS discourses surrounding, explaining and attempting to intervene in the epidemic is necessary. Equally important to understanding the course of the evolution of an epidemic is an examination of the psychology of gender, language and professional discourses.

Beyond the new geography of dissident gender-sexual identity categories: Masculinities, homosexualities and intimate partner violence in Namibia
Robert Lorway

The homosexual transmission of HIV in Africa now receives significant attention as health and development initiatives begin to target African men who have sex with men (MSM). This chapter critically examines interventions that foster sexual self-recognition among sexual minorities in Namibia, placing particular emphasis upon the gendered subject positions that surface within communities of young, feminine males. These men's idioms of 'uncontrollable and unexplainable' desire for violent men as sexual partners reveal the ironies surrounding these interventions, which celebrate gender/sexual non-conformity as they depoliticize gender inequalities between males. Drawing upon long-term ethnographic research, this chapter illustrates the cultural politics through which a new geography of homosexuality proliferates. It argues that the notion of MSM as a universal, decontexualised risk group or as a global typology of fixed cultural identities must be reconceptualized within HIV prevention policy to account for how emerging sexualities interact with local gender and power inequalities between men and women.

Neglecting gender in HIV prevention and treatment programmes: Notes from experiences in West Africa
Joséphine Aho and Vinh-Kim Nguyen

In HIV interventions, 'gender' is often reduced to differentiating women from men, and they fail, therefore, to engage with the realities of power that shape relationships between individuals in everyday life. Using epidemiological and anthropological approaches and qualitative and quantitative methodologies, the chapter presents examples of some unintended consequences of HIV prevention and treatment programmes in two West African settings. In the case of prevention, the chapter examines the impact of an intervention targeting a core group of high-risk sex workers. The chapter also explores the impact of antiretroviral therapy programmes on women, who are their principal beneficiaries. It argues that it is necessary to assess and take into account the unexpected consequences of interventions as they, in turn, may shape the epidemic and responses to interventions. The chapter provides a critique of conventional behavioural and biomedical indicators and concludes that multidisciplinary approaches are necessary in this respect.

AIDS, gender and access to antiretroviral treatment in South Africa
Nicoli Nattrass

This chapter explores the role of gender in shaping the HIV and AIDS epidemic and structuring access to highly active antiretroviral therapy (HAART) in South Africa. South African women are at greater risk of HIV infection than men but are more likely to access HAART once they become sick with AIDS. Using regression analysis of survey data, the chapter argues that the main reason for the under-representation of men in HAART programmes is that constructions of masculinity militate against accessing care for all illnesses. The chapter argues that policies to increase access to HAART should therefore focus more closely on the cultural and ideational barriers faced by men.

Section IV: Cultures of Measurement

Epidemiological fallacies: Beyond methodological individualism
Catherine Pirkle

Although no single measure can capture every gender dimension of the epidemic, certain measures may be better suited than others. Whereas it is broadly accepted that gender plays a determining role in many HIV epidemics across the world, this chapter demonstrates the inadequacies of conventional methodologies in measuring such impacts. Gender is not well-captured by predominant epidemiological methods, which have difficulties linking gender, as a structural characteristic, to individual outcomes. Women's social vulnerability to HIV stems from gender norms shaped at levels that reach beyond the individual; it is therefore very difficult to alter at the level of the individual. As a result, interventions based solely on the assumption that gender is a malleable behavioural characteristic will be innately flawed as they will fail to recognize that gender is constrained by social norms and expectations.

Measuring the gendered consequences of AIDS: Household dynamics and poverty in South Africa
Jeremy Seekings

This chapter examines the indirect effects of AIDS on African women in South Africa, using quantitative and qualitative research. Indirect effects include the impact of the syndrome on caregivers and dependants. The scope of such effects depends on the 'radius of responsibility' among and between kith and kin. South African women living with HIV and AIDS now have increased access to employment opportunities and public grants, but they still have limited access to resources for themselves or their children. Their access to resources from kin (especially husbands and kin through marriage, or paternal kin for children) is also diminishing. Whereas the 'extended family' accommodates almost all orphaned children, the radius of responsibility among kin has shrunk dramatically for the sick or adults without assured sources of income. Responsibilities are also exercised more often through co-habitation rather than financial remittances. The changing nature of kinship has implications for research on AIDS and poverty; it is therefore important to focus more closely on the claims that individuals can make on, and their responsibilities towards, other people.

Measuring the impacts of the HIV epidemic on household structure and gender relations
Patrick Heuveline

This chapter presents a review of the impacts of the HIV epidemic on households, focusing on orphans from populations with high HIV prevalence in eastern and southern Africa. The HIV-related mortality that first attracted the attention of demographers is now recognized as only one of the potential social impacts of the epidemic on the demographic systems of these populations (such as fostering, marriage, household structures, gendered relationships, etc.). In order to exemplify the challenges of documenting any such consequences, the chapter focuses on one of the epidemic's least ambiguous effects: its impact on orphans. It addresses the paucity of our knowledge about ex ante social institutions, the multifaceted social changes contemporaneous with the epidemic and the use of broad empirical categories as limiting factors in understanding the mechanisms through which the epidemic operates and on our ability to inform policies that would mediate its effects on orphans.

Behind the scenes of sex and sexual debut: Unpacking measurement
Charlotte Watts

The HIV epidemic has led to extensive research on sexual behaviour around the world and across different cultures and settings. Most population research focuses on quantifying numbers of sexual partners, sex acts and condom use. The chapter presents evidence of physical and sexual violence against women, including at sexual debut and from women's partners, to illustrate the dangers of using simple reductionist measures to understand sexual behaviour, and argues that current methods of quantifying and understanding risk need to be overhauled. Research priorities focus on how to move beyond categorizations of patterns of sexual behaviour to documentation of the levels and drivers of coerced, unwanted and unsafe sex. The chapter concludes that a more nuanced understanding of the power structures and contexts that underpin risk, including the role of gender, economic and power inequalities, is more likely to provide meaningful insights for prevention.

From unpaid to paid care work: The macroeconomic implications of HIV and AIDS on women's time-tax burdens
Rania Antonopoulos and Taun Toay

This chapter considers public employment guarantee programmes in the context of South Africa as a policy tool that has the ability to address the nexus of poverty, unemployment and unpaid work burdens, all factors exacerbated by HIV and AIDS. To be effective as an intervention, the authors argue, public job creation must be gender-informed, particularly so in view of the HIV and AIDS pandemic. Paying particular attention to mitigating the 'time-tax' burdens of women, the chapter focuses on a South Africa Government initiative, the Expanded Public Works Programme. This job creation programme, in addition to physical infrastructure works, includes projects designed to redress social sector service delivery deficits. To help offset the destabilizing effects of HIV and AIDS and endemic poverty, the chapter highlights the need for scaling up resource allocation for community home-based care. The authors conclude with results from macroeconomic simulations for such an enlarged programme, using a Social Accounting Matrix framework, and set out its implications for participants and policy-makers.

Contributors

Joséphine Aho is a doctoral candidate in epidemiology and public health at the Université de Montréal. She also studies the evaluation of health interventions, and holds a master's degree in microbiology and immunology from the Université de Montréal. Her research interests include the epidemiology of infectious diseases in vulnerable populations and the ethics of HIV and AIDS programs and research. Her thesis focuses on HIV and AIDS prevention among female sex workers. She is also involved in a multicenter longitudinal study on antiretroviral therapy outcomes in a cohort of patients in West Africa.

Rania Antonopoulos is a research scholar and director of the Gender Equality and the Economy program of the Levy Economics Institute of Bard College. Prior to her present positions, she taught economics at New York University for ten years. Her current research focuses on the intersection of paid and unpaid work, public job creation as it relates to inclusive growth, human development and gender equality, and micro-macro simulation modelling that traces the economic impacts of employment guarantee policies.

Francisco Inácio Bastos is a physician and senior researcher at the Oswaldo Cruz Foundation (FIOCRUZ), Brazil. He has been involved in the planning and management of the WHO multicity project on HIV/AIDS and viral hepatitis among injecting drug users. He has also been involved in analyses aiming to assess the status and trends of the AIDS epidemic in Brazil as well as modelling on the impact of HAART on AIDS deaths and the spread of other STIs.

Orkideh Behrouzan is a Ph.D. candidate studying medical anthropology in the science studies program (HASTS) at MIT. She has studied molecular genetics in the Department of Clinical Medicine at Oxford. Prior to that, she graduated from medical school at the University of Tehran, Iran. She is a blogger and a poet and has worked as a freelance writer for medical and literary journals.

Cynthia J. Buckley is an endowed fellow of the Institute for Innovation, Creativity, and Capital at the University of Texas at Austin, a faculty member of the Department of Sociology and a faculty affiliate of the Center for Women's and Gender Studies and the Center for Russian, East European and Eurasian Studies. She is interested in examining the interplay between migration, health and gender, in addition to the generation of culturally acceptable interventions in the area of sexual health.

Mary Crewe is the director of the Centre for the Study of AIDS at the University of Pretoria. She is on the editorial boards of *Sex Education: Sexuality, Society and Learning; The Journal of Higher Education in Africa;* and *AIDS Education and Prevention*. She works with UN agencies, such as UNAIDS, UNICEF and UNESCO, and with the SADC and has links with local, regional and international tertiary institutions, research institutions, parliamentarians and NGOs. She is the editor of the *Annual AIDS Review* of the Centre for the Study of AIDS and is the author of a book and many articles.

Veena Das is Krieger-Eisenhower Professor of Anthropology at Johns Hopkins University. She also serves on the executive board of the Institute of Socio-Economic Research on Development and Democracy in India. She studied at the Delhi School of Economics at the University of Delhi and taught there from 1967 to 2000. Her research interests include feminist movements, gender studies, sectarian violence, medical anthropology and post-colonial and post-structural theory.

Inês Dourado is an associate professor and researcher at the Collective Health Institute of the Federal University of Bahia, Brazil. She is a physician, with a master's degree in public health from the University of Massachusetts and a doctorate in epidemiology from the School of Public Health at the University of California, Los Angeles (UCLA). Her research is on the epidemiology of infectious diseases, and she has been deeply involved in the study of human retrovirus epidemiology and prevention in Brazil.

Judy El-Bushra manages the Great Lakes Regional Programme of International Alert, a British-based non-governmental agency that works for peace in over twenty countries and territories and internationally. She has worked on issues of gender, conflict and peacebuilding since the early 1990s, mainly with NGOs, such as ACORD, CARE International and International Alert. Her work has included project management and evaluation, research, training and policy influencing.

Margaret Emodu-Walakira is a public health nurse. She heads the Community-Based Health Care Program of Mengo Hospital in Kampala, Uganda. She has over ten years experience running community public health outreach clinics in the suburbs of Kampala.

Didier Fassin is James Wolfensohn Professor of Social Science at the Institute for Advanced Study at Princeton University and director of study at the Ecole des Hautes Etudes en Sciences Sociales in Paris. An anthropologist and a medical doctor, he directs IRIS, the Interdisciplinary Research Institute for Social Sciences. Former vice-president of Médecins sans Frontières, he is currently president of the Comité Médical Pour les Exilés.

Kelly K. Hallman is an associate in the Poverty, Gender, and Youth Group at the Population Council. Trained as an economist, she works in interdisciplinary teams to analyse health, economic development and population issues. Her present research examines the ways in which social and economic factors influence sexual and reproductive health behaviours and outcomes, including the ability to adopt and sustain HIV-preventive behaviours. She received her Ph.D. in economics from Michigan State University.

Patrick Heuveline holds a Ph.D. in sociology and demography from the University of Pennsylvania. He is a professor in the Department of Sociology and the International Institute at the University of California, Los Angeles (UCLA), and is a research associate in the California Center for Population Research. He is currently working on an international study of the institutional context in which families operate and, in particular, how the relationship between the family and the state affects youth well-being.

Johannes John-Langba is social policy and monitoring and evaluation specialist in the Children and AIDS Section at the UNICEF-Eastern and Southern

Africa Regional Office. He holds a Ph.D. in social work and a Master of Public Health in behavioural and community health, both from the University of Pittsburgh (Pennsylvania). He also holds a Master of Social Work degree (with a field of practice in displaced populations) from Howard University. His research interests include social protection, gender and HIV, sexual violence and exploitation, child poverty, maternal and child health, social and behavioural determinants of health, forced migration and health, adolescent sexual and reproductive health/rights, and monitoring and evaluation.

Jennifer F. Klot is senior adviser for Social Science Research Council programs on HIV/AIDS, gender and security. Prior to this, she served as a senior adviser on governance, peace and security at the United Nations Development Fund for Women (UNIFEM). Between 1994 and 2000, she served as a policy adviser on peace and security at the United Nations Children's Fund (UNICEF).

Robert Lorway is an assistant professor in the University of Manitoba Centre for Global Public Health. He conducted nine years of community-based HIV prevention research in eastern Canada before pursuing his Ph.D. in medical anthropology at the University of Toronto. As a medical anthropologist he has extensive experience in working with sexual minority youth in Namibia on issues related to sex work, homophobia and HIV vulnerability.

Nicoli Nattrass is professor of economics and director of the AIDS and Society Research Unit at the University of Cape Town. She has a Ph.D. from Oxford and has published widely on economic and AIDS policy in South Africa and on the global roll-out of antiretrovirals. Her most recent books are *Class, Race, and Inequality in South Africa* (Yale University Press, 2005), co-authored with Jeremy Seekings, and *Mortal Combat: AIDS Denialism and the Struggle for Antiretrovirals in South Africa* (University of KwaZulu-Natal Press, 2007).

Vinh-Kim Nguyen is an HIV physician and medical anthropologist. He practices at the Clinique Médicale l'Actuel and is also an associate professor in the Department of Social and Preventive Medicine at the Université de Montréal. His research has focused on the political and cultural dynamics of the response to the HIV epidemic, particularly in West Africa. For this work, he was recently awarded the Aurora Prize by the Social Sciences and Humanities Research Council of Canada.

Stella Nyanzi is a medical anthropologist based at the Law, Gender and Sexuality Research Project of the Faculty of Law at Makerere University in Kampala. She has twelve years of social science research experience in the broad areas of sexualities, gender, health and society in Uganda and Gambia. Her most recent book is the co-authored *How to Be a 'Proper' Woman in the Times of HIV and AIDS,* published by the Nordic Africa Institute.

Colleen O'Manique's research focuses on the interconnections between gender relations, globalization and human health, with a specific focus on the gender dimensions of the HIV and AIDS pandemic. She is an associate professor at Trent University in Peterborough, Canada, where she holds a cross-appointment between politics and women's studies, and has a Ph.D. in political science from York University.

Vera Paiva is a professor at the Department of Social Psychology at the Psychology Institute of the University of São Paulo, Brazil. She has also been a visiting professor and researcher at the Department of Sociomedical Sciences at the Mailman School of Public Health at Columbia University. Her research and teaching are in the areas of social psychology and public health, with emphases on gender, sexuality, technologies for health promotion and HIV and AIDS. She co-coordinates NepAids-USP, an interdisciplinary group that brings together teachers from various departments of the University of São Paulo and from other universities and research institutions.

Alton Phillips is a doctoral candidate in the Department of Sociology at New York University. From 1995 to 1998, he worked on HIV prevention programming at the Massachusetts Departments of Education and Public Health. He is currently a researcher for the Social Science Research Council's HIV/AIDS, Gender and Security Program. Recent publications include contributions to *Practicing Culture* (edited by Craig Calhoun and Richard Sennett). His current research focuses on nevirapine and the cultures of response to the global HIV and AIDS pandemic.

Catherine Pirkle is a doctoral student in epidemiology at the Université de Montréal and a Canada Vanier Scholar. Her current research looks into the linkages between HIV and maternal mortality. In addition, she works as a research coordinator at the International Health Unit of the Université de Montréal, where she has been involved in a multicentre study of antiretroviral therapy outcomes in a cohort of patients in West Africa. She holds a master's degree in community health from the Université de Montréal and a bachelor's degree in environmental science from McGill University.

David Plummer is a senior advisor at the Royal Tropical Institute in Amsterdam and adjunct professor in public health at the University of Texas, Houston. At the time of writing, he held the post of Commonwealth/UNESCO Caribbean Chair in Education (HIV Health Promotion) and was based at the University of the West Indies in Trinidad. His research is in gender, sexual health, marginalization and health, and stigma and discrimination. He is the lead researcher for a major project researching masculinities in the Caribbean and their relationship to education, crime and health.

Lisa Ann Richey is an associate professor of development studies in the Department of Society and Globalisation at Roskilde University in Denmark. She conducts research on health, gender and international development in Africa. She is the author of *Population Politics and Development: From the Policies to the Clinics* (Palgrave Macmillan, 2008). Her current research interests are therapeutic citizenship, the politics of antiretroviral therapy for HIV/AIDS in South Africa and Uganda, and Brand Aid.

Lydia Rebecca Ruprecht is a political sociologist. She holds a B.Sc. in political science from the Université de Montréal and a Maîtrise and D.E.A in international affairs and political sociology from the Université de Paris I-Sorbonne. She has pursued social science studies at Essex University in the United Kingdom and Ph.D. studies in political sociology at the Ecole des Hautes Etudes en Sciences Sociales in France. She is currently a programme specialist working in the Division for Gender Equality in the Office of the Director-General of UNESCO.

Hakan Seckinelgin is a lecturer in international social policy in the Department of Social Policy at the London School of Economics. More specifically, he is working on the impact of international HIV and AIDS policies on the disease in sub-Saharan Africa by analysing the agency of international actors and their knowledge claims. Another aspect of his research is related to politics of knowledge production and discussions of evidence/evidence-based policy. He is involved in gender studies research and looked at the relationship between Islam and democratic processes and their gendered impact on women's welfare in Turkey. At the moment he is writing a book on conflict, gender and HIV in Burundi.

Jeremy Seekings is professor of political studies and sociology at the University of Cape Town in South Africa and a visiting professor at Yale University (Fall 2009). His books include *The UDF: A History of the United Democratic Front in South Africa, 1983–1991* (2000) and *Class, Race, and Inequality in South Africa* (co-authored with Nicoli Nattrass, 2005). He co-edits the *International Journal of Urban and Regional Research* and directs a range of research projects in Cape Town on topics such as adolescence, everyday violence, kin relationships, housing and community, and social and political attitudes.

Wilberforce Serwaniko is a social worker based in the Community-Based Health Care Program of Mengo Hospital in Kampala, Uganda. He is also a community leader in Kasubi-Kawaala, with extensive experience as a Local Council chairman.

Philip Setel is a medical anthropologist involved in international health and health development research and practice for the past twenty years, mostly in East Africa. Currently he heads a unit at the Bill and Melinda Gates Foundation that supports measurement, evaluation and evidence-based learning for improving the strategic focus and impact of the foundation's Global Health Program.

Shao Jing received his Ph.D. in anthropology from the University of Chicago in 2000. He has taught cultural and medical anthropology at Vassar College and McGill University and is currently associate professor of anthropology in the Department of Sociology of Nanjing University, China. Since 2002, he has conducted extensive field research among HIV-infected commercial plasma donors in rural central China.

Taun Toay is a research analyst at the Levy Economics Institute of Bard College, where he works on macroeconomic modelling and gender-aware analysis. He was a Fulbright Research Grantee to Greece for 2005–2006 and an affiliate to the University of Piraeus, where his work examined the socio-economic impacts of inflation patterns surrounding the adoption of the euro. He is currently pursuing his Ph.D. at the New School for Social Research in Manhattan.

Charlotte Watts is Sigrid Rausing Professor in Gender, Violence and Health at the London School of Hygiene and Tropical Medicine. She has been conducting international research on gender-based violence for the past ten years and on HIV for fifteen years. She is a core research team member for the WHO multicountry study on women's health and domestic violence and senior advisor to the IMAGE microfinance and gender participatory training intervention in rural South Africa.

Index

Food security, 47, 227, 416, 475, 484
  farm subsidies and price supports, 47
  food crises, 46
  subsistence agriculture, 43, 429, 474, 475
    and women, 47, 111
Forced sex. *See* Sex, coerced
Ford Foundation, 118
Fortes, Meyer, 427–28
Foucault, 272, 278
Fourth Wave
    as a new paradigm, 17–18
    defined, 16–17
Frames and frameworks. *See also* Cultures of
    intervention; Cultures of measure-
    ment; Cultures of response; Gender
  biomedical, 18–23, 38–40, 237, 277, 280,
    321, 332, 372–74
  cultural, 159–60
  dominant culture, 271, 273–75
  emergency, 20, 190–91, 195–98, 203–09,
    249
  epidemiological paradigm, 159–60
    changing perspective on, 20–23, 29, 38,
      332–33
    fallacies of, 407–19
    poverty of epidemiology, 34, 121–22, 131
  gendered, 12, 18, 257–62, 264, 275–76
  human rights, 17, 48, 219, 226–27, 236,
    250, 272, 277, 287, 292, 371
  individual behaviour paradigm, 16, 21, 23,
    30, 33, 40, 41, 54, 73–74, 153, 331, 415
  macroeconomic, 43, 47, 473–74, 489–90
  migration, 96
  rescue paradigm, 19–20, 23, 161, 162, 174,
    275
  semiotics, 20, 319–43
  sexual and reproductive health, 283–85,
    287, 289

Frames and frameworks (*continued*)
  sexual violence in conflict, 253–54, 257
  sexual-gender typology, 347–48
  socio-psychological, 259
  virtualism, 164–66, 175, 178, 181
Garrett, Laurie, 45
Gates Foundation, 169, 172, 183
Gender, 18, 118–21. *See also* Femininity;
    Masculinity; Relations, social
  analysis, 15, 19, 21, 48, 251, 261
  and blood products, 34, 124–125
  and the global political economy, 38, 39,
    48
  and widowhood, 295–315
  concept of, 30, 257–58, 264, 365, 412–13,
    414, 416
  definition of, 258, 407
  disparities, 15, 17, 19, 40, 208, 223, 478
  dynamics, 11, 16, 21, 254, 259, 272, 361,
    371
  inequality, 11, 12, 15, 19, 103, 169, 177,
    220, 221, 223, 226, 230, 249, 274, 348,
    352, 355, 358–59, 360, 361, 381, 418,
    463, 466, 467, 469, 475
  language and meaning, 319–43
  norms, 11, 20, 33–35, 103, 108, 159–60,
    182–83, 190, 254–55, 282, 314, 371,
    373–74, 379, 381, 387, 391–94, 412,
    426–27, 451–52
    in Sierra Leone, 103–13
    in southern Caucasus, 82, 87, 90, 92, 95
  Western concepts of, 21, 159, 180–81,
    323, 373
Generics. *See under* Drugs
Geography of HIV, 17–19, 29–35, 48, 81, 119,
    128, 218, 222, 323
Georgia, Republic of, 82–98
Ghana, 91, 173, 175, 384

Spousal abuse. *See* Sexual violence and exploitation, intimate-partner violence

Stigma, 17, 18, 21, 22, 37, 40, 53, 60, 86–87, 98, 108, 111, 140, 150, 159–60, 219, 221, 223, 231–36, 248, 257, 271, 292, 296–99, 320, 322, 323, 324, 325, 328–29, 330–31, 336, 337, 338, 341, 366, 367, 368, 436, 480, 485, 487

Stokvels (voluntary savings clubs), 58, 60–61, 67, 70–71

Structural adjustment programmes, 30, 39, 41–43, 478

and undermining of state capacities, 41–42

impact on women, 42–43

Sub-Saharan Africa, 15, 16, 17, 19, 37–48, 53–57, 59, 67, 74, 173, 177, 193–95, 222, 234, 284, 295, 380, 383, 409, 412, 445, 446, 447, 452, 454, 463, 464, 468, 474

Subepidemics, 15, 18, 48

Brazil, 226

China, 16, 17, 34, 121–22

India, 16, 17

Russian Federation, 17

southern Caucasus, 16

sub-Saharan Africa, 15, 16

Swaziland, 173, 481

Tanzania, United Republic of, 462, 464

Tawil, Osama, 338

Technologies of governance, 34, 277

Thailand, 118, 200, 450, 454

Third World Network, 43

Togo, 384

Trade policies, 38, 39, 41, 43–45, 164, 167, 182, 195–96, 198–03, 407, 473. *See also* Liberalization, economic; TRIPS

Trade policies (*continued*)

agricultural, 39, 46–47

in sub-Saharan Africa, 46–47

new variant famine hypothesis, 46

Trafficking, 81

drug, 83, 227, 235, 326, 335

of women, 112, 465

Treatment Action Campaign, 43, 56

Treichler, Paula, 166, 173, 319, 321, 336

TRIPS (Trade-Related Aspects of Intellectual Property Rights), 43–46, 199–203, 286

Uganda, 17, 192, 197, 204, 205, 247–64, 272, 295–315, 448, 454

Ukraine, 82–98

UN Action against Sexual Violence in Conflict, 250

UNAIDS (Joint UN Programme on HIV/AIDS), 38, 83, 84, 160, 190, 196, 231, 279, 283, 284, 285, 295, 338, 347, 381, 404, 467

UNDP (United Nations Development Programme), 110, 222, 338, 496

UNESCO, 15, 16

Culture, HIV and AIDS program, 26

UNFPA (United Nations Population Fund), 231

UNICEF (United Nations Children's Fund), 90, 196

United Nations (UN), 107, 165, 247, 274, 287–89

Unsafe sex. *See under* Sex

USAID (US Agency for International Development), 206–07, 347, 404

Vaccine, 18, 45, 410, 455

Vanity Fair, 166, 173–79, 182–83

Vertical transmission. *See* Mother-to-child transmission